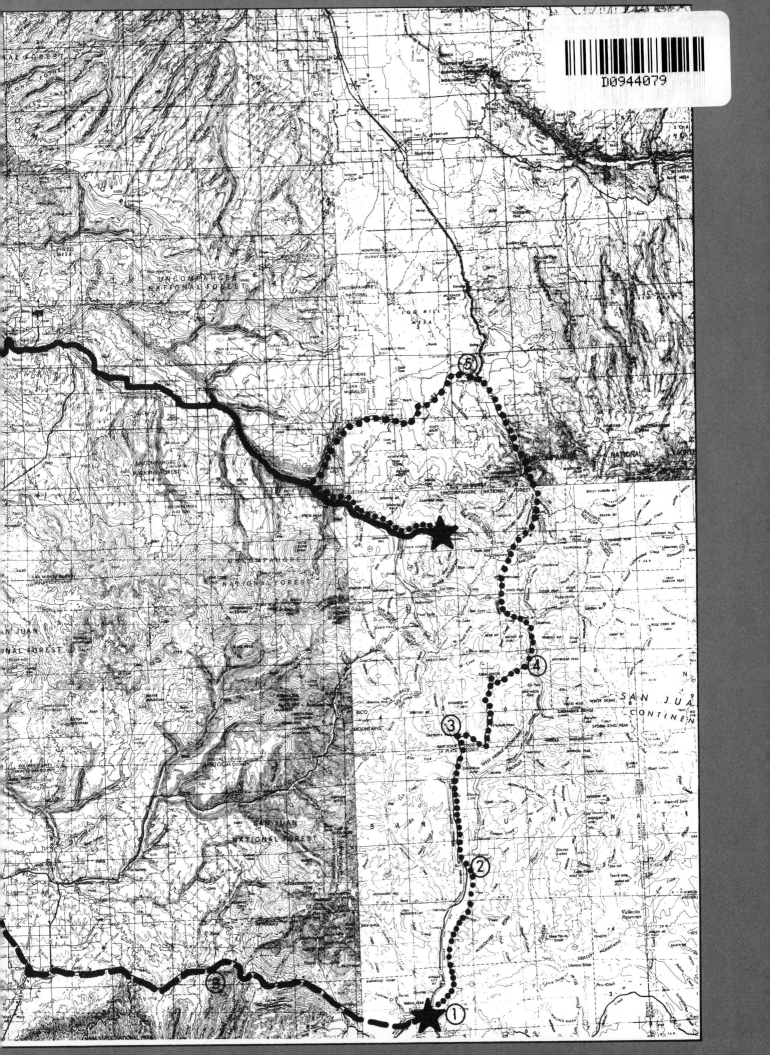

GEOLOGY of the PARADOX BASIN

EDITED BY

DEL L. WIEGAND

PUBLISHED BY

ROCKY MOUNTAIN ASSOCIATION OF GEOLOGISTS
DENVER, COLORADO

1981

ROCKY MOUNTAIN ASSOCIATION OF GEOLOGISTS

OFFICERS 1981

President	Dudley W. Bolyard	Bolyard Oil & Gas, Ltd.
President-Elect	Joseph P.D. Hull	Ensource, Inc.
1st Vice President	Bruce O. Tohill	Peppard-Souders & Associates
2nd Vice President	Wilson W. Bell	Excoa Oil & Gas, Inc.
Secretary	Mary P. Frush	Texas Gas Exploration
Treasurer	Phillip T. Kinnison	Conoco, Inc.
Councilor	Kenneth H. Holmes	Mobil Oil Corporation
Past President	John M. Parker	Consultant

FIELD CONFERENCE COMMITTEE

General Chairman	Kenneth T. Smith	Sinclair Oil Corporation
Guidebook Editor	Del L. Wiegand	C & K Petroleum, Inc.
Associate Editors	Jan Earle	Champlin Petroleum Company
	Bruce Rubin	C & K Petroleum, Inc.
	N.D. Thomaidis	Wexpro Company
	Ken Altschuld	C & K Petroleum, Inc.
Publication Manager	Raymond G. Marvin	Consultant
Field Trip Chairman	C. Dennis Irwin	Consultant
Field Trip Assistants	Eugene L. Howard	Terrascan Group
	Richard B. Powers	U.S. Geological Survey
Road Log Chairman	C. Dennis Irwin	Consultant
Road Logging	Donald L. Baars	Consultant
Housing Chairman	Phillip T. Kinnison	Conoco, Inc.
Registration Chairman	Charles E. Stark	Conoco, Inc.
Catering & Social Chairman	Philip J. McKenna	Polaris Oil & Gas
Transportation Chairman	W. Merle Freeman	Banner Oil & Gas
Publicity & Finance Chairwoman	Kay Waller	Petroleum Information
Advertising Chairman	Donald E. Dayhuff	Florida Exploration Company
Advertising Assistant	Susan Romero	Florida Exploration Company
Sketches	Andrew G. Alpha	Consultant
	Darwin Spearing	Marathon Oil Company
Photographer	John H. Rathbone	Consultant

PRESIDENT'S MESSAGE

This field conference and guidebook are dedicated to the conviction that significant petroleum and other resources in the Paradox Basin await discovery. The decision to conduct this project was made because the basin is indeed a paradox to petroleum explorationists. This is one of the largest onshore geologic provinces in the lower 48 states that contains major oil and gas fields but is as yet only sparcely explored. Petroleum source beds, reservoir rocks, vertical and lateral seals, structural complications, stratigraphic variability, and abundant indications of hydrocarbons all point to the probability of significant undiscovered petroleum accumulations. Surely the application of modern geological and geophysical methods will unravel the paradox of this basin.

I wish to express my gratitude to Kenneth Smith who as General Chairman has expedited and coordinated the project, and to Del Wiegand who is the Editor of this book. The credit for the project is largely due to Ken and Del who have given so generously and enthusiastically of their time, expertise and talents.

Dudley W. Bolyard, President
Rocky Mountain Association of Geologists

INTRODUCTIONS

This conference is designed to expose the participants to both the diverse geology and spectacular scenery of that part of the Colorado Plateau occupied by the Paradox Basin.

The combination of massive bounding uplifts, the rugged abruptness of towering laccolithic intrusions, and the structural relief and areal expanse of the salt anticlines together create one of the most complete geological workshops located anywhere. Stir in the myriad of subsurface elements and it would be difficult to find a better place for learning the true exploration and business insignificance of the phrase "regional understanding."

The Paradox Basin itself is "big country" and these three days will have traversed less than 25% of this province. It would require many of these trips to see the entire basin. The remaining part of the basis is no less important although it enjoys a higher density of exploration than the interior basin. Because the fringes of this truly evaporite basin contains equivalent shelf carbonates, it also hosts the major producing fields. The Greater Aneth Area of southeastern Utah, for example, has already recovered over 307 million BO and 294 BCF of gas, and is still producing about 40,000 BOPD — one of the new giants in the Rocky Mountain Area.

Many satellite accumulations of hydrocarbons are present in this shelf portion of the basin, and represent analogs of others yet to be found in the basin.

All of the fields in the Paradox Basin are worthy of investigation. This Guidebook has not included these data; however, the recently issued Oil and Gas Fields of the Four Corners Area (in two volumes), published by the Four Corners Geological Society does contain the field data.

Our especial thanks to the many authors that were willing to submit papers helping us meet the goals of the conference. Further, this excursion was made possible because of the many months of time and energy dedicated by the very interested people listed under Field Conference Committee, as well as numerous people who were willing to give a few hours of their time at our request. These efforts have not gone unappreciated, and we know that only through their effectiveness that this trip became a reality.

Del Wiegand
Guidebook Editor

Dennis Irwin
Field Trip Chairman

PREFACE

Since the 1973 embargo, there haven't been enough good prospects to keep up with the simple demand for new domestic hydrocarbons. Thanks to new prices for the raw materials, the industry has the incentive for generating wildcat prospects. Unfortunately, the shortage of professionals has forced industry investments to go where the old files and experience lie — primarily in the most mature producing provinces.

Many of the areas already demonstrate major producing capabilities; however, others contain geologic complexities that dampen projected exploratory programs.

The Paradox Basin of Utah and Colorado is one of these dampened areas. While there is existing production, vast areas containing township after township have never seen the drill. The lack of exploration drilling and the exploration opportunities that abound in the basin today are very simply explained by the same reason — managers and people tend to run from complicated situations.

The Paradox Salt seems to be the primary culprit of complexity. It also is directly related to, and offers the key to, understanding prospects in rocks both below and above the salt.

The Paradox Salt formation is much more than a "nothing" rock — it is an ideal *seal*, it is surely the major *source* rock in the basin and it occasionally enjoys *reservoir* properties. Without offering a great amount of detail here, perhaps a few comments regarding the salt section are warranted.

Flowage does not destroy the sealing qualities of the salt for the Mississippian and older reservoirs — in fact, uplifting and faulting of the pre-salt rocks (causes of flowage) rearranges the seal geometrically. In many instances the salt seal and source are then around or even lower structurally than the pre-salt reservoir. The Lisbon Field, for example, which produces from the Mississippian, is totally "encased" in Paradox Salt.

The black shales within the Paradox Salt are not only source beds — they may be traced throughout the basin. Gross salt interval work is of regional value, but subdividing the total salt section by use of these shale markers and then working with many different smaller intervals contributes a wealth of knowlege to the history and growth of the basin. This approach allows one to separate normal from abnormal, and reconstruct normal thickness in flowage areas.

By dealing *only* with the Paradox Salt in this manner is by far the most thorough and productive method for gaining a truly regional understanding of this basin.

As to reservoirs within the salt, these same black shales and clastic breaks become reservoirs when fractured. The Cane Creek zone is the most prominent of these, and produces in several localities. One well completed in this fractured shale interval has produced over 767,000 BO, and is still flowing.

The totally impermeable nature of the uppermost salt bodies and the source within the salt have combined to create an overpressured regime that is self-contained within this Paradox Salt formation. A pressure gradient sometimes as high as 0.65 to 0.70 exists when fluids are encountered within the salt section, as compared with a normal 0.43 gradient in the underlying Mississippian. The Cane Creek mentioned above, and any other fractured clastic break will enjoy overpressured conditions.

Without knowing why, or how to purposefully locate it, just pure and plain halite zones yield large volumes of heavy exotic brines sometimes with associated oil and gas. Both oil and gas occur in unadulterated halite. Some day we may learn how to complete and produce these mysterious accumulations as evidence to date suggests commercial extent.

There is at least one known instance of a core of salt (with some minor anhydrite content) that showed measurable porosity and permeability by commercial core analysis.

To say it again — the Paradox Salt formation is much more than a "nothing" rock.

In many parts of the basin, ancestral adjustments triggered salt flowage, and throughout Permian Cutler times depositional overloading caused additional salt flowage. The Cutler thickens, and compensates for salt loss, and we are usually dealing with thousands of feet of differential. One can visualize the many sub-basins created in this manner, at varying distances from the source of the clastics, in some cases with sufficient depths for local carbonate deposits. The industry has barely scratched the surface of this stratigraphic potential. With the advent of CDP techniques (only sparingly utilized to date in the Paradox Basin), this exploration workshop may be mapped regionally, and dealt with locally.

These are but a very few of the cause-and-effect geological concepts in the Paradox Basin. It boggles one's mind to imagine the economic resource potential associated with the extremes and variations that exist in this basin.

Most of the technology is available — unravelling and resolution of the untapped potential of the Paradox Basin is simply in the keen minds of men. We trust our aim to contribute a slight "nudge" in the correct direction will become successful.

Kenneth T. Smith
General Chairman

TABLE OF CONTENTS

GEOPHYSICAL

URANIUM, GEOTHERMAL, GEOHYDROLOGY AND EXPLORATION

GEOLOGIC ENGINEERING

OTHER PAPERS

We completed a rectified multispectral-scanner band-ratioed composite image of the northern Paradox Basin. Landsat multispectral scanner (MSS) scene 5165-17030 (which covers Salt Valley, Fisher Valley, Castle Valley, and Gibson Dome) was used in preparing spectral band ratios 4/5, 4/6, and 6/7. Three quarter scenes were concatenated to make geometrically corrected images of 2100 scan lines and 1900 pixels, the maximum size allowable on USGS optronics equipment. Because a 2% histogram stretch for each ratioed image resulted in scenes of low contrast, a cumulative-frequency-function (CDF) histogram stretch was also applied. The CDF stretch increased the contrast among the least frequent values. The CDF-stretched data resulted in high-constrast, black and white images. A color-ratio composite was made from the data for these three ratios using the USGS color-write system and 50 278 Ektachrome film with filters red (4/5), blue (4/6), and green (6/7). The colors of the resulting positive transparency are directly related to several mappable features of the surface, notably, distribution of vegetation and outcrop areas of specific lithologic units of the Phanerozoic sequence in the Paradox basin (e.g., the Cutler and the Moenkopi Formations of Permian and Triassic age, and the Wingate sandstone of Triassic age.

Jules D. Friedman

"Alwright folks, step over here for a look
at some real salt tectonics . . . . ."

CHARACTERISTICS OF SURFACE FAULTS IN THE PARADOX BASIN

Catherine A. Kitcho

ABSTRACT

Surface faults of the Paradox Basin were mapped to identify tectonic activity and its effect on subsurface stratigraphy. Faults mapped in the Abajo Grabens and Lockhart Basin areas were mapped on the ground in detail, and their surface characteristics were compared with faults in the salt anticline belt and the Needles fault zone. Faults in the Abajo Grabens area and Lockhart Basin have smaller displacements than the faults in the salt anticline belt, and are expressed as shear zones 1 to 30 feet wide rather than as single faults bounding the diapiric salt anticlines. This comparison suggests that there is less structural complexity in the southwestern part of the Paradox Basin than elsewhere. Faults in the Abajo Grabens and Lockhart Basin area are commonly cemented or mineralized with calcite, but those in the Needles zone are open or alluvial-filled fractures, suggesting a difference in ground-water movement or age of formation between these two structural areas.

INTRODUCTION

As part of a siting investigation in the Paradox Basin for the Office of Nuclear Waste Isolation of Battelle Memorial Institute (a prime contractor to the U.S. Department of Energy), Woodward-Clyde Consultants has been mapping faults in southeastern Utah (Figure 1). Surface faults are being studied to help define (1) future tectonic activity; and (2) the likelihood that these faults might provide conduits for moving ground water to the surface.

The combined approaches of remote sensing interpretation, compilation of faults from literature, and field mapping were used in this study to identify and assess the faults in southeastern Utah. The index map (Figure 2) shows the area for which remote sensing interpretation was completed. The remote sensing interpretation yielded approximately ten previously unmapped faults or extensions of faults.

Figure 3 shows the area where interpreted lineaments and faults from literature were mapped on the ground. Several of the mapped faults from literature were actually found to be features other than faults, and so were removed from the fault compilation. During ground-based mapping of faults and during helicopter reconnaissance of the larger fault systems, several previously unmapped faults or splays were found, especially in the areas of Shay Graben and Lockhart Basin.

Data from the area shown on Figure 3 were then compared with published data from two other structural areas in the Basin, the Needles fault zone and the Salt anticline belt, to identify similarities or differences in structural characteristics. This comparison study was done to better understand the structural evolution of the Paradox Basin.

The fault reconnaissance and mapping showed that there does not seem to be one specific method for reliably identifying faults in the Paradox Basin. Because this area is arid and open, it would seem that surface faults would clearly be expressed on aerial photos. However, as Figures 4A and 4B show, there is only a subtle linear expression on the photos, and that appears only because in that particular area (Shay Graben), the fault is enhanced by a line of trees. Another problem in identifying faults in the Paradox Basin is the character of surface formation that crops out in an area. In areas where the surface is dominated by the Jurassic Navajo Sandstone (a massive eolian crossbedded sandstone), a hummocky erosional rock surface has developed that tends to obscure expression of linear features such as faults. Many of the previously unmapped faults were located only by ground traverse or very low-level aerial reconnaissance in these areas.

PREVIOUS WORK

The southeastern Utah portion of the Paradox Basin was mapped in the 1950s chiefly by investigators from the Atomic Energy Commission (AEC) and the U.S. Geological Survey (USGS). Publications with fault data include USGS bulletins and professional papers. The maps prepared by AEC investigators were published as a series of U.S. Geological Survey "MF" or "I" Series maps; the latter were published at a scale of 1:24,000. The majority of the maps were based on photogeology, not ground mapping. In the 1960s, fault data from previous publications were selectively compiled at a scale of 1:250,000 and became part of the 2° geologic quadrangles published for southeastern Utah (Williams, 1964; Haynes and others, 1972; Williams and Hackman, 1971; Hackman and Wyant, 1973).

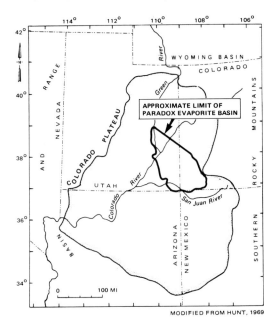

MODIFIED FROM HUNT, 1969

Figure 1. Location Map of the Paradox Basin

REGIONAL STRATIGRAPHY AND STRUCTURE

Paleozoic and Mesozoic sediments up to 20,000 feet thick are present in the Paradox Basin. Dissection by the Colorado River and post-Cretaceous structural evolution of the area have provided excellent surface exposure of the Mesozoic and part of the Paleozoic stratigraphic section. This has facilitated mapping of surface faults for most of the Paradox Basin.

Folded structures in and around the Paradox Basin consist of monoclines bordering major uplifts, and a system of salt anticlines with intervening synclines (Figure 5). The uplifts and monoclines trend north, northwest or northeast; the salt anticlines and intervening synclines trend northwest. Most of the faulting in the Paradox evaporite basin is associated with diapiric salt anticlines, and results from solution and collapse along the crest of the anticlines.

Concentrated faulting is also located in the Needles area south of the confluence of the Green and Colorado Rivers, and in the graben systems near the laccolithic Abajo Mountains. Figure 6 shows the generalized distribution of faulting taken from the 1:250,000 scale published compilations. Most of the faults in the Paradox Basin are vertical, or at least steeply dipping. Relative displacement on faults is usually normal, and a few are thrust faults. Normal faults usually occur along valleys or bases of cliffs.

The first known episode of faulting in what was to be the Paradox depositional basin occurred during Precambrian time and produced the major northwest trend that was to control evaporite deposition and subsequently the formation of salt anticlines in the northeast half of the basin. Baars (1966) suggested that faulting may have continued through the end of Mississippian time, and thereafter was quiescent until Cretaceous time.

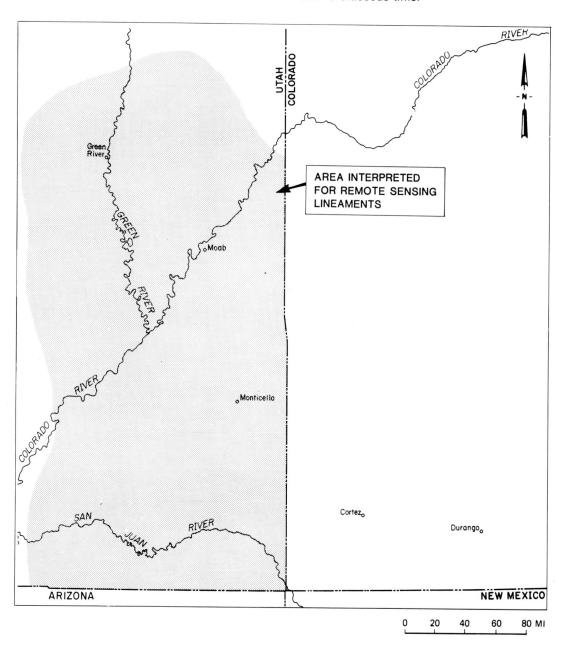

Figure 2.   Area of Remote Sensing Interpretation

The Laramide orogeny in Late Cretaceous-Early Eocene probably played the most significant role in producing the structures visible on the surface in the Paradox Basin. During this time the Colorado Plateau was subjected to northeast-southwest compression that produced broad northwest-trending folds and subsequent normal faults along the collapsing salt anticlines.

FAULTS OF THE SALT ANTICLINE BELT

Faults in the northeastern part of the Paradox Basin were studied primarily by literature review and secondarily by limited field reconnaissance. Abundant descriptions of structures are available for this part of the basin because of major mineral and petroleum exploration during the 1950s.

Faults in this part of the basin are associated with the deposition, flowage, folding and solution of evaporites and share an unusual structural history compared to the rest of the basin.

Pre-Pennsylvanian fault escarpments formed northwest-trending ridges that controlled evaporite deposition during the Pennsylvanian. Later, during the Late Pennsylvanian and Permian, folding caused the thickened salt ridges to form anticlines that were elongated along these northwest trending faults. Salt flowage into the anticlines and piercement along the crest of the folds took place during the Laramide orogeny. During the late Laramide, collapse occurred on the salt anticlines and normal faults or grabens were produced along the crest of the anticlines. A second stage of collapse in the Later Tertiary or Early Quaternary time (Richmond, 1962; Biggar and others, this volume) produced the high-angle normal faults bounding the flanks of the anticlines that are visible at the surface today (Woodward-Clyde Consultants, 1980). Figure 7 illustrates the sequence of faulting associated with the anticlines.

The faults that bound the diapiric salt anticlines form steeply dipping fault scarps along the topographically flat

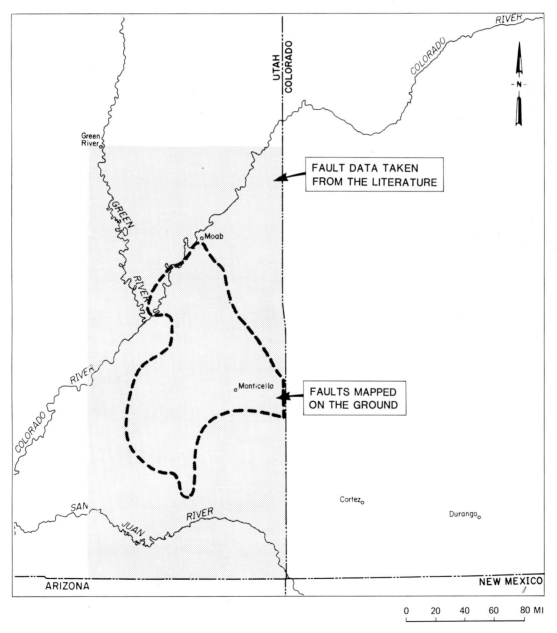

Figure 3. Sources of Fault Data

breached anticlinal valleys. Figure 8 shows the Spanish Valley anticline as an example. Displacements up to 2,500 feet have been estimated for some of the faults.

The Moab fault forms one of the boundaries of the Moab Valley anticline (Figures 5 and 6). McKnight (1940) describes it as a normal fault with 2,500 feet of downthrow to the east, and suggested that it formed as a result of tensional stress caused by collapse of the Moab anticline. It is observable for 29 miles, and trends N40° to 50°W. The dip of the fault plane is 50 to 62 degrees to the northeast.

The Lisbon Valley anticline is similar to the other salt anticlines in the area in that salt has flowed to form the anticline, but here the salt has not pierced overlying strata (nondiapiric anticline). The Lisbon Valley fault is a normal fault along the crest of the anticline and is 41 miles long (Figures 5, 6, and 9). It is downthrown 4,000 feet on the northeast, and the fault plane dips 58 degrees northeast (Figure 10). The surface fault was probably formed from flowage of underlying salt (Hite and Lohman, 1973); it is not yet known whether the surface fault extends downward through the salt sequence.

NEEDLES FAULT ZONE

The Needles fault zone is located just southwest of the confluence of the Green and Colorado rivers. The fault zone is a system of accurate, shallow grabens that have formed on the east side of the Colorado River.

Figure 11 shows the array of grabens in this fault zone as mapped by Lewis and Campbell (1965). Individual grabens in this zone are 75 to 300 feet deep and 300 to 1,200 feet wide. The bounding faults of the grabens in this area have average dips of 80 to 85 degrees.

The major grabens consist of two or more en echelon elements, with one boundary fault shared by both elements. This suggests a scissors motion on the shared fault (McGill and Stromquist, 1979).

Recent theories of the Needles fault zone assume that tensile stresses developed on a brittle plate gliding on underlying mobile evaporites, thus creating grabens along pre-existing joint trends. The evaporites flowed downdip, in a northwest direction toward the Colorado River, creating the arcuate grabens that are concave in the direction of dip (McGill and Stromquist, 1979).

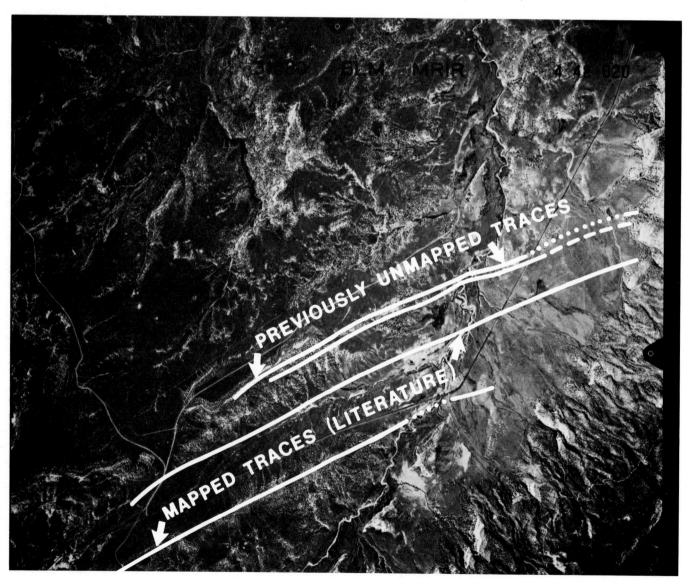

Figure 4A. Aerial Photograph of the Shay Graben Area

ABAJO GRABENS

A group of grabens near the Abajo laccolithic mountains exhibit similar characteristics and appear possibly to be related in origin. This group includes the Salt Creek Graben, Bridger Jack Graben and Shay graben northwest of the Abajo Mountains, and the Verdure and Hammond grabens south of the Abajos (Figure 6). Figures 12, 13, 14, and 15 show the detailed location of these grabens, which are unique in trend (northeast or east-trending and are thought to have controlled placement of the Abajo laccoliths (Witkind, 1964).

The surface faults mapped in the Abajo area affect a stratigraphic section ranging from Permian to Quaternary. Some of these grabens either splay or develop into several parallel faults at their ends. These grabens commonly contain step faults, or at least small parallel faults. Displacements on faults range from 1 to 350 feet, with 10 feet being the most common. Sense of movement on faults is normal. Fault planes are mostly near vertical; dip ranges from 51° to 90°. The zones are commonly altered, with limonite staining and calcite mineralization in the fracture itself. Occasionally the fault zone is bleached to a white or yellow-brown color. Brecciation of the fault or fault zone is characteristic. The typical surface expression of a fault is a low bedrock ridge or scarp commonly enhanced by lines of trees (Figure 16). Slickensides, frequently found on the scarp, are vertical, and occasionally are weathered out (Figure 17).

Of this group, the Shay graben has been more thoroughly studied than the others, both by previous investigators and Woodward-Clyde Consultants. This graben is about 20 miles long and ½ mile wide, and has a maximum displacement of 320 feet. Both faults of the graben are dip-slip. The south Shay fault is generally better exposed than the north one, and the middle of the structure is marked by strong faceted spurs on the flank of Shay Mountain (Figure 18). There is strong geomorphic and stratigraphic suggestion at this location that the fault displaces a gravel-covered pediment on the north side of Shay Mountain, implying an episode of rejuvenation has taken place since emplacement of laccoliths in the Eocene.

Several previously unmapped faults were mapped at the northeast terminus of the Shay graben (Figure 13). They are north of the main part of the graben and may be downstepping faults toward the graben. Alternatively, the graben itself may actually be wider at this location with parallel faults within it.

The Verdure Graben (Figure 15) was also mapped, but not

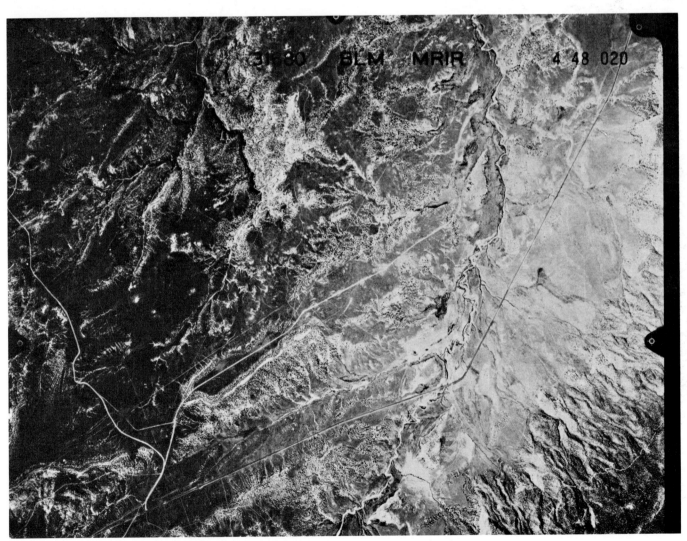

Figure 4B.   Aerial Photograph of the Shay Graben Area

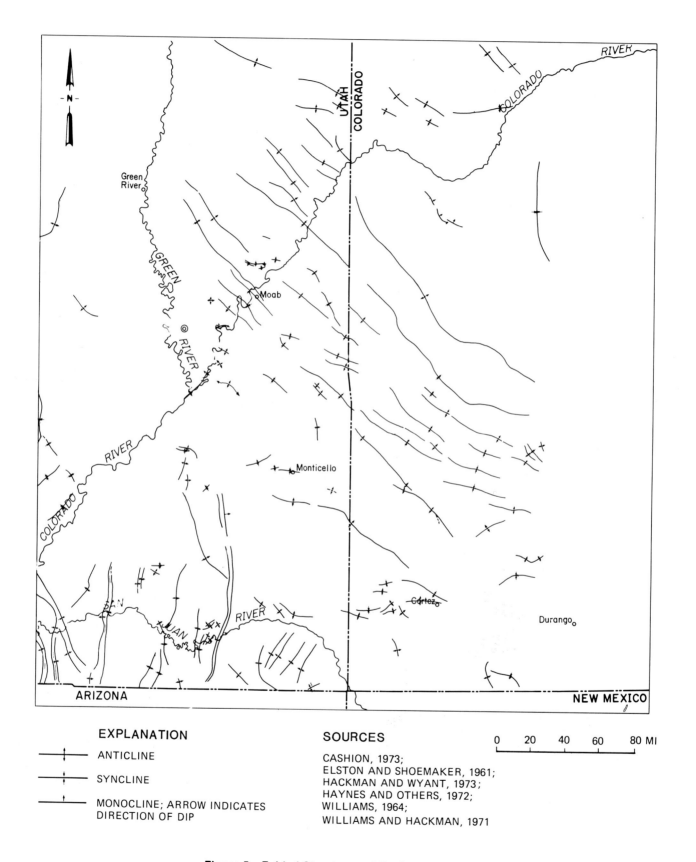

EXPLANATION

—|— ANTICLINE

—+— SYNCLINE

—↑— MONOCLINE; ARROW INDICATES
        DIRECTION OF DIP

SOURCES

CASHION, 1973;
ELSTON AND SHOEMAKER, 1961;
HACKMAN AND WYANT, 1973;
HAYNES AND OTHERS, 1972;
WILLIAMS, 1964;
WILLIAMS AND HACKMAN, 1971

0   20   40   60   80 MI

Figure 5.   Folded Structures of the Paradox Basin

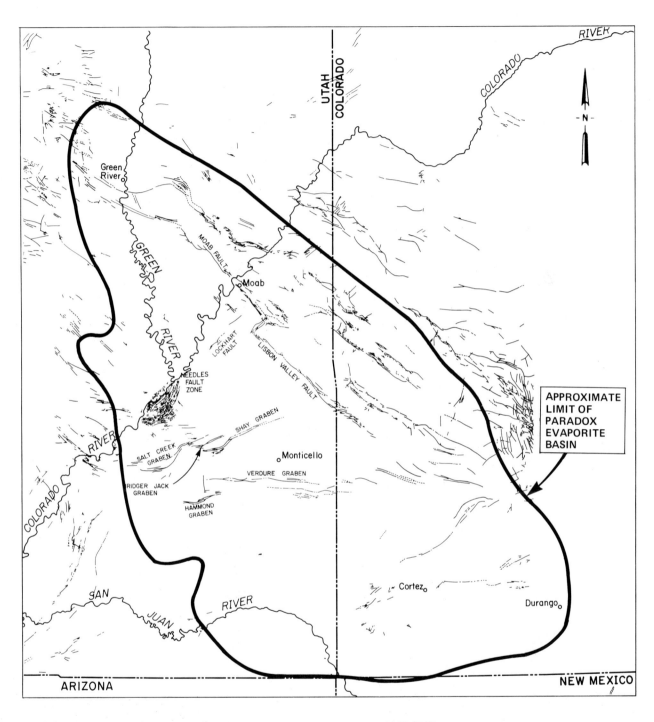

EXPLANATION

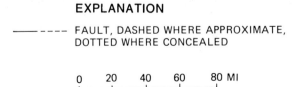

FAULT, DASHED WHERE APPROXIMATE,
DOTTED WHERE CONCEALED

0   20   40   60   80 MI

SOURCES

(1:250,000 SCALE MAPS) CASHION, 1973;
ELSTON AND SHOEMAKER, 1961;
HACKMAN AND WYANT, 1973;
HAYNES AND OTHERS, 1972;
WILLIAMS, 1964;
WILLIAMS AND HACKMAN, 1971;
WITKIND AND OTHERS, 1978

Figure 6. Faults of the Paradox Basin

A. PRECAMBRIAN AND PALEOZOIC ROCKS DURING DEPOSITION OF THE PARADOX FORMATION
(MIDDLE PENNSYLVANIAN) AFTER EARLY DOWNFAULTING AND SUBSIDENCE OF DEEP
PART OF PARADOX BASIN AND UPLIFT OF UNCOMPAHGRE UPLIFT.

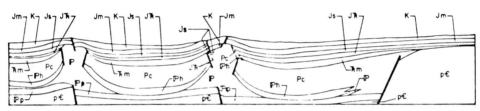

B. PRECAMBRIAN AND PALEOZOIC ROCKS NEAR END OF CUTLER DEPOSITION.
Development of salt cores well advanced.

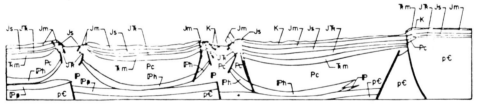

C. PRECAMBRIAN, PALEOZOIC AND MESOZOIC ROCKS DURING FIRST STAGES OF CRESTAL
COLLAPSE OF SALT ANTICLINES (EARLY TERTIARY).

D. PRECAMBRIAN, PALEOZOIC AND MESOZOIC ROCKS SINCE PLEISTOCENE TIME.
Renewed faulting on southwest border of Uncompahgre Plateau during late Tertiary and Pleistocene.

EXPLANATION   Modified from Cater, 1970

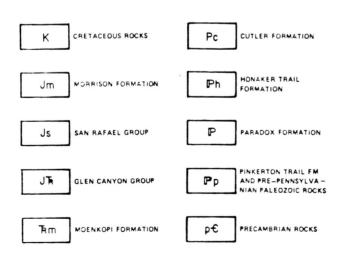

K	CRETACEOUS ROCKS	Pc	CUTLER FORMATION
Jm	MORRISON FORMATION	Ph	HONAKER TRAIL FORMATION
Js	SAN RAFAEL GROUP	P	PARADOX FORMATION
JR	GLEN CANYON GROUP	Pp	PINKERTON TRAIL FM AND PRE-PENNSYLVA- NIAN PALEOZOIC ROCKS
Rm	MOENKOPI FORMATION	p€	PRECAMBRIAN ROCKS

Figure 7. Structural Evolution of Salt Anticlines

in as much detail as the Shay Graben because exposures are not as abundant. The Verdure Graben widens and narrows erratically and is about 14 miles long. The faults are dip-slip and range in dip from 80° to vertical; maximum displacement is 180 feet.

The Hammond Graben (Figure 15) is another east-west trending graben, parallel to the Verdure Graben but quite distant from it. The graben is actually made up of two en echelon grabens. The north fault of the west end of the graben becomes the south fault of the east end of the graben. This is a scissors fault with the pivot point at Comb Ridge. Maximum displacement is 100 feet on the north fault.

The juxtaposition of the Hammond Graben with te Verdure Graben and its similar trend suggests a common structural origin. They both probably formed prior to the Monument Upwarp (Lewis and Campbell, 1965). The Hammond Graben now exhibits a bend where it crosses the nose of the Monument Upwarp; the Verdure Graben is wholly outside the boundary of the Monument Upwarp. Lewis and Campbell (1965) indicated that most of the Abajo grabens resulted from tension caused by differential compaction of sediments overlying Precambian crystalline rocks. The position of the Abajo grabens during Tertiary time may have been a controlling factor in location of laccolithic emplacement.

LOCKHART BASIN

Lockhart Basin was totally remapped on the ground; an extensively revised fault map is shown on Figure 19. The Lockhart fault has a maximum of 240 feet of down-to-the-south displacement; all of the other mapped faults in the basin have very small displacements of 1 to 20 feet. The appearance of the faults is similar to the faults in the Abajo Grabens area.

The Lockhart fault trends northeastward through the northern end of Lockhart Basin. The basin itself has collapsed because of solution of underlying salt; approximately 1,100 feet of stratigraphic collapse has taken place. The role of the Lockhart fault in the basin collapse is suggested to be that of a conduit for ground-water movement to the Paradox salt (Huntoon and Richter, 1979; Thackston and others, this volume). Initial formation of the fault was caused by salt flowage, which in turn was caused by regional compression.

Figure 8. Spanish Valley Anticline

COMPARISON OF FAULT AREAS

A comparison of faults shown in the mapped area of Figure 3 to those in the Salt anticline belt and Needles zone has identified some basic differences in faulting that offer clues regarding the cause and age of faulting, and the question of rejuvenation of faults in the mapped area.

Nearly all of the faults in the mapped area (Figure 3) were cemented or mineralized with calcite, whereas those in the Needles fault zone are not. In the Needles zone (Figure 11) those faults exposed along the Colorado River occur as open or alluvial filled fractures that are not cemented (Figure 20). These features are described in more detail by Biggar and others (this volume). This suggests that different mechanisms may be at work, or that ground-water movement in the areas may have been different. McGill and Stromquist (1979) suggested that the Needles faults formed along pre-existing joints in the Permian Formation and that the whole zone acted as a gliding block on top of the Pennsylvanian salt when flowage toward the river occurred. Moreover, the faults in the Needles zone are thought to be very young (Biggar and others, this volume), which may account for the lack of the type of cementation observed in the mapped area.

The topographic configuration of the faults mapped is quite different than those of the collapsed salt anticlines in the northeastern part of the Paradox basin. The effects of breaching and collapse of salt anticlines has created abrupt vertical normal faults that bound the sides of the present day anticlinal valleys. Single faults or faults within grabens in the mapped area often occur in zones (or appear as shear zones) 1 to 30 feet wide. Faults bounding diapiric anticlines in the salt anticline belt, in contrast, are sharp single planes instead. Only three faults (Lockhart, Shay and Salt Creek) in the mapped area have displacements greater than 200 feet, which is generally much smaller than displacements in the salt anticline belt. This may be a reflection of difference of structural complexity in the subsurface in these two parts of the Paradox Basin.

AGE OF MOVEMENT ON FAULTS

Most surface faults in the Paradox Basin are thought to be Laramide (Late Cretaceous-Early Eocene) or older. However, a general scarcity of Mid and Late Tertiary and Quaternary deposits prevents a more definitive dating of the basin faults. The time of last movement on faults has yet to be documented; a candidate site for further investigation is the south fault of the Shay Graben, where pediment gravels of probable Late Tertiary or Early Quaternary age (Biggar and others, this volume) appear to be dispaced by the fault. A trench across this fault is planned for future studies.

ACKNOWLEDGEMENTS

The author wishes to thank DOE-Office of Nuclear Waste Investigations for support of investigations, and also appreciates the assistance of Noah A. Frazier and Stephen J. Kowall for review of this manuscript.

REFERENCES

Baars, D. L., 1966, Pre-Pennsylvanian paleotectonics — key to basin evaluation and petroleum occurrences in Paradox Basin, Utah and Colorado: American Association of Petroleum Geologists Bulletin, v. 50, no. 10, p. 2082-2111.

Cater, F. W., 1972, Salt anticlines within the Paradox Basin, in Geologic Atlas of the Rocky Mountain Region, United States of America: Rocky Mountain Association of Geologists, p. 137-138.

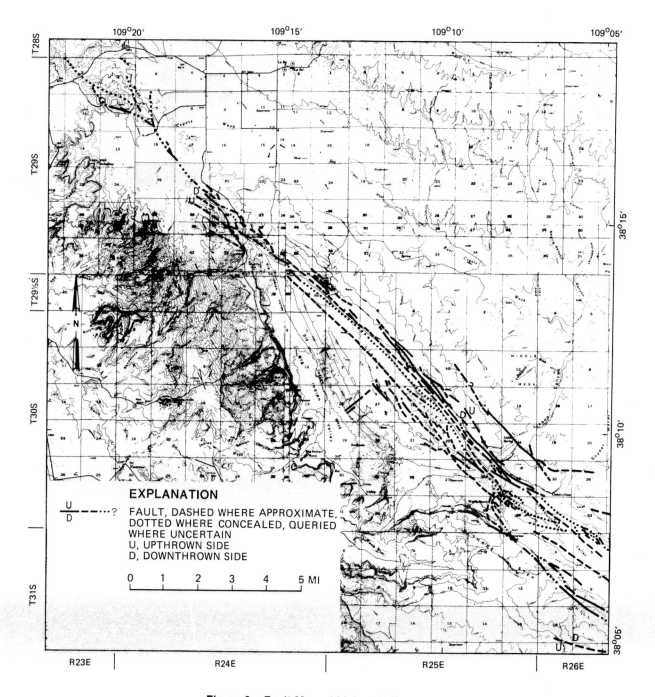

Figure 9. Fault Map of Lisbon Valley

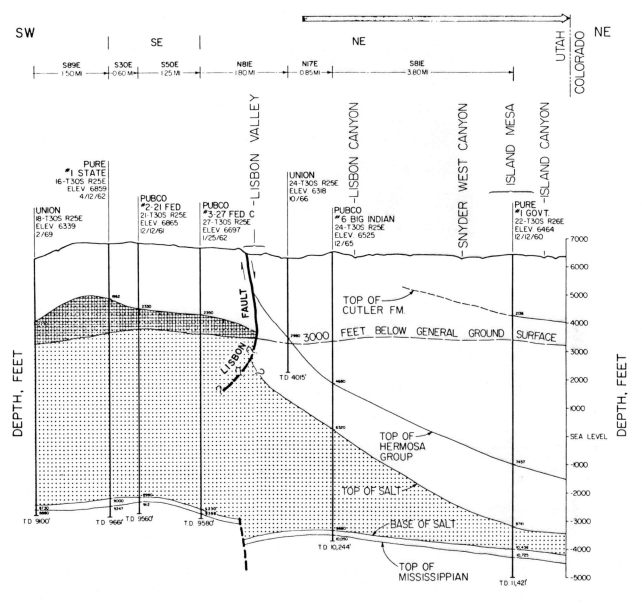

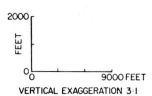

EXPLANATION

— — — ? FAULT, DASHED WHERE LOCATION UNCERTAIN, QUERIED WHERE INFERRED

— — — ? CONTACT, DASHED WHERE LOCATION UNCERTAIN, QUERIED WHERE INFERRED

ZONE OF PARADOX SALINE FACIES BETWEEN 1000 AND 3000 FEET BELOW GROUND SURFACE

SALINE FACIES OF PARADOX FORMATION

Adapted from Hite (1978); Heylmun and other others (1965); and unpublished well data (M. J. System, Inc.)

VERTICAL EXAGGERATION 3·1

Figure 10.   Cross Section of Lisbon Valley Area

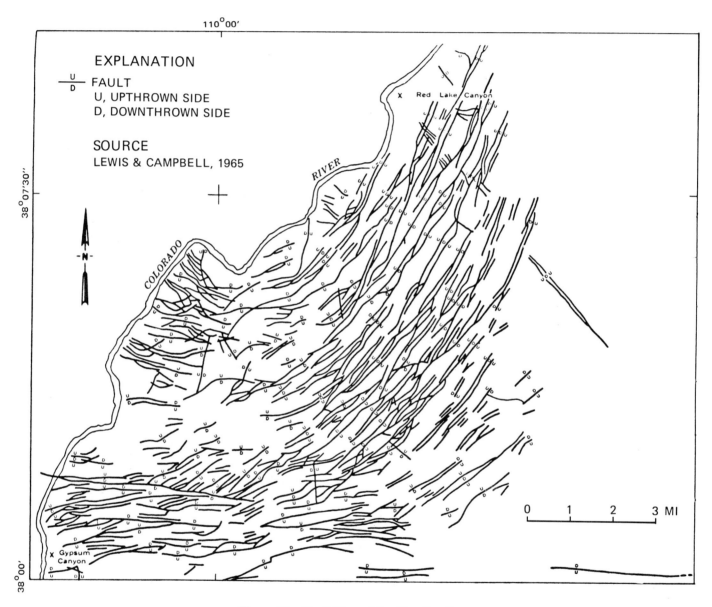

Figure 11.   Fault Map of the Needles Zone

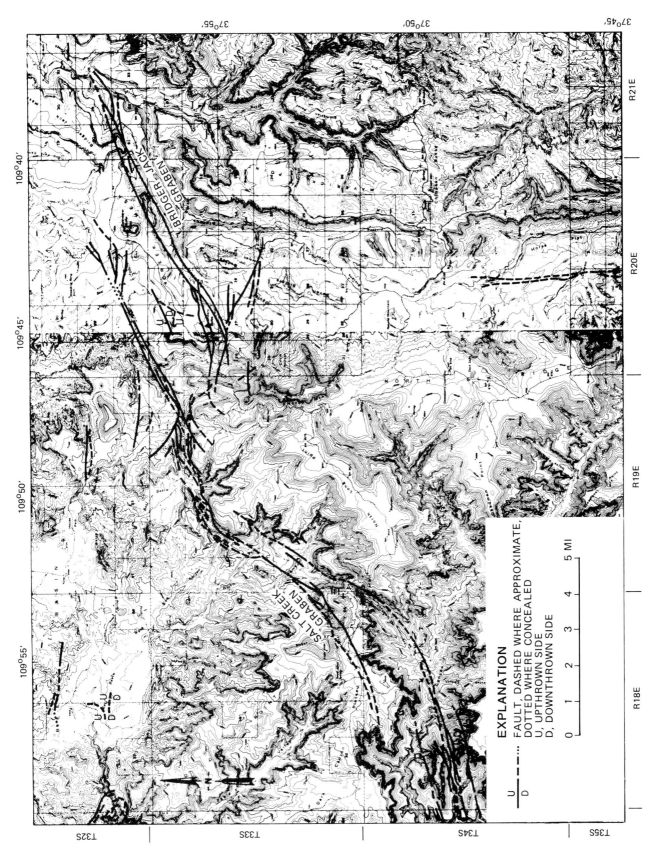

Figure 12. Fault Map of the Western Abajo Mountains

EXPLANATION

FAULT, DASHED WHERE APPROXIMATE,
DOTTED WHERE CONCEALED
U, UPTHROWN SIDE
D, DOWNTHROWN SIDE

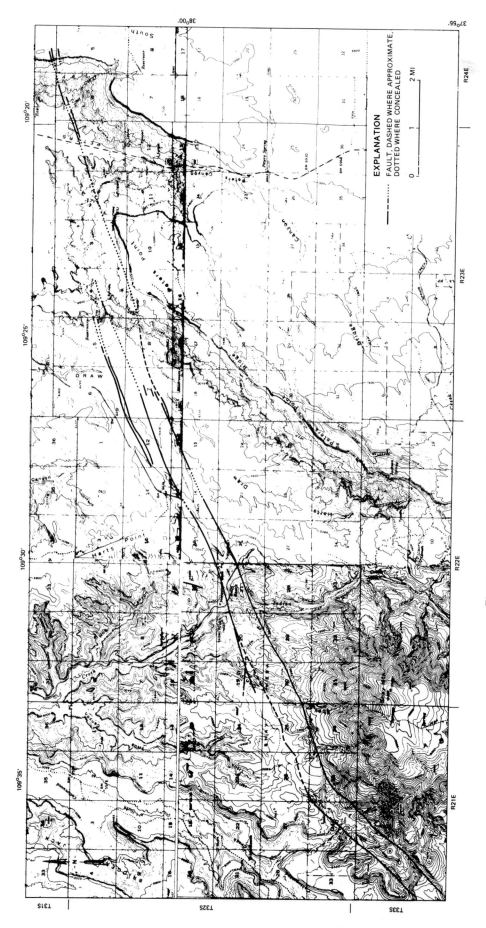

Figure 13. Fault Map of the Shay Graben Area

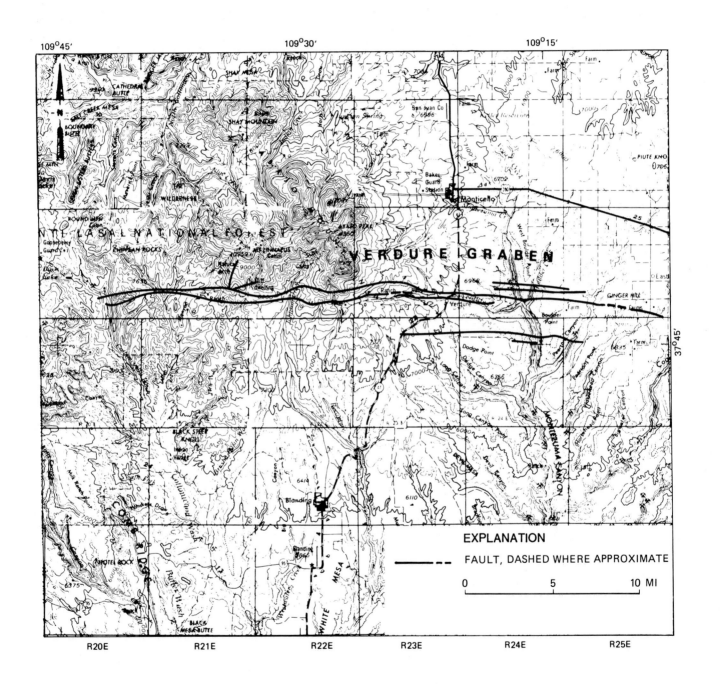

Figure 14. Fault Map of the Verdure Graben Area

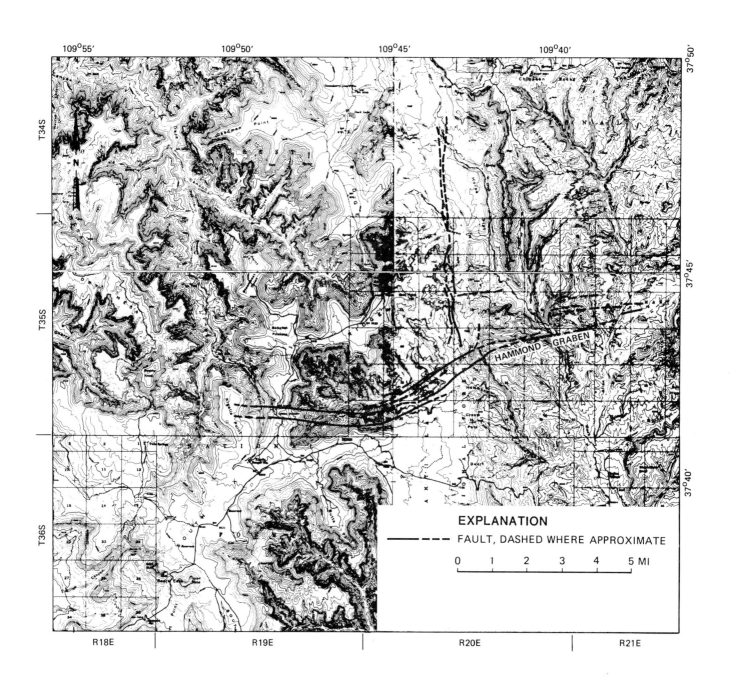

Figure 15. Fault Map of the Hammond Graben Area

Figure 16. Typical Ground Expression of Faults

Figure 17. Example of Slickensides

Figure 18. Aerial View of Shay Graben

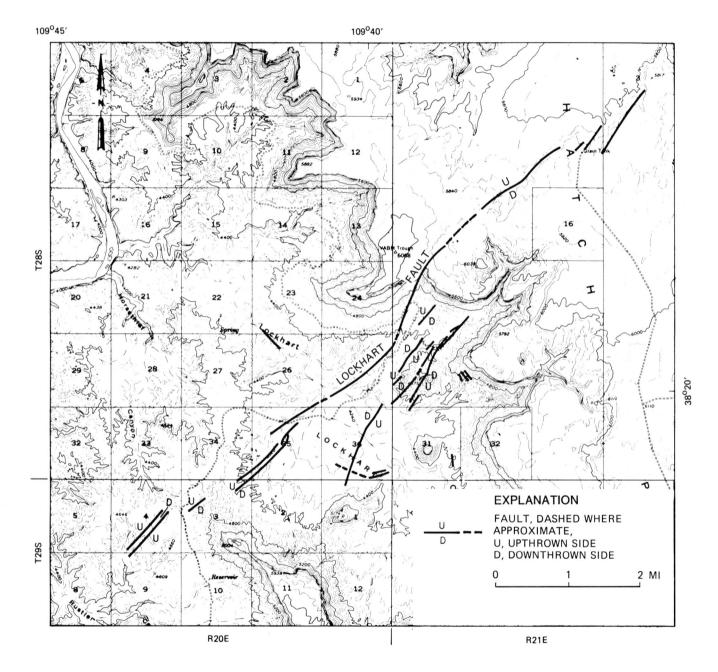

Figure 19. Fault Map of Lockhart Basin

Open fractures typical of   Alluvium-filled fracture   Close-up of alluvium in
this zone   fracture

Figure 20. Tensional Faults — Needles Fault Zone

Cashion, W. B., 1973, Geologic and structure map of the Grand Junction Quadrangle, Colorado and Utah: U.S. Geological Survey Map I-736, Scale 1:250,000, two sheets.

Elston, D. P., and Shoemaker, E. M., 1961, Preliminary structure contour map on top of salt in the Paradox Member of the Hermosa Formation in the Salt Anticline region, Colorado and Utah: U.S. Geological Survey Oil & Gas Investigations Map OM-205, scale 1:250,000.

Hackman, Robert J., and Wyant, Donald G., 1973, Geology, structure and uranium deposits of the Escalante quadrangle, Utah and Arizona: U.S. Geological Survey Map I-744, 1:250,000 scale.

Haynes, D. D., Vogel, J. D., and Wyant, D. G., 1972, Geology, structure and uranium deposits of the Cortez quadrangle Colorado and Utah: U.S. Geological Survey Map I-629, 1:250,000 scale.

Heylmun, E. B., Cohenour, R. E., and Kayser, R. B., 1965, Drilling records for oil and gas in Utah 1954 to 1963: Utah Geological and Mineralogical Survey Bulletin 74, 518 p.

Hite, R. J., and Lohman, S. W., 1973, Geological appraisal of Paradox Basin salt deposits for waste emplacement: U.S. Geological Survey Open File Report 73-114, 75 p.

Hite, R. J., 1978, Geology of the Lisbon Valley potash deposits, San Juan County, Utah: U.S. Geological Survey Open File Report 78-148, 21 p.

Hunt, C. B., 1969, Geologic history of the Colorado River: U.S. Geological Survey Professional Paper 669-C, p. 59-130.

Huntoon, P. W., and Richter, H. R., 1979, Breccia pipes in the vicinity of Lockhart Basin, Canyonlands area, Utah: Four Corners Geological Society Guidebook, 9th Field Conference, p. 47-53.

Lewis, R. G., and Campbell, R. H., 1965, Geology and uranium deposits of Elk Ridge and vicinity, San Juan County, Utah: U.S. Geological Survey Professional Paper 474B, 69 p.

McGill, G. E. and Stromquist, N. W., 1979, The grabens of Canyonlands National Park Utah: Geometry, mechanics and kinematics, Journal of Geophysical Research, v. 84, no. 89, p. 4547-4563.

McKnight, E. T., 1940, Geology of area between Green and Colorado Rivers, Grand and San Juan Counties, Utah: U.S. Geological Survey Bulletin 908, 147 p.

Richmond, G. M., 1962, Quaternary stratigraphy of the La Sal Mountains, Utah: U.S. Geological Survey Professional Paper 324, 135 p.

Williams, P. L., 1964, Geology, structure, and uranium deposits of the Moab quadrangle Colorado and Utah: U.S. Geological Survey Map I-360, 1:250,000 scale.

Williams, P. L., and Hackman, R. J., 1971, Geology, structure, and uranium deposits of the Salina quadrangle Utah: U.S. Geological Survey Map I-591, 1:250,000 scale.

Witkind, I. J., 1964, Geology of the Abajo Mountains area, San Juan County, Utah: U.S. Geological Survey Professional Paper 453, 110 p.

Witkind, I. J., Lidke, D. J., and McBroome, L. A., 1978, Preliminary geologic map of the Price 1x2 Quadrangle, Utah: U.S. Geological Survey Open File Report 78-465, scale 1:250,000.

Woodward-Clyde Consultants, 1980, Overview of the regional geology of the Paradox Basin Study Region, Sections 5 and 6, Office of Nuclear Waste Isolation, ONWI-92.

Twin Rocks near Bluff, Utah (Photo by Jack Rathbone)

TECTONIC EVOLUTION OF THE PARADOX BASIN, UTAH & COLORADO

D. L. BAARS
Consulting Geologist
Evergreen, Colorado

and

G. M. STEVENSON
Tierra Petroleum Corp.
Denver, Colorado

INTRODUCTION

The Paradox basin of the eastern Colorado Plateau Province is a paleotectonic depression of Late Paleozoic age. The boundaries of the basin are ususally defined by the geographic extent of salt deposited during Middle Pennsylvanian time in the Paradox Formation. Consequently, there is little or no reflection of the buried basin at the surface, except for the salt diapirs in the "Paradox fold and fault belt". The basin is bounded on the northeast and east by the Uncompahgre uplift segment of the Ancestral Rockies orogenic system, and is surrounded along the remainder of its periphery by paleotectonically controlled (shallow-water) shoals. The ovate basin has a northwesterly orientation, extending from Durango, Colorado and Farmington, New Mexico on the southeast to Green River, Utah on the northwest.

Although much has been said about the Laramide deformation of the Colorado Plateau and Paradox basin, the fact is that the structural fabric of the region was fixed by Late Precambrian time and repeated rejuvenations of the basement structure, including the Laramide episode, only modified the original framework. Tectonic features seen at the surface today were enhanced by Laramide forces acting from west to east, but the features were invariably present in some form by Late Precambrian time, caused by stresses directed from the north.

In the now classic work of Kelley (1955) it was suggested that the peculiar orientation of surface structures on the Plateau may be more closely related to deep-seated structure than to the Laramide overture. He was unable at the time to pinpoint the nature of the basic controls, but mapped several northwest-trending "lineaments" that he believed to be Precambrian or Paleozoic features. In the meantime, structural geologists have belabored the peculiarities of the Laramide "orogeny" to the exclusion of examining the older framework. Baars (1966) and Baars and See (1968) documented the Precambrian origin of several northwesterly faults in the eastern Paradox basin, and found evidence to support rejuvenation of the structures throughout much of Paleozoic time. It was not until 20 years after Kelley's publication that Baars (1976) attached regional significance to the northwesterly basement fractures and Warner (1978) described the northeasterly Colorado Lineament that together define a conjugate set of shears that unravel the mystery of the "Laramide" structural orientations.

BASEMENT FRAMEWORK

It was sometime around 1,700 m.y.b.p. that activity got underway on two major rift systems that transect the Paradox basin as we know it today (Figure 1). One, the dominant northwest-trending swarm of faults that passes through the San Juan Mountains of southwest Colorado and on into the subsurface of the salt-intruded anticlines of the basin, may extend as far to the northwest as Vancouver Island, B. C. and toward the southeast into Oklahoma's Wichita aulacogen (Baars, 1976). The subordinate northeasterly swarm of faults forming the conjugate set of fractures extends from Grand Canyon and beyond in Arizona through the Colorado Mineral Belt to Lake Superior (Warner, 1978). The northwest-trending set, called the Olympic-Wichita Lineament by Baars (1976), appears to have had right-lateral strike-slip displacement, and its timing can be bracketed to the interval 1,720 m.y. to 1,460 m.y. in the San Juan Mountains. The northeast-trending Colorado Lineament, dated at 1,700 m.y. by Warner (1978), displaced the basement rocks in a left-lateral sense. The two continental-scale rift systems form a conjugate set that bisect one another in the vicinity of Moab, Utah. Such a basic fracture pattern can only be formed from a situation where compressive forces were directed from the north in Precambrian time, or perhaps a more reasonable solution is a right-lateral wrenching stress imposed on the western United States that Wise (1963) referred to as the "outrageous hypothesis". The underlying mechanism, i.e., the "outrageous hypothesis" of Wise or compression from the north as proposed by Moody and Hill (1956), is a moot point at this state of knowledge. Recognition of the basic tectonic fabric provides a basis for understanding the "peculiar" structural features of the Colorado Plateau and Southern Rockies.

A review of the strain ellipsoid oriented to properly represent the conjugate fractures described above (Figure 2) indicates that we should expect north-south oriented normal faults to occur (east-west extension) in conjunction with the wrench faults. It is a consensus of many authors that the large monoclinal folds of the Colorado Plateau are drape structures over normal basement faults of Precambrian age; thus the monoclines originated as third order features of the stress field. Furthermore, the large bounding faults of the Colorado Rockies (the Gore, Mosquito, Cotopaxi, etc. faults) are north-northwest-trending normal faults that originated in Precambrian time (Tweto, 1980a) and appear to have resulted from the same basic mechanism. Also, back to the strain ellipsoid (Figure 2), we should expect east-west-trending folding and thrusting (north-south compression) which readily explains the "maverick" east-west-trending thrusted anticlines of the Uinta Mountains. Unconformities

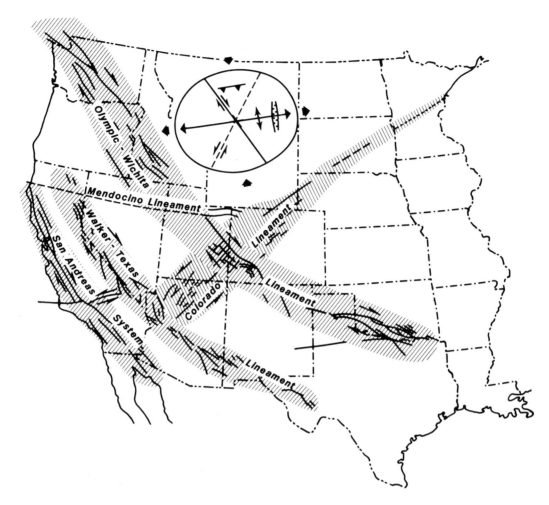

Figure 1. Map showing the location of major lineaments of the western United States. The sense of strike-slip offset is shown by arrows; northwesterly lineaments are right lateral, northeasterly are left lateral. The stress-strain ellipsoid is oriented such that maximum compressive stress is directed from the north.

between the Precambrian Uinta Mountain Group and the overlying Cambrian strata clearly indicate that the east-west-trending fold of the Uinta Mountains is of Precambrian origin, and fits the stress field described. Thus the tectonic stage was set long before Laramide time, and most likely by about 1,700 m.y.b.p.

THE GRENADIER GRABEN

The Grenadier Range of the San Juan Mountains in southwest Colorado is a remarkable exposure of a segment of the Olympic-Wichita Lineament. The range is composed of more than 8,500 feet of quartzite and slate of the younger Precambrian Uncompahgre Formation, isoclinally folded and complexly thrust faulted, then eroded into an alpine array of craggy peaks. The younger Precambrian metasediments are faulted into juxtaposition with older metamorphic sequences, both terrains being buried by Paleozoic sedimentary rocks. When the significance of this setting was first described by Baars (1966) and Baars and See (1968) the range was naively believed to be a simple graben resulting from extensional vertical movements. It was recognized, but not fully accepted, that "yo-yoing" vertical displacement along the bounding faults recurred throughout at least Early Paleozoic time, as determined from detailed stratigraphic studies. A similar history was described for the Sneffels fault block near Ouray, Colorado.

It has now finally been realized that these large structural

features are but segments of a continental-scale wrench fault system (Baars, 1976). In the first place, the highly complex "crumpling" of the Uncompahgre Formation in the fault blocks is not consistent with vertical tectonics and the volume of sedimentary rocks "crammed" into the fault blocks is excessive. Secondly, the alternating sense of displacement along the faults is to be expected only in a wrench fault zone. The "yo-yo" effect was found to be present along the extension of the faults in the Paradox basin (Baars, 1966) and is common along basement faults throughout the Colorado Rockies (Tweto, 1980a). Tweto (1980b) further suggested that the thick Uncompahgre sequence was deposited only within or along, the rifted troughs. This seems unlikely since the volume of the palinspastically reconstructed basin is inconsistent with the available space. A better explanation for the limited distribution of the thick section is that it was rifted to its present site, perhaps from the sedimentary basin of the Uinta Mountain Group in the vicinity of the western Uinta Mountains. That the Uncompahgre Formation is presently dated as somewhat older than the Uinta Mountain Group using limited and indirect data is not conclusive evidence to nullify this interpretation.

FAULT REJUVENATIONS

The Colorado Plateau and Southern Rockies were relatively quiescent during Early Paleozoic time, however,

Baars (1966) and Baars and See (1968) presented conclusive evidence that minor rejuvenations along the Olympic-Wichita Lineament in the Paradox basin occurred during Cambrian, Devonian and Mississippian times. Although Early Paleozoic displacement on the faults was minor, sufficient vertical movement occurred to create local shoaling conditions and alter sedimentary facies on a local scale. This structural activity was responsible for isolating offshore sand bars in the Late Devonian McCracken Sandstone Member of the Elbert Formation and provided high fault blocks for the generation of crinoidal bioherms in the Mississippian Leadville Formation. The shallow-water sand bars and bioherms were to become petroleum reservoirs at such places as Lisbon Valley, S. E. Lisbon, Big Flat and Salt Wash fields. Where vertical structure was more severe, as at Wray Mesa on the southwest flank of Paradox Valley, the Mississippian reservoir was removed by erosion.

LATE PALEOZOIC HOLOCAUST

The relatively mild nature of the Early Paleozoic tectonic activity took a dramatic change by the beginning of Middle Pennsylvanian (Atokan) time. Vertical displacement along the basement faults of the Paradox basin and Southern Rockies began slowly, but picked up momentum as Middle Pennsylvanian (Des Moines) time progressed. The major uplifts of the Ancestral Rockies developed during this time as tilted fault blocks rising from the Precambrian wrench faults to become major sources of coarse, arkosic, clastic sediments. The Uncompahgre uplift rose to a height of several thousand feet, shedding uncounted cubic miles of clastic debris into the subsiding Paradox basin on its southwest flank. Up to 15,000 ft., perhaps as much as 20,000 ft. locally, of coarse clastics were dumped from the upland into the adjacent, deeper parts of the structural trough of the eastern Paradox basin. Although vertical displacement became definitely dominant over the former rift zones, east to west extension was the primary mechanism, perhaps accompanied by epeirogenic uplift, suggesting little change from the Precambrian stress field.

UNCOMPAHGRE-SAN LUIS UPLIFT

The Uncompahgre uplift, sometimes referred to as the Uncompahgre-San Luis uplift, has a complex history that is not completely understood because of poor exposures and limited subsurface data. Major uplift of the faulted highland began in about Atokan time from its southern extremity just east of Santa Fe, New Mexico northwestward to about Ouray, Colorado. Clastic sediments of Atokan age are relatively thick in the Sandia Formation of north-central New Mexico and an 800 ft. thick wedge of deltaic clastics in the Animas Valley north of Durango, Colorado attest to the early growth. This segment is the San Luis uplift of early workers. The San Luis segment continued its relatively modest rate of uplift well into Permian time.

A pronounced westerly arc, or flex, occurs in the shape of the highland just east of Ouray, paralleling a similar westward bend in the adjacent Sneffels and Grenadier graben (Figure 1). This arcuate bend in the basement faults is interpreted to be a left-lateral drag fold of enormous proportion caused by the Colorado Lineament. It also appears to occur at the northwestern termination of the San Luis (Atokan) positive feature. From Ouray northwestward to the northwestern plunge of the surface Uncompahgre plateau near Cisco, Utah, the middle segment of the Uncompahgre uplift did not begin shedding massive amounts of arkose until Desmoinesian (middle Pennsylvanian) time, but continued its positive tendencies well into Permian time. This northwesterly termination of the

Uncompahgre plateau also marks the emergence of the Colorado Lineament into the Paradox basin and Colorado Plateau. In other words, the middle segment of the Uncompahgre uplift, from Ouray to Cisco, is at least partially controlled by the right-lateral offset of the Colorado Lineament by the Olympic-Wichita Lineament, complicated by the left-lateral offset of the Olympic-Wichita Lineament by the Colorado Lineament.

The Northwestern element of the Uncompahgre uplift extends from about Cisco to the overthrust belt in the Wasatch Mountains just east of Provo, Utah (in the subsurface). This segment is known from subsurface and geophysical data to underlie the Book Cliffs and form the southern flank of the Uinta structural basin. It did not shed significant arkosic clastics until Early Permian time.

Thus, the "Uncompahgre uplift" appears to be comprised of three separate elements, with somewhat different histories of structural uplift, segmented at least in part by the basement rifts.

PARADOX BASIN

The Paradox basin formed adjacent to the southwestern bounding faults of the Uncompahgre uplift as a complimentary faulted depression (Figure 3). The deepest part of the basin lies immediately adjacent to the uplift, having stepped down structurally in a series of half-graben from the western and southwestern shelves, or structural hingeline (Figure 4). Restricted marine circulation resulted in evaporite sedimentation throughout most of Desmoinesian (Middle Pennsylvanian) time. Salt deposition began in very early Desmoinesian time in the deeper faulted troughs (Hite, 1960) and slowly filled the structural basin, burying the basement faults by the end of the epoch. Simultaneously, the Uncompahgre uplift was supplying ever increasing amounts of arkosic debris to the northeastern margin of the basin. The highland was continuously or episodically rising throughout the remainder of Pennsylvanian time, as the basin was sinking along the continuously active basement faults.

Normal marine waters entered the basin from several structural sags to replenish the salt supply to the Paradox Formation. The larger entryways were from the south through the paleo-San Juan basin, where carbonate rocks of Paradox age are thick, and from the northwest through a reentrant from the Oquirrh basin in the vicinity of Provo, Utah. The San Juan sag was bounded on the east by the San Luis (southeastern Uncompahgre) and Nacimiento uplifts and on the west by the Zuni and Defiance positive elements, all being high structural features from Cambrian through Pennsylvanian time. The Oquirrh entryway was bounded on the east by the northwest Uncompahgre segment and on the south by the Emery uplift, a positive structure beneath and west of the San Rafael swell growing during Pennsylvanian time and culminating in erosional stripping of the Pennsylvanian System at the close of the Period. Other connections to the open Middle Pennsylvanian sea may have been from the west (south of the Emery uplift) and from the southwest through the paleo-Black Mesa basin of northern Arizona. For details of the Pennsylvanian stratigraphy of the Paradox basin see Szabo and Wengerd (1975).

Most, if not all of the smaller structural features of the Paradox basin were in place and growing during Paradox time. These folds exist at the surface today, having been enhanced by Laramide compression, but they were sufficiently prominent in Middle Pennsylvanian time to significantly alter salt thickness. The best demonstrable example is the Monument upwarp, with its many smaller superimposed structures. The anticlinal and monoclinal

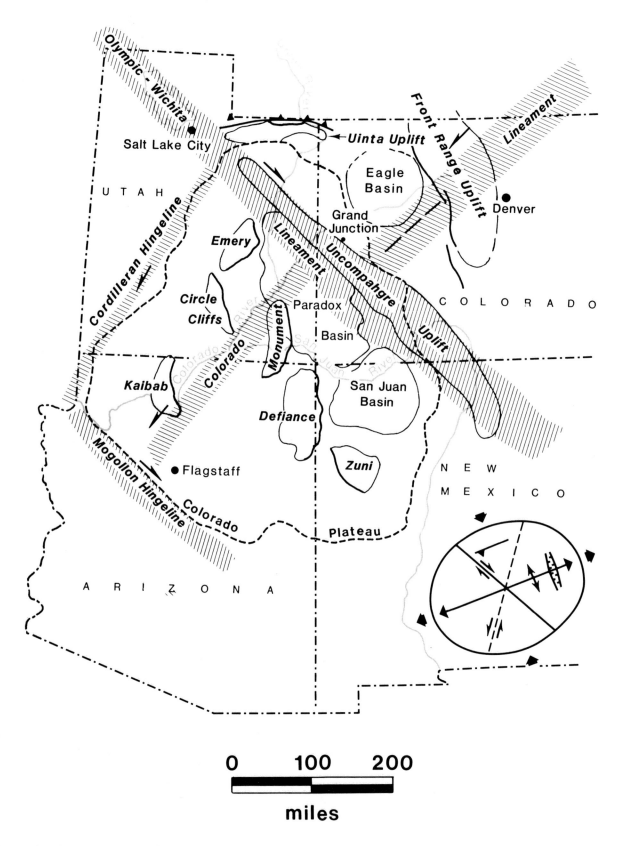

Figure 2. Map showing location of Colorado Plateau and relationship to major orthogonal set of lineaments. Northwest-trending lineaments are right lateral, northeast-trending lineaments are left lateral. Stress-strain ellipsoid oriented such that maximum compressive stress is directed from the north.

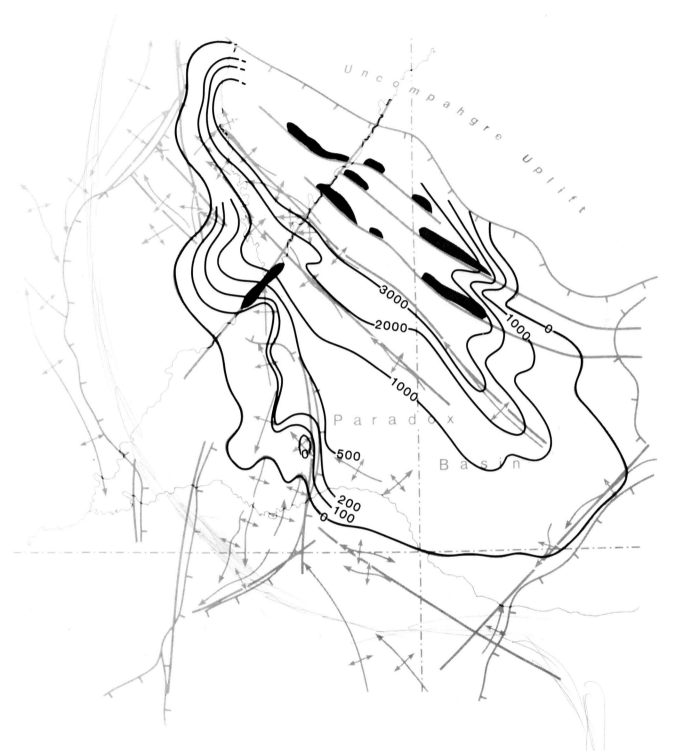

Figure 3.   Location map of Paradox basin. Basin outline is defined by the distal limit of Paradox salt. Contours are net salt isoliths of the Paradox Fm. Major anticlines and monoclines in the area are taken from Kelley (1955). Salt anticlines shown in gray with related northwest-tending basement faults (from Baars 1966).

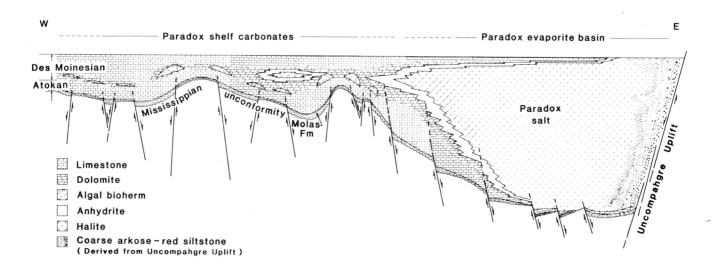

Figure 4. Schematic cross section across Paradox basin at lake Middle Pennsylvanian time, showing relationship of shelf carbonate to evaporite facies. Algal bioherms are shown in general relationships to basement structures. Salt diapirs are not shown.

structures on Figure 3 were taken from Kelley (1955) and superimposed on a net salt isolith map. It may be clearly seen that the zero salt isopach irregularly crosses the middle of the upwarp, and in some cases avoids small anticlines, such as Lime Ridge and Cedar Mesa. The salt also thins to zero over the Fish Creek anticline just to the north. The 100 through 500 ft. contours generally outline the Comb Ridge monocline and carefully wrap around the northern plunge of the Monument upwarp in the vicinity of the confluence of the Green and Colorado rivers. Farther to the northwest, the salt outlines Nequoia arch, a southeast-trending structural segment or extension of the Emery uplift. Thus, even the minor structures were affecting salt deposition during the Middle Pennsylvania Epoch, and definitely predate Laramide deformation.

Even less prominent positive structures directly related to basement fractures are present along the southwest shelf of the Paradox basin in the vicinity of the Blanding basin. These structures will be documented and their relative significance to the localization of Middle Pennsylvanian reservoir facies will be described in Baars and Stevenson (1981, in press).

SALT ANTICLINES

Perhaps the most obvious and certainly the most interesting structural features of the Paradox basin are the large, positive structures formed by salt flowage and diapirism in east-central Utah and west-central Colorado (Figure 3). This broad region, termed the "Paradox fold and fault belt" by Kelley (1955), overlies the deeper structural depression of the Paradox basin where depositional salt thickness may have reached 5000 to 8000 ft. The oldest and thickest salt deposits lie in the basement-controlled half-graben described above (Hite, 1960), but massive salt flowage has totally obscured other depositional characteristics.

The larger salt anticlines are strongly elongated in a northwesterly direction, paralleling the Uncompahgre frontal faults. This relationship prompted Stokes (1948, p. 14) to conclude "This regional uniformity of trend is evidently a reflection of important deep-seated breaks in the basement rocks that are part of a system of earth structures initiated in the Late Paleozoic at the time of the creation of the Ancestral Rockies." This interpretation was proven

essentially correct when Cater and Elston (1963), following geophysical studies by Joesting and Byerly (1958) and using subsurface well control, documented the existence of major pre-salt faults underlying the southwest flanks of the major diapirs. Further documentation of the existence of deep-seated faults was provided by Baars (1966), who also presented evidence to show their Precambrian age. A multitude of seismic surveys in the area in the past twenty years have left no doubt as to the existence of pre-salt faulting, and have shown the extreme complexity of the subsurface faulting.

As salt thickness reached a few thousand feet over the half-graben, thick arkose wedges, or alluvial fans, were being deposited along the transition between the Uncompahgre highland and the low-lying evaporite basin. The directional nature of the clastic overburden must have been a large factor in the initiation of salt flowage toward the southwest and toward the large basement faults (Figure 5). Drilling has proven nearly 6000 ft. of displacement along the fault underlying Paradox Valley anticline, and seismic surveys suggest that displacement may exceed this figure in some cases. Nearly 14,000 ft. of diapiric salt was penetrated in Paradox Valley. Thus, the deep-seated faults were major buttresses to lateral salt movement. Repeated displacement along the faults must have also contributed to triggering salt flowage. Rapid deposition of the arkose of the Cutler Formation kept the upward flow of the salt walls relatively rapid, and in turn the surface topography formed by the upward migration of the salt directed sediment-laden Pennsylvanian and Permian streams around the diapirs. The salt bulges may have reached the surface at times, causing sediments to lap up against the margins, but at other times sediments buried the structure only to be later truncated by piercement of the salt. Upward salt flowage was rapid in Late Pennsylvanian and Early Permian times, but slowed considerably in Triassic time. By the close of the Jurassic Period, the available salt had been depleted to the point it could no longer flow, and the growth of the salt anticlines died a natural death. The upward growth of the Uncompahgre source area ended in Permian time, and it was stripped by erosion and buried by sediments in Late Triassic and Jurassic times. The source of the ever-thickening clastic

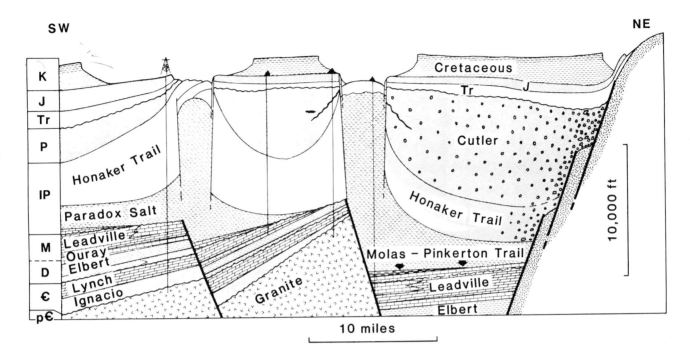

Figure 5. Schematic structural cross-section drawn normal to tectonic strike in eastern Paradox basin through Lisbon field and Wray Mesa region, showing relation between pre-salt faults and salt flowage structures (from Baars, 1966).

overburden was cut off as the supply of salt diminished, marking the close of an era.

Smaller salt pillows and bulges developed west of the larger diapirs, where the salt thinned by deposition and the arkosic overburden also thins. The salt definitely flowed to form these anticlines over basement fractures, as seen by salt thicknesses in drill holes and in underground potash mines in the Cane Creek anticline west of Moab. Besides the Cane Creek, other prominent anticlines that show salt bulges are Shafer dome, Lockhart anticline, Dolores anticline, and perhaps others. These were all actively growing in Permian time, at least, as indicated by thinning of the Cutler Formation along their axes. Meander anticline is a low-relief salt diapir formed over a northeast-trending basement fault of the Colorado Lineament. Upheaval dome in northern Canyonlands National Park is a circular, very sharp structural dome with a rim syncline. Although there has been much discussion regarding its origin, Upheaval dome is without doubt a salt dome of a type more similar to Gulf Coast domes than to the Paradox elongate anticlines.

THE GREAT COVER-UP

Growth of the major structures in the vicinity of the Paradox basin was for the most part completed by the end of Pennsylvanian time. Notable exceptions to this are the salt diapirs, which were still actively growing into the Mesozoic. The Uncompahgre uplift had probably reached its zenith by Permian time, except for the northwestern segment, and was undergoing denudation for the first half of the Permian Period, still supplying great quantities of arkosic sediments to the lowlands during its demise.

The Permian red beds from the Uncompahgre uplift finally buried the Nacimiento, Zuni and Defiance basement uplifts

to the south of the Paradox basin. They also buried the Emery uplift which had been stripped to the Mississippian level by Late Pennsylvanian erosion, and probably buried most of the salt diapirs, at least temporarily. The Monument upwarp remained sufficiently positive to cause major facies changes along its crest and flanks during the Permian.

There appears to have been little tectonic activity during the pre-Laramide Mesozoic Era, although, like the Permian strata, Triassic rocks thin over the larger structures such as the Monument and Defiance uplifts.

LARAMIDE DISTURBANCE

The Laramide orogeny is generally considered to be the wave of compressional tectonism that reshaped the western North American continent from the west toward the east during Latest Cretaceous through Early Eocene time. During this event the Colorado Plateau, as a whole, resisted the extensive thrust faulting that occurred to the west and south. It is interesting that the major tectonic lineaments of the region not only pre-date the Laramide, but in fact became the buttresses that resisted the thrusting. The northeast-trending Wasatch line (Cordilleran Hingeline of Figure 2), that marks the eastward extent of Laramide (Sevier) thrusting, had its roots in Precambrian time (Stokes, 1976), and defines the western margin of the Plateau. Similarly, the northwest-trending Walker Lane-Texas Lineament (Mogollon Hingeline of Figure 2) lies along the southern limits of the Plateau, terminating thrusting from the southwest. Where the two lineaments meet near Las Vegas, Nevada, the intersection forms a square corner (the "Grand Canyon bight") at the southwestern terminus of the province. Although not involved with extensive thrusting, the eastern limit of the Plateau is the Uncompahgre uplift on the

Olympic-Wichita Lineament. This rigid basement fault block may have played a major role in deflecting Sevier thrust faulting west of the Uinta Mountains as described by Stokes (1976). The southeastern limb of the rhombic Colorado Plateau "mini-plate" is the Rio Grande rift. The latter appears to have had a Paleozoic, if not Precambrian, history as well as the better known Tertiary movements.

The primary effects of the Laramide orogeny on the Colorado Plateau were the enhancement of pre-existing structures and the overturning of drape folds, generally toward the east. The amplitude on virtually all of the folded structures on the Plateau was increased considerably by this west to east compression, changing minor, low-amplitude folds into structures of major significance. Major monoclines formed over the larger north-south-oriented basement normal faults, having the effect of overturning the deep-seated faults toward the east and creating asymmetric folds with their steep flanks facing eastward. The west-facing monoclines of the northern and eastern Plateau (Kelley, 1955) were formed as draping folds over northwest or northeast-trending basement wrench faults. The east-west-trending Uinta Mountain arch and its marginal thrusted monoclines are simply greatly enhanced basement structure, as previously described.

Rather surprisingly, the principal structures of the Paradox basin proper show little or no effects from the Laramide disturbance. Most of these structures were salt-generated in Late Paleozoic time and were apparently little affected by Laramide compression. The salt-enclosed structures appear to have reacted like a "bowl of jello". The middle and southeastern parts of the Uncompahgre uplift were positive features at this time.

THE LARAMIDE SAN JUAN DOME

While the various elongate surface structures have been pondered endlessly by structural geologists, the relatively symmetrical San Juan dome has been overlooked, despite the fact that its domal shape is very un-Laramide-like. Although the major uplift had a complex Precambrian and Paleozoic tectonic history, the major elevation of the structure as seen today was of Laramide age.

The answer to the unusual symmetry seems apparent. As previously discussed, the basement fault blocks of the Grenadier, Sneffels and Uncompahgre structures bend sharply westward in exposures in the mountains, probably due to structural drag created by sinistral displacement on the Colorado Lineament in Precambrian time. This sharp flexure in generally vertical faults created a circular zone of weakness in the crust at the locus of flexure into which the Eolus Granite (1,460 m.y.) was intruded. The flexed basement faults along with the circular granitic body within the flexure are anomalous in plateau structure, but became the vertical manifestation of Laramide compressional strain, forming a circular uplift.

LARAMIDE CONCLUSIONS

We will only concede that the structural configuration of the Colorado Plateau and Paradox basin are of Laramide origin if the time framework for the Laramide is extended to include all structural events since about 1,700 m.y.b.p. The Laramide, as now defined, merely represents the disfiguration of pre-existing (basement) structure. Tweto (1980a) has presented a similar case for the origin of structures of the Colorado Rockies. Thus, in our opinion, there is no longer any mystery to the structural configuration of the Colorado Plateau.

AFTERMATH

Tectonic events following the Laramide disturbance have more effect on the geomorphology than anything else. Beginning shortly after the termination of Laramide time (probably during the Eocene) the entire Colorado Plateau province was gently, but bodily, uplifted and tilted toward the north. A regional vertical doming of central Arizona seems to have been the cause of the tilting. The end result was that surface drainage gained potential energy and surface erosion was accelerated. The early denudation of the province provided considerable amounts of sediments that were carried northward into a large lake (Lake Uinta) that formed between the structural buttresses of the northwestern Uncompahgre uplift and the Uinta Mountain arch on the north. The Paradox basin region was merely subjected to surface erosion.

The most prominent topographic features on the Plateau are the so-called laccolithic ranges that stand to elevations exceeding 13,000 ft. There are eight in all, and they appear to have been emplaced along basement lineaments (Kelley, 1955) or more likely at intersections of northwest- and northeast-trending basement lineaments (Witkind, 1975). Within the individual ranges, intrusive igneous rocks are exposed in the form of stocks, dikes, sills, laccoliths and cactoliths. They appear to have been emplaced at two distinctive time intervals. One group, including the Ute, Carrizo, La Plata and Rico Ranges, have been dated at between 61 and 84 m.y., or about Laramide time. The others, including the Henry, LaSal and Abajo Ranges were intruded around 24 to 48 m.y., or Middle Miocene-Early Pliocene (Witkind, 1975). It is interesting that the LaSal Mountains east of Moab were intruded along the basement faults underlying Paradox and Castle Valley salt structures and actually pierced the heart of the salt anticline. The resulting igneous rocks are peculiar aegirine-augite-rich syenite porphyries (soda-enriched) as a result of the intrusion through halite. The range was named LaSal (salt) Mountains by the early Spanish explorers, because they found saltwater springs in the mountains.

Late in the episode of regional tilting and during the intrusion of the younger laccoliths, general elevation of the Plateau occurred. Surface and groundwater drainage increased, and was gradually diverted toward the southwest along the Colorado River system, perhaps by a series of stream piracies along the route. Groundwater began to remove near-surface salt by solution on the larger salt diapirs; consequently, solution collapse of the anticlinal crests began. Overlying strata of all ages, from Permian to Cretaceous, slumped into the weakened crests of the salt anticlines, leaving them with gravity faults along the high flanks and jumbled slump folds depressed into the terminations of the anticlines as we see them today. Superimposed streams cut downward into the structures, sometimes at right angles to the anticlines, creating "paradoxical" river courses that cut across the structures rather than flow along the axial valleys. Thus, the name was derived for Paradox Valley, from which the name was derived for the Paradox Formation and subsequently the Paradox basin.

CONCLUSIONS

The tectonic evolution of the Paradox basin may be summarized as follows:

1. A conjugate set of shear zones transected the Paradox basin in about 1,700 m.y.b.p. The northwesterly rift has been named the Olympic-Wichita Lineament, the northeasterly set the Colorado Lineament. They resulted from relative compression from the north.

2. Related basement fractures were north-south-oriented normal faults from extension and east-west-oriented folds from compression.

3. Small-scale vertical relief along the fracture system was rejuvenated throughout Cambrian, Devonian and Mississippian time, creating localized reservoir facies on the high, shoaling fault blocks.

4. The Uncompahgre uplift and the compensatory Paradox basin formed along the Olympic-Wichita Lineament in Pennsylvanian time due to extreme E-W extension of the crust.

5. Salt-thickened and diapiric structures formed in Pennsylvanian through Jurassic time because clastic overburden on the eastern basin caused the salt to flow against and upward along the basement faults.

6. Laramide compressional forces from the west in Late Cretaceous to Early Eocene time enhanced the existing structures and overturned them toward the east in most cases. The salt structures were little affected. Monoclines were formed over the north-south-oriented basement normal faults, and the east-trending Uinta Mountain arch was enhanced.

7. Regional tilting of the Plateau province toward the north caused surface drainage to fill Lake Uinta with sediments stripped from the south in Early Tertiary time.

8. Intrusive igneous laccolithic magmas were implaced during Laramide and Middle Tertiary times at intersections of basement lineaments.

9. Major surface structures of the Colorado Plateau were not formed, only enhanced from rejuvenation of basement structure, in Laramide time. They resulted from a continuum of tectonic activity originating about 1,700 m.y.b.p. and continuing until the present.

REFERENCES

Baars, D. L., 1966, Pre-Pennsylvanian Paleotectonics-Key to Basin evolution and petroleum occurrences in Paradox basin, Utah and Colorado: Am. Assoc. Petroleum Geologists Bull., v. 50, p. 2082-2111.

_____ 1976, The Colorado Plateau aulacogen-Key to Continental scale basement rifting: Proc. 2nd International Conf. on basement tectonics, ed. Podwysocki and Earle, p. 157-164.

Baars, D. L., and See, P. D., 1968, Pre-Pennsylvanian stratigraphy and paleotectonics of the San Juan Mountains, southwestern Colorado: Geol. Soc. Am. Bull., v. 79, p. 333-350.

Baars, D. L., and Stevenson, G. M., 1981 (in press), Subtle stratigraphic traps in Paleozoic rocks of the Paradox basin, in Geological and geophysical rationale related to the deliberate search for the subtle trap: Amer. Assoc. Petroleum Geologists Mem.

Cater, F. W., and Elston, D. P., 1963, Structural development of salt anticlines of Colorado and Utah: Am. Assoc. Petroleum Geologists Memoir 2, Backbone of the Americas, p. 152-159.

Hite, Robert J., 1960, Stratigraphy of the saline facies of the Paradox Member of the Hermosa Formation of southeastern Utah and southwestern Colorado: Four Corners Soc. Guidebook, 3rd Field Conf., p. 86-89.

Joesting, H. R., and Byerly, P. E., 1958, Regional geophysical investigations of the Uravan area, Colorado: U. S. Geol. Surv. Prof. Paper 316-A, p. 1-17.

Kelley, V. C., 1955, Regional tectonics of the Colorado Plateau and relationships to the origin and Distribution of Uranium: Univ. New Mexico Press, Albuquerque, 120 p.

Moody, J. D., and Hill, M. J., 1956, Wrench fault tectonics: Geol. Soc. Am. Bull., v. 67, p. 1207-1246.

Stokes, Wm. Lee, 1948, Geology of the Utah-Colorado Salt Dome Region, with Emphasis on Gypsum Valley: Guidebook to the Geol. of Utah, No. 2 Utah Geol. and Min. Surv.

_____ 1976, What is the Wasatch Line?, in Geology of the Cordilleran Hingeline, ed. Hill, J. Gilmore, Rocky Mountain Assoc. Geologists, p. 11-25.

Szabo, Ernest, and Wengerd, Sherman A., 1975, Stratigraphy and tectogenesis of the Paradox basin: 8th Field Conf. Guidebook, Four Corners Geol. Soc., Canyonlands Country, p. 193-210.

Tweto, Ogden, 1980 (a), Tectonic history of Colorado: in Colorado Geology, ed. Kent and Porter, Rocky Mountain Assoc. Geologists, p. 5-9.

_____ 1980 (b), Precambrian geology of Colorado: in Colorado Geology, ed. Kent and Porter, Rocky Mountain Assoc. Geologist, p. 37-46.

Warner, L. A., 1978, The Colorado Lineament: a middle Precambrian wrench fault system: Geol. Soc. America Bull., v. 89, p. 161-171.

Wise, Donald U., 1963, An outrageous hypothesis for the tectonic pattern of the North American cordillera: Geol. Soc. Am. Bull., v. 74, p. 357-362.

Witkind, Irving J., 1975, The Abajo Mountains: an example of the laccolithic groups on the Colorado Plateau: Four

Witkind, Irving, J. 1975, The Abajo Mountains: an example of the laccolithic groups on the Colorado Plateau: Four Corners Geol. Soc. Guidebook, 8th Field Conf., Canyonlands Country, p. 245-252.

How are ya supposed to spell "Uncompaghre"
when ya can't even pronounce it . . . ?

COLLAPSE STRUCTURES IN THE PARADOX BASIN

Ray Sugiura and Catherine A. Kitcho

ABSTRACT

Circular to elliptical shaped collapse structures have been mapped in five areas of the Paradox Basin and San Rafael Swell regions of the Colorado Plateau. The collapse structures range in size from a few tens of meters to several kilometers in diameter and consist of a central block or core of infolded strata or brecciated clasts derived from overlying younger formations that have been displaced downward a few tens of meters to several hundred meters. The structures are exposed in sedimentary rocks that range from the Honaker Trail Formation (Pennsylvanian) through the Mancos Shale (Cretaceous).

The mapped collapse structures can be separated into two types on the basis of their size, type of downdropped block or core material and origin. The larger structures generally have a diameter of a kilometer or more, consist of a coherent block of infolded strata and are postulated to have originated from the downward movement of ground water, dissolution of underlying soluble sediments (limestone and/or salt), and collapse of overlying strata. The smaller collapse structures generally have diameters of a few tens of meters to several hundred meters and a core that consists of highly brecciated clasts. These structures are also hypothesized to have formed by dissolution of soluble subsurface strata by ground water. However, after the initial removal of soluble strata and subsequent collapse, these structures are hypothesized to have advanced upward by a stoping mechanism.

Most of the collapse structures in the Paradox Basin and San Rafael Swell regions appear to be associated with minor structural features, cross warping and small folds, that are superimposed on larger more regional structures. The time of origin of the collapse structures is not known, however, on the basis of structural and stratigraphic data, most of the structures are hypothesized to have formed before or during Tertiary time.

INTRODUCTION

Numerous circular to elliptical shaped collapse structures have been mapped in the Paradox Basin and San Rafael Swell regions of the Colorado Plateau. These structures range in size from a few tens of meters to several kilometers in diameter and are exposed in sedimentary rocks that range from the Honaker Trail Formation (Pennsylvanian) through the Mancos Shale (Cretaceous). The collapse structures consist of infolded strata or a core of brecciated clasts derived from overlying younger units. The structures are similar in appearance to collapse structures mapped in the Grand Canyon area of northern Arizona and parts of northwestern New Mexico. In the literature, some of the mapped features have been referred to by various names: diatremes, breccia pipes, explosive breccia, and cryptovolcanic structures. In this paper, the term collapse structure is preferred because it describes its general surficial expression.

Collapse structures were investigated as part of a regional geologic study for the Battelle Office of Nuclear Waste Isolation, a prime contractor to the U.S. Department of Energy, to evaluate the feasibility of siting an underground nuclear waste repository in the Paradox Basin. These features are of interest because they crop out on the surface and are known or postulated to extend vertically downward through several stratigraphic formations and could thus form possible conduits for ascending and descending fluids.

The purpose of this paper is to summarize the present knowledge of collapse structures: their characteristics, theories of origin, time of formation, and relationships to structures or other pertinent features. The data presented in this paper are based on a compilation of published literature and on limited field reconnaisance.

PREVIOUS WORK

Most of the collapse structures in the Paradox Basin and San Rafael Swell areas were mapped during the past three decades by government and industrial investigations involved in the exploration for mineral resources, primarily uranium. The most recent studies of collapse structures in the Paradox Basin include: Huntoon and Richter (1979), Cater (1970), Lewis and Campbell (1965), Weir and others (1961), and Gableman (1957). In the San Rafael Swell area, the most recent and detailed work was completed by Hawley and others (1965, 1968), Kerr and others (1957), and Keys and White (1956).

In addition, there are a number of references that describe the characteristics and origins of collapse structures mapped in the Grand Canyon region of northern Arizona: Shoemaker (1956), Barrington and Kerr (1963), Gableman and Boyer (1968), Gornitz and Kerr (1970), Bowles (1965; 1977), Watkins (1975), Hoffman (1977), Baillieul and Zollinger (in press), and O'Neill and others (in press).

OCCURRENCE AND CHARACTERISTICS

The collapse structures mapped in the Paradox Basin and San Rafael Swell regions of the Colorado Plateau occur in five areas: Spanish Valley, Lockhart Basin, the Beef Basin-Gypsum Canyon-Lean To Canyon area, Dolores River, and within the San Rafael swell (Figure 1). The following discussion briefly summarizes the characteristics of the collapse structures mapped in each of the five areas.

SPANISH VALLEY

The numerous collapse structures that have been mapped in the southeastern part of Spanish Valley (Figure 2) are located on the northeast flank of a syncline (Weir and others, 1961). The collapse structures are circular to oval in plan view, range in size from 30 m to 60 m in diameter, are bounded by semi-arcuate faults (Weir and others, 1961), and consist of a core of brecciated clasts derived from the adjacent wall rock and overlying younger formations. They are exposed in strata that range from the Navajo Sandstone (Triassic-Jurassic) through the Mancos Shale (Cretaceous) and are generally expressed as low mounds that rise from a

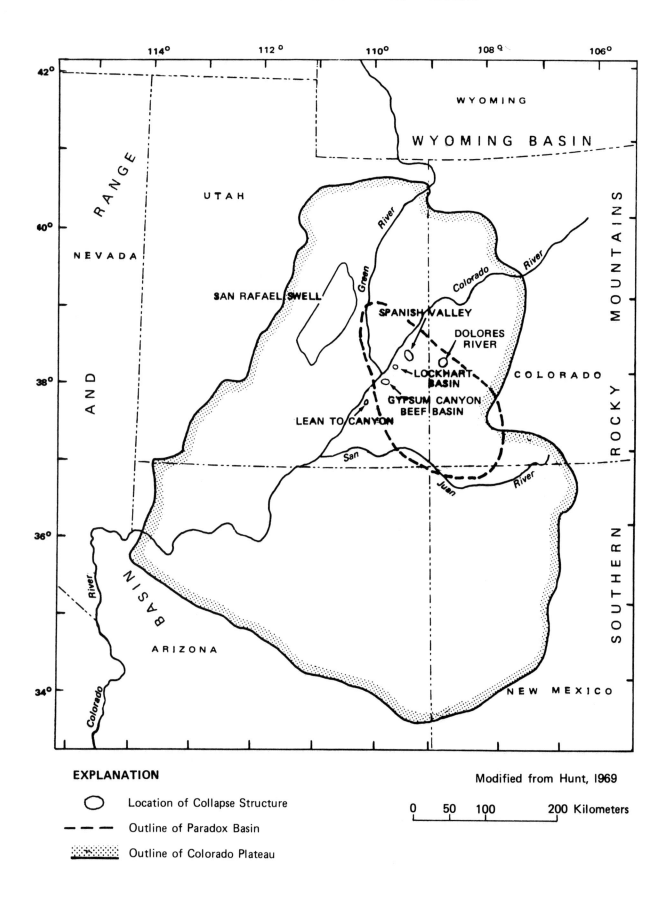

Figure 1. Index map showing the location of collapse structures in the Paradox Basin — San Rafael Swell Region of the Colorado Plateau.

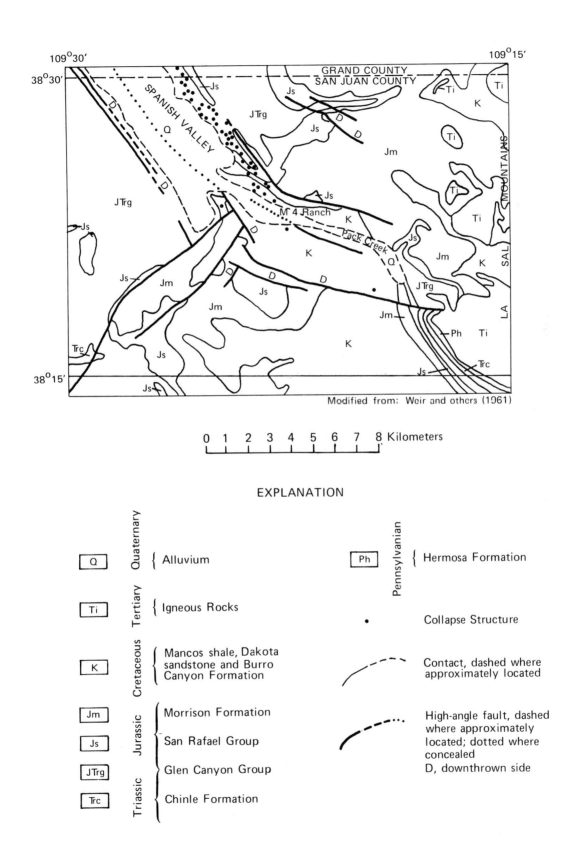

0 1 2 3 4 5 6 7 8 Kilometers

EXPLANATION

Q	Quaternary	{ Alluvium
Ti	Tertiary	{ Igneous Rocks
K	Cretaceous	{ Mancos shale, Dakota sandstone and Burro Canyon Formation
Jm	Jurassic	Morrison Formation
Js		San Rafael Group
JTrg		Glen Canyon Group
Trc	Triassic	Chinle Formation

Ph Pennsylvanian { Hermosa Formation

• Collapse Structure

Contact, dashed where approximately located

High-angle fault, dashed where approximately located; dotted where concealed
D, downthrown side

Figure 2. Generalized geologic map of the southern Spanish Valley area showing the locations of collapse structures.

few meters to 30 m above the adjacent terrain (Figure 3). Weir and others (1961) estimated a downward displacement of 60 m to 450 m for the brecciated clasts found in the collapse structures and hypothesized that the structures extend downward to and bottom out in the Honaker Trail Formation (Pennsylvanian).

Figure 3.   Aerial view of a typical collapse structure in Spanish Valley.

LOCKHART BASIN

Lockhart Basin is located approximately 8 km east of the Colorado River and 29 km southwest of Moab, Utah. The basin has a diameter of about 6 km and is characterized by infolded sedimentary rocks. Lockhart Basin was hypothesized by Huntoon and Richter (1979) to be a large collapsed basin similar in origin to the collapsed salt anticlines located to the north and east. They attributed the collapse of the basin and subsequent inward folding of strata to be the result of dissolution of salt in the Pennsylvanian Paradox Formation. An alternative origin for Lockhart Basin is given by Thackston and others (this volume).

Approximately 20 collapse structures have been mapped in Lockhart Basin (Huntoon and Richter, 1979, and Huntoon and Billingsley, unpublished data). On the basis of our field reconnaissance, twelve additional collapse structures were identified (Figure 4). Although the features are scattered throughout the basin, most are located in areas of minor folding, along trends of major inflection points of folds associated with the inward dipping strata, and along faults or within fault bounded blocks.

The exposed collapse structures consist of a core of brecciated clasts derived from units found higher in the stratigraphic section. The collapse features crop out in formations that range from the Cutler Formation (Permian) to the Moss Back Member of the Chinle Formation (Triassic) and are hypothesized to bottom out in the Honaker Trail or Paradox Formation (Huntoon and Richter, 1979).

The features are circular to elliptical in plan view, range from 10 m to 150 m in diameter, and form mounds of cemented breccia that rise from a meter or less to 30 meters above adjacent terrain. In most cases, the central part of the collapse structures are covered by talus. Where exposed, the

contact between the brecciated core and wall rock exhibits a distinct inward dip of the wall rock toward the brecciated core (Figure 5).

Most of brecciated material in the collapse structures is altered and/or bleached to a white or light yellowish brown that is distinct from the darker reddish brown to maroon color of the adjacent wall rock strata. In a few of the features, several distinct zones of alteration can be mapped that range from well-cemented unaltered brecciated clasts to highly altered clasts in a matrix of poorly cemented silt and sand (Huntoon and Richter, 1979). Individual clasts in the brecciated core vary in size from a centimeter or less to 3 m on a side. On the basis of identifiable brecciated clasts, Huntoon and Richter (1979) estimated a minimum downward displacement of strata of approximately 30 m and possibly more.

Figure 5.   Collapse structure in Lockhart Basin. Note the inward dipping strata (center of photograph) towards the brecciated core (left side of photograph).

GYPSUM CANYON, BEEF BASIN, AND LEAN TO CANYON AREAS

The Gypsum Canyon, Beef Basin, and Lean To Canyon areas are located at the north end and along the northwest flank of the Monument Upwarp, respectively.

The Gypsum Canyon collapse structure is located near the head of Gypsum Canyon (Figure 6). It is oval in plan view and consists of a downdropped block of strata approximately 1.5 km in diameter (Lewis and Campbell, 1965). The downdropped strata consist of the Permian Halgaito/Elephant Canyon Formations and the Cedar Mesa Sandstone Member of the Permian Cutler Formation. The downdropped block is bounded by several arcuate faults that dip nearly vertical to steeply toward the downdropped block. Displacement on the bounding faults increases from the ends of the faults toward the middle. Downward displacement of the block is approximately 40 m to 45 m. Strata surrounding the downdropped block generally dip toward the center of the block, which suggests that the block may have slowly sagged downward instead of being

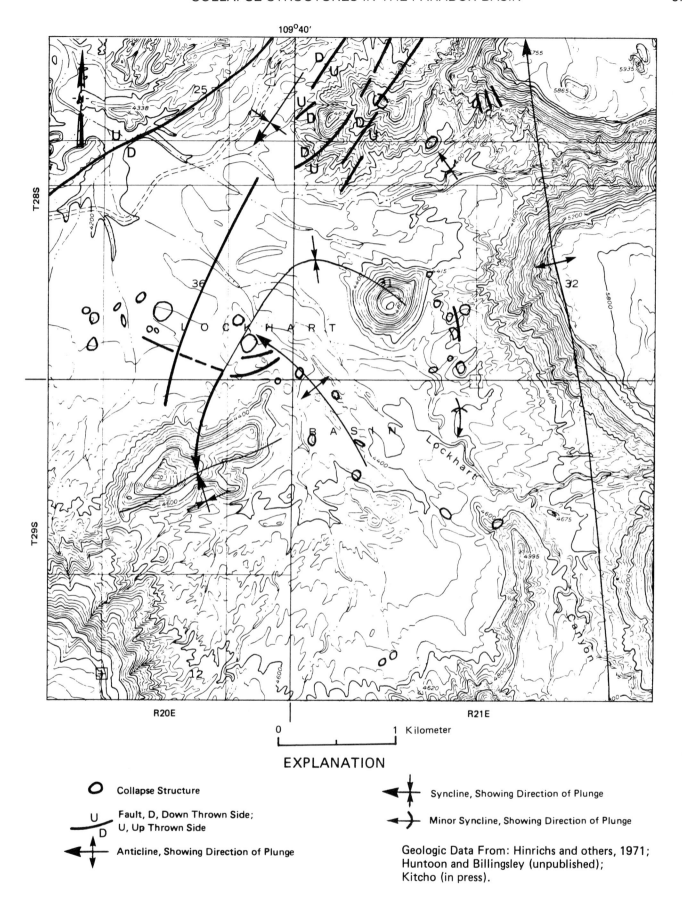

EXPLANATION

⬭ Collapse Structure

Fault, D, Down Thrown Side;
U, Up Thrown Side

Anticline, Showing Direction of Plunge

Syncline, Showing Direction of Plunge

Minor Syncline, Showing Direction of Plunge

Geologic Data From: Hinrichs and others, 1971;
Huntoon and Billingsley (unpublished);
Kitcho (in press).

Figure 4. Map showing location of collapse and generalized geologic structure in the Lockhart Basin area.

displaced abruptly by movement along the bounding faults.

Beef Basin (Figure 6) is inferred to be a collapse structure on the basis of its structural relationship with the Monument Upwarp, primarily because of the reversal in dip of the strata on the north plunging nose of the upwarp (Lewis and Campbell, 1965). Field reconnaissance along the south side of the Beef Basin also showed a steepening of dip from east to west along the anticlinal bend mapped by Lewis and Campbell (1965).

The collapse structure in Lean To Canyon (Figure 7) is similar to the Gypsum Canyon and Beef Basin features, but it is approximately 100 m in diameter and the downdropped block is bounded by linear faults. The downdropped block is composed of the Pennsylvanian Honaker Trail and Permian Halgaito/Elephant Canyon formations. Displacement along the bounding faults is greatest in the vicinity of the downdropped block and decreases toward the ends of the faults.

DOLORES RIVER

The Dolores River collapse structure is located along the Dolores River approximately 4 km northeast of the edge of Paradox Valley (Figure 8). The feature is circular in plan view and is bounded by concentric arcuate faults (Cater, 1970). The downdropped block (Figure 9) is capped by the Salt Wash Member of the Morrison Formation (Jurassic). Cater (1970) estimated a displacement of about 275 m for the downdropped block.

SAN RAFAEL SWELL AREA

Eleven collapse structures have been mapped in the San Rafael Swell area (Figure 10) (Hawley and others, 1968; Kerr and others, 1957; Keys and White, 1956). Eight of the features are located near Temple Mountain in the southeastern part of the swell. The other features are located north of Tomsich Butte on the west side of the swell and west of Window Butte at the north end of the swell. The collapse structures in the San Rafael Swell are the most well known in the Paradox Basin-San Rafael Swell area and were studied in detail during the exploration for uranium deposits during the 1950s and 1960s.

In general, all the collapse structures in the San Rafael Swell area are circular to elliptical in plan view, range in average diameter from 10 m to 150 m, and have a distinct brecciated core that consists of clasts from both the adjacent wall rock and overlying younger formations. Strata around the collapse structures dip inward toward the brecciated core. Most of the collapse structures are located within areas of cross warping or subsidiary folding (Hawley and others, 1968).

The largest and most studied of the collapse structures in the swell area is the Temple Mountain collapse (Figure 11). This collapse structure is approximately 600 m long and 150 m wide and involves exposed strata ranging from the Moenkopi Formation (Triassic) through the Wingate Formation (Triassic). Strata around the edge of the collapse area dip inward toward the center of the collapse with dips as steep as 31°. The material in the downdropped brecciated core is bleached to a white to light yellowish brown color, primarily because of the reduction or removal of iron oxides from the original red colored strata (Keys and White, 1956). Intensity of the bleaching decreases from the center of the core outward toward the unbrecciated wall rock strata. The lateral extent of bleaching occurs most in the Chinle and Wingate formations and least in the Moenkopi Formation. On the basis of drillhole data, 90 m of downward displacement of strata has occurred at the Temple Mountain collapse structure (Keys and White, 1956).

The other collapse structures in the San Rafael Swell area have characteristics similar to the Temple Mountain feature except that they are smaller in areal extent. The maximum downward displacement reported in any collapse structure was approximately 240 m in the Reds Canyon collapse (Keys and White, 1956). Drillhole data from one collapse structure indicates that the collapse structures are probably not pipelike cyclindrical features but rather have irregular sides that widen or flare irregularly with depth (Keys and White, 1956). Keys and White also indicated that with the exception of the South Reds Canyon collapse structure, most of the collapse structures bottom out at or near the top of the Coconino Sandstone. Drillhole data from South Reds Canyon features indicate that this feature bottoms out well into or below the Coconino Sandstone (Hawley and others, 1968).

COLLAPSE STRUCTURE ORIGIN

The origins of the Dolores River, Gypsum Canyon, and Beef Basin collapse structures have been attributed to dissolution or flowage of salts in the Paradox Formation (Lewis and Campbell, 1965; Cater, 1970). Evidence that supports this hypothesis is the fact that two of the collapse features are located close to major structures that have undergone dissolution or flowage or salt in the Paradox Formation. The Dolores River feature is approximately 4 km northeast of the collapsed Paradox Valley diapiric anticline, and the Gypsum Valley and Beef Basin features are about 3.5 km south of the Needles fault zone, which is an area of major salt flowage (McGill and Stromquist, 1979).

The origin of the Lean To Canyon collapse structure is more difficult to explain, because it is located about 22 km southwest of the Needles fault zone, the nearest area to have been affected by salt dissolution or flowage. This structure, however, may be identified as a collapse structure on the basis of its similarity to the Gypsum Canyon, Beef Basin and Dolores River features and also because it lies at the intersection of two large canyons, Lean To Canyon and Dark Canyon, that have eroded deeply into the Pennsylvanian Honaker Trail Formation. Unloading of the overburden in this area may have resulted in the development of fractures in the Honaker Trail and underlying formations. Migration of ground-water along the fractures is hypothesized to have caused dissolution of soluble strata within the Honaker Trail or underlying formations, resulting in the formation of the collapse structures.

The origin of the smaller collapse structures in Spanish Valley and Lockhart Basin are hypothesized to be caused by dissolution of soluble subsurface strata (limestone and/or salt) by the movement of ground water, which created an initial void or cavities into which the overlying strata collapsed (Weir and others, 1961; Huntoon and Richter, 1979). These authors inferred that the collapse structures continued to advance upward by a stoping process. Primarily, ground water migrating upward along fractures resulted in removal of carbonate cement and weakening of the overlying rocks, which then collapsed into new voids or cavities.

Several theories have been advanced for origin of the collapse structures in the San Rafael Swell area. These include landslides, diatreme-like explosive volcanism and sinkhole collapse. Kerr and others (1957) cited evidence against these theories and postulated that the collapse structures are caused by dissolution and removal of soluble strata at depth, mainly the Kaibab Limestone and parts of the Moenkopi Formation, resulting in the collapse of the overlying strata. Keys and White (1956) and Hawley and others (1968) also supported this latter theory.

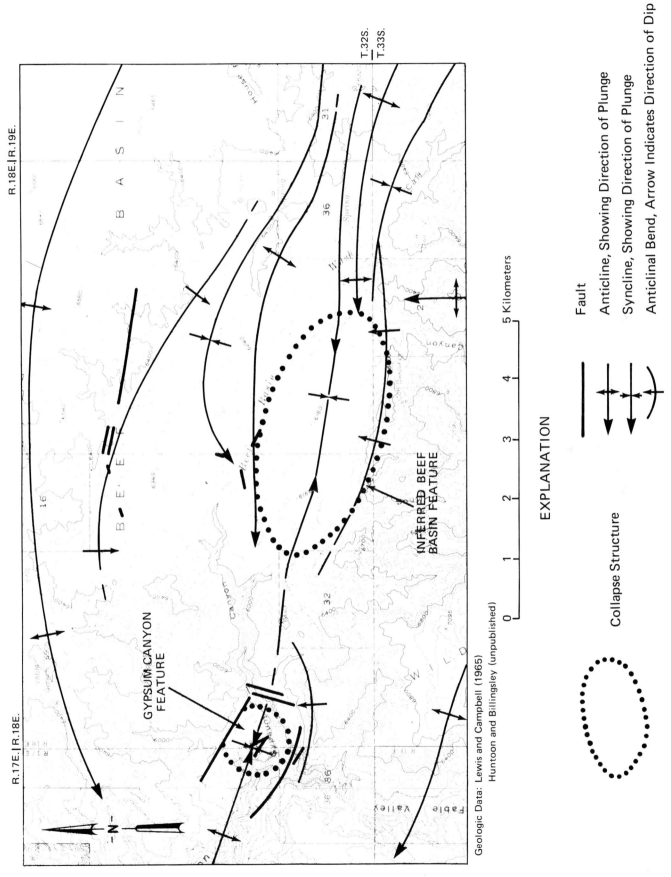

Geologic Data: Lewis and Campbell (1965)
            Huntoon and Billingsley (unpublished)

EXPLANATION

Fault

Anticline, Showing Direction of Plunge

Syncline, Showing Direction of Plunge

Anticlinal Bend, Arrow Indicates Direction of Dip

Collapse Structure

Figure 6.   Map showing location of Gypsum Canyon and Beef Basin collapse structures.

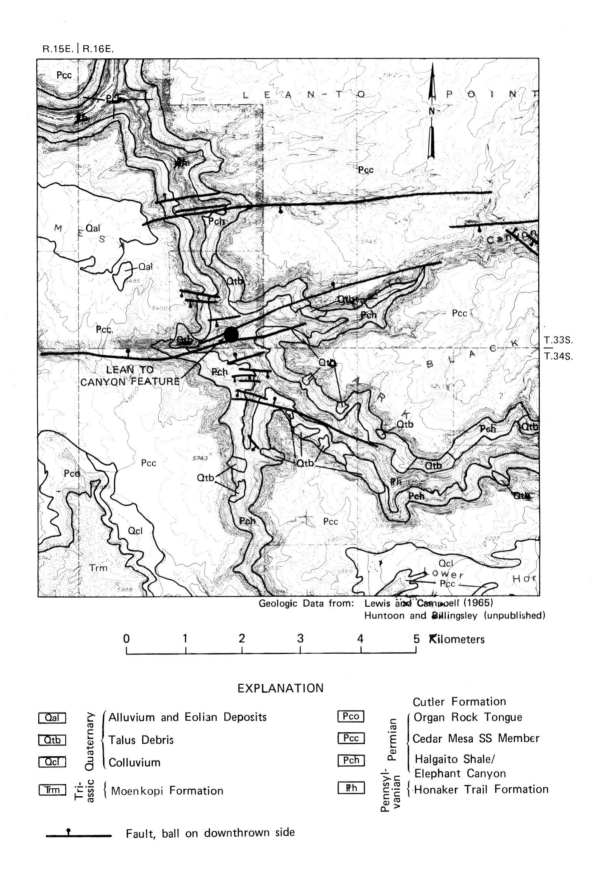

Geologic Data from: Lewis and Campbell (1965)
Huntoon and Billingsley (unpublished)

0   1   2   3   4   5 Kilometers

EXPLANATION

Qal	Quaternary	Alluvium and Eolian Deposits
Qtb		Talus Debris
Qcl		Colluvium
Trm	Triassic	Moenkopi Formation

Cutler Formation

Pco	Pennsyl-Permian	Organ Rock Tongue
Pcc		Cedar Mesa SS Member
Pch		Halgaito Shale/ Elephant Canyon
Ph		Honaker Trail Formation

Fault, ball on downthrown side

Figure 7.   Geologic map of the Lean To Canyon collapse structure area.

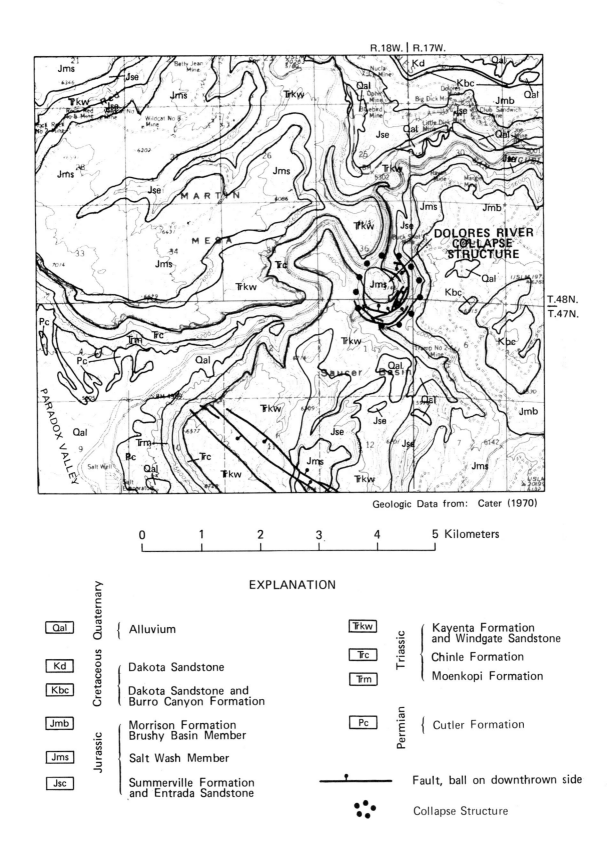

Geologic Data from: Cater (1970)

0 1 2 3 4 5 Kilometers

EXPLANATION

Quaternary	Qal	Alluvium
Cretaceous	Kd	Dakota Sandstone
	Kbc	Dakota Sandstone and Burro Canyon Formation
Jurassic	Jmb	Morrison Formation Brushy Basin Member
	Jms	Salt Wash Member
	Jsc	Summerville Formation and Entrada Sandstone

Triassic	Trkw	Kayenta Formation and Windgate Sandstone
	Trc	Chinle Formation
	Trm	Moenkopi Formation
Permian	Pc	Cutler Formation

——•—— Fault, ball on downthrown side

Collapse Structure

Figure 8.   Geologic map of the Dolores River collapse structure area.

Figure 9. Aerial view of the Dolores River collapse structure. The down dropped block in the center of photograph is capped by the Salt Wash Member of the Morrison Formation.

The collapse structures in the Grand Canyon region of northern Arizona, which have similar characteristics to the Spanish Valley, Lockhart and San Rafael Swell features, are hypothesized to have a similar origin: collapse of overlying rocks into caverns or voids followed by upward advancement by a stoping process (O'Neill and others, in press). The cavern collapse and upward stoping theory (Bowles, 1965, 1977; Gornitz and Kerr, 1970; and O'Neill and others, in press) proposes that the features were formed by collapse of overlying rocks into caverns or voids formed by migrating fluids (ground water or other aqueous solutions). Continued movement of the fluids into the developed cavern or voids and the above collapse zone dissolves additional carbonate rocks and cement, resulting in the formation of additional void space and continued collapse of overlying rocks.

RELATIONSHIP OF COLLAPSE STRUCTURES TO LOCAL GEOLOGIC STRUCTURE

Most of the collapse structures in the Paradox Basin appear to be related to local structural features. Detailed studies of features in the San Rafael Swell area indicate that they are located in areas that consist of localized minor cross warps and folds superimposed on the San Rafael Swell (Hawley and others, 1968). Similarly, the features in the Spanish Valley are located on a synclinal fold superimposed on the collapsed salt anticline (Weir and others, 1961).

Collapse structures in Lockhart Basin are confined to the collapsed or downsagged portion of the basin (Huntoon and Richter, 1979). Specifically, the collapse structures are located in areas of minor folding, along trends of inflection points of folds associated with the inward dipping strata and adjacent to faults. The Gypsum Canyon and Beef Basin collapse structures are associated with folds that appear to be superimposed across the nose of the Monument Upwarp.

The only features that do not appear to be within or be directly associated with structures are the Dolores River and Lean To Canyon features. Both these features, however, are located in or adjacent to major, deeply incised drainages.

TIME OF ORIGIN

Little direct evidence is available to evaluate the age of formation or last collapse for most of the features. The youngest formation affected by the collapse structures is the Mancos Shale (Cretaceous) and the oldest are the Honaker Trail and/or Paradox Formations (Pennsylvanian).

The Gypsum Canyon, Beef Basin, Lean To Canyon, and Dolores River features are probably related in time to the latest collapse of the major salt anticlines, which was estimated to have occurred during the Middle to Late Tertiary (Cater, 1980), or Early Quaternary time (Richmond, 1962; Biggar and others, this volume). A Tertiary age is estimated for the Spanish Valley features (Weir and others, 1961) because they affect strata as young as Late Cretaceous and are overlain by Pleistocene deposits. A Tertiary age is also probable for the Lockhart Basin structures, because the collapse structures were apparently formed after the collapse of the old Lockhart anticline, which probably occurred at about the same time as the collapse of the major salt anticlines in the area (Huntoon and Richter, 1979). The San Rafael Swell collapse features are believed to have formed at or about the same time as the formation of the San Rafael anticline, which occurred during Early Tertiary time (Hawley and others, 1965, 1968; and Kerr and others, 1957).

SUMMARY

Collapse structures in the Paradox Basin and San Rafael Swell areas have certain common characteristics:

- All are circular to elliptical in plan view

- Strata surrounding the collapse structures are generally infolded

- The downdropped portion of the collapse structures consists of sedimentary strata or clasts from units found higher in the stratigraphic section

- They extend downward from the surface to depths of several tens of meters to possibly several hundred meters or more

- All have hypothesized origins that are related to the dissolution or flowage of subsurface strata.

Mapped collapse structures can be separated into two types on the basis of their size, type of downdropped material and origin. The first type includes the Gypsum Canyon, Beef Basin, Lean To Canyon, and Dolores River features. These collapse structures are generally larger in size and the downdropped portion of the features are composed of a coherent block of strata. This type of feature is hypothesized to have originated from the downward movement of ground water, resulting in the dissolution of the underlying soluble salts in the Paradox Formation. The other type of collapse structure includes the Spanish Valley, Lockhart Basin, and San Rafael Swell features. These are smaller in areal extent, and the downdropped portion of the features consist of highly brecciated clasts in a coarse- to fine-grained matrix. Individual clasts range in size from a centimeter to a few meters in diameter. These features are also hypothesized to have formed by the dissolution of soluble subsurface strata (limestone and salt) by ground water. After the initial removal of the soluble strata and subsequent collapse, the features are hypothesized to have advanced upward by a stoping mechanism (Figure 12).

Most of the collapse structures mapped appear to be associated with minor structural features, cross warping and folds, that are superimposed on larger more regional structures. The two features not directly associated with

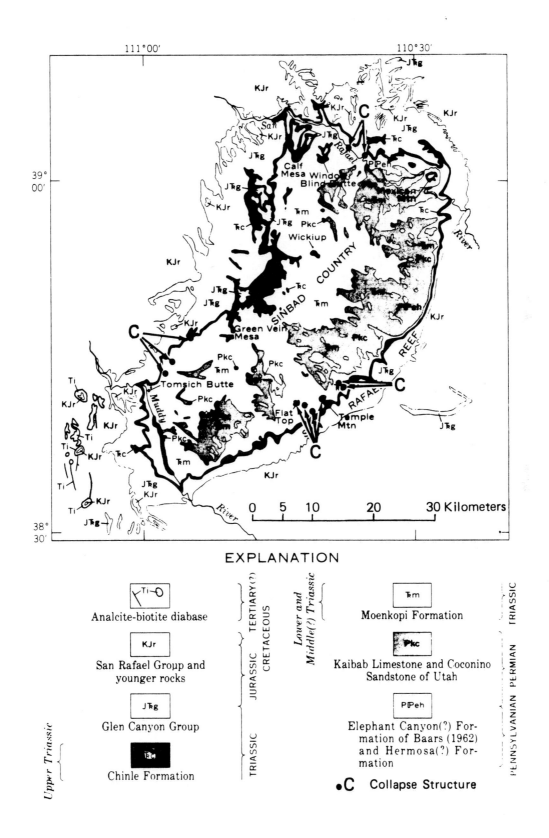

EXPLANATION

Upper Triassic

Analcite-biotite diabase

KJr

San Rafael Group and younger rocks

JŦg

Glen Canyon Group

Chinle Formation

TERTIARY(?)
CRETACEOUS
JURASSIC
TRIASSIC

Lower and Middle(?) Triassic

Ŧm

Moenkopi Formation

Pkc

Kaibab Limestone and Coconino Sandstone of Utah

PⱣeh

Elephant Canyon(?) Formation of Baars (1962) and Hermosa(?) Formation

●C   Collapse Structure

TRIASSIC
PERMIAN
PENNSYLVANIAN

Figure 10. Generalized geologic map of the San Rafael Swell area showing distribution of major rock units and collapse structures (From Hawley and others, 1968).

Figure 11. Temple Mountain collapse structure, San Rafael Swell area. Note the inward dipping strata adjacent to the light colored down dropped material (center of photograph).

structures are the Lean To Canyon and Dolores River collapse structures. These features, however, are located in or adjacent to major deeply incised drainages.

Although there is little direct evidence (such as datable material) for estimating the time of origin of the collapse structures, most of the features are hypothesized to have formed before or during Tertiary time on the basis of structural and stratigraphic data.

ACKNOWLEDGEMENTS

The authors wish to thank Peter Huntoon of the University of Wyoming for his guidance and for sharing current technical data of the Lean To Canyon and Lockhart Basin areas.

The authors also wish to extend thanks to Charles A. Jones of Bendix Field Engineering, Grand Junction, Colorado, for his assistance in locating information for northern Arizona, and to the Battelle Office of Nuclear Waste Isolation (prime contractor to the Department of Energy) for supporting these studies of collapse structures in the Paradox Basin area.

REFERENCES

Baillieul, T. A., and Zollinger, R. C., in press, National uranium resources evaluation, Grand Canyon quadrangle, Arizona: U.S. Department of Energy, Open-File Report.

Barrington, J., and Kerr, P. F., 1963, Collapse features and silica plugs near Cameron, Arizona: Geological Society of American Bulletin, v. 74, p. 1237-1258.

Bowles, C. G., 1965, Uranium-bearing pipe formed by solution and collapse of limestone: U.S. Geological Survey Professional Paper 525-A, p. A12.

Bowles, C. G., 1977, Economic implications of a new hypothesis of origin of uranium- and copper-bearing breccia pipes, Grand Canyon, Arizona, in Campbell, J. A., Short papers of the U.S. Geological Survey, Uranium-Thorium Symposium, 1977: U.S. Geological Survey Circular 753, p. 25-27.

Cater, F. W., 1970, Geology of the salt anticline region in southwest Colorado, with a section on stratigraphy by W. Carter and L. C. Craig: U.S. Geological Survey Professional Paper 637, 80 p.

Gableman, J. W., 1957, The origin of collapsed plug pipes: Mines Magazine, v. 47, p. 67-72 and 79-80.

Gableman, J. W., and Boyer, W. H., 1958, Relation of uranium deposits to feeder structures, associated alteration and mineral zones, in Proceedings, United Nations International Conference on the Peaceful Uses of Atomic Energy, v. 2, p. 338-350.

Gornitz, V., and Kerr, P. F., 1970, Uranium mineralization and alteration, Orphan Mine, Grand Canyon, Arizona: Econ. Geology, v. 65, p. 751-768.

Hawley, C. C., Robeck, R. C., and Dyer, H. B., 1968, Geology, altered rocks and ore deposits of the San Rafael Swell, Emery County, Utah: U.S. Geological Survey Bulletin 1239, 115 p.

Hawley, C. C., Wyant, D. G., and Brooks, D. B., 1965, Geology and uranium deposits of the Temple Mountain District, Emery County, Utah: U.S. Geological Survey Bulletin 1192, 154 p.

Hinrichs, E. N., Krummel, W. J., Jr., Connor, J. J., and Moore, H. J., II, 1971, Geologic map of southwest quarter of the Hatch Point quadrangle, San Juan County, Utah: U.S. Geological Survey Miscellaneous Geologic Investigation Map I-670, scale 1:24,000.

Hoffman, M. E., 1977, Origin and mineralization of breccia pipes, Grand Canyon District, Arizona: M.S. thesis, University of Wyoming, Laramie, 47 p.

Huntoon, P. W., and Richter, 1979, Breccia pipes in the vicinity of Lockhart Basin, Canyonlands area, Utah: Four Corners Geological Society Guidebook, 9th Field Conference, Permianland, p. 47-53.

Kerr, P. F., Bodine, M. W., Jr., Kelley, D. R., and Keys, W. S., 1957, Collapse features, Temple Mountain uranium area, Utah: Geological Society of America Bulletin, v. 68, no. 8, p. 933-982.

Keys, W. S., and White, R. L., 1956, Investigation of the Temple Mountain collapse and associated features, San Rafael Swell, Utah, in Page, L. R., Stocking, H. E., and Smith, H. B., compilers, Contributions to the geology of uranium and thorium by the United States Geological Survey and Atomic Energy Commission for the United Nations international conference on peaceful uses of Atomic Energy, Geneva, Switzerland, 1955: U.S. Geological Survey Professional Paper 300, p. 285-298.

Kitcho, C. A., this volume, Characteristics of surface faults in the Paradox Basin.

Lewis, R. Q., Jr., and Campbell, R. H., 1965, Geology and uranium deposits of Elk Ridge and vicinity, San Juan County, Utah: U.S. Geological Survey Professional Paper 474-B, p. B-1 to B-69.

McGill, G. E., and Stromquist, A. W., 1979, The grabens of Canyonlands National Park, Utah Geometry, Mechanics and Kinematics: Journal of Geophysical Research, v. 84, no. 89, p. 4547-4563.

O'Neill, A. J., Nystrom, R. J., and Thiede, D. S., in press, Uranium resource evaluation, Williams quadrangle, Arizona: U.S. Department of Energy Open-File Report.

Richmond, G. M., 1962, Quaternary stratigraphy of the La Sal Mountains, Utah: U.S. Geological Survey Professional Paper 324, 135 p.

Shoemaker, E. M., 1956, Structural features of the central Colorado Plateau and their relations to uranium deposits, *in* Page, L. R., Stocking, H. E., and Smith, H. B., compilers, Contributions to the geology and uranium and thorium of the United States Geological Survey and Atomic Energy Commission for the United Nations International Conference on Peaceful Uses of Atomic Energy, Geneva, Switzerland, 1955: U.S. Geological Survey Professional Paper 300, p. 155-170.

Watkins, T. A., 1975, The geology of the Copper House, Copper Mountain, and Parashant breccia pipes: Western Grand Canyon, Mohave County, Arizona: M.S. thesis, Golden, Colorado School of Mines, 83 p.

Weir, G. W., Puffett, W. P., and Dodson, C. L., 1961, Collapse structures of southern Spanish Valley, Southeastern Utah, *in* U.S. Geological Short Papers in the Geologic and Hydrologic Sciences, Articles 1-46, Geological Survey Research: U.S. Geological Survey Professional Paper 424-B, p. 173-175.

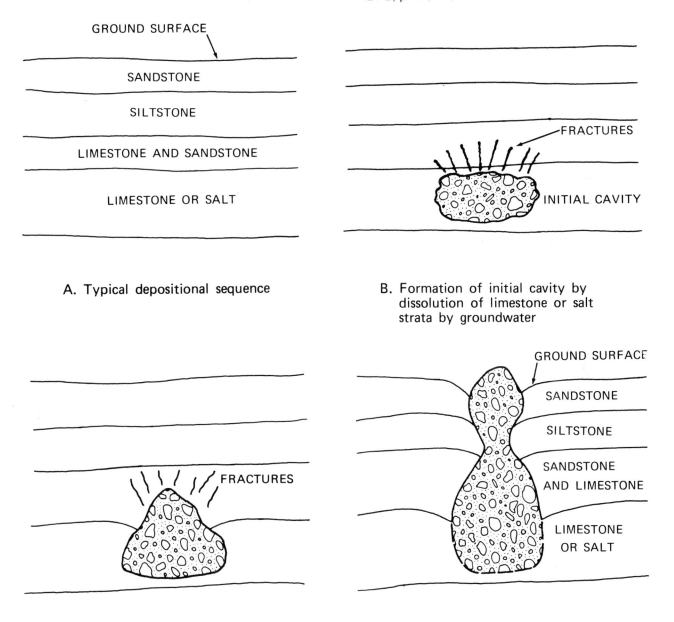

A. Typical depositional sequence

B. Formation of initial cavity by dissolution of limestone or salt strata by groundwater

C. Collapse of overlying strata into the initial cavity and formation of fractures in strata overlying the cavity

D. Continued development of the collapse structure to the ground surface by an upward stoping process, accompanied by inward dipping of adjacent strata

Figure 12. Schematic diagram showing hypothetical development of a typical collapse structure found in the Lockhart Basin, Spanish Valley and San Rafael Swell areas.

Delicate Arch, Arches National Park (Photo by Jack Rathbone)

BUG FIELD
T. 36 S., R. 25 & 26 E.
San Juan County, Utah

CONNIE M. KRIVANEK
Wexpro Company
Farmington, New Mexico

INTRODUCTION AND LOCATION

The Bug Field is located in the Paradox Basin in San Juan, County, Utah, near the Colorado-Utah border (Figure 1). The field produces oil and gas from a stratigraphic trap in the lower Desert Creek zone of the Paradox Formation. Age of the Paradox Formation is Des Moinesian. The field is 5 miles long and 1 mile wide. Nearest lower Desert Creek production is Papoose Canyon Field located 3 miles southeast in Dolores County, Colorado. Dove Creek Field, one mile east of Papoose Canyon Field also produces from the lower Desert Creek. Bug Field is divided by the northeast trending 800 foot deep Monument Canyon. The canyon's base elevation is 5800 feet and its top elevation is 6600 feet. The steep sides of the canyon pose a problem for future development well locations. The Dakota and Morrison sandstone formations are exposed on the canyon walls. Bug No. 1, 2 and 3 wells were drilled on the northwest side of the canyon on Cedar Point. Bug No. 4, 10 and 14 wells were drilled on the southeast side of the canyon on Bug Point, thus the derivation of the Bug Field name.

The 1980 Bug Field discovery was made 10 years after the Papoose Canyon Field discovery. The two key wells used to map the prospect were the Amerada No. 1 Federal Connelly well (Sec. 13, T. 36 S., R. 25 E.) drilled in 1971 and the Mountain Fuel Supply Company No. 1 Monument Canyon well (Sec. 31, T. 35 S., R. 26 E.) drilled in 1974 (Figure 2). Twenty feet of lower Desert Creek porosity was cored in the downdip Amerada well. A drill stem test of the zone, produced 2943 feet of salt water with gas to surface in 45 minutes, too small to measure. The shut-in pressure gradient was 0.62 pounds per foot. The Mountain Fuel No. 1 Monument Canyon well was drilled updip and the lower Desert Creek porosity was missing. An updip lower Desert Creek porosity pinch out was mapped over a broad southwest plunging nose in the area (Figures 3 and 4). The Bug No. 1 discovery well was drilled between the Amerada and Mountain Fuel wells. Kenai Oil & Gas, Inc. participated in the discovery well and is participating in the development of the field.

STRUCTURE

Regional dip across Bug Field on the Desert Creek Formation is southwest at 35 feet per mile away from the San Juan Mountain Uplift located in southwest Colorado. Dakota sandstone rocks that cap Cedar and Bug Points dip southerly 10 to 20 feet per mile.

The oil-water contact in the lower Desert Creek reservoir at Bug Field is about 35 feet low to the oil-water contact in the Papoose Canyon Field. The Bug Field reservoir is on depositional strike to the Papoose Canyon Field. The two fields are either separated by a gentle syncline or the reservoirs are not continuous.

REGIONAL PARADOX STRATIGRAPHY

The Paradox Formation is divided into five substage divisions. The Alkali Gulch is the oldest followed by the Barker Creek, Akah, Desert Creek and Ismay. With the exception of the Ismay, all have salt facies equivalents from Dove Creek, Colorado, northeast 60 miles to the Uncompahgre mountain front near Norwood, Colorado. The Paradox Basin trends 200 miles northwest from Durango, Colorado, to Price, Utah. Aneth, the largest oil field in Utah, is located 25 miles southwest of Bug Field. Aneth has produced 305,000,000 barrels of oil and 293,000,000 MCFG from Desert Creek algal mounds and oolite banks.

LOWER DESERT CREEK STRATIGRAPHY

Conventional cores retrieved from the lower Desert Creek in Bug No. 2, 4 and 10 wells exhibit a leached and dolomitized algal boundstone reservoir (Figures 6 and 7). These mounds show abundant Ivanovia leaves with good intercrystalline and vuggy porosity. Carbonate mud trapped by the algal blades is also dolomitized but exhibits poorer porosity. The mound exhibits thin interbedded zones of breccia and desiccation cracks. Faint and spotty fluorescence with abundant asphalt residue is found throughout the core. Anhydrite replacement is less than one percent. Average core porosity at Bug. No. 2, Sec. 7, T. 38 S., R. 26 E. is 11 percent and average permeability is 67 millidarcys. The interpreted environment of deposition for the Bug Field reservoir is an intertidal and supratidal algal flat. The zone attains a maximum thickness of 23 feet drilled at Bug Well No. 12, Sec. 19, T. 38 S., R. 26 E. The porosity trends northwest-southeast. Cores show the oil-water contact at plus 291 feet. The updip facies that forms the trap at Bug Field was cored at Bug No. 3 well (Sec. 7, T. 36 S., R. 26 E.). The cored facies between 6335 feet to 6346 feet (6342 feet to 6353 feet log depth) is mudstone, dark gray to black, dolomitic, dense, with no presence of oil and gas.

SECONDARY OBJECTIVES

Gas recoveries of 220 MCFGPD (DST 1, 4992 feet to 5070 feet) and 170 MDFGPD (DST 3, 5104 feet to 5142 feet) were recovered from Honaker Trail sandstones in Bug Well No. 4 (Figure 5). In the same well, 99 MCFGPD (DST 8, 6159 feet to 6182 feet) was recovered from the lower Ismay limestone. The lower Ismay also made 92 MCFGPD from DST 5 (6157 feet to 6198 feet) in Bug No. 12 well.

DRILLING PROCEDURES

A 12¼ inch hole is drilled to approximately 2000 feet into the Chinle Formation. The hole is cased with 9⅝ inch casing. This is required by the United States Geological Survey to protect fresh water sandstone aquifers beneath Federal acreage in the area. An 8¾ inch hole is drilled to total depth,

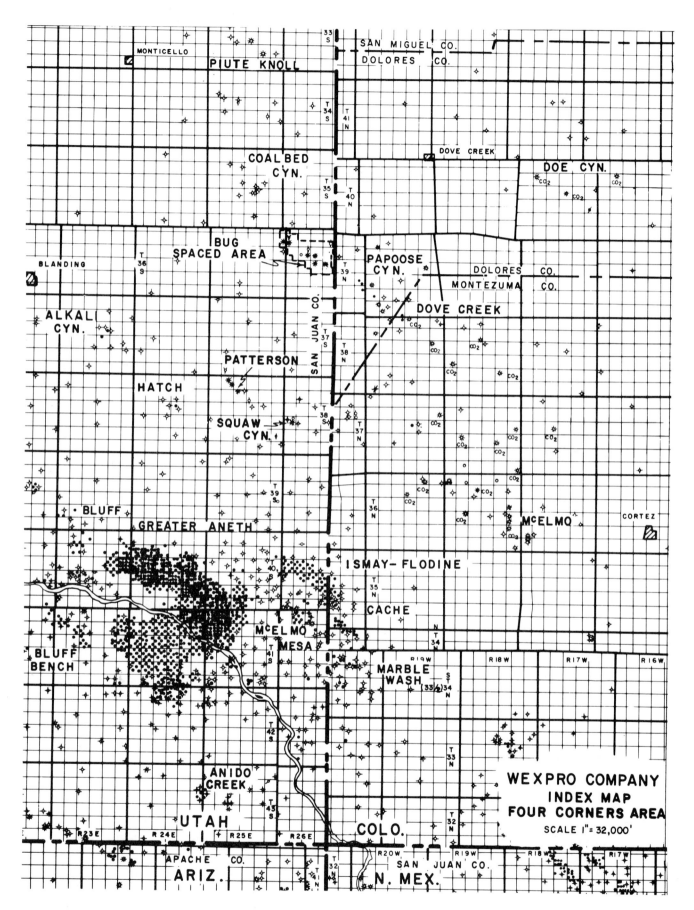

Figure 1

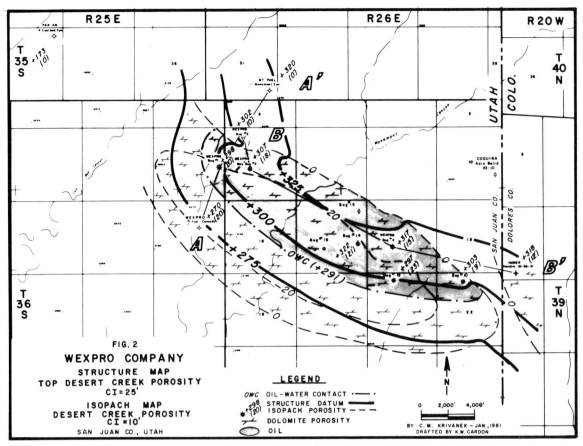

Figure 2

approximately three feet into the Akah salt. A fully manned logging unit is employed from 4000 feet to total depth. Gas shows that are detected by the mud logging unit are tested as the well is drilled. In most wells a 60 foot conventional core is cut from the lower Desert Creek porosity. A Dual Induction Laterolog and Compensated Neutron Formation Density Log are run below surface casing to total depth. The well is drilled with 9.1 pounds per gallon mud into the B Zone shale then increased to 11.4 pounds per gallon before drilling or coring the lower Desert Creek over pressured zone. If porous sandstone intervals in the Shinarump, Cutler and upper Honaker Trail formations have water flows or will not support the 11.4 pounds mud by losing circulation, a string of 7 inch intermediate casing will be run and the well completed by drilling a 6⅛ inch hole to total depth. To complete this well 4½ inch casing would be run to total depth.

COMPLETION PRACTICES

Assuming commercial oil and/or gas is indicated from drill stem tests, mud log gas shows, cores and/or log data, 5½ inch casing is run to total depth in the 8¾ inch hole.

The lower Desert Creek is perforated and 2⅞ inch tubing is hung above the perforated zone. No stimulation is necessary in wells with good porosity and permeability. Bug No. 4 was stimulated with 7500 gallons of 28 percent hydrochloric acid. Bug No. 10 was stimulated with 1500 gallons of 15 percent hydrochloric acid and 10,000 gallons of 15 percent crosslinked hydrochloric acid. Bug No. 3 well was plugged back to 1880 feet and surface casing perforated at 1096 feet to 1116 feet in the Entrada for a fresh water source well. While flow testing Bug No. 1 well the flow chokes were obstructed by salt crystals. It became necessary to flush metering equipment and tubing with fresh water. The standard completion procedure for wells that produce formation water and oil is to inject fresh water down the casing-tubing annulus to retard precipitation of salt crystals.

WELL COSTS

In 1980, a 6300-foot dry hole in Bug Field cost approximately $470,000. A completed well cost approximately $660,000.

OIL, GAS, WATER AND PRESSURE CHARACTERISTICS, SPACING AND MARKET OUTLET

The API oil gravity for the field is 47 degrees. The color of the crude is reddish brown. Gas BTU is 1197 with a specific gravity of 0.70. Formation water has 331,831 ppm total dissolved solids with a ph of 5.

The initial potential flow test for Bug No. 2 well was 838 BOPD, 1597 MCFGPD and 2 BWPD through a 19/64 inch choke. Flowing tubing pressure was 1700 psi and casing pressure was 2000 psi. Extrapolated shut-in pressure at Bug No. 1 well is 3579 psig at 6300 feet. The reservoir at Bug Field is assumed to produce under a solution gas and/or limited water drive. No gas cap has been found to date.

Bug Field is presently shut-in and waiting on a gas pipeline connection. A 12 mile gas pipeline will be laid northeast to Dove Creek, Colorado, where a gas plant will be built to strip liquids before the gas enters the 26 inch Northwest gas pipeline. A 12 mile oil pipeline will be laid southwest to Patterson Field then six miles west and connect to the Ute oil pipeline that connects Lisbon Field with Aneth Field.

The Utah Oil and Gas Commission approved 160 acre spacing in February, 1980. An extension to the spaced area was approved in October, 1980. An additional spaced area was added in December, 1980, by another operator on the northeast side of the field.

CONCLUSION

Undoubtedly, continued exploratory drilling in the Paradox Basin will produce new discoveries similar to Bug Field.

REFERENCES

Miesner, James F., Papoose Canyon Field, Four Corners Geological Society, Oil and Gas Fields of the Four Corners Area, Volume 1, page 154-155, 1978.

Wexpro Company, company files.

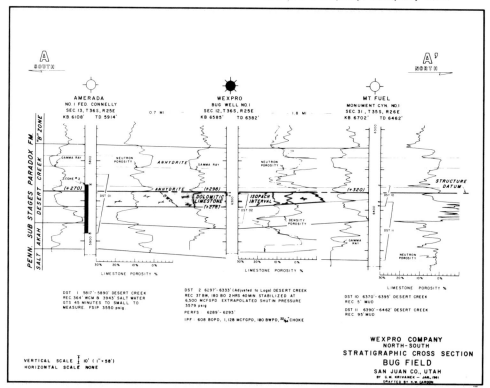

Figure 3

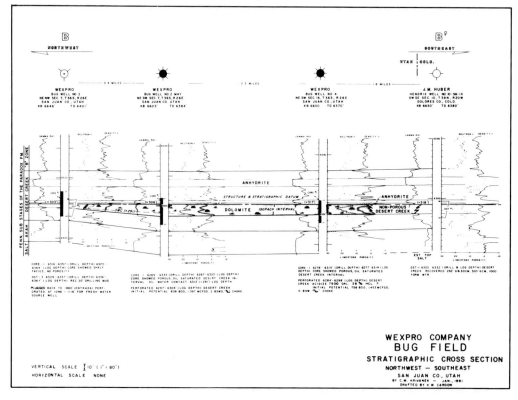

Figure 4

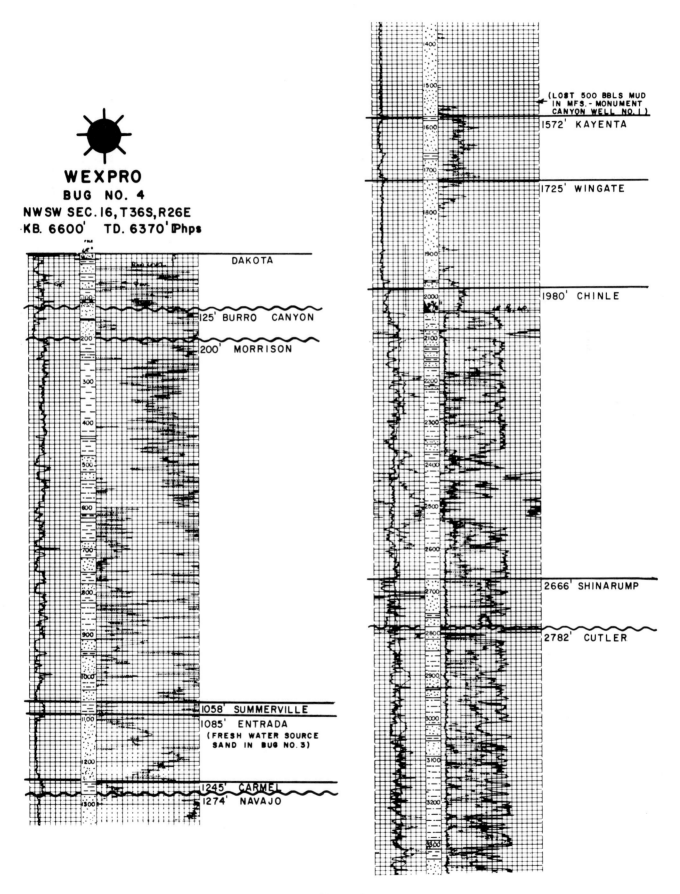

WEXPRO
BUG NO. 4
NWSW SEC.16,T36S,R26E
KB. 6600'   TD. 6370' Phps

DAKOTA

125' BURRO CANYON

200' MORRISON

1058' SUMMERVILLE
1085' ENTRADA
(FRESH WATER SOURCE
SAND IN BUG NO.3)

1245' CARMEL
1274' NAVAJO

(LOST 500 BBLS MUD
IN MFS.- MONUMENT
CANYON WELL NO.1)

1572' KAYENTA

1725' WINGATE

1980' CHINLE

2666' SHINARUMP

2782' CUTLER

Figure 5

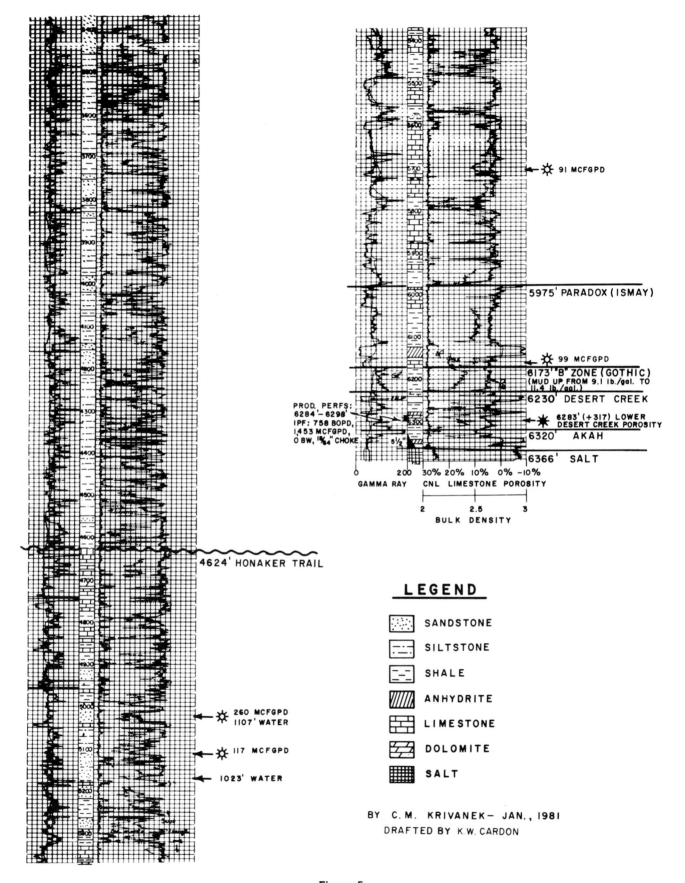

Figure 5

Wexpro Bug No. 2-May
Sec. 7, T. 36 S., R. 26 E.
San Juan County, Utah

Lower Desert Creek Porosity 6298.5' (+ 304.5')
KB 6603'
Core 1 6289'-6333', Cut 44', Rec. 44', Lower Desert Creek

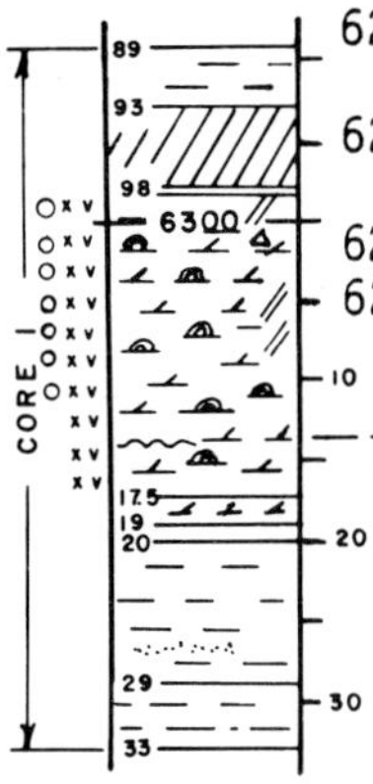

FOOTAGE INTERVAL		ROCK TYPE	COLOR	DESCRIPTION
6289'-6293'	(4)	Shale	Black	2⁰-3⁰ dips, estimated, thin laminated bedding.
6293'-6298'	(5)	Anhydrite	Gray	Massive, flat bedded.
6298'-6298.5'	(0.5)	Shale	Black	
6298'.5-6317.5	(19)	Dolomite Ivanovia Boundstone	Gray-Brown	Fine grained, intercrystalline and vuggy porosity, ¼" wide vugs. Asphalt residue near top of porosity, brown stain, fluorescence and cut 6298.5'-6314'. 6304' Breccia, algal heads and leaves. 6306' anhydrite replacement. 6308' anhydrite replacement. 6308' anhydrite in vugs, 6310' clay increase 1-2'. 6312' algal-mud cracks, anhydrite replacement.
6317.5'-6319'	(1.5)	Dolomite	Dark Gray	Hard, fine grained, no vugs. Carbonaceous material 6320'.
6319'-6320'	(1)			
6320'-6329'	(9)	Mudstone	Dark Gray Black	None calcareous. 6327' light weight, crumbly.
6329'-6333'	(4)	Shale	Black	Platy
6333'				

* OWC 6314' (+289)

DST No. 2 6301'-6333' (32)

IHP	3843
IFP	1307-2512 (35)
ISIP	3534 (70)
FFP	1093-3184 (180)
FSIP	3534 (180)
FHP	3789

Recovery
Flowed 64 BO and reversed out 15 BO 2½ hours.
Flowed 950 MCFGPD rate 12/64" choke, trace of water.

Core analyzed and slabbed by Core Lab, Farmington, New Mexico
Description by C. M. Krivanek
* Core is 2' low to logs.

See Legend for Core Descriptions Fig. 7

VERTICAL SCALE 1" = 20'

Figure 6.

Wexpro Bug No. 4
Sec. 16, T. 36 S., R. 26 E.
San Juan County, Utah

Lower Desert Creek Porosity 6284' (+316)
KB 6600'
Core 1 6278'-6315', Cut 37', Recovered 37'

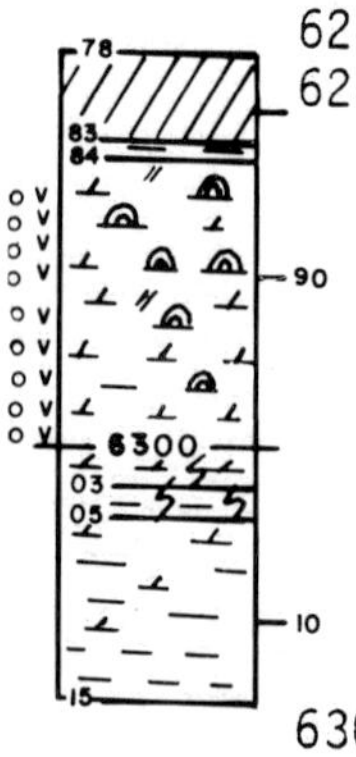

FOOTAGE INTERVAL		ROCK TYPE	COLOR	DESCRIPTION
6280'-6283.2'	(3)	Anhydrite	Gray	Faintly color banded top half, massive lower half.
6283.2'-6284.2'	(1)	Shale	Black	Fine bedded, carbonaceous, 5° dips±
6284.2'-6300'	(16)	Boundstone	Dark-gray top foot, then gray below	Dolomite, abundant Ivanovia leaves, swirly texture, good vuggy porosity with tight dolomitic mud matrix. At 84'-85' very slightly bleeding brine. Faint fluorescence 84'-86', spotty fluorescence 6286'-6300', 30-50% of rock. Abundant asphalt residue. Fresh break has good odor. Scattered Anhydrite replacement less than 1% has small percent of intercrystalline porosity.
6300'-6303'	(3)	Dolomite	Gray-Black	Dense, vert. fractures healed, 02-04 vertical fractures healed.
6303'-6305'	(2)	Shale	Black	Carbonaceous, non-calcareous, vertical fractures healed.
6305'-6315'	(10)	Mudstone	Gray	Dolomitic, bottom 2' crumbly.

DST No. 9 6285'-6316' (31') FP 773-1037 (30), ISIP 3494 (90), FFP 899-1671 (73) SI-
surface gas leak, FSI 3480 (181).
IO GTS (23) WCTS (25) 3/4" choke.
FO GTS immediately, flowed 767 MCFGPD. WC unloaded (23) OTS (33) 3/4" choke.

Core analyzed and slabbed by Core Lab, Farmington, New Mexico
Description by Connie M. Krivanek, July 22, 1980.

LEGEND FOR CORE DESCRIPTIONS, BUG WELLS NO. 2 & 4

– –	SHALE	IO	INITIAL FLOW
↲↲	DOLOMITE	ISI	INITIAL SHUT-IN
////	ANHYDRITE	FF	FINAL FLOW
//	ANHYDRITIC	FSI	FINAL SHUT-IN
⌒	ALGAL FACIES	WCTS	WATER CUSHION TO SURFACE
x	INTERCRYSTALLINE POROSITY	FO	FINAL OPEN
v	VUGGY POROSITY	GTS	GAS TO SURFACE
o	OIL STAIN & FLUORESCENCE	OTS	OIL TO SURFACE
		( )	MINUTES
		DST	DRILL STEM TEST

VERTICAL SCALE 1"= 20'

Figure 7.

LISBON FIELD — LESSONS IN EXPLORATION

Kenneth T. Smith[1][2] and Orley E. Prather[1][3]

INTRODUCTION

The Lisbon Field, San Juan County, Utah, has produced 42.7 million barrels of 54° gravity oil, 363 BCF of associated gas, and 11.4 million barrels of extracted liquids since discovery by The Pure Oil Company in 1960, and through December, 1980. Twelve of the 24 originally completed oil wells in this gas-condensate-oil field are still producing (flowing) about 2000 BOPD. Three of these original wells have *each* surpassed cumulative production of 5,000,000 BO exclusive of associated gas and liquids, and two of the three are presently flowing over 340 BOPD *each*.

Drilled on 160-acre spacing, these three specific wells have *each* yielded a recovery-to-date exceeding 30,000 BO/acre — not a bad reservoir by anyone's standards. Average field recovery-to-date (3000 acres of oil ring) is over 14,000 BO/acre, and still climbing —an *average* economic factor that will favorably hold its own when comparing different basins for future potential. These recoveries are *exclusive* of gas and natural gas liquids that have been produced. Extracted liquid recovery-to-date averages about 4000 bbls/acre.

The gas cap (2000 acres) contains reserves well in excess of 100 BCF/section. To date, most of the associated gas produced with the oil has been recycled into the gas cap. When eventually produced, the gas will require stripping of the inerts and other contaminants, but even so, ultimate pipeline gas and associated liquids constitute a substantial hydrocarbon reserve independent of the major after-the-fact oil reserves.

Based on total fluid production, the cumulative water cut for the excellent reservoir in this field is only 29.5%! This fact will significantly influence the future of this 21-year-old oil field, which has abundant gas-condensate reserves yet to be recovered.

An accumulation of this quality deserves a penetrating review by the explorationist, covering both individual field characteristics and the exploration maturity of its host province. The following comments are intended to contribute to any evaluation of the future and remaining potential in the basin of the "Paradox".

PRE-DISCOVERY EXPLORATION METHODS

An outstanding feature of the Paradox basin is the thick evaporite cover sealing the older Paleozoics. In the early Fifties, however, the magnitude of surface anticlines, regardless of flowage effects, was visualized as a clue to similarly large pre-salt structures. In other words, the "Sheepherder Anticline" concept could still be applied, and the true worldwide significance of the tremendous reserves established in evaporite basins and their source-seal-reservoir relationships were perhaps mistakenly assigned a lesser role at the time.

The area covered by the Pennsylvanian Paradox Salt conservatively encompasses 12,000 sq mi, about 7000 sq mi in Utah and 5000 sq mi in Colorado.

In 1955, this 12,000 sq mi area (7,680,000 acres) included a total of 30 wells that had daringly drilled below the top of the

penetrated the Mississippian and drilled deeper to determine what pre-Mississippian rocks might exist. Even in 1981, predicting pre-Mississippian rock type and distribution remains a regional stratigraphic puzzle.

Importantly, in 1955, these 30 widely scattered control points for the Mississippian essentially broadcast to the prospect-seeking professional that the widely distributed carbonates of this vintage certainly exhibited commercial reservoir qualities in much more of the Four Corners Area than the 12,000 sq mi expanse touched on here.

This simple, but important, conclusion in 1955 led to the commitment for a regional seismic sampling. One of the objectives was to establish a relationship (or lack of any) between the large surface anticlines and the subsurface Mississippian. Hopefully, salt flowage could then be given dimensional values and be better understood.

An examination of the complete salt section in the 30 wells mentioned suggested the Paradox Salt was more susceptible to flowage where depositional thickness exceeded + 3000 ft. In general, the northwest-southwest-trending Dolores Arch-Lisbon Valley-Big Flat lineament is associated with this critical original thickness, and separates the fold-fault belt (or extreme flowage area) to the northeast from the less disturbed platform area to the southwest. Where original salt deposits are less than 3000 ft (southwest of the "hinge"), the Paradox Salt tends to behave like any other competent sedimentary rock.

The lure of the unknown in the complex flowage area along and basin-ward of the Lisbon "hinge" obviously appeared to offer unlimited exploration opportunities. Therefore, this vast, complex area was selected for implementation of the seismic program.

In 1955, gravity coverage over most of the basin was available. The effect of the salt anticlines overwhelmed any conventional gravitational features. Also, very little topographic control existed then for handling obviously severe influences equal to or greater than the magnitude of normal gravity prospect indicators. Consequently, the *reconnaissance* value of gravity data was quickly reduced.

Magnetics on a widely flown grid were available. Early seismic mapping failed to confirm structurally what were otherwise good magnetic leads. At that time the use of magnetics for regional screening and high-grading was terminated. (There was one notable exception: a true basement uplift with some of the pre-salt rocks missing due to erosion. Based on the several wells drilled on this feature, it is so far non-productive.)

In the beginning, there were no velocity surveys, and attempts to estimate thicknesses and convert to depth were wild guesses. The early velocity surveys proved most assumptions to be grossly erroneous, especially regarding the velocity of the Paradox Salt and interval velocities of the overlying Permo-Penn sediments.

Early in the program, acquisition of usable seismic data became the primary consideration. In the beginning months, it also became apparent that the cost of per-mile coverage was no small matter. Logistics, especially in the Utah Canyon Country, were very difficult in the Fifties, even though the uranium "boom" had opened areas that otherwise would have remained inaccessible.

[1] Formerly with The Pure Oil Company.
[2] Vice President - Exploration & Production, Sinclair Oil Corporation, Denver, Colorado.
[3] Consultant, "Prather & Bremkamp", Littleton, Colorado.

With time, certain relationships between usable data and the age and pattern of outcrops became apparent, and many poor, or "no data" areas were avoided. This, on more than a few occasions, presented obvious problems in total definition of a prospect.

As mapping progressed, it also became evident that some faulting was associated with almost every prospect worthy of drilling. Because clean fault cuts were rarely seen seismically, faults could only be interpreted by correlation. Amounts of throw were quite speculative, and salt flowage effects sometimes produced reflections that would dip across and override any Mississippian reflections. Areas of "no data" were to be expected. Economics, and other pertinent reasons, caused distances between shot points and group intervals to be quite lengthy, and spreads with up to ½ mile between shot points were not uncommon. For geological and accessibility reasons, line and loop ties were usually impractical, and by no means a standard practice.

Considering the combination of all these factors, and most of them came into play on every line, mapping and interpreting this area with 100% data called for reliance on basics and hard work. It required an imaginative approach to sort out the most logical interpretation; then it required daring and conviction to defend and support this conclusion, especially when amounts of fault throw and inferred dips were based on correlations sometimes extracted from no more than 20% of the records taken.

After mapping about half a dozen interesting Mississippian anomalies, the two best were selected for drilling — to be spudded simultaneously. Because all of the anomalies demonstrated such different geophysical characteristics, combined with the dramatic variation in geological conditions from prospect to prospect, a multi-well commitment was made. These first two wildcat wells were the discovery wells at Lisbon Field, San Juan County, Utah, and at McIntyre Canyon Field, San Miguel County, Colorado. (In passing, the McIntyre Canyon anomaly consists of a subsurface faulted anticline lying beneath a surface syncline.)

ANATOMY OF THE FIELD

Because the Lisbon Field is the only Mississippian accumulation of its kind in the Paradox basin in terms of size and quality, an in-depth examination of its geological and geophysical characteristics can be helpful in locating new prospects elsewhere in the basin.

To the best of our knowlege, the Lisbon Field has not been comprehensively mapped using CDP techniques. Therefore, direct observations and comparisons with the limited stacked coverage existing in the basin today cannot be made. Within the Lisbon Field, those observed structural conditions from the 100% data would simply be confirmed by improved and refined CDP coverage along-side the old lines. Those patches of "no data" within the area of production will most likely remain as such, even after CDP.

Within the producing area, the major fault at the Mississippian level was never actually seen on the records; it was inferred by correlation. A greater number of more closely spaced shot points may improve upon this situation in some localities, but not necessarily on every line. Although reverse dip on the Mississippian averages 7°, nowhere were seismic dips (based on valid data) this great; the maximum was only about 4.5°. Segments of valid "zero dip" were observed within this same productive area.

Examination of all of the well logs in the field provides many lessons that may be applied regionally, and allows certain realistic assumptions in the interpretation of stacked seismic lines recorded elsewhere in the basin.

The Lisbon Field encompasses about 5000 acres (3000 acres of oil ring, and 2000 acres of gas cap). Structural closure is very near 2000 ft, and this is one of those rare accumulations that contains commercial fluids to the "spill point." Figure 1 represents the authors' concept of the structural interpretation for this field. We believe there are many more smaller faults in the field area than the number shown on the map. Many comments to follow will be related to this interpretation.

Regionally, the Lisbon Valley salt structure is a non-breached, faulted anticline in the center of the aforementioned "hinge" dividing the basin. The surface fault has about 4000 ft of displacement (down to the northeast). Reverse dip to the southwest along the upthrown block extends for slightly more than 6.5 mi, and has about 4400 ft of structural relief on top of the Paradox Salt. The surface fault loses identity within the salt, and does not cut pre-salt rocks.

Regional dip on top of the Mississippian is estimated at 1½° to the northeast around and across the Lisbon Valley area.

The fault at the Mississippian level is several miles removed (southwest) from the surface fault, and is *not* parallel to the surface fault trace. This subsurface fault dies out upward within the salt. The "controlling fault" at Lisbon Field is believed to be a zone (or series) of connected faults, varying both in strike and in segment length. A "fault segment" may be cleanly displaced, but some segments appear to be a jumbled mass of slivers and blocks across the displacement zone.

Mississippian fault displacement at the Lisbon Field is probably more than 2500 ft across the crest of the closure. Maximum reversal is about 2100 ft, covering a distance of 3.4 mi. in the dip direction (7° southwest dip). The authors do not believe there is any rollover into the main fault, merely a sharp break at the crest of the half-anticline as indicated on Figure 1.

The entire producing area at the Lisbon Field is totally "encased" in salt. Interestingly, the datum of the closing "spill point" contour in the field is about the same as the datum of the base of the Paradox Salt on the downside, or northeast side, of the controlling subsurface fault. The black shales in the salt are considered to be the major source for the Lisbon Field, and any other Mississippian accumulations in, or to be found in, the Paradox basin.

Cumulative production data certainly confirm that vertical and horizontal fracturing in the thick Mississippian carbonates contribute additional porosity and permeability not measured by conventional tools. This is most obvious when a review of the field history shows cumulative fluid production to be several times greater than earlier volumetric estimates. Faulting within the field may be contemporaneous with fracturing, and such faults only tend to horizontally displace fluid boundaries, not create barriers. To reiterate, this entire reservoir-fluid regime is totally enclosed by Paradox Salt.

Ongoing regional work in the late Fifties and the increased use of the sonic log combined to demonstrate the widespread sedimentary distribution of the black shales separating the individual salt bodies. Through use of these interval correlations, one may separate normal from abnormal data, and use the salts most reliably for regional patters. Of the 29 separate salts identified in the Paradox basin, 28 of these are represented in the Lisbon Field area. However, some of the individual salt bodies below the Cane Creek clastic zone (salts #22 through #28) are missing locally, and are believed here to be absent due to non-deposition rather than to flowage "wipeout".

The Cane Creek shale break in the Paradox Salt (in the lower half, between salts #21 and #22) was the first major widespread intervening clastic deposited across the entire basin. By dealing with the interval between the Cane Creek and the base of the salt interval, one may interpret post-Mississippian to pre-Cane Creek movement, or recognize sea floor irregularities. Early Pennsylvanian (pre-Cane Creek) adjustments definitely occurred in the Lisbon Field area, as concluded by the authors.

The Lisbon Field area is the only location in the basin with sufficient well data to examine in detail those phenomena that result from flowage and distortion of the Paradox Salt. Within the distance separating the subsurface Mississippian fault from the Lisbon Valley surface fault, the salt interval "balloons" from a thin of less than 3000 ft over Lisbon Field to over 7000 ft at the thickest part of the salt structure, all due to flowage. Sonic logs from wells drilled in this zone graphically demonstrate overturned and repeated shale sections (repeated as many as five times), loss of breaks due to "wipeout", and fluid and re-crystallization anomalies within the salt bodies, all of which are due to flowage and distortion. Across the uplifted area of the Lisbon Field, similar conditions are also in evidence in a much thinner salt interval, but here the loss of shale breaks is mostly due to horizontal distortion and flowage "wipeout". The internal deformation in the salt due to faulting of the Mississippian within the Lisbon Field is clearly evident on the logs, which provide a portion of the criteria important for the interpretation of Figure 1.

Based on similar detailed analysis of the salt interval, it appears conclusive that the Cane Creek shale break itself is missing in about half of the wells within the field area due to flowage "wipeout" caused by faulting and uplift, rather than from non-deposition. If so, missing or severely altered Cane Creek, indicated by well logs, is a clue to localized Mississippian faulting, or flowage caused by local faulting. This is another underlying factor in the structural interpretation of Figure 1.

Well log data in the Lisbon Valley area (and work by others throughout the basin) readily show areas of thick Permian Cutler deposits compensating for salt thins. This indicates localized salt flowage triggered by structural adjustments throughout the basin in Late Pennsylvanian and Early Permian times. The effects of depositional overloading (continuous through all of Cutler time) amplified this situation in varying amounts from place to place. The middle Pennsylvanian Honaker Trail section does not vary in thickness, and the entire unit follows the attitude of the top of the salt, unless faulted.

Northeast of the Lisbon Field (a few miles northeast of the Lisbon Valley surface fault trace), maximum compensating amplification is demonstrated by a loss of about 4000 ft of Paradox Salt. This is the main source area for the salt in the Lisbon Valley salt anticline. Withdrawal and flowage volumes were replaced by the very thick cause-and-effect Cutler deposits resulting from the depositional overloading and salt movement.

Around the flanks of the Lisbon Field, ancestral uplift caused enough salt movement (in the updip direction) to cause compensating thickening in the Cutler. To say this differently, a "halo" of thicker Permian - thinner Paradox Salt, locally a more subtle condition, surely extends around the uplifted field area.

The dissection of the Lisbon Field area presented here includes those geological and geophysical factors that are considered to be the most important for exploration guidance and assistance elsewhere in the province. There are many other practical observation that may be learned from this same exercise, but they are not covered here.

(For additional information on the Lisbon Field, please refer to "Lisbon Field Area, San Juan County, Utah", by John M. Parker, elsewhere in this volume. Many details of the reservoir appear there, along with fluid analyses, stratigraphy, and other comprehensive statements pertaining to this field.)

POST-DISCOVERY EXPLORATION PHILOSOPHY

In 1981, as in the late Fifties, the deeper unexplored portions of the Paradox basin will require a concentrated and coordinated seismic-subsurface effort to locate wildcat anomalies indicating Mississippian (and older) potential. Even with the tremendous impact of CDP methods, one should expect accessibility limitations and variations in quality of deep seismic data, and the ever-present threat of cost limitations. The many lessons learned from understanding the geology of the Lisbon Field may be utilized to overcome and control these possible constraints when they become evident during future exploration.

Lisbon teaches us the paramount necessity for having an understanding of regional control. An awareness of the areal extent and magnitude of regional variations is a must, in order to know when to modify a technique or alter the approach altogether. This background may be the positive difference in recognizing a good prospect even though certain conditions will permit only partial documentation or delineation.

Earlier, all of the massive salt anticlines (breached and unbreached) were grouped together regarding genesis, structural characteristics, etc., and would vary only in size. A close examination will reveal that no two are alike. Each has characteristics peculiar only to that salt structure, and these must be sorted and weighed in order to sensibly relate them characteristically to the subsurface, or conversely, to better interpret the subsurface information obtained in the vicinity of a specific salt structure. Each of these structures is replete with stratigraphic and structural subtleties, some of which may not occur on any of the other flowage features. Other forms of surface subtleties will prove to be associated with less extreme subsurface anomalies, such as "salt pillows" or other completely buried prospects essentially masked by Cutler-Paradox Salt compensations of low relief.

Identification of major faults cutting the Mississippian and older rocks will not necessarily be obvious from stacked data. Reasons for this, other than limited surface accessibility, include (1) the apparent segmented nature of the faulting, including the sudden transition from a clean fault to a fault zone, and abrupt changes in strike; (2) highly distorted salts and shale breaks within the salt section which form the "umbrella effect" just above the Mississippian faults. Contorted "pods" of salts and shales within the total Paradox Salt interval may easily extend a mile or more and assume shapes and angles that have no relationship with the attitudes of the upper and lower salt boundaries. These probably have experienced "recrystallization" and may produce reflections of an extraneous character. These events may even override the Mississippian reflection, indicating locally erroneous dips on the Mississippian.

Many of the individual Mississippian prospects yet to be found will take the general shape of and be no larger than one of the faulted pie slices of Figure 1, but will still yield prolific recoveries. About the only seismic evidence for such an anomaly may be regional dips disappearing as the anomaly is approached, with extremely limited valid data on the anomaly itself; or the true prospect may be indicated only by flat seismic reflections murkily separated from regional

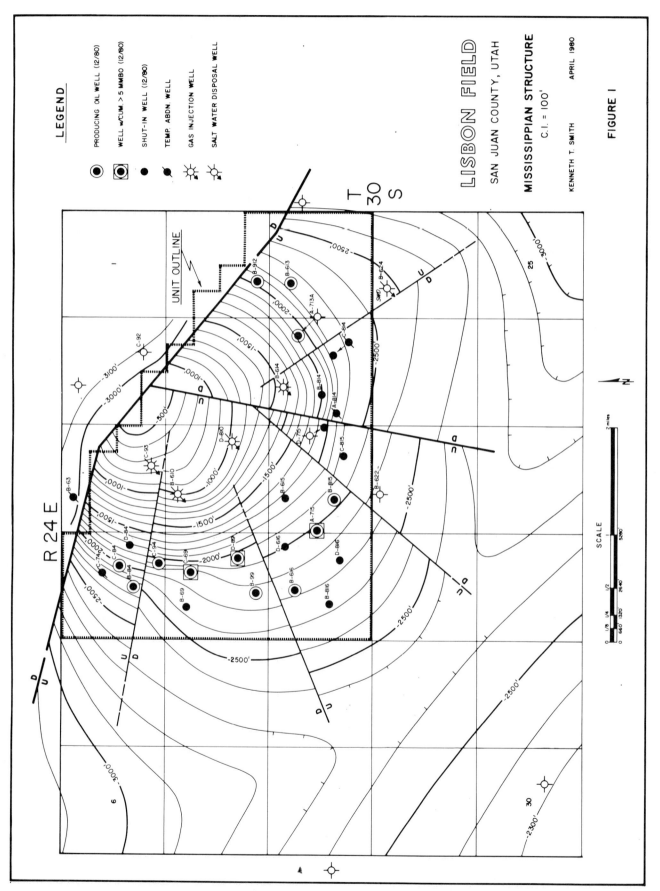

Figure 1.

geology by barely discernible faults of questionable correlation and displacement.

Dealing with the Cutler and Paradox Salt intervals may indirectly provide clues to the extent of Mississippian anomalies. Remember, the top of the Permian Cutler Formation will not vary much; the anomalous compensating variations are totally within the Cutler or salt intervals. While such Cutler-Paradox Salt clues may be upwards of 100 mils, they can be abrupt, and cover short distances. Seismically, this might appear as a diffraction. Processing can eliminate some of these clues altogether.

While the presence of salt over and around the pre-salt anomalies is most desirable (for seal and source), those areas of "zero salt" may be associated with complex subsurface structure. Absence of salt actually provides a "window" or "migration hatch" for hydrocarbons generated within the total salt and black shale section to escape into younger or older rocks that otherwise may never have been in proper juxtaposition with the source-seal properties of the Paradox Salt.

In addition to the pre-salt potential, the Permo-Penn clastics and carbonates offer objectives today that were not very well understood as recently as fifteen years ago. Wells drilled during this period of time, combined with stacked seismic data, now allow one to explore around the basin and make sensible geological projections. Future drilling will only serve to expand the list of potential locales and types of traps, especially those which are stratigraphic in nature.

Mississippian prospects southwest of the "hinge" are expected to be of a different type, and probably of a lower magnitude of structural relief. However, there are examples of buried "blocks" or "plugs" of pre-salt rocks that have been elevated as much as 2000 ft, yet do not affect the structure at the top of the Pennsylvanian. These sharp, faulted anomalies are probably very Early Pennsylvanian in origin. Obviously, a seismic program is required to locate more of these.

While Mississippian well control is still insufficient for localizing areas for stratigraphic traps in the Mississippian, this future potential is now recognized, and the more gentle portions of the basin southwest of the Lisbon trend present a more likely spot for this type of exploration. First of all, depths to the Mississippian are more reasonable. Some of the existing dry holes have experienced a complete lack of any permeability in the entire Mississippian and Devonian, thus paving the way for drilling downdip, or projecting permeable fairways across structural noses otherwise not yet deserving of a wildcat test.

Last, but certainly not least, an outstanding example of the importance of regional knowledge is related to drilling costs. To the uninitiated, drilling cost estimates for wells in the Paradox basin will appear to be prohibitive. The nearest wells to the prospect may not even be the proper wells for examining drilling histories. Only the geologist with the proper regional understanding is able to select wells with geology similar to the undrilled wildcat prospect, and those wells may be many miles from the proposed location.

In spite of the complexities of this evaporite basin, the Paradox basin offers to the enterprising explorationist a greater range of opportunities than in most of those partially explored areas left in the lower 48 states.

SELECTED REFERENCES

Cater, F.W., 1970, Geology of the salt anticline region in Southwestern Colorado: U.S. Geological Survey Professional Paper 637, 80 p.

Clark, C.R., 1978, Lisbon Field, in Oil and Gas Fields of the Four Corners Area: Four Corners Geological Society, Volume II, p. 662-665.

Elston, D.P., and Shoemaker, E.M., 1963, Salt anticlines of the Paradox Basin, Colorado and Utah, in Symposium on Salt: Northern Ohio Geological Society, Inc., p. 131-146.

Hite, R.J., 1960, Stratigraphy of the saline facies of the Paradox Member of the Hermosa Formation of southeastern Utah and southwestern Colorado Geology of the Paradox Basin fold and fault belt, in Four Corners Geological Society Guidebook, 3rd Field Conference, 1960, p. 86-89.

Hite, R.J., Carter, F.W. and Liming, J.A., 1972, Pennsylvanian rocks and salt anticlines, Paradox Basin, Utah and Colorado, in Geologic Atlas of the Rocky Mountain Region: Rocky Mountain Association of Geologists, 1972, p. 133-138.

Lekas, M.A., and Dahl, H.M., 1956, The geology and uranium deposits of the Lisbon Valley anticline, San Juan County, Utah, in Geology and economic deposits of east central Utah: Intermountain Association of Petroleum Geologists Guidebook, 7th Annual Field Conference, 1956, p. 161-168.

Parker, J.M., 1968, Lisbon Field Area, San Juan County, Utah: American Association of Petroleum Geologists, Memoir 9, Natural Gases of North American, p. 1371-1388 (updated and in this volume).

Shoemaker, E.M., Case, J.E., and Elston, D.P., 1958, Salt anticlines of the Paradox Basin (Colorado-Utah), in Guidebook to the geology of the Paradox Basin: Intermountain Association of Petroleum Geologists Guidebook, 9th Annual Field Conference, 1958, p. 39-59.

Agathla Peak (Photo by Jack Rathbone)

PATTERSON FIELD
San Juan County, Utah

GREGORY W. MARTIN
Wexpro Company
Farmington, New Mexico

INTRODUCTION

The Patterson Oil & Gas Field is located in the Paradox Basin in Township 37 and 38 South, Range 25 East, San Juan County, Utah (Figure 1). The field which produces oil and gas from the Ismay zone of the Paradox Formation is comprised of a northwest-southeast trending porous carbonate bank or mound at depth ranging from 5400 to 5600 feet. Additional hydrocarbon zones have not been encountered at the field.

Five wells have been drilled in the field on 160 acre spacing since 1974. Three are shut-in oil and gas producers awaiting pipeline construction, and two are dry holes (Figure 2). The discovery well, the Wexpro Company Patterson Canyon Well No. 1 (NE NW, Sec. 9, T. 38 S., R. 25 E.) was drilled in the spring of 1974, farmed out from the Mobil Oil Corporation. The well potentialed (pumping) for 62 BOPD, 195 BSWPD, with gas too insignificant to gauge. The Patterson Field discovery was drilled as a result of regional and local geologic interpretations coupled with geophysical interpretation of seismic profiles shot in the area. The key to the discovery was the Mobil Oil Corporation No. 1 Federal "HH" well (SE NW, Sec. 15, T. 38 S., R. 25 E.), drilled in November, 1971. The well encountered 65 feet of porosity in the Ismay zone which was drill stem tested and determined to be wet. The well was plugged and abandoned. The data indicated the porosity zone penetrated in the Mobil "HH" extended in a northwest direction updip to the dry hole.

The second field well was drilled in August, 1974. The Wexpro Company Patterson Canyon Well No. 2 (NE NE, Sec. 9, T. 38 S., R. 25 E.), a 160 acre offset to the east, was drilled to test the eastern limit of the porosity. The well was plugged and abandoned on August 31, 1974 when porosity was not encountered above the interpreted oil-water contact (Figures 2 & 3). The Wexpro Company Patterson Canyon Well No. 3 (NE SE, Sec. 5, T. 38 S., R. 25 E.), a 160 acre diagonal offset northwest of the discovery, was drilled in August and September, 1977. This well resulted in the extention of the productive reservoir.

The area was approved for unitization on November 5, 1979 (see unit outline, Figures 1 & 2) with Wexpro Company and Mobil Oil Corporation the major leaseholders. The initial unit well, the Wexpro Company Patterson Unit Well No. 1 (NE NW, Sec. 5, T. 38 S., R. 25 E.) was drilled in March 1980, as a 160 acre diagonal offset northwest of the Patterson Canyon No. 3. The well penetrated the productive Ismay zone and became the unit qualifying well while extending the field to the northwest (Figures 2 & 3). The most recent well drilled at the field was the Wexpro Company Patterson Unit Well No. 2 (NE SW, Sec. 32, T. 37 S., R. 25 E.). This well was drilled in May and June of 1980 and was a 160 acre offset north of the Unit Well No. 1. The well did not encounter effective porosity in the Ismay zone and was plugged back and completed as a fresh water well in the Entrada Sandstone. In the near future, unit well names will be given to all field wells to prevent confusion created by the present well titles.

JURASSIC
MORRISON FORMATION (undifferentiated)

The Morrison Formation outcrops at the Patterson Field, and mainly consists of variegated sandstones, siltstones, and shales, with minor limestones. The sandstones are grayish-green, orange-red, and cream colored, and generally consist of medium grains subrounded which are moderately to well sorted. The shales and siltstones generally are light green, red, red-brown or orange, and occasionally are very limey. The Morrison Formation at this location ranges in thickness from 400 to 600 feet.

BLUFF SANDSTONE

The Bluff Sandstone is the uppermost member of the San Rafael Group, and mainly consists of eolian sandstones, with minor siltstones present. The sandstone is light pink, orange, and cream colored with medium to coarse, subrounded grains, moderately to well sorted, exhibiting good intergranular porosity. A faster drilling rate is associated with this sandstone which is 40 to 60 feet thick at this location.

SUMMERVILLE FORMATION

The Summerville Formation was deposited in a fluvial to marginal marine environment and consists of thinly bedded sandstones, siltstones, and shales. The sandstones are red-brown to light orange, very fine to fine grained, and is moderately to poorly sorted. The shales are light to dark red and often sandy. The unit is about 20 to 40 feet thick in the area and is associated with a slower drilling rate at this location than the overlying Bluff Sandstone or underlying Entrada Sandstone.

ENTRADA SANDSTONE

The Entrada Sandstone consists of eolian sandstones which generally are white, occasionally light orange to red, with fine to medium, subrounded to rounded grains. The sandstone is moderately to well sorted, exhibiting good intergranular porosity. This sandstone is 140 to 160 feet thick in the area.

CARMEL FORMATION

The Carmel Formation is the lowest member of the San Rafael Group and was deposited in a continental to marginal marine environment. This formation consists almost entirely of siltstones and shales which are red to red-brown and slightly calcareous. Occasionally, thin, red to red-brown sandstones are present and actually may be reworked Navajo Sandstone. This formation is about 30 feet thick at this locality and has a slower drilling rate than the overlying Entrada Sandstone.

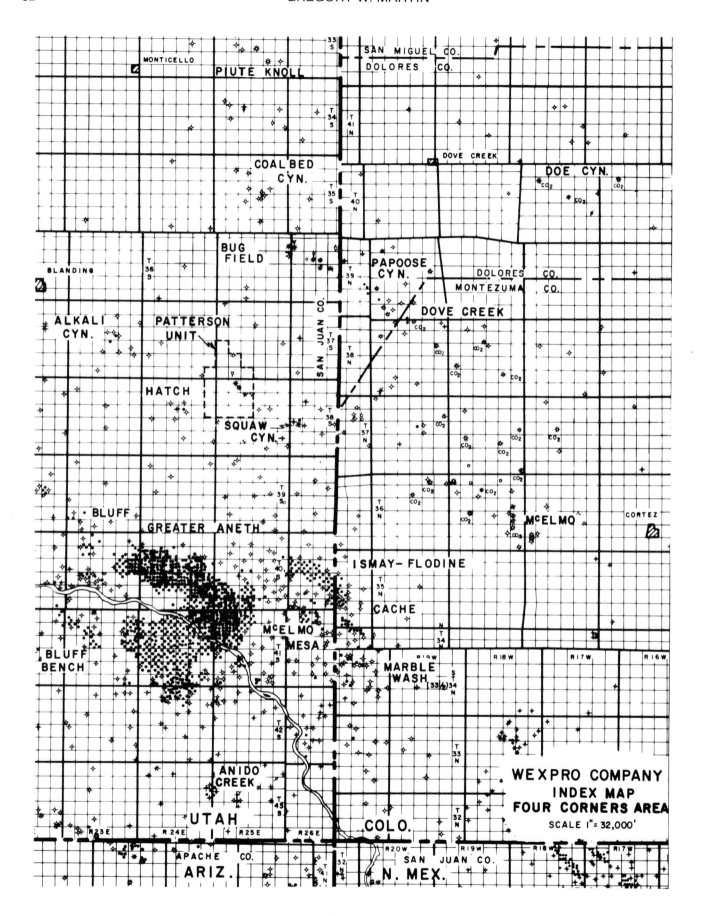

Figure 1

TRIASSIC

NAVAJO SANDSTONE

The Navajo Sandstone is the uppermost member of the Glen Canyon Group and is eolian in origin. The sandstone is light orange to red, white to buff, occasionally clear, and is composed of very fine to fine, subrounded to rounded grains which are often frosted. This sandstone is moderately to well sorted, displays good intergranular porosity, is associated with a faster drilling rate than the overlying Carmel Formation, and is about 340 feet thick at this location.

KAYENTA FORMATION

The Kayenta Formation consists of fluvial sandstones with less prominent thinly bedded shales and siltstones. The sandstones are white, lavender and light tan, very fine to fine grained, subangular to subrounded, displays poor to moderate sorting, and exhibits fair intergranular porosity. The shales and siltstones are red to red-brown. The Kayenta is about 150 feet thick at this location and is associated with a slower drilling rate than the overlying Navajo Sandstone or the underlying Wingate Sandstone.

WINGATE SANDSTONE

The Wingate Sandstone is the lowermost member of the Glen Canyon Group and is comprised almost entirely of eolian sandstone. The Wingate is light to bright orange, very fine to fine grained, well sorted, subrounded, and slightly silty. The sandstone exhibits good intergranular porosity and has a faster drilling rate than the underlying Chinle Formation, and is about 240 feet thick at this location.

CHINLE FORMATION

The Chinle Formation consists almost entirely of continental shales and siltstones, with occasional sandstones. The upper 100 feet of the Chinle predominantly consists of sandstones similar, yet siltier than the Wingate. The upper Chinle is characterized by a gradual decrease in the drilling rate due to an increasing silt content in the sandstones with depth. The remainder of the Chinle Formation above the basal Shinarump member consists of red to red-brown siltstones and shales, with occasional thin limestones. The Chinle Formation excluding the Shinarump member is about 800 to 850 feet thick at this location.

SHINARUMP MEMBER OF THE CHINLE FORMATION

The Shinarump Sandstone is a member of the Chinle Formation. This unit is composed of predominantly fine to medium grained sandstone; the grains generally are white, light gray to clear, subangular, and exhibit poor to moderate sorting. The sandstone was deposited by fluvial processes and exhibits poor to moderate intergranular porosity. The entire unit exhibits a faster drilling rate than the Chinle Formation, and is about 80 to 100 feet thick at this locality.

MOENKOPI FORMATION

The Moenkopi Formation unconformably overlies the Permian Cutler Formation. It was deposited by mudflat, fluvial, and lacustrine processes and is mainly composed of variegated calcareous shales, mudstones and siltstones, red to brown, and gray to grayish-green. The formation contains minor sandstones which generally are thin and silty, of white to gray, medium sized subangular grains. The sandstones are moderately to well sorted. Noticeable change in the drilling rate through the Moenkopi was not observed from the overlying Shinarump Sandstone nor underlying Cutler Formation, and is about 130 to 150 feet thick at this location.

PERMIAN

CUTLER FORMATION (undifferentiated)

The Cutler Formation consists of about 1900 feet of alternating shales, silt-stones and sandstones deposited in a fluvial to continental environment. The shales and siltstones usually are red, orange to orange-red, and occasionally light gray to grayish-green. The sandstones are white, clear, light red to orange, generally subangular, often arkosic, with varying degrees of sorting. Many sandstones have good intergranular porosity and drill at a much faster rate than the shales and siltstones. Occasionally, thin, white, light gray or pink limestones are present. These limestones usually are dense and highly siliceous.

PENNSYLVANIAN

HONAKER TRAIL FORMATION

The Honaker Trail Formation is the uppermost member of the Hermosa Group. This formation is about 1000 feet thick at this location and represents the transition from the marine, evaporite Paradox Formation below, to the continental, Cutler Formation above. The upper boundary of the Honaker Trail is stratigraphic and generally is picked at the first occurrence of a thick marine limestone. The upper half (500 feet +) consists of cyclical sequences of marine limestones and shales, and deltaic to continental sandstones, siltstones and shales. The Honaker Trail Formation becomes increasingly marine with depth. The shales and siltstones of the upper half of the formation range in color from bright red to dark gray. The sandstones are more abundant towards the upper portion of the upper half of the formation and usually are light to medium gray, and sometimes white to clear in color. They generally are very fine to fine grained, subangular, well sorted and calcareous. The limestones generally are light to medium gray, finely crystalline, clean to highly argillaceous and often fossiliferous.

The lower half of the Honaker Trail Formation is almost entirely marine and generally devoid of sandstones. This lower portion of the Honaker Trail is comprised of limestones and silty shales. The limestones generally are white or light to medium gray, cryptocrystalline to finely crystalline, often fossiliferous, clean to argillaceous, and dense. The shales are not true shales but rather appear to be highly argillaceous cryptocrystalline limestones which often are partially dolomitized. Perhaps, they should be more properly classified as marlstones.

DESERT CREEK

The Desert Creek zone is 90 to 100 feet thick at the Patterson Field and is comprised of dense anhydrite, shale, siltstone and dolomite. The sediments were deposited in a restricted marine environment, and the anhydrites and shales are identical to those described in the Ismay zone. The dolomites are brown, and often exhibit an earthy texture.

PARADOX FORMATION

The Paradox Formation is the middle member of the Hermosa Group and consists of five zones, in descending order: the Ismay, Desert Creek, Akah, Barker Creek and Alkali Gulch. The upper three zones of the Paradox Formation have been penetrated by the wells at the Patterson Field.

ISMAY ZONE

The upper boundary of the Ismay is picked at the first occurrence of a thick (5 feet) anhydrite, a good time marker throughout the area. The productive reservoir at the Patterson Field lies within this interval and is comprised of limestones and dolomites. The limestones are white to medium gray, finely crystalline, dolomitic, clean to slightly argillaceous and occasionally fossiliferous. The dolomites are light to medium brown, finely crystalline, clean and occasionally fossiliferous. Highly porous zones are associated with faster drilling rates and mud gas shows. A detailed reservoir description is seen on Figure 4.

The anhydrites of the Ismay zone often are thickly bedded and occasionally nodular. They are white to light gray and exhibit a soft, chalky texture. A noticeable increase in mud viscosity usually occurs while drilling through the anhydrites.

The mudstones and shales of the Ismay zone are dark gray to dull black, dense, calcareous and dolomitic. Many authors consider these "shales" as cryptocrystalline, sapropelic dolomites. High mud gas shows usually are observed while drilling through these shales or mudstones. The Ismay zone is about 200 to 240 feet thick at the field, and was deposited in restricted to normal marine waters in subtidal to supratidal environments.

AKAH ZONE

The Akah zone has an undefined thickness at the Patterson Field since only the upper part has been penetrated. This interval is comprised of anhydrite, shale, siltstone and salt. The anhydrite, siltstone and shale is identical in appearance to those of the Desert Creek zone. The wells at the field generally are drilled a few feet into the salt whose upper boundary is picked by an extremely fast drilling rate (1 foot per minute), and a slight increase in mud chloride content. The Akah sediments at the field were deposited in a restricted marine environment.

STRUCTURE

The Paradox Basin is a northwest-southeast trending depositional trough which experienced major subsidence during the Pennsylvanian Period and continued to a lesser degree into the Permian Period. The Patterson Field is actually located in the Blanding Basin, a poorly defined Laramide (Late Cretaceous and Early Tertiary) structural feature superimposed onto the greater Paradox depositional basin. Laramide tectonism modified the paleodip (to the northeast) and created a gentle, southwest sloping surface at the Patterson Field. Figure 2 illustrates this slope which is mapped on top of the producing interval or its equivalent in wells which did not produce (also see Figure 3). Dips generally range from ¾ degree to 1 degree, or about 75 feet to 100 feet per mile. The porous carbonate bank facies is bounded by nonporous, anhydrite, shale, and dense carbonate facies (Figures 2 & 3). Hydrocarbons, influenced by regional southwest dip, migrated through the porous carbonate bank and were trapped by the northeast pinchout of the porous facies. The hydrocarbon trapping mechanism to the northwest presently is undefined. The oil-water contact of -241 feet is structurally controlled and obliquely traverses the bank trend. A gentle southerly plunging nose on the eastern end of the field appears to have negligible influence on hydrocarbon accumulation. Faulting has not been observed at the field.

GENERAL STRATIGRAPHY

Stratum of the Jurassic, Triassic, Permian and Pennsylvanian Periods are penetrated by wells drilled at the Patterson Field. Since this paper mainly discusses subsurface geology, the following brief rock descriptions are derived from drill cuttings from wells in the field. It is hoped that individuals working with subsurface geology will find this a more useful approach than descriptions from surface outcrops.

STRATIGRAPHY OF THE PRODUCING INTERVAL

The productive interval at the Patterson Field consists of a porous carbonate bank or mound which trends northwest-southeast. Porosity in the carbonate bank predominantly is vugular and was created by the preferential leaching of fossils. The downdip limit of the oil reservoir is determined by the oil-water contact at -241 feet. The updip northwest and northeast limits of the reservoir have not been adequately defined.

Figure 2 shows an effective porosity isopach map of the Patterson Field. The porosity contours illustrate the bank or mound-like morphology of the reservoir. The greatest porosity encountered is 115 feet in the Patterson Unit Well No. 1. (Note: the 40 feet of porosity displayed for the Patterson Canyon Well No. 2 is below the oil-water contact, and the productive portion of the bank has been replaced by laterally equivalent anhydrite, Figures 2 & 3).

Figure 4 is a type log of the Ismay reservoir from the Patterson Unit Well No. 1 on a scale of 5 inches equals 100 feet. Figure 4 lists detailed core and sample descriptions and displays the gamma ray and sidewall neutron porosity curves.

The carbonate bank is comprised of fossiliferous wackestone, a carbonate rock containing more than 10 percent grains by volume supported in a mud matrix. The predominant constituent of the carbonate bank is lime mud indicating deposition occurred in a relatively low energy environment. Partial to complete dolomitization of the lime mud is noted in most cores and samples. The predominant grain constituents of the bank are benthonic foraminifers and crinoid fragments; brachiopods and algae are present to a much lesser degree (Figure 4).

The bank was created by a combination of bioclastic and biogenic deposition. Abundant fauna living at this site served to generate organically derived carbonate sediment in life, and became clastic carbonate particles in death. The growing carbonate bank acted as a physical barrier to restrict currents carrying carbonate sediments from adjacent generating sites, thus permitting deposition.

Core data indicates that the bank was bathymetrically higher than the surrounding seafloor, was deposited in a shallow subtidal environment and underwent episodes of intertidal to supratidal exposure (Figures 3 & 4). Crinoids and benthonic foraminifers are abundant in cores from Patterson Unit Well No. 1 and Patterson Canyon Well No. 3. Crinoids are filter feeding organisms and prefer the shallower, slightly agitated waters circulating around bank crests while foraminifers prefer normal marine water. Neither organism is evident in cores from Patterson Canyon Well No. 2 or Patterson Unit Well No. 2 which did not intersect the carbonate bank. Instead, these wells cored laterally equivalent evaporite and dense carbonate facies (Figures 2 & 3). The porous portion of the bank was not cored in Patterson Canyon Well No. 2.

Sponge spicules are present in the dense carbonate, off-bank facies found in the lower portion of core 3 from Patterson Unit Well No. 2 (Figure 3). Although the spicules are not overly abundant in relation to the total rock, they are diagnostic since they are not present in cores which penetrated the bank. This sponge facies was interpreted by Elias (1963), to have been deposited in a low energy, very muddy, shallow water environment. He also stated this environment was untenable for organisms which extract their nutrients from sea water and were unable to survive in muddy waters. The sponges preferred the gently circulating

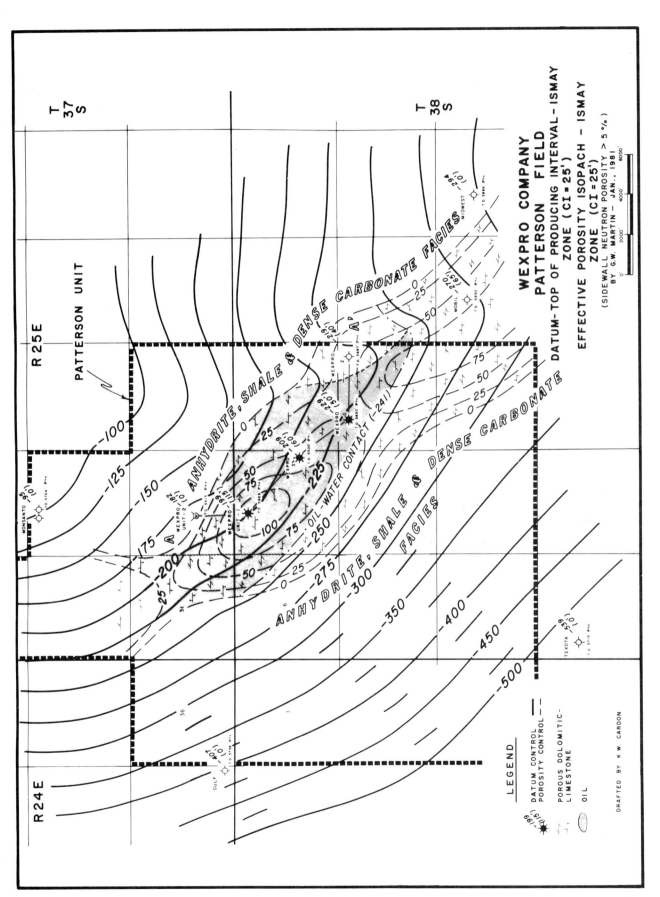

WEXPRO COMPANY
PATTERSON FIELD
DATUM-TOP OF PRODUCING INTERVAL - ISMAY ZONE (CI = 25')
EFFECTIVE POROSITY ISOPACH - ISMAY ZONE (CI = 25')
(SIDEWALL NEUTRON POROSITY > 5 %)
BY G.W. MARTIN - JAN., 1981

LEGEND

DATUM CONTROL ——
POROSITY CONTROL – – –

POROUS DOLOMITIC-
LIMESTONE

OIL

DRAFTED BY K.W. CARDON

Figure 2

PATTERSON UNIT WELL NO. 2

Core 1 5509'-5569'
Core 2 5570'-5630'
Core 3 5630'-5689'
No tests
Plug back to 1650'. Well will be completed in the Entrada Sandstone as fresh water source.

PATTERSON UNIT WELL NO. 1

Core 1 5508'-5568' (5501'-5561' Log Depth)
DST 1 5510'-5568' (5502'-5561' Log Depth) Misrun
April 18, 1980, PERFS: 5532 - 5532' 2 SPF
Treat formation with 750 gallons 15% hydrochloric acid.
IPF 294 BOPD, 720 MCFGPD, 20 BSWPD 3 day production test ending May 14, 1980
Cumulative 601 BO, 2700 MCFG, 9 BSW
At end of test, well was producing at a rate of 159 BOPD, 1 MMCFGPD, 24 BSWPD.
Bottom Hole Pressure Survey - 6.5 day shut-in after 3 day production test.
Extrapolation of data indicates SIP is between 2450-2475 psig. pressure did not change from pre-production pressure of 2462 psig.
Well currently shut-in, waiting on pipeline.

PATTERSON CANYON NO. 3

Core 1 5332'-5392' (5327'-5387' Log Depth)
Core 2 5392'-5452' (5387'-5447' Log Depth)
DST 1 5320'-5392' (5315'-5387' Log Depth) Misrun
DST 2 5354'-5392' (5349'-5387' Log Depth)
IFP 225-586 (30); ISIP 2473 (120); FFP 463-663 (419); FSIP 2470 (631)
Extrapolated shut-in pressure 2529#
Gas to surface 18 minutes into IFP Oil to surface 48 minutes into FFP
Flowed 55 BO in 210 minutes
Flowed gas from TSTM to rate of 450 MCFGPD on 3/8" choke.
Pipe recovery, 822' Oil
DST 3 5392'-5452' (5387'-5447' Log Depth)
IFP 237-364 (30); ISIP 2276 (119); FFP 448-969 (122); FSIP 2150 (209)
Flowed gas to surface, 5 minutes into ISIP. Gas TSTM
Gas remained through FFP. Gas TSTM
Pipe recovery, 1120' SW, 420' O& GCM

Sept. 29, 1977, PERFS: 5362'-5373' 2 SPF, no stimulation.
Set pumping unit. IPP 197 BOPD, gas not gauged, 0 BSWPD.
Cumulative, 226 days on pump, 12,939 BO, approximately 88,000 MCFG, 0 BSW.
Last 60 day test averaged 35 BOPD, 407 MCFGPD, 0 BSWPD, Well currently shut-in, waiting on pipeline.

PATTERSON CANYON NO. 1

DST 2 5430'-5504' (5414'-5488' Log Depth)
IFP 155-364 (30); ISIP 2423 (118); FFP 415-1197 (243); FSIP 2415 (359)
Recovered 120' Oil, 2391' SW, 93' GCM, GTSTM
DST 3 5509'-5529' (5493'-5513' Log Depth) Misrun
DST 4 5513'-5529' (5497'-5513' Log Depth)
IFP 41-211 (31); ISIP 2395 (87); FFP 223-491 (120); FSIP 2320 (227)
Recovered 931' MSW, 30'VSGCM
DST 7 Straddle 5460'-5480'
IFP 20-88 (30); ISIP 2472 (118); FFP 82-264 (243); FSIP 2473 (259)
Recovered 597' Oil, 100' SW, 60' HOGCM

June 27, 1974, PERFS: 5464'-5476'. Acidize with 5,000 gallons 5% hydrochloric acid plus 5,000 gallons 28% hydrochloric acid displaced with 6,000 gallons crude oil.
IPP 62 BOPD, GTSTM, 195 BSWPD This well was put on 25 day pump test. At the end of the test the well was making 64 BOPD, 175 MCFGPD, 215 BSWPD.
Cumulative for 25 day test, 1748 BO, 4375 MCFG, 5899 BSW.
Total cumulative, 2212 BO, 4375+ MCFG, 7069 BSW.
Well currently shut-in, waiting on pipeline.

PATTERSON CANYON NO. 2

Core 1 5353'-5413' (5356'-5416' Log Depth)
Core 2 5413'-5452' (5416'-5455' Log Depth)
Core 3 5452'-5510' (5455'-5513' Log Depth)
DST 1 Straddle 5453'-5540'
IFP 27-73 (32); ISIP 2365 (89); FFP 86-172 (120); FSIP 2310 (240)
Recovered 250' mud, NGTS
P&A August 31, 1974

WEXPRO COMPANY
PATTERSON FIELD
TESTS, CORES, & PRODUCTION DATA

Figure 3

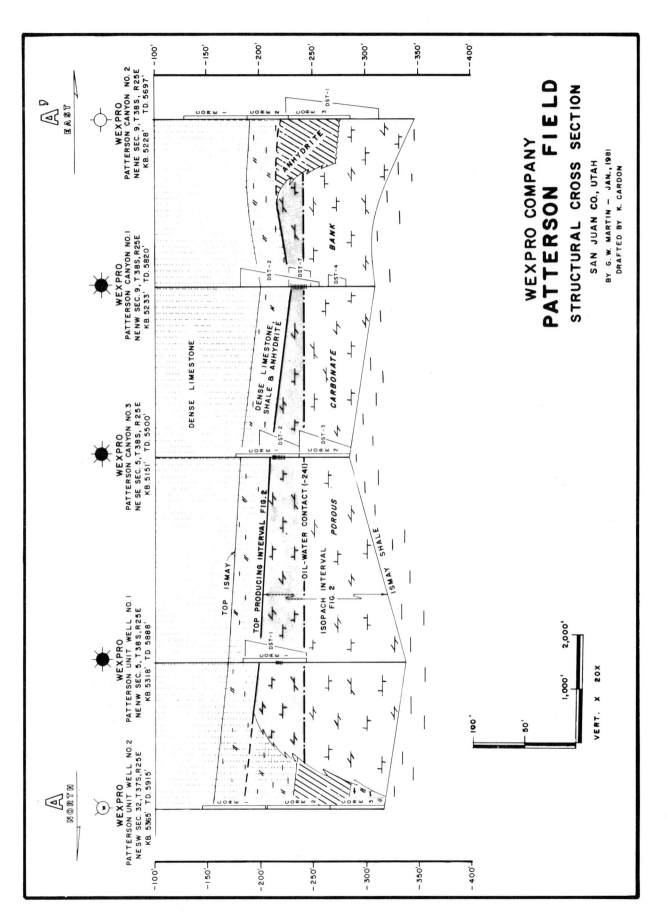

WEXPRO COMPANY
PATTERSON FIELD
STRUCTURAL CROSS SECTION

SAN JUAN CO., UTAH

BY G. W. MARTIN – JAN., 1981
DRAFTED BY K. CARDON

Figure 3

waters around the bank to the more strongly circulating waters on the bank. As was stated by Moore (1952), "they are animals of quiet waters, for if sediment is agitated by waves or currents it tends to clog their pores."

Additional evidence supporting subareal exposure of the carbonate bank is the desiccation breccia found in cores which penetrated the bank, and the total lack of this feature in off-bank cores. This feature was imparted to the bank during intermittent periods of subareal exposure which allowed the lime mud to dry and crack. Also, the fossil leaching and lithification of the bank probably occurred during these periods of exposure as fresh waters from rains migrated through the bank.

RESERVOIR CHARACTERISTICS AND MARKETING PROCEDURES

Detailed reservoir and production data for individual wells in the Patterson Field is shown in Figure 3. Production tests recovered a total of 15,752 BO and 100,000 plus MCFG from the three producing wells at the field. Most of the oil and gas was produced from the Patterson Canyon No. 3 on a 226 day test period. The oil was collected and transported and the gas vented.

The original static reservoir pressure, extrapolated from drill stem test data, was 2529 psig. Reservoir data indicates that the field will produce under a solution gas drive and probably will be placed on a pressure maintenance program in the early stages of production if economically feasible. The primary recovery using no pressure maintenance is estimated between 15 to 20 percent of the oil in place. The bubble point pressure of the reservoir presently is unknown.

Whole core analysis shows a porosity range through the reservoir interval of 0 to 29 percent with the average porosity running 11 to 12 percent. The average permeability for the reservoir is about 5 to 10 millidarcys and ranges from 0 to 50 millidarcys (Figure 4). The average water saturation through the oil filled portion of the reservoir is 40 to 44 percent.

Laboratory samples of oil taken from production tests show the oil to have a specific gravity of 0.82 at 60 degrees Fahrenheit, and an API gravity of 42 degrees at 60 degrees Fahrenheit. The pour point of the oil is below 0 degrees Fahrenheit and the total sulphur is about 0.09 percent by weight.

Gas analysis indicates a heating value of about 1200 BTU per cubic foot and a specific gravity of 0.72. The gas yields about 75 percent methane, 12 percent ethane, 5 percent propane, 2 percent nitrogen, 0.07 percent carbon dioxide, and others 2.93 percent.

Formation water analysis indicates total dissolved solids (sodium chloride equivalent) to be about 220,000 ppm with an observed ph of 7.0.

The existing field wells have been drilled on 160 acre spacing. Future plans are to drill and test the undefined northwest and northeast limits of the field (Figure 2).

Pipeline construction for marketing Patterson Field oil and gas should begin early in 1981. A six inch gas pipeline will be constructed from the Patterson Field northeast to Bug Point where it will join the six inch gas line from the newly discovered Bug Field. From that junction, an eight inch line will be constructed to the sales point at Dove Creek, Colorado, where the natural gas liquids will be stripped from the gas. The dry gas will be transported by the Northwest Pipeline.

A six inch oil pipeline will be constructed from the Bug Field southwest to the Patterson Field. From that point the line will bear west where it will intersect the Ute Oil line at Antelope Flat. The Ute line connects the Lisbon Field to the Aneth Field.

DRILLING AND COMPLETION PRACTICES

The present drilling method used at the Patterson Field involves the drilling of a 12¼ inch hole to a depth of about 50 feet. The hole is then underreamed to 17½ inches and a 14 inch conductor pipe is set. A 12¼ inch hole is then drilled into the Chinle Formation at a depth of about 1600 feet, and 9⅝ inch surface casing is set. Current Federal law requires that surface pipe be set into the Chinle Formation on Federal leases to protect shallow, fresh water aquifers. The shallow San Rafael and Glen Canyon Group sandstones are characterized by lost circulation and water flow zones. The present drilling method was not utilized in the Patterson Canyon Well No. 1 and 700 barrels of drilling fluid were lost into the Navajo Sandstone before regaining circulation. An 8⅜ inch or 8¾ inch hole is then drilled from below the surface casing to total depth and 5½ inch casing is set if the well is productive. Fresh water generally is an adequate drilling fluid from the surface to 3000 or 4000 feet; barite must then be added. The mud weight at total depth generally is 9.1 to 9.5 pounds per gallon. Overpressured zones have not been encountered. The cost of a dry hole at the Patterson Field averaged from $450,000 to $500,000 in 1980. The cost of a completed well ranges from $625,000 to $700,000.

A two man logging unit was employed on the discovery well from 600 feet to total depth. On subsequent wells, a two man logging unit was used 200 to 300 feet above the top of the Honaker Trail Formation. All mud gas shows are tested immediately by conventional drill stem tests. Occasionally, straddle tests will be run to retest the productive reservoir (Figure 3) or to test a zone which was bypassed but appears attractive on the mud and mechanical logs.

Coring of the productive interval has been pursued in all field wells with the exception of the discovery well (Figure 3). The coring program was designed to continue until sufficient data was gathered about the productive interval to enable a determination of a sensible geologic depositional model, and to gain a full understanding of the reservoir parameters and fluid contacts. In the future only stepout wells testing the unknown field limits will be cored.

The mechanical logging program for the field consists of running a Dual Induction log from total depth to the bottom of surface pipe. A Sidewall Neutron Porosity log with a Gamma Ray and Caliper is run from total depth to surface pipe. The Gamma Ray is then continued through pipe to the surface. A Dipmeter is utilized for the bottom 2000 feet of the hole for stratigraphic control. A Borehole Compensated Sonic log was run in the first three field wells from total depth to surface pipe to aid the geophysicists in acoustic modeling and velocity control.

The Patterson Canyon Well No. 1 was perforated from 5464 feet to 5476 feet with two shots per foot (Figure 3). The formation was acidized with 5000 gallons of five percent hydrochloric acid plus 5000 gallons of 28 percent hydrochloric acid displaced with 6000 gallons of crude oil. The well would flow oil, gas and formation water intermittently load up and cease flowing. A pumping unit was set and 2⅞ inch tubing was run to 5432 feet. A 2½ inch by 2 inch by 16 foot pump was installed and pumping began. A 25 day test was run with 1748 BO, 4375 MCFG and 5899 BSW recovered. Cumulative production for this well is 2212 BO, 4375+ MCFG and 7069 BSW (Figure 3).

The Patterson Canyon Well No. 3 was perforated from 5362 feet to 5373 feet with two shots per foot. Stimulation treatment was not applied to the formation. A pumping unit was set immediately and 2⅞ inch tubing was run to 5401 feet. A 2½ inch by 2 inch by 16 foot pump was installed. Pumping continued for a total of 226 days. At that time 12,939 BO, approximately 88,000 MCFG and 0 BSW had been recovered (Figure 3).

The Patterson Unit Well No. 1 had 2⅞ inch tubing set to 5412 feet. The well was perforated using a through-tubing perforating gun from 5532 feet to 5538 feet with 2 shots per foot. After swab runs the well would flow oil and gas intermittently and then load up. The formation was treated with 750 gallons of 15 percent hydrochloric acid. After a few swab runs the well kicked off and began to flow. On a 3 day production test the well flowed a total of 601 BO, 2700 MCFG and 9 BSW (Figure 3).

SUMMARY

The following are conclusions resulting from this study:

1. The Patterson Field is a northwest-southeast trending stratigraphic trap;

2. Laramide tectonism modified the paleodip and created a gentle southwest dipping surface at the field (Figure 2);

3. The downdip limit of the field is defined by the oil-water contact at -241 feet. The updip northeast and northwest limits are undefined (Figure 2). Future field wells will test these limits;

4. The reservoir is a porous carbonate bank or mound bounded on the northeast and southwest by anhydrite, shale and dense carbonate facies (Figures 2 & 3);

5. The bank was created by a combination of bioclastic and biogenic depositional processes;

6. The carbonate bank is classified as a fossiliferous wackestone. The major fossil constituents are crinoids and foraminifers with algae and brachiopods present to a lesser degree;

7. The porosity in the carbonate bank is vugular and was created by the preferential leaching of fossils;

8. The carbonate bank was bathymetrically higher than the surrounding seafloor, was deposited into a subtidal environment and underwent episodes of intertidal to supratidal exposure. Leaching and lithification of the bank occurred during these periods of exposure when fresh waters from rains migrated through the bank;

9. Partial to complete dolomitization of the bank has occurred;

10. The average porosity of the reservoir is 11 to 12 percent and the average permeability is 5 to 10 millidarcys;

11. The original static reservoir pressure extrapolated from drill stem test data was 2529 psig. The reservoir will produce under a solution gas drive. Some form of pressure maintenance will be pursued if economically feasible;

12. In a stratigraphic field such as the one discussed in this paper, the success of the drilling program is dependent upon the correct interpretation of the location of the porous facies, coupled with an understanding of where the porosity is in relation to the structural elevation.

13. A pipeline will be constructed and production is scheduled to begin in 1981.

REFERENCES CITED

Baars, D. L., 1963, Petrology of carbonate rocks, in Guidebook to shelf carbonates of the Paradox Basin: Four Corners Geological Society, symposium, p. 101-129.

Choquette, P. W., and Traut, J. D., 1963, Pennsylvanian carbonate reservoirs, Ismay Field, Utah and Colorado, in Guidebook to shelf carbonates of the Paradox Basin: Four Corners Geological Society, symposium, p. 157-184.

Craig, L. C., and Cadigan, R. A., 1958, The Morrison and adjacent formations in the Four Corners area, in Guidebook to the geology of the Paradox Basin: Intermountain Association of Petroleum Geologists, Ninth Annual Field Conference, p. 182-192.

Eardley, A. J., 1958, Physiography of southeastern Utah, in Guidebook to the geology of the Paradox Basin: Intermountain Association of Petroleum Geologists, Ninth Annual Field Conference, p. 10-15.

Elias, G. K., 1963, Habitat of Pennsylvanian algal bioherms, Four Corners area, in Guidebook to shelf carbonates of the Paradox Basin: Four Corners Geological Society, symposium, p. 185-203.

Friedman, G. M., and Sanders, J. E., 1978, Principles of sedimentology: John Wiley and Sons, New York, 792 p., p. 144-163, p. 521-536.

Kelley, V. C., 1958, Tectonics of the region of the Paradox Basin, in Guidebook to the geology of the Paradox Basin: Intermountain Association of Petroleum Geologists, Ninth Annual Field Conference, p. 31-38.

Krivanek, C. M., 1978, Patterson Field, in Oil and gas fields of the Four Corners area: Four Corners Geological Society, V. II, p. 688-690.

Mack, G. H., and Miller, M. L., 1980, Pennsylvanian mud mound, Hermosa Group, southwestern Colorado: The Mountain Geologist, v. 17, no. 2, p. 37-43.

Moore, R. C., Lalicker, C. G., and Fischer, A. G., 1952, Invertebrate fossils: McGraw-Hill, New York, 766 p., p. 39-98, p. 574-581, p. 675-714.

Peterson, J. A., and Ohlen, H. R., 1963, Pennsylvanian shelf carbonates, Paradox Basin, in Guidebook to shelf carbonates of the Paradox Basin: Four Corners Geological Society, symposium, p. 65-79.

Robeck, R. C., 1958, Chinle and Moenkopi Formations, southeastern Utah, in Guidebook to the geology of the Paradox Basin: Intermountain Association of Petroleum Geologists, Ninth Annual Field Conference, p. 169-171.

Wexpro Company, company files.

Needles Mountains in the heart of the San Juan Dome looking east. (Photo by Jack Rathbone)

SQUAW CANYON FIELD
San Juan Co., Utah

Duane H. Buckner and Wilson Groen[1]

INTRODUCTION

On August 1, 1979, MCOR Oil and Gas (then McCulloch Oil and Gas) established Desert Creek production in Squaw Canyon from the #1-19 Federal test drilled in the SE NE of section 19 in T. 38 S., R. 26 E., San Juan County, Utah. Squaw Canyon is located between Desert Creek production in the Aneth Area 13 miles to the south-southwest and the Papoose Canyon-Bug trend 12 miles to the north-northeast (Figure 1). Although there is also potential for production from the Upper Ismay zone in the well, which is actually the reason that MCOR ran production casing to attempt completion, the Desert Creek is the only zone that has been production tested in the #1-19 to date. Therefore, this paper will discuss the data concerning the drilling, completion, and production performance of the Desert Creek zone alone.

These data present a true paradox, considering our accustomed way of evaluating a zone's potential to produce oil and gas. As Baars (1980) reported about the #1-19 well in his review of developments in 1979 in the Four Corners Area, "an alarming aspect of that well is that the induction log indicates salt water in the productive zone." However, virtually no water has been recovered with the 72,130 barrels of oil and 77 MMCFG produced over a total test period of six months. This suggests that either the induction log may not have been truly representative of the zone's virgin resistence or a seemingly miraculous completion job connected the perforations to an oil saturated zone not seen by the borehole.

DRILLING & LOGGING OF THE #1-19 WELL

The Desert Creek was drilled on July 9, with a mud weight of 11.3 lbs/gal, which was necessary to control uphole water flows. The drilling rate broke from 6-7 min/ft. to 1½-2 min/ft. for a 12 foot interval which corresponds with the porosity zone indicated on subsequent logs. Although circulated samples were fairly good above and below the porosity, no samples were seen from the interval of the drilling break exhibiting porosity of the magnitude shown by logs or permeability of the magnitude indicated later by the production performance of the well. There was a significant mudlogger show throughout the interval of the break, and there was a slight but noticeable increase in the mud pit volume with the mud becoming slightly gas cut.

Before logging, it appeared that the Desert Creek was not only porous, but also oil and gas saturated. However, the Dual Induction Log showed the porosity zone with an R_t as low as 0.9 ohms (Figure 2). The porosity log suite corresponding to that interval indicated dolomite of porosity up to 20%. Thus, assuming a saturated R_w of 0.023 ohms at 130° F, the water saturation calculates from the logs to be a very discouraging 80%.

Even though water saturations appeared to be very high, log calculations at 2' increments precisely matching measured depths on the porosity logs to the induction log suggested a transition from water saturations of 100% in the base of the zone to 80% in the highest porosity in the middle of the zone to about 50% in the top of the porosity zone. It was because of these calculations and the shows encountered while drilling that MCOR perforated the top 2 feet of the Desert Creek porosity as the first step in an overall production testing program planned for the well. It is interesting to note that if the induction log values are read only 1 foot deeper than corresponding porosity values so that the character match between the corresponding curves improves, the resulting values of water saturation show no transition zone but, rather, are fairly uniform at about 65 - 90% throughout the porosity zone.

On August 1, the SITP was 820 psi. The well was opened and when tubing pressure bled to 100 psi, it started flowing oil, producing 11 BO before dying in 5 minutes. It was then swabbed down to the seating nipple, recovering about 15 BO. At that time, the zone was acidized with 2000 gallons of 28% NE HC1. Acid was pumped at an initial rate of 2 BPM requiring 3000 psi. When the acid hit the perfs, the pressure dropped from 3200 psi to 3100 psi. After 30 bbls were pumped, the pressure was 3200 psi and the pumps were shut down for the acid to soak with the initial SIP 2600 psi and 700 psi after 10 minutes. Pumping was resumed at 2 BPM and 2600 psi. The rate was changed to 3 BPM and 3600 psi, then back to 2 BPM and 3100 psi. The last acid was pumped at 2 BPM and 2800 psi and the flush (1% KC1) was started at 2 BPM and 2700 psi. After 7 bbls were pumped, the pressure was 2700 psi, after 10 bbls pumped 2400 psi, after 14 bbls pumped 2300 psi, and after 24 bbls of flush were pumped, the pressure was 1600 psi (total acid 48 bbls and flush 24 bbls). The initial SIP was 1100 psi and 550 psi after 5 minutes. The job was complete at 10:40 AM and the well was opened to the reserve pit with 275 psi on tubing which bled immediately to zero. At that time, three swab runs were made. On the third, the well kicked off flowing oil, gas and acid water to the reserve pit. It was immediately hooked up to the frac tank and flowed through a 2" opening at 225 psi. A ⅜" positive choke was installed at 1:30 PM and flowing TP was 780 psi. At 2:30 PM the FTP was 680 psi and recovery was gauged at 30 BO. At 3:30 PM the FTP was 650 psi with the last hour's recovery at 29 BO. At 4:00 PM the FTP was 680 psi with 20 BO recovered, at 5:00 PM 680 psi and 20 BO, and at 6:00 PM 680 psi and 24 BO.

PRODUCTION PERFORMANCE OF THE #1-19 WELL

The next few days' reports clearly illustrate the productive capability of the well. On August 2, the SITP was 1040 psi. The well was opened at 7:30 AM on a ⅜" choke. Flowing tubing pressures and recoveries were gauged as follows during the day:

```
 8:00 AM  740 psi TP  25 BO Recovered
 9:00 AM  660 psi TP  14 BO Recovered
10:00 AM  680 psi TP  29 BO Recovered - changed to a ½"
                                          choke
11:00 AM  680 psi TP  32 BO Recovered
12:00 PM  550 psi TP  28 BO Recovered
 1:00 PM  550 psi TP  49 BO Recovered
```

[1]McAdams, Roux, O'Connor Associates, Denver, Colorado.
The authors wish to thank MRO Associates and MCOR Oil and Gas Corporation for permission to publish the data contained in this report. We also appreciate the specific contributions of the following people: Jr. Hickman of MCOR for his field supervision of the completion of the #1-19 well, Jack Severns and Jim Endacott of MCOR for their petrophysical evaluations and engineering supervision of the well, Thomas S. Ahlbrandt of MRO for critically reviewing the article, and Lynn Corrales of MRO for help in preparing the figures and typing the text.

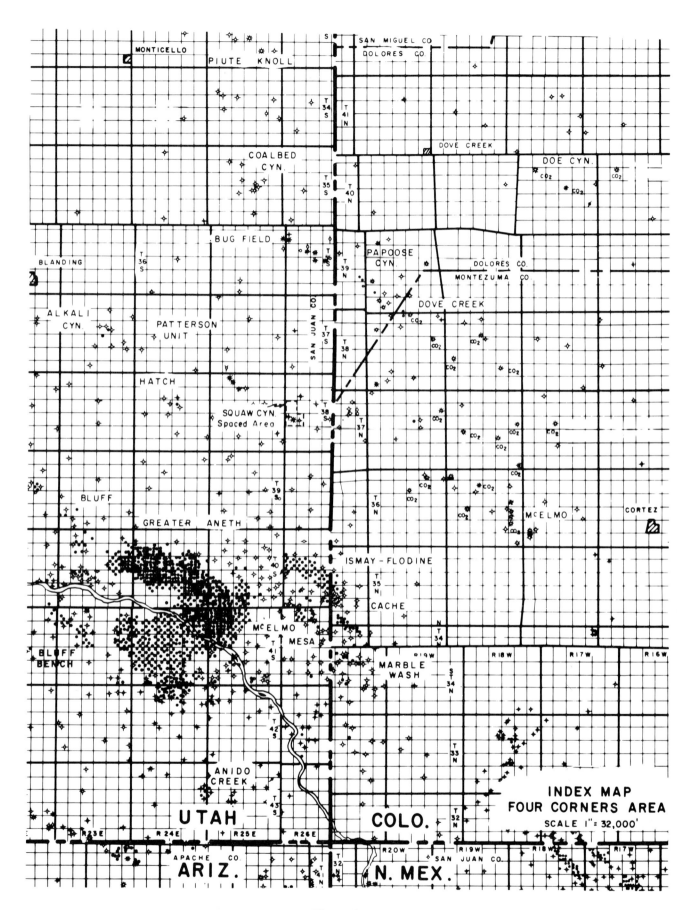

Figure 1

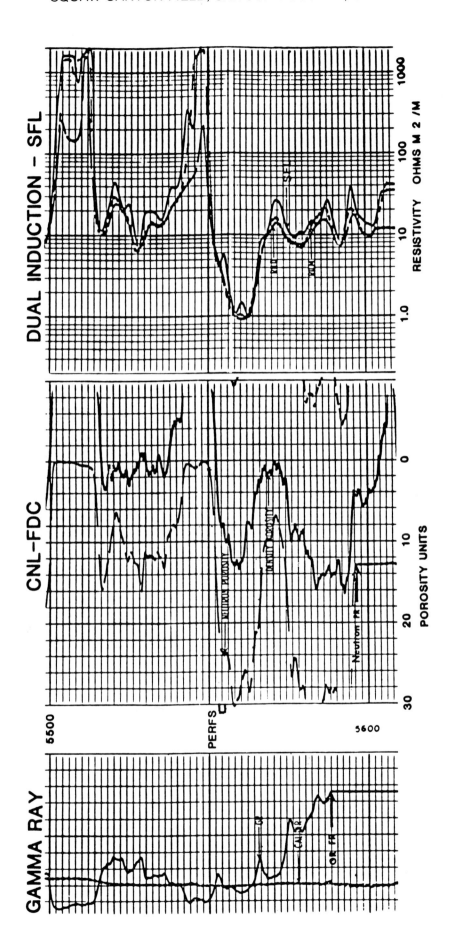

Figure 2

2:00 PM 550 psi TP 38 BO Recovered
2:15 PM 550 psi TP 10 BO Recovered - shut in waiting on
                                        second frac tank
4:30 PM 900 psi TP   - hooked up to new
                                        tank
5:00 PM 550 psi TP 45 BO Recovered
6:00 PM 550 psi TP 32 BO Recovered - SION

The next morning, August 3, SITP was 1050 psi. The well was flowed on a ½" choke for 8 hours at a FTP of 520 psi with recovery of 333 BO. The first bottom hole pressure survey was then run for a 72 hour buildup. Formation pressure was found to be 2480 psi.

The next gauge of production was on August 7 after producing 22½ hours through a ⅜" choke at a flowing TP of 630 psi with a separator on line. Recovery was 685 BO, 2.19 BW, with a gas rate of 503 MCFPD.

On August 8, 24 hours of production was gauged at 717 BO, 497 MCF gas and 2 BW at 630 psi FTP.

The next day, 24 hours of production gauged at 755 BO, 461 MCF gas, and 1 BW. The choke was then changed to ½" and during the next 24 hour period, the well produced 822 BO, 633 MCF gas, and 4.54 BW, which was the reported initial potential.

COMPLETION OF THE #1-19 WELL

On July 28, the Desert Creek zone was perforated from 5553-5555' with 2JSPF (4 holes). After tripping in the hole with packer and tubing, the tubing was swabbed down to 5000 feet and shut in over night. The next morning, July 29, was Sunday. Shut in tubing pressure was 260 psi.

On the morning of July 30, SITP was 300 psi. The fluid level was found at 3800 feet. Swabbing recovered water with a slight trace of oil. The zone was then acidized with 250 gal of 28% NE HC1 and flushed with 1% KC1 water. Initial shut in pressure was 3400 psi and after five minutes the SIP was 2850 psi. The well was opened with 1800 psi and immediately bled to zero. Fluid level was swabbed to 4000 feet into the reserve pit; the line was then hooked to the frac tank and swabbing was resumed down to the seating nipple, recovering an estimated 3 BO and 12 BW.

The next morning, July 31, SITP was 650 psi. The well was opened to the reserve pit and blew gas for 5 minutes, then flowed oil with 50 psi TP. It was hooked up to the frac tank, swabbed down to the seating nipple, and subsequently swabbed every 45 minutes during the day. The fluid level came up approximately 200 feet between runs and recovery for the day was 40 barrels of fluid of which an estimated 30 barrels was oil.

We contend that all of the data except the induction log suggests that the entire zone was oil and gas saturated before being penetrated by the bit; but, because the formation pressure of 2840 psi was over-balanced by a mud pressure of about 3260 psi, the formation fluids were affected by drilling fluids in such a way as to result in the low induction log reading. If so, a phenomenon somewhat different from a true annulus ring would have to be responsible for the low resistivity since an annulus would have lowered the zone's resistence to only about 3 ohms, not less than 1 ohm. However, we believe that a situation which could cause this phenomenon is conceivable. In formations like the Desert Creek, which is well known for its super salt saturated formation waters and, particularly, for porosity

which is sometimes salt plugged to varying degrees, it may be possible to move hydrocarbons away from the borehole with filtrate water that then dissolves some of the salt in the formation to effectively reduce the resistence of the invading filtrate water to levels much lower than that of pure filtrate water. The magnitude of permeability exhibited by the Desert Creek production in the #1-19 well suggests that such a phenomenon may account for the low induction log reading.

CONCLUSIONS FROM THE #1-19 WELL

We have presented unusual detail concerning the drilling, completion, and production of the Desert Creek in the #1-19 well, because we believe that it offers an excellent example to show that our usual methods of evaluating a well's potential to produce oil and gas are not necessarily foolproof. As explorationists, we must keep in mind that there are phenomena in the subsurface that we don't understand and/or have not yet calibrated. In the #1-19 well MCOR was fortunate to discover through a prudent completion program that the induction log did not tell the whole truth: but, how many tests have been drilled and plugged primarily on the basis of log analysis without cores or tests? This example painfully points up the value of gathering as much data as possible during the drilling process — especially cores. If the Desert Creek had been cored in the #1-19 and then interpreted in light of the other data, it probably would have made the answers to our questions obvious and MCOR probably would have run production casing because of the Desert Creek's potential as well as the Upper Ismay's. Because the Desert Creek wasn't cored, the reader must decide from where the oil is actually being produced based on the data that is available.

FIELD DEVELOPMENT

MCOR has drilled two attempts to extend production in the Squaw Canyon Field (Figures 3 & 4). Neither of those tests encountered porosity development in the Desert Creek, so those tests serve only to help define the field's boundaries. The Utah Oil and Gas Commission has established a temporary spacing order for 80 acre drilling and production units. At the time of this writing the operators are making drilling plans for the spring and summer to develop the field. Future drilling should also test and define the extent of the Upper Ismay reservoir in Squaw Canyon.

REFERENCE CITED

Baars, D. L., 1980, Developments in Four Corners-Intermountain Area in 1979: AAPG Bull., v. 62, p. 1340-1344.

SOME THEORIES FOR THE #1-19 WELL

Understandably, a controversy ensued concerning the identification of the oil producing zone. One possibility is that the induction log shows that the main porosity zone must be wet and the production performance proves that it therefore must be impermeable since no water was produced. So, one would conclude that the oil must be coming from a zone removed from the borehole and not seen by logs but reached by the acid job. Another explanation is a lensing of porosity zones may be responsible, with the top two feet of one lens filled with oil sitting on top of the main body of another lense that is wet.

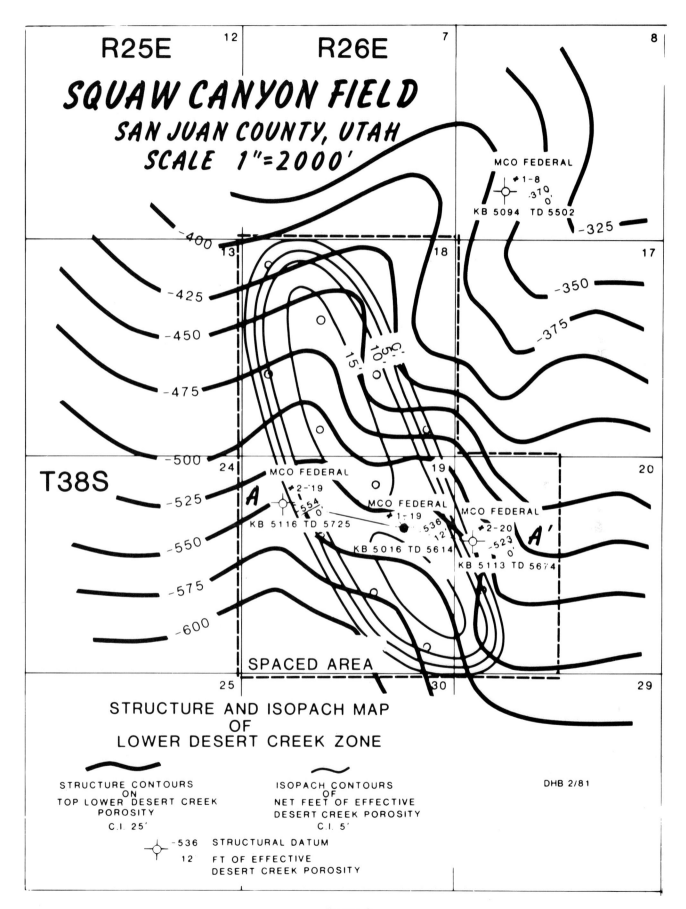

R25E 12 **R26E** 7 8

SQUAW CANYON FIELD
SAN JUAN COUNTY, UTAH
SCALE 1"=2000'

MCO FEDERAL
1-8
-370
0'
KB 5094 TD 5502
-325

13 18 17

-400

-425 -350

-450 -375

-475

-500

T38S 24 19 20

-525 MCO FEDERAL
2-19
A -554
0'
KB 5116 TD 5725

-550 MCO FEDERAL
1-19
-536 MCO FEDERAL
2-20
A' -523
0'

-575 12 KB 5113 TD 5674

KB 5016 TD 5614

-600

SPACED AREA

25 30 29

STRUCTURE AND ISOPACH MAP
OF
LOWER DESERT CREEK ZONE

STRUCTURE CONTOURS
ON
TOP LOWER DESERT CREEK
POROSITY
C.I. 25'

ISOPACH CONTOURS
OF
NET FEET OF EFFECTIVE
DESERT CREEK POROSITY
C.I. 5'

DHB 2/81

-536 STRUCTURAL DATUM

12 FT OF EFFECTIVE
DESERT CREEK POROSITY

Figure 3

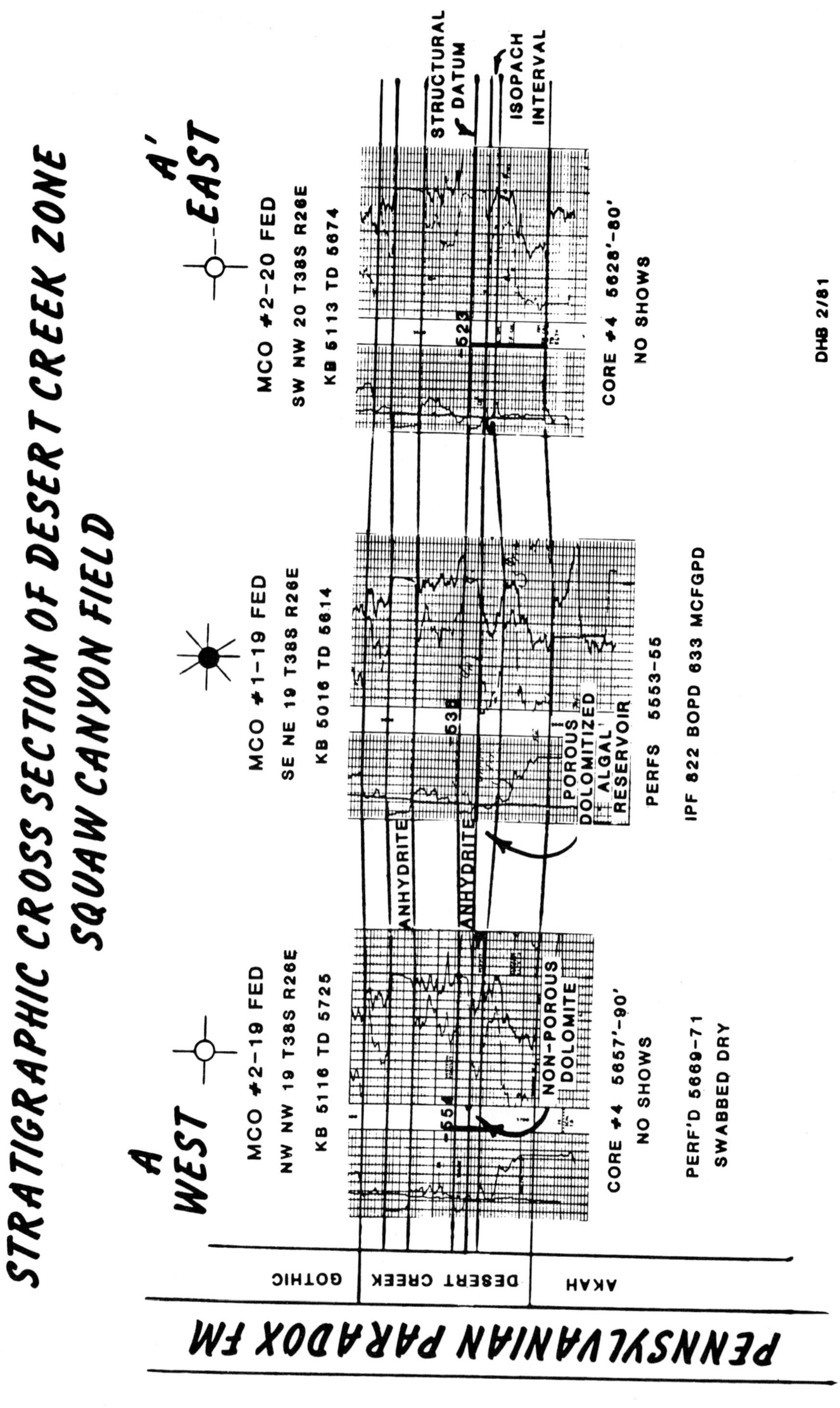
STRATIGRAPHIC CROSS SECTION OF DESERT CREEK ZONE
SQUAW CANYON FIELD
A
WEST
MCO #2-19 FED
NW NW 19 T38S R26E
KB 5116 TD 5725
CORE #4 5657'-90'
NO SHOWS
PERF'D 5669-71
SWABBED DRY
-554
NON-POROUS
DOLOMITE
ANHYDRITE
ANHYDRITE
MCO #1-19 FED
SE NE 19 T38S R26E
KB 5016 TD 5614
-538
POROUS
DOLOMITIZED
ALGAL
RESERVOIR
PERFS 5553-55
IPF 822 BOPD 633 MCFGPD
A'
EAST
MCO #2-20 FED
SW NW 20 T38S R26E
KB 5113 TD 5674
-523
CORE #4 5628'-80'
NO SHOWS
STRUCTURAL DATUM
ISOPACH INTERVAL
DHB 2/81
GOTHIC
DESERT CREEK
AKAH
PENNSYLVANIAN PARADOX FM

Figure 4

NEW FIELDS AND EXPLORATION DRILLING PARADOX BASIN UTAH AND COLORADO

CONNIE M. KRIVANEK
Wexpro Company
Farmington, New Mexico

INTRODUCTION

This report discusses successful exploration and development drilling programs during 1979 and 1980 in the Paradox Basin of southwestern Colorado and southeastern Utah. Brief summaries and listings of the geology of the new fields and types of traps are discussed.

COLORADO

1. McELMO FIELD

The Shell and Mobil Oil Corporations have completed 13 producible carbon dioxide gas wells ranging in depth from 7000 to 9000 feet from the Mississippian Leadville and Devonian Ouray carbonates. The McElmo Field is divided into seven Federal units in Montezuma County of southwestern Colorado. Shell and Mobil plan to drill an additional 130 gas wells in the greater McElmo Field located between the McElmo Dome Field to the south, Sections 13 and 24, T. 36 N., R. 18 W. and the Dove Creek Field to the north, Sec. 3, T. 38 N., R. 19 W. The field is 18 miles long and 10 miles wide (see activity maps). This project, sponsored by the two companies, is the largest single drilling program in the Paradox Basin since the discovery of the Aneth Field in 1956.

At McElmo Dome, on the southern end of the field, the Leadville has about 500 feet of closure. The gas accumulation in the greater McElmo Field shows a vertical relief in excess of 1300 feet. The gas is trapped in the Leadville-Ouray limestones and dolomites which are about 350 feet thick throughout the field. The porosity, mostly in dolomite, ranges from a gross thickness of 120 feet in the center of the field to 50 feet on the updip, east end of the field where wells produce water. It is possible that hydrodynamic processes are involved with the gas entrapment outside of the McElmo Dome closure.

The age and origin of the gas is related to the mid-Miocene/early Pliocene intrusion of the Ute Mountain laccolith into the Mississippian-Devonian carbonate host rocks south of the field.

Shell and Mobil's seven Federal units collectively contain 150,000 acres. The unit names are Cow Canyon, Hovenweep Canyon, Yellow Jacket, Moqui, Woods, Risley Canyon, and Sand Canyon. Gas reserves at the McElmo Dome and McElmo Field are estimated at 10 trillion cubic feet. Mobil's Risley Canyon Unit No. 1 well, Sec. 10, T. 36 N., R. 19 W. produced 40,000 MCFGPD without choke from gross perforations at 7082 to 7240 feet. The calculated absolute open flow equaled 220,000 MCFGPD. This well is the best producer in the field.

The unit areas at McElmo Field will not be developed on regular interval spacing. The Bureau of Land Management prefers the area to be developed by cluster drilling to reduce the impact of new roads in the area. Two or three wells will be drilled 300 to 500 feet apart from a common location.

The carbon dioxide gas will be transported through the 480 mile long Cortez pipeline. The line will originate at the field west of Cortez, Colorado, and terminate in Denver City, Texas, at the Denver Unit of Wasson Field. The carbon dioxide gas will be injected into the Permian San Andres Formation primarily consisting of dolomites. The participating companies claim that as much as 280 million additional barrels of oil should be recovered by this method.

Development drilling of the Leadville and Ouray Formations within the Federal units likely will result in oil and gas discoveries in the shallower Ismay-Desert Creek zones of the Paradox Formation.

2. DOE CANYON FIELD

Shell's Doe Canyon area in Dolores county, T. 40 N., R. 16 & 17 W., produces from three carbon dioxide wells. Doe Canyon is a large carbon dioxide field with an areal extent of 15,000 acres. The gas accumulation is trapped on the upthrown side of an east-west trending fault that borders the south side of an east-west trending anticline. Displacement is down to the south.

Mississippian rocks have been truncated at the crest of the structure. The field has a gas column with a vertical relief of 500 feet in the Leadville-Ouray Formations. The maximum reservoir porosity thickness at the Doe Canyon Field is 40 feet.

3. NORTHEAST DOVE CREEK AREA

Tipperary Oil and Gas Company set 4½ inch casing to 4645 feet in their No. 1 Fury well, NW NW, Sec. 21, T. 41 N., R. 18 W., Dolores County, Colorado. From perforations in the Honaker Trail Formation, the well flowed 400 MCFGPD. The zone flowed 1,500 MCFGPD when air drilled. The operator plans additional drilling for this area. The gas was recovered from lenticular arkosic sandstones.

3. NORTH DOLORES AREA

Lear Petroleum Company set 5½ inch pipe to 5621 feet at their No. 1 Bales well, SE NW, Sec. 25, T. 39 N., R. 15 W., Montezuma County, Colorado. It is rumored that some oil was recovered from the Ismay zone. The operator is not releasing data on the well.

5. HAMM CANYON FIELD

Champlin Petroleum Company completed the Hamm Canyon 14-26 No. 1 well, Sec. 26, T. 45 N., R. 18 W., San Miguel County, Colorado. Pipe was set at 10,007 feet and perforated from 9562 to 9578 feet, 9582 to 9596 feet, and 9602 to 9620 feet in the Hamm Sandstone (Honaker Trail Formation) for an initial potential flow of 1,164 MCFGPD.

The gas trap at the Hamm Canyon Field is controlled by a fault bordering the northeast side of the northwest-southeast trending Big Gypsum Valley salt anticline. The

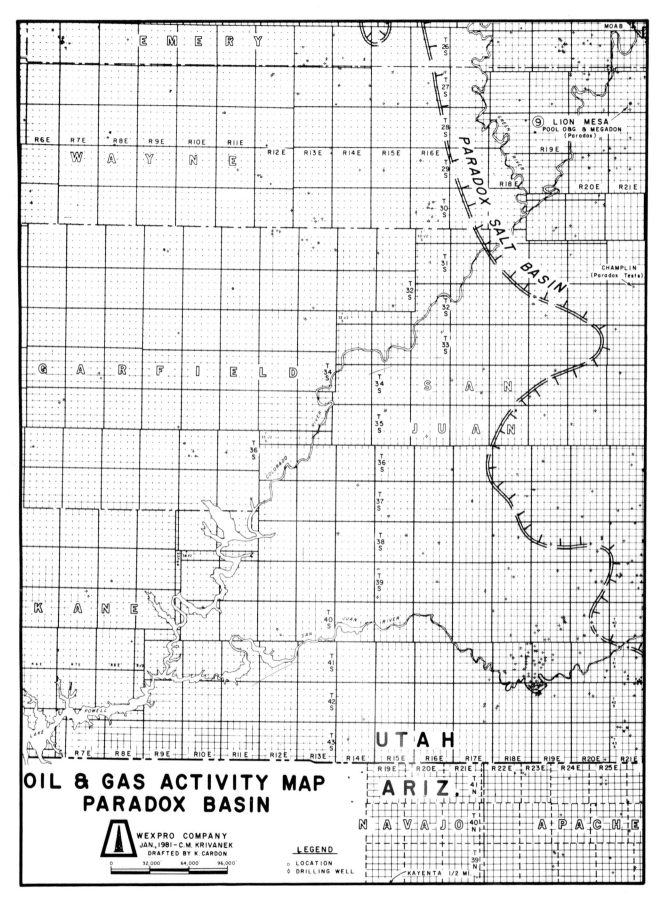

MAP 1

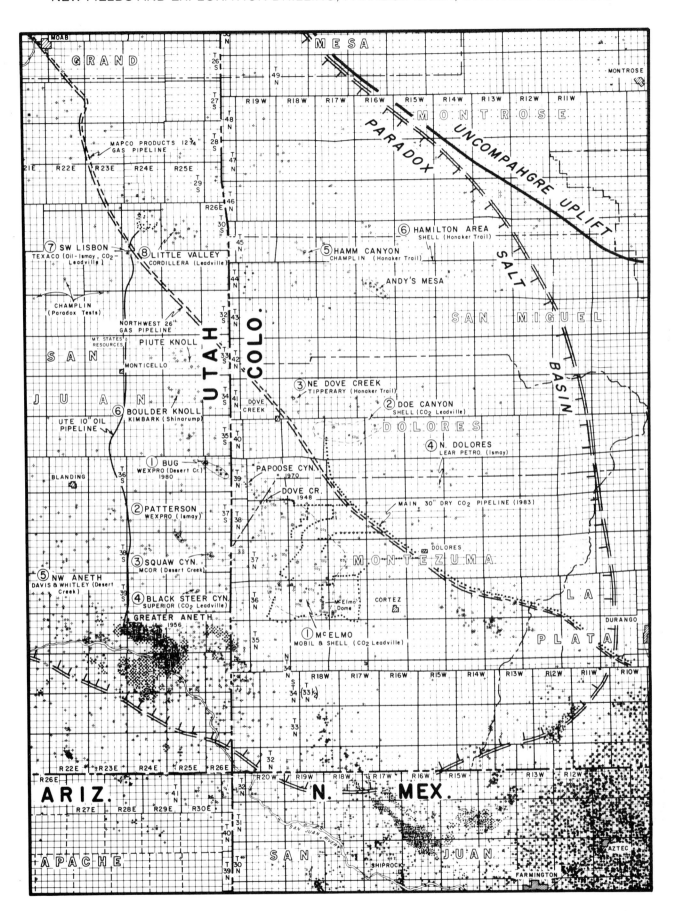

MAP 2

arkosic sandstones are down-thrown and in fault contact with petroliferous black shales and salt beds of the Paradox Formation. The new field is located 10 miles northwest of Union Oil's Andy's Mesa Field (T. 43 & 44 N., R. 16 W.). The Andy's Mesa Field also is located on the northeast limb of the Big Gypsum Valley salt anticline and produces gas from a similar type of trap.

At the No. 2 Hamm Canyon well, NW NE, Sec. 27, T. 45 N., R. 18 W., 5½ inch casing was set at 10,000 feet and perforated from 9766 to 9797 feet. The well was swabbed and produced 56 barrels of water and 9 barrels of load condensate. The zone was squeezed. After perforating from 9718 to 9736 feet the well produced 24 MCFGPD and 12 BGCW. This well is shut-in.

6. HAMILTON AREA

Shell Oil has set 7 inch pipe to 8545 feet in their Federal 1-1 well, SW NE, Sec. 1, T. 44 N., R. 15 W., San Miguel County, Colorado. This could be a gas discovery from the Honaker Trail Formation. Shell drilled a faulted anticline.

UTAH

1. BUG FIELD

The second largest single drilling project presently underway in the Paradox Basin is the development of Bug Field (T. 36 S., R. 26 E.), San Juan County, Utah, by Wexpro Company. Six wells are currently capable of oil and gas production from a stratigraphic trap in the Desert Creek zone. Approximately 10 to 15 additional wells will be drilled at this field on 160 acre spacing (see Bug Field report in this guidebook).

2. PATTERSON FIELD

Wexpro Company completed the Patterson Unit Well No. 1, Sec. 5, T. 38 S., R. 25 E., San Juan County, Utah. The well flowed with an initial potential of 294 BO, 720 MCFGPD and 20 BWPD. The Patterson Field produces from a stratigraphic trap in the Ismay zone (see Patterson Field report in this guidebook).

3. SQUAW CANYON

McCulloch Oil Corporation, now MCOR, discovered the Squaw Canyon Field, Sec. 19, T. 38 S., R. 26 E., San Juan County, Utah. The Squaw Canyon Field produces from a stratigraphic trap in the Desert Creek zone. The 1-19 well, Sec. 19, T. 38 S., R. 26 E., was completed in October, 1979, flowing 504 BOPD and 433 MCFGPD through a ⅜ inch choke. Further development of this one-well field is scheduled for 1981 (see Squaw Canyon report in this guidebook).

4. BLACK STEER CANYON AREA

At Superior's Black Steer Canyon 14-33 well, NW SE, Sec. 14, T. 39 S., R. 25 E., San Juan County, Utah, 3,900 MCFPD of carbon dioxide gas and 2,800 BWPD were recovered from the Leadville Formation after a 7,000 gallon acid fracture. Perforations at 7530 to 7540 feet and 7640 to 7650 feet have been squeezed. Production perforations are from 7572 to 7612 feet. The trap is a low relief anticlinal closure.

5. NORTHWEST ANETH AREA

Bill Whitley set 4½ inch casing at 5580 feet in his 1-24 Federal well, SW SE, Sec. 24, T. 40 S., R. 22 E., and perforated the Desert Creek zone from 5526 to 5534 feet. The well flowed 216 BO and 56 MCFGPD through a 12/64 inch choke.

An offset, Whitley's 1-25 3-E Federal well, NE NE, Sec. 25, T. 40 S., R. 22 E., recovered oil and water from the Desert Creek zone. The well was plugged back and perforated in the Ismay from 5375 to 5380 feet and pumped an initial potential of 6 BO and 17 BWPD.

Davis Oil Company set 5½ inch casing to 5560 feet at the McCracken Point No. 1 Federal, NW SW, Sec. 19, T. 40 S., R. 23 E. Gross perforations in the Desert Creek are from 5428 to 5600 feet. The well pumped 5 BO and 55 BWPD.

At the Davis Oil Nathan Fee No. 1, NW NE, Sec. 16, T. 40 S., R. 22 E., 5½ inch casing was set at 5914 feet and perforated in the Desert Creek zone at 5690 to 5710 feet and acidized with 35,000 gallons. The well pumped an initial potential of 70 BO and 66 BWPD.

6. BOULDER KNOLL AREA

Kimbark Operating Company set 4½ inch casing to 2706 feet in their Boulder Knoll State No. 1 well, SE NW, Sec. 16, T. 34 S., R. 25 E., San Juan County, Utah. The casing was perforated in lenticular sandstones of the Shinarump member of the Chinle Formation from 2610 to 2614 feet, 2634 to 2642 feet, 2647 to 2650 feet and 2654 to 2658 feet. The well flowed 285 MCFGPD and 10.5 BWPH following an acid and sand fracture treatment.

7. SOUTHWEST LISBON AREA

Texaco completed the No. 1 Government Evelyn Chambers, NE NE, Sec. 6, T. 31 S., R. 24 E., San Juan County, Utah. Seven inch pipe was set to 8728 feet. The Mississippian Leadville Formation was perforated from 8118 to 8149 feet and 8040 to 8054 feet. Commingled flow rates for both zones were 1,700 MCFGPD of 30.8 percent nitrogen, 33 percent carbon dioxide and 36 percent methane. The gas accumulation is controlled by a fault on the southwest side of an anticline. The Cane Creek zone at 7792 to 7818 feet was perforated and produced carbon dioxide at a rate of 1,230 MCFGPD. The zone was squeezed. The Ismay zone was perforated from 4836 to 4860 feet and 4670 to 4682 feet and acid fractured through 2⅞ inch tubing set at 4659 feet. A 24 hour pump test recovered 12 BO and 4.5 MCFG and 60 BW. The gravity of the oil is 40.2 degrees API. The methane gas is vented at the wellsite. The productive carbon dioxide gas zones in this well are shut-in. Texaco plans to drill several offset wells at this new field.

8. LITTLE VALLEY

Cordillera Corporation re-entered a temporarily abandoned hole in SW SW, Sec. 16, T. 30 S., R. 25 E., San Juan County, Utah. Their well is the No. 1 State in the Little Valley Field. Four and one half inch liner was set from 4520 to 9507 feet. Gross perforations in the Leadville are from 9048 to 9421 feet. The well had an initial potential flow of 3,516 MCFGPD and 72 BCPD. An offset by another operator in Sec. 21, T. 30 S., R. 25 E., was dry. Cordillera had set 5½ inch casing to 9508 feet in their 1-2 Federal well, NE NE, Sec. 20, T. 30 S., R. 25 E. They have selectively perforated from 9328 to 9434 feet and are preparing to acidize. The oil and gas trap at Little Valley Field is controlled by a fault on the northeast side of an anticlinal closure.

9. LION MESA

Pool Oil & Gas-Megadon Energy Corporation ran 5½ inch pipe to 7995 feet at their 27-1A Hatch Point (Lion Mesa Unit) well, NE SW, Sec. 27, T. 27 S., R. 21 E., San Juan County, Utah. The well is plugged back to 7746 feet. The gross interval perforated in the Paradox Cane Creek zone is from 7378 to 7464 feet. Estimated production rate is 50 to 75 BOPD and 50 MCFGPD. This zone flowed 30 to 40 BOPH on a drill stem test. The gas has a heating value of 1579 BTU's per cubic foot. The operator plans to drill 3 additional wells to test this zone and the deeper Mississippian rocks on the structure in this area. Also, 7 Mississippian tests in the western part of the Paradox Basin are planned in 1981.

FUTURE DEVELOPMENT DRILLING TRENDS

The most extensive drilling activity in the Paradox Basin will occur in western Montezuma County, Colorado, to develop the large carbon dioxide deposit in the Leadville-Ouray Formation at McElmo Field. One hundred thirty additional wells are planned for this area. Oil and gas discoveries in the shallow Ismay and Desert Creek zones should occur as the carbon dioxide field is developed.

Bug Field will require an additional 10 to 15 wells to develop this oil and gas stratigraphic trap in the Desert Creek in northeast San Juan County, Utah.

At the Aneth Field in southern San Juan County, Utah, 15 to 20 wells are scheduled along this field's downdip oil-water contact.

FUTURE EXPLORATORY DRILLING TRENDS

The area west and northwest of the Aneth Field will continue to be an active exploration area for stratigraphic traps of the Ismay and Desert Creek carbonates. Well control in this area of the Paradox Basin is excellent. Ten to twenty exploratory tests will be drilled in the area.

The area near the Bug, Patterson and Squaw Canyon fields will continue to be explored for stratigraphic traps in Desert Creek and Ismay carbonates.

Three to four wells will be exploring for stratigraphic traps in the Ismay-Desert Creek zones in an area 15 to 20 miles southwest of the Lisbon Field.

The large pie-shaped area between the Colorado and Green Rivers of northern San Juan County and Grand County, Utah, will have 5 to 10 exploratory wells drilled this year prospecting for structural traps in the Leadville-Ouray carbonate formations and McCracken Sandstone member of the Elbert Formation. Shallower objectives in this area are the fractured petroliferous shales in the Cane Creek zone of the Paradox Formation. Also, Honaker Trail and Cutler Formations are additional objectives. Geophysical activity has been increasing in this area.

The sparsely drilled area along the eastern shelf of the Paradox Basin in eastern Wayne and Garfield counties will continue to have several exploratory tests for structural traps in Devonian-Mississippian rocks by a few daring wildcaters. Pennsylvanian algal bioherms are stratigraphic objectives in this area.

The Paradox fold and fault belt in Dolores, San Miguel and Montrose Counties, Colorado, has had increased geophysical activity the past two years. The exploration activity in this area should continue to have 5 to 10 wells drilled per year prospecting for structural traps in the Devonian, Mississippian, Pennsylvanian and Permian rocks.

In summary, there are large areas within the Paradox Basin that can be demonstrated, geologically and geophysically, to contain a variety of structural and stratigraphic traps for hydrocarbons and carbon dioxide.

REFERENCES

Communications with company operators mentioned in report.

Communications with Bureau of Land Management personnel, Santa Fe, New Mexico.

Krivanek, C. M., 1978, McElmo Field, in Oil and gas fields of the Four Corners area: Four Corners Geological Society, p. 148-151.

Latch, B. F., 1978, Little Valley Field, in Oil and gas fields of the Four Corners area: Four Corners Geological Society, p. 670-672.

Petroleum Information Corporation, Jan. 15, 1981, Rocky Mountain regional reports, Vol. 54, No. 9.

"This field work is great but don't you
think it's time to analyze our samples
in the lab . . . ?"

PRODUCTIVE PENNSYLVANIAN CARBONATE MOUNDS SOUTHEAST OF THE ANETH AREA, UTAH

Donald D. Lehman[1]

ABSTRACT

Isolated Pennsylvanian algal mounds and oolite banks are responsible for prolific oil and gas production near the Greater Aneth producing complex in Southeast Utah. Three fields, Southeast McElmo Creek, Rockwell Springs and the Navajo 116, all located in the southern half of T. 41 S., R. 25 E., San Juan County, Utah, have produced more than 3.7 MMBO and 5.1 BCFG from the Desert Creek Zone of the Pennsylvanian Hermosa Formation. These structurally and stratigraphically controlled fields are similar to each other, yet they also display several basic differences. They all possess the excellent reservoir parameters characteristic of the Desert Creek; however, each produces from a different zone (or zones) from within the Desert Creek. The Lower Ismay Zone is also a potential producer in Rockwell Springs field. Although small in aerial extent, the shallow drilling depths and excellent productive qualities makes these types of carbonate reservoirs extremely attractive exploration targets.

INTRODUCTION

Southeast McElmo Creek, Rockwell Springs and the Navajo 116 are located from two to four miles southeast of the Greater Aneth producing complex (figure 1), with the San Juan River disecting the area from northwest to southeast. During Pennsylvanian time this area was the southwest carbonate shelf of the Paradox Basin. The environment was very conducive to the growth of the algae *Ivanovia*, particularly during Desert Creek, Lower Ismay and Ismay time, as shown by the excellent reservoir parameters encountered at Rockwell Springs and Southeast McElmo Creek fields. Shoaling on the shelf during late Desert Creek time was responsible for the development of oolites on top of some existing algal mounds. Subsequent leaching of the oolites and dolomitization formed excellent oomoldic porosity in the Upper Desert Creek Zone at the Navajo 116 and Rockwell Springs fields. McComas (1963) and Irwin (1963) describe in detail, these types of reservoirs and their characteristics in the Aneth area. Many excellent accounts of the stratigraphy, and sedimentary and tectonic history of the Paradox Basin have also been published; Hite (1973), Peterson (1966), Peterson and Ohlen (1963), Picard (1960) and Wengard (1962).

Although the algal mounding and formation of oolites have been responsible for primary stratigraphic hydrocarbon accumulations, present day structure and paleothinning over the Desert Creek are observed in relation to the production in this area (figures 2 and 3). Structurally low wells generally are water wet or without sufficient algal buildup and porosity. Paleohighs at the end of Desert Creek time are observed by thinning of the overlying Gothic Shale, usually corresponding to a thicker than normal Desert Creek section. Figure 3 displays paleohighs at all three producing fields. Other paleohighs are nonproductive in this area because (1) the porosity has been destroyed by anhydrite plugging or (2) the reservoir is water wet.

NAVAJO 116

The Navajo 116 is a one well field, discovered utilizing subsurface techniques, by Zoller-Danneberg and Duncan Oil at the 116-1 Navajo, located in the NW/SE of Section 31-41S-25E. It was completed in November, 1963, flowing 255 BOPD. The well is currently operated by Walter Duncan Oil

Properties and has produced 632,425 BO and 982,596 MCFG. Current production is 46 BOPD and 132 MCFGPD. The Desert Creek section is 190 feet thick, nearly 90 feet more than the regional thickness (figure 4). The 28 feet of net productive pay is from the oomoldic porosity in the upper portion of the Desert Creek. The average porosity of this interval is approximately 14 percent. Solution gas is the reservoir drive, with an original reservoir pressure of about 1985 psi. Figure 5 displays the log character of this zone.

SOUTHEAST McELMO CREEK

Southeast McElmo Creek Field is a four well field, separated by dry holes from the giant McElmo Creek Unit in the Greater Aneth complex, two miles to the northwest. The discovery well, the Humble and Superior #1 Navajo 125, in the SW/SW of Section 21-41S-25E was drilled on the basis of subsurface and surface information. It was completed in February, 1962, flowing 646 BOPD. Three additional producing wells were completed in the field by July, 1962. Cumulative production from the field is 2,549,110 BO and 3,463,339 MCFG and current production from the four wells is 103 BOPD and 205 MCFGPD. The gross Desert Creek thickness at Southeast McElmo Creek is nearly regional (figure 4), the trap being formed primarily by dolomitized algal porosity surrounded by tight carbonate rock in the lower part of the Desert Creek. Porosities range from 6 to 20 percent with a 26 foot average net pay thickness. The original reservoir pressure was 2130 psi and the primary drive mechanism appears to be solution gas. A type log for this field is shown in Figure 6.

ROCKWELL SPRINGS

The two well, Rockwell Springs field, was discovered by Superior Oil at the Navajo 34-42, located in the SE/NE of Section 34-41S-25E, on a farmout from Walter Duncan Oil Properties. It was completed in August, 1978, flowing 1298 BPD of 41° API gravity oil. A north offset, the 34-31 Navajo, was drilled and completed in the Lower Ismay, which produced only 122 BO before being abandoned. This well encountered a normal section of Desert Creek with no porosity. A second producer, the Navajo 34-43, NW/SE of Section 34-41S-25E, was completed in June, 1979, flowing 707 BOPD on a 16/64" choke. The cumulative field

[1]Walter Duncan Oil Properties, Denver, Colorado

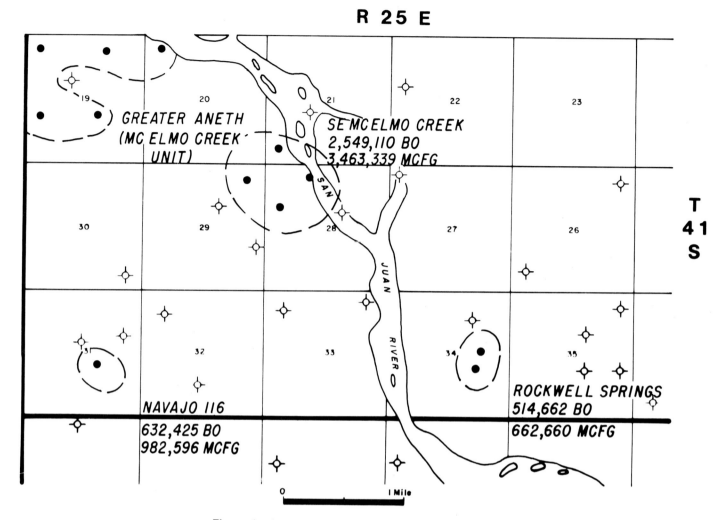

Figure 1.   Location map and cumulative production.

production is 514,662 BO and 662,660 MCFG and is currently producing 392 BOPD and 1,012 MCFGPD. All three wells were drilled on seismic anomalies. The Desert Creek attains a maximum thickness of 174 feet at Rockwell Springs, about 75 feet more than regional thickness. The Desert Creek produces from the upper oomoldic zone and the lower algal zone, with an average total net pay thickness of 49 feet. An oil-water contact exists at -844 subsea. Core porosities in the dolomitized oomoldic zone range from 7.4 to 24.3 percent and permeabilities range from less than one to 114 millidarcies. The dolomitized algal zone has porosities ranging from 7.8 to 27.8 percent and permeabilities ranging from less than one to 47 millidarcies. The original reservoir pressure in the Desert Creek was approximately 1950 psi. The drive mechanism is primarily solution gas with a possible weak water drive.

The Lower Ismay pay at Rockwell Springs is behind casing and has not yet produced (except at the Navajo 34-31). The lithology is limestone with much of the original algal porosity and characteristics preserved. The core porosities from the Navajo 34-43 average 9.0 percent and permeabilities average 143 millidarcies. Average net pay thickness in the field is 20 feet. Figure 7 displays the Lower Ismay and Desert Creek pays in this field.

SUMMARY

The Desert Creek and Lower Ismay fields discussed herein should provide encouragement for additional exploration and development activity in this part of the Paradox Basin. With many of these features less than a half section in size, the potential exists for the discovery of additional productive algal mounds in this area.

REFERENCES CITED

Hite, R. J., 1973, Shelf carbonate sedimentation controlled by salinity in the Paradox Basin, Southeast Utah: The Mountain Geologist, v. 9, nos. 2-3, p. 329-344.

Irwin, C. D., Jr., 1963, Producing carbonate reservoirs in the Four Corners area, in shelf carbonates of the Paradox Basin: Four Corners Geological Society 4th annual field conference, p. 144-148.

McComas, M. R., 1963, Productive core analysis characteristics of carbonate rocks in the Four Corners area, in shelf carbonates of the Paradox Basin: Four Corner Geological Society 4th annual conference, p. 149-156.

Peterson, J. A., 1966, Stratigraphic vs. structural controls on carbonate mound hydrocarbon accumulation, Aneth area,

Paradox Basin: American Association Petroleum Geologists Bulletin, v. 50, no. 10, p. 2068-2081.

_____ and Ohlen, H. R., 1963, Pennsylvanian shelf carbonates, Paradox Basin, in shelf carbonates of the Paradox Basin: Four Corners Geological Society 4th Annual field conference, p. 65-79.

Picard, M. D., 1960, Geology of Pennsylvanian gas in the

Four Corners region: American Association Petroleum Geologists Bulletin, v. 44, no. 9, p. 1541-1569.

Wengerd, S. A., 1962, Pennsylvanian sedimentation in Paradox Basin, Four Corners region, in Pennsylvanian System in the United States: American Association Petroleum Geologists Special Volume, p. 264-330.

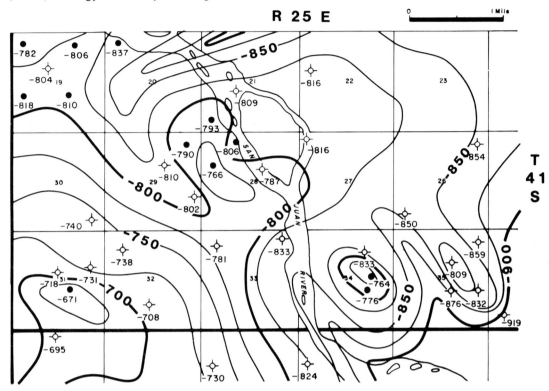

Figure 2.   Structure map constructed on the top of the Desert Creek.

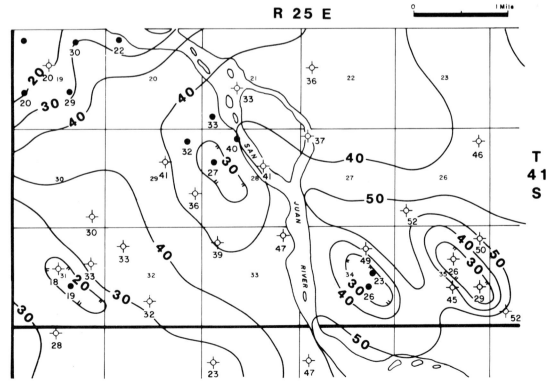

Figure 3.   Isopach map of the Gothic shale.

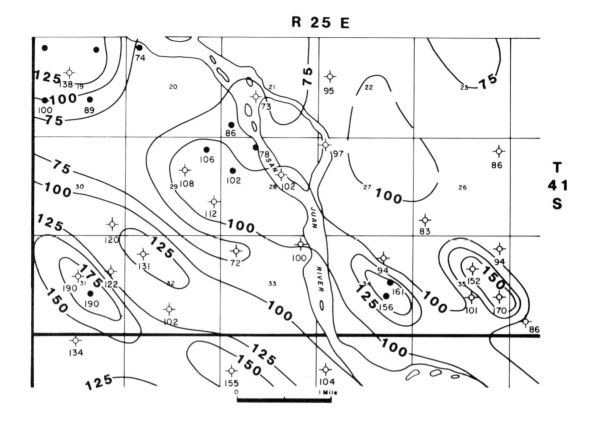

Figure 4.   Isopach map of the Desert Creek.

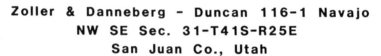

Zoller & Danneberg - Duncan 116-1 Navajo
NW SE Sec. 31-T41S-R25E
San Juan Co., Utah

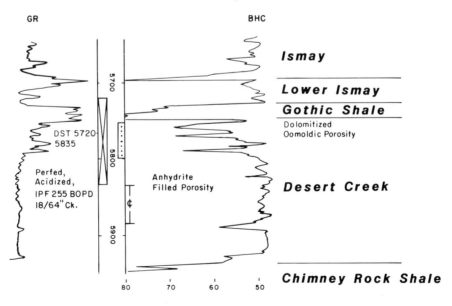

Figure 5.   Example log from the Navajo 116 area.

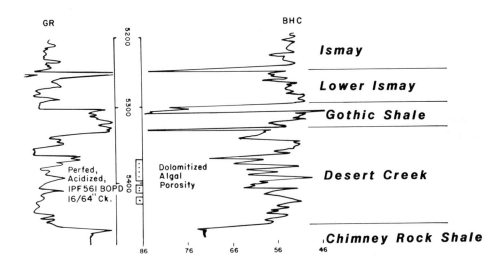

Superior 29 McElmo-Q
NE NE Sec. 29-T41S-R25E
San Juan Co., Utah

Figure 6.   Example log from the Southeast McElmo Creek Field.

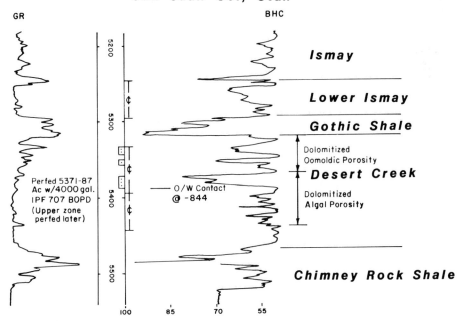

Superior 34-43 Navajo
NW SE Sec. 34-T41S-R25E
San Juan Co., Utah

Figure 7.   Example log from the Rockwell Springs Field.

Sleeping ute

LISBON FIELD AREA, SAN JUAN COUNTY, UTAH[1]

John M. Parker[2]

ABSTRACT

The Lisbon field oil and gas accumulation is trapped in a faulted anticline. Reservoirs are in five zones — the McCracken and Ouray of Devonian age, the Leadville of Mississippian age, and the middle Paradox and Honaker Trail (upper Hermosa) of Pennsylvanian age. Only the Mississippian oil, condensate, and gas reservoir is of commercial importance at the present time. Oil production from the Mississippian from 1960 to September 1965 was 11,801,530 bbls. Remaining oil reserve is estimated to be 39 million bbls. Gas reserve is estimated to be 240 billion cu ft. The gas now being produced is injected into the Mississippian in a pressure-maintenance program. It is estimated that gas sales will begin in 1973. The gas has a high nitrogen and carbon dioxide content (775 + Btu) and will require beneficiation.

INTRODUCTION

The Lisbon field is an oil, condensate, and gas field in the salt-anticline fold-and-fault belt on the southwest flank of the Paradox basin. Porous zones in the Mississippian Leadville dolomite beds form the primary reservoir; the trapping mechanism is a large faulted anticline. The Mississippian anticline is beneath the west flank and 2,500 ft downdip from the crest of the well-exposed Lisbon Valley salt anticline. Minor oil production in the Lisbon field has been developed from limestone and dolomite of the Devonian Ouray Limestone, from the Devonian McCracken Sandstone Member of the Elbert Formation, and from a clastic zone in the Pennsylvanian Paradox Formation.

Two undeveloped Mississippian dolomite gas reservoirs are present near the main Lisbon field, the Big Indian area on the north and the Little Valley area on the southeast. There is one undeveloped oil and gas field in Honaker Trail (Upper Pennsylvanian) sandstone in the Little Valley area northeast of the Little Valley Mississippian accumulation.

DISCOVERY HISTORY AND METHOD OF EXPLORATION

The Lisbon surface anticline was mapped in the early 1900's. The anticline is 21 mi long; a normal fault along the crest has displaced beds on the northeast flank downward 4,600 ft (Figure 1). The upthrown southwest block has surface closure of 3,000 ft. Union Oil Company of California drilled a 5,010 ft cable-tool test in 1927 on the crest of the surface structure. This test bottomed in the salt member of the Paradox Formation without finding commercial production.

Pure Oil Company spudded their No. 1 Northwest Lisbon area wildcat (NE ¼, NW ¼, Sec. 10, T. 30 S., R. 24 E.) on August 14, 1959. Commercial gas distillate was drill-stem tested in the Mississippian in October, 1959. The well was drilled to a total depth of 8,442 ft into the Devonian Aneth formation, and was completed on January 4, 1960, in the Devonian McCracken Formation, with an initial production, flowing, of 587 bbls a day of 44° API-gravity green crude oil on a 14/64-in choke. (This McCracken production declined rapidly, partly because of mechanical problems, and the well subsequently was recompleted in the Mississippian. Still later, the discovery well was converted to a McCracken oil producer and a Mississippian reservoir gas-injection hole.)

[1]Manuscript was originally received May 25, 1966, and was published in AAPG Memoir 9, Vol. 2, Natural Gases of North America, 1968. At the request of the editor of this 1981 RMAG Guidebook, John M. Parker has revised the maps and the production statistics and the article is here reprinted, courtesy of AAPG.

[2]Consulting Geologist
Surface geologic mapping and magnetic and gravity surveys performed by the USGS have been very helpful. The writer acknowledges the use of two reports on the field area, one by Allan Fullerton, Pure Oil Co., and one by James Albright, Pubco Petroleum Corp.

TABLE I. LISBON FIELD DATA, SEPTEMBER 30, 1965

Reservoir	No. of Producing Wells	No. of Injection Wells	Productive Area (acres)
Mississippian (gas, condensate, and oil)	18	3 (gas injection)	5,500
Ouray	1[1]	0	320
McCracken	2[2]	1[2] (water injection)	800
Paradox	1[3]	0	40

[1] Two wells (one in NE ¼ NE ¼, Sec. 16, and one in NE ¼ NW ¼, Sec. 15, T. 30 S., R. 24 E.) were producing from the Ouray until 1963 when the well in Sec. 15 was recompleted in the Mississippian.

[2] Three wells originally were completed in the McCracken (one in the NE ¼ NW ¼, Sec. 10, one in the NE¼ SE ¼, Sec. 10, and one in the NE ¼ NW ¼, Sec. 14, T. 30 S., R. 24 E.). In 1963 the McCracken well in Sec. 14 at the lowest structural position was converted to a water-injection well in a pilot flood attempt designed for secondary recovery from this reservoir. The flood did not work, and the water-injection well is shut in. The McCracken oil in the other two wells is produced through tubing, and in the same well bore Mississippian gas is injected down the annulus into the Mississippian reservoir.

[3] This well was plugged and abandoned in 1963.

This wildcat was staked after a massive and persistent exploration program in the Paradox basin by the Pure Oil Company which had gone on continuously for more than 10 years and included surface, gravity, and extensive seismic work, the drilling of several dry wildcats, and the discovery of the mediocre Mississippian production in the Big Flat field, Grand County, Utah, in 1957.

PRODUCTION AREA AND NUMBER OF WELLS

Productive areas in the Lisbon field and number of wells drilled as of September 30, 1965, are shown in Table I.

STRATIGRAPHY

Table II is a tabulation of the stratigraphic column in the area.

LOCAL STRUCTURE

The Lisbon Field has six different structural configurations caused by different periods of uplift, folding, and faulting, and by different periods of salt flowage and contemporaneous subsidence. The configurations are formed by (1) the units above the Cutler Formation (this is the folding and faulting expressed at the surface), (2) the units from the top of the Cutler down to the unconformity between the upper and lower Cutler, (3) the units from the Cutler unconformity down through the uppermost part of the Paradox salt, (4) the middle and lower parts of the Paradox salt, (5) the presalt Paleozoic strata, and (6) the crystalline basement rocks.

Figures 1-8 show details of structural development (the locations of the cross sections are shown on the contour maps).

The Mississippian petroleum reservoir (Figure 3) at Lisbon

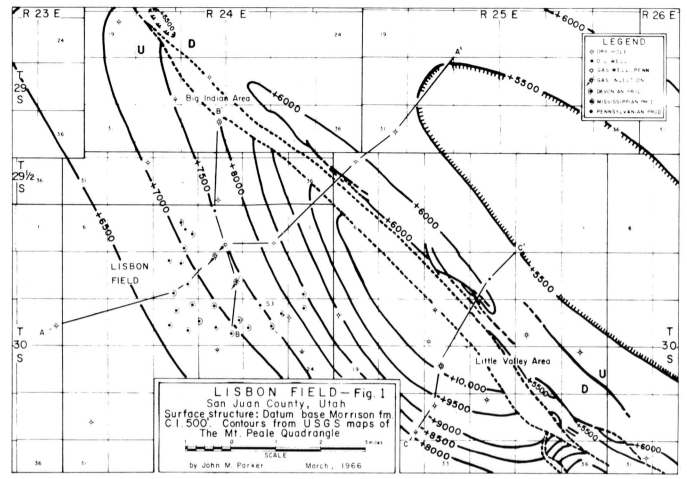

Figure 1.   Surface structural contour map, Lisbon field; datum is base of Morrison Formation.

Field is a faulted anticline with 1,900 ft of closure. The gas, condensate, and oil column is 1,870 ft high; thus the structure is filled nearly to the spill point. The top of the anticline at the Mississippian level is at -700 ft, the oil-water contact is at -2,570 ft, and the closing contour is -2,600 ft.

Where there is no well control, the structural interpretation shown on the maps and cross sections is conjectural. The easternmost northwest-trending fault shown at the Mississippian level (Figure 3) is not necessary in a subsurface interpretation.

REGIONAL RELATIONSHIPS

The geologic history of the general area of Lisbon field, with specific emphasis on the Lisbon structural complex, may be summarized as follows:

1. Uplift and faulting occurred in Precambrian time (Baars, 1966).

2. Cambrian through Mississippian rocks were deposited (Ordovician and Silurian strata are absent or unidentifiable).

3. Uplift and faulting occurred in Late Mississippian time.

4. Oil and gas accumulated in the Mississippian and Devonian reservoirs (?).

5. Erosion occurred during Late Mississippian and Early Pennsylvanian times.

6. Pennsylvanian rocks were deposited; during Molas, Pinkerton Trail, and early salt deposition, local areas continued to rise slightly, with accompanying erosion. Oil and gas accumulated in the Mississippian and Devonian reservoirs from source beds on the Molas, Pinkerton Trail, and lower Paradox salt and black shale section (?).

7. Lower Permian rocks were deposited, and Paradox salt

flowage was initiated by recurrent growth of the graben and half-graben regional system of faults developed in Mississippian time. Salt flowage continued because of differential loading. Salt flowage began during Cutler time and most of the flowage took place after development of the unconformity dividing the Cutler Formation. There was relief on the presalt surface prior to and during the early part of salt deposition, but it is believed to have been no more than a 300-400-ft differential in an area 5-15 mi across. Thus, salt thickness originally was nearly uniform in local areas, and an average total depositional thickness of 3,000 ft for the middle Paradox Formation is postulated for the Lisbon area. After deposition of the lower Cutler and the initiation of salt movement, large local depressions were formed over the areas from which the salt had flowed. These depressions formed immediately after development of the unconformity dividing the Cutler Formation. Landslides and erosion from the hills and ridges surrounding the depressions initiated the later Cutler deposition, then huge volumes of sediment from distant sources were brought in by streams and tidal bores. Thus, in late Cutler time, the lower few feet or hundreds of feet came from local sources, and most of the upper thousands of feet came from distant sources. This sequence explains the local angular unconformities between essentially flat upper Cutler beds over upwarped (by salt flowage) lower Cutler beds. The loading of thousands of feet of upper Cutler beds in the local depressions caused the salt to continue to flow out of the loaded areas into the adjacent salt anticlines. In some of these areas of thick Cutler deposition, salt flowage continued until no salt was left, and

TABLE II. STRATIGRAPHY OF LISBON FIELD AREA

Age	Formation	Lithologic Description	Thickness (ft)
Upper Cretaceous	Mancos	Gray marine shale.	500 + (top not exposed in area)
	Dakota	Open-marine to shoreline and stream-channel sandstone, conglomerate, shale, mudstone, and coal.	200
	– – – (unconformity) –		
Lower Cretaceous	Burro Canyon	Lagoonal, shoreline, stream-channel, and mud-flat sandstone, conglomerate, and variegated mudstone.	200
Upper Jurassic	Morrison	Variegated mudstone, sandstone, and thin limestone beds. Brushy Basin unit at top (225 ft ±) contains mostly mudstone and Salt Wash unit at base (325 ft ±) contains more sandstone.	550
	Summerville	Mudstone and sandstone.	130
	Entrada	Cross-bedded sandstone.	180
Upper and Middle Jurassic	Carmel	Siltstone and sandstone.	75
	– – – (unconformity) –		
	Navajo	Cross-bedded sandstone.	100–300
	Kayenta	Fine-grained sandstone.	75–250
Upper Triassic	Wingate	Cross-bedded sandstone.	300
	Chinle	Sandstone, conglomerate, and mudstone. Shinarump sandstone and conglomerate unit at base.	400–700
	– – – (unconformity) –		
Middle (?) and Lower Triassic	Moenkopi	Mudstone, siltstone, and fine-grained sandstone.	0–550
Permian	Upper Cutler	Conglomerate, siltstone, mudstone, arkosic sandstone, local chert and limestone.	550–4,500
	– – – (unconformity) –		
	Lower Cutler	Mudstone and sandstone.	500–800
Pennsylvanian	Honaker Trail (Upper Hermosa)	Gray fossiliferous, marine limestone, interbedded with sandstone, siltstone, mudstone, and gray shale. Fewer red arkosic sandstone beds in basal part.	1,600–1,900
	Upper Paradox	(Ismay carbonate cycle of Four Corners area.) Dolomite, siltstone, gray to black shale, anhydrite.	325–400
	Middle Paradox	Salt with thin beds of black shale, anhydrite, siltstone, and a few earthy dolomite beds.	500–8,000
	Pinkerton Trail (Lower Hermosa)	Dolomite and limestone, gray-brown, dense, some gray dolomitic siltstone, thin anhydrite beds, some chert in the limestone. Thin gray-green and dark gray shales.	15–170
	Molas	Shale, red-brown, gray, green, purple, silty and sandy.	20–60
	– – – (unconformity) –		
Mississippian	Leadville	Dolomite and limestone.	330–500
Devonian	Ouray	Limestone.	70–130
	Elbert	Dolomite, gray-brown, interbedded with green shale.	100–160
	McCracken	Sandstone and sandy dolomite.	70–140
	Aneth	Dolomite, glauconitic with siltstone partings.	200 ±
	– – – (unconformity) –		
Upper Cambrian	Lynch	Dolomite.	200 ±
Middle and Lower Cambrian	Ophir	Shale, gray, green; siltstone, tan.	125 ±
	Tintic	Gray-green shale and siltstone at top, grading downward to red, pink, and buff coarse-grained sandstone.	400 ±
	– – – (unconformity) –		
Precambrian		Granite, pink. 30% quartz, 60% feldspar, 10% biotite.	

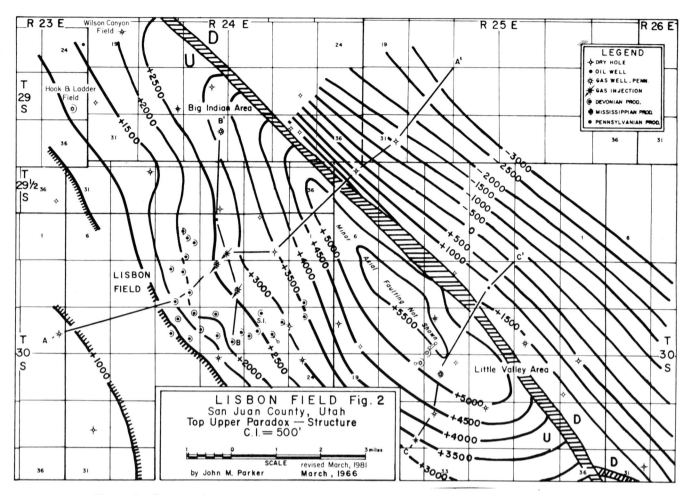

Figure 2. Structural contour map, Lisbon field; datum is top of upper Paradox Formation.

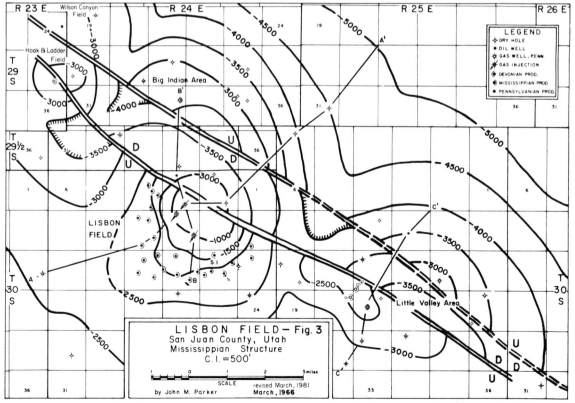

Figure 3. Structural contour map, Lisbon field; datum is top of Mississippian.

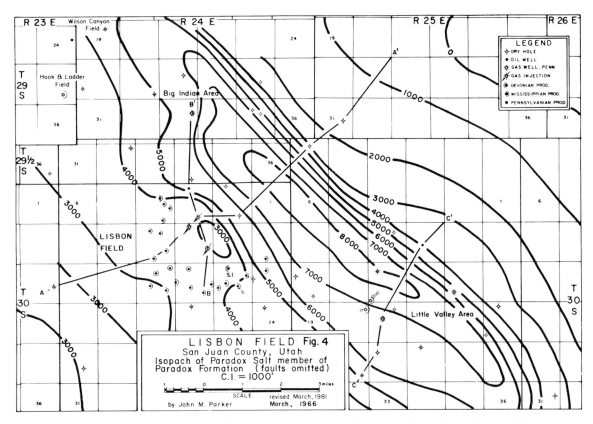

Figure 4. Isopachous map of Paradox salt member of Paradox Formation, Lisbon field.

the upper Paradox Ismay beds now lie directly on the lower Hermosa Pinkerton Trail Formation (see zero salt isopach area on Figure 4).

8. Triassic through Upper Cretaceous rocks were deposited and salt movement recurred primarily in Triassic and Jurassic times as loading overcame flow resistance. This recurrent pushing upward of the salt anticlines caused the thinning and, in some instances, nondeposition of all units from the Moenkopi through the Morrison over the crests and high on the flanks of the salt anticlines.

In summary, it is estimated that 90 percent of the salt movement occurred in late Cutler and Triassic times. At a rate of salt movement of 0.3 mm/yr (Trusheim, 1960) and in a time span of 60 my (45 my for the Triassic Period and 15 my of Late Permian upper Cutler time), total movement of an individual salt crystal was 9.7 mi. A distance of 9 + mi is compatible with the distance of 6 mi between the present zero salt thickness and 8,000-ft salt thickness shown on Figure 4. The dimensions, form, density contrasts, and boundary conditions of the salt mass in the Lisbon structural feature (and other Paradox basin salt features) are substantially different from the theoretical models postulated for the study of salt-dome dynamics in Germany and the United States Gulf Coast. Because the relationship of salt structures to the mother salt bed is better known in the Paradox basin than in the Gulf Coast, a review of salt-movement theory based on Paradox basin parameters would be valuable (see general theory assumptions by Danes [1964] based on German and Gulf Coast models). Persian Gulf salt anticlines have characteristics similar to those of Paradox basin salt anticlines.

9. Laramide orogenic pulses in latest Cretaceous time through Eocene time slightly accentuated the already strongly folded and faulted area, but little or no new folding or faulting occurred.

10. Major normal faulting occurred on the flanks of the salt anticlines in Miocene (?) time and later as the whole Colorado Plateau area was uplifted; then normal faulting took place with the development of reverse drag (beds dip 20-25° into the edge of the downthrown block). The phenomenon of reverse drag has been studied by Hamblin (1965), but he did not study reverse drags of faults over salt anticlines, and the translation of downward movement sideways into a markedly thinning salt section poses problems in mechanics (Figures 5-7).

11. After the regional uplift, streams breached the salt anticlines, salt solution took place, and anhydrite cap rocks formed. Isolated adjustment of the large salt masses is going on at the present time.

PRODUCING FORMATIONS

McCracken reservoir.—The McCracken reservoir consists of white to light-brown, silicious sandstone with very fine to coarse, subrounded to rounded grains. This unit includes sandy, gray-brown, finely crystalline dolomite at the top of the formation; the basal McCracken is very fine grained to silty, dolomitic, and micaceous. Only a few wells have penetrated the McCracken; net pay ranges from 10 to 40 ft and porosity and permeability are very erratic, generally poor.

Ouray reservoir.—The Ouray is composed of gray to light-brown, dense, very finely crystalline to chalky, fractured limestone, containing crinoid fragments and thin green shale streaks. Five- to 20-ft, dark brown, very finely crystalline, argillaceous dolomite beds within this limestone unit constitute the oil reservoir. Only a few wells have penetrated the Ouray; net pay ranges from 5 to 15 ft and porosity and permeability are poor to very poor. The Mississippian-Ouray contact is hard to identify conclusively in certain areas. The similarity of the Ouray crude oils and

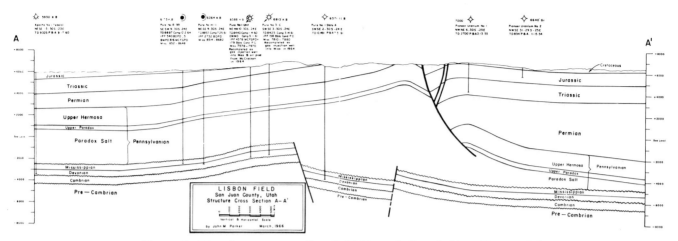

Figure 5. Structure cross section A-A'. Trace is line A-A' on Figures 1-4.

gases to those in the Mississippian and the proximity of the Ouray reservoir beds to fractures in the Mississippian cast coubt on the assumption that the Ouray is a primary reservoir.

Mississippian reservoir.—The Mississippan consists mainly of gray to brown dolomite, dense to finely crystalline to saccharoidal with vugs. It commonly is fractured, is pelletoidal and oolitic in places, and contains a few thin beds of dark brown to white translucent chert. Limestone may constitute 10-50 percent of the Mississippian. The limestone beds are white to light gray to tan, dense, chalky to finely crystalline, generally pelletoidal or oolitic, and contain crinoids and a few corals. The primary oil-bearing beds are porous zones within the dolomite (Figure 8).

Reservoir parameters are as follows.

Average depth	8,500 ft
Average gross pay	343 ft
Average net pay	234 ft
Effective porosity	6%
Permeability	Low in matrix; fracture porosity provides effective communication
Oil gravity	52° API in oil ring; 71° API in gas cap
Gas/oil ratio	1,200 in base of oil ring; 37,500 in top of gas cap
Gas Btu	Ranges from 1,207 in oil ring to 750 in gas cap
CO_2 content	20+% in oil ring; 22+% in gas cap

Paradox reservoir.—Gray-brown, earthy, anhydritic dolomite composes the Paradox oil zone. Production is from a 15-ft bed within the salt section. Production is noncommercial because of thin reservoir, lack of continuity, low permeability, and mechanical production problems.

Hermosa reservoir.—The Hermosa is not productive at Lisbon because the productive sandstone beds crop out or are buried only a few hundred feet on the upthrown block of the large Lisbon surface fault. Hermosa sandstone is productive on the downthrown block of this fault in the Little Valley area (Figure 7).

The sandstone is arkosic, very fine to fine grained. Six to 10 sandstone beds in this section are capable of production. Because of low productivity, the two Little Valley area wells completed in this section are shut in. This productive section is shown in the northernmost well in structure cross section *C-C'*, Figure 7.

Reservoir parameters are as follows.

Average depth	4,000 ft
Average gross pay	93 ft
Average net pay	54 ft
Porosity	23%
Permeability	Fair to good
Oil gravity	47° API
Gas Btu content (trace of CO_2)	1,154
IP of well No. 3	IPF 100 Mcf and 8 bbls/day of oil
IP of well No. 4	IPF 2,300 Mcf/day (before treatment to remove water block)

These Hermosa sandstone beds have been altered during drilling and completion, and a water block has been induced. The Pure No. 4 Big Indian well was treated with alcohol and liquid CO_2 to remove the water block. Productivity after a 30-day production test had been increased 33 percent by the treatment.

CHARACTER OF ACCUMULATION AND TYPE OF TRAP

The Lisbon field is a faulted anticline. Oil and gas fill the structure almost to the structural spill point.

The Little Valley area Mississippian gas trap southeast of Lisbon has no associated oil ring, but the gas-water contact is at the same datum as the oil-water contact at Lisbon. The Big Indian area Mississippian gas trap north of Lisbon also has no oil ring, but the gas-water contact there is at -3,000 ft, or 430 ft lower than at Lisbon. Thus, the greater Lisbon area is an example of differential entrapment. The rocks now exposed along the crest of the surface axis directly northeast of the 4,600-ft fault (Figures 1-3, 5-7) were once approximately that much higher. How much of the movement was translated straight down during the time of this faulting is conjectural. Most of the translation was northeast rather than down, but it seems possible that a substantial downward displacement did occur in the Mississippian and older rocks. If this is the case, most or all of the Mississippian and Devonian accumulations may have been "X" hundred feet higher structurally, and "X" feet laterally from their present location. Thus, secondary or tertiary migration of those accumulations is a distinct possibility, with attendant complications of differential entrapment.

This accumulation is unique for the Rocky Mountain area because the folding and faulting that effect the trap are in part of pre-Pennsylvanian age and in part of Late Pennsylvanian-Permian age. The structural form of most Rocky Mountain structural traps developed during the Laramide series of orogenies, whereas most of the Lisbon

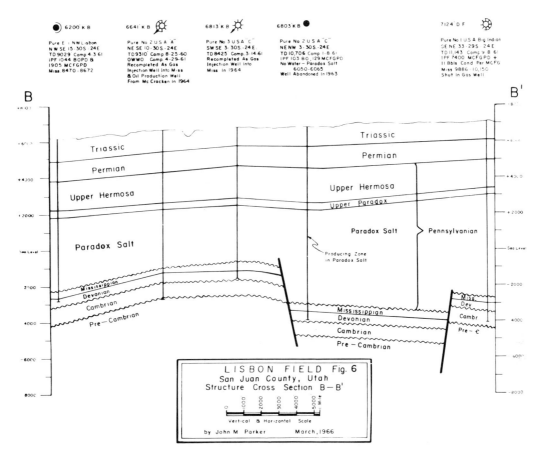

Figure 6. Structure cross section *B-B'*, Lisbon field. Vertical and horizontal scale equal. Trace is line *B-B'* on Figures 1-4.

structural form had been established long before Laramide time. The top of the Mississippian trap is 2,500 ft structurally below the top of the surface structural axis (Figures 2, 3), and this also makes the Lisbon pool a paradox. Approximately 145 ft of the Mississippian Leadville Dolomite was removed by erosion on the Lisbon structural feature before the deposition of the Molas Formation, because the Molas and the basal member of the Paradox Formation (the Pinkerton Trail Formation) do not thicken over the areas of maximum preserved Mississippian section. This thickening and thinning of the Mississippian is the result of structural uplift or growth before Molas deposition, and is not caused by the development of a topography unaccompanied by uplift or folding. The coincidence of the thinned Mississippian strata with the present structural configuration is direct evidence for the presence of a substantial fold in Late Mississippian or Early Pennsylvanian time.

The poor to fair continuity of the pelletoidal and dolomitized zones in the Mississippian is shown on stratigraphic cross section *B-B'*, Figure 8. Good reservoir development does not appear to be a function of present structural position or preservation of the porosity zones in the Mississippian.

As shown by structure cross sections *A-A'*, *B-B'*, and *C-C'*, good arguments can be advanced for the indigenous presence of oil and gas in each of the Devonian, Mississippian, and Pennsylvanian reservoirs, depending on the differential pressures assumed along the major faults during geologic time. The juxtaposition of shale, carbonate, and sandstone beds in the lower Hermosa Pennsylvanian Pinkerton Trail Formation to reservoir beds in the Mississippian and Devonian since Jurassic time could have allowed migration of oil and gas from Pennsylvanian beds up the fault zone into the older Paleozoic beds if the proper differential pressures were present to allow the fault zones to act as conduits. Comparison of analyses of the Aneth area Pennsylvanian Hermosa oil and gas with those of the Lisbon area Devonian and Mississippian oil and gas can be used as argument that the Lisbon oil is not indigenous to the Devonian and Mississippian, but migrated into those rocks from Pennsylvanian strata. However, in the Lisbon area, crude oil and gas compositions in the Devonian, Mississippian, and Hermosa are each unique even though they have somewhat similar correlation indices.

The composition of gas and crude from a Lisbon Mississippian well three fourths of the way down the field hydrocarbon column is shown in Table III. Compositions of gases from the upper Hermosa and Mississippian formations in the general Lisbon area are shown on Table V. The most significant differences in composition between the upper Hermosa and Mississippian gases are the higher percentages of nitrogen, CO_2, and helium in the Mississippian. The argon and helium in the Mississippian reservoir may have originated from the radioactive shale in the Mississippian and Devonian sections or they may have originated in the very radioactive Molas regolith and Molas shale above the regolith. Picard (1962) has summarized ideas on the occurrence of exotic Mississippian gases in the Paradox basin.

Many important questions remain to be answered concerning the origin and migration of the oil and gas in the Lisbon area.

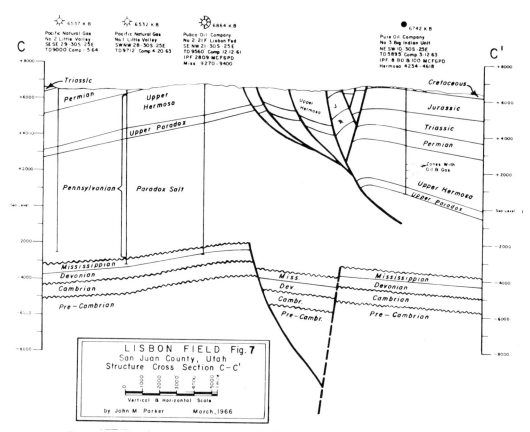

Figure 7. Structure cross section *C-C'*. Trace is line *C-C'* on Figures 1-4.

RESERVOIR CHARACTERISTICS

Only the Mississippian reservoir is discussed because the other producing units are of minor importance at this time.

The Leadville Dolomite (Mississippian) reservoir, with an 1,870-ft petroleum column, shows gravity segregation with arbitrary zones listed in Table VI.

The potentiometric surface in the Lisbon area at the Mississippian level shows an anomalous flattering in a regional westward-dropping gradient. The potentiometric surface in the field is calculated to be 4,500-4,600 ft above sea level.

An analysis of gas and oil from a well (Unit well B-815) in NE ¼, SW ¼, Sec. 15, T. 30 S., R. 24 E., with a datum of -1,966 ft, is shown in Table III.

The reservoir produces by a combination of solution-gas drive, gas-cap expansion, and limited water drive. A compositional material balance derived in 1962 showed that total oil recovery would be approximately 21 percent of the original oil in place. Recovery calculations with partial pressure maintenance showed that approximately 44 percent of the stock-tank oil in place in the oil zone would be recovered. In addition, retrograde condensation in the reservoir would be minimized, and the condensate recovery would increase to approximately 22 standard bbls/MMcf compared with approximately 14.5 standard bbls/MMcf under primary operations.

The Utah Oil and Gas Conservation Commission called a hearing pertaining to gas being flared from the Lisbon field in November 1960, and issued an order in December 1960 limiting high-GOR oil production.

The field was unitized for the Mississippian beds on May 1, 1962. On the basis of the calculations of reservoir performance, a partial pressure-maintenance program was planned and gas injection was begun on July 31, 1962. Reservoir pressure near the base of the oil ring, measured on December 6, 1964, was 2,860 psig (datum -2,477 ft). Initial reservoir pressure at a datum of -2,460 ft was 2,945 psig.

TABLE III.
LOW-TEMPERATURE FRACTIONAL-DISTILLATION ANALYSIS, LISBON FIELD, MISSISSIPPIAN RESERVOIR, WELL B-815

Component	Separator Gas (mol %)	GPM	Separator Liquid Mol %	Separator Liquid Liquid Vol %
Acid gases	27.75	—	7.60	4.67
Noncondensables	14.89	—	2.49	1.21
Methane	42.94	—	12.66	5.40
Ethane	8.72	—	10.21	5.38
Propane	3.46	0.952	9.71	6.95
Isobutane	0.49	0.160	2.60	2.21
N-butane	1.00	0.315	6.58	5.40
Isopentane	0.20	0.073	3.21	3.06
N-pentane	0.31	0.112	3.71	3.50
Hexanes	0.13	0.053	5.97	6.38
Heptane plus	0.11	0.054	35.26	55.84
Total	100.00	1.719	100.00	100.00

Separator pressure (psig)	860
Separator temperature (°F)	102
Specific gravity (air =1.000)	0.997
Heating value (Btu/cu ft at 14.7 psia, 60° F)	757
Heptanes plus	
Molecular weight	154
Density at 60° F	0.801
Gravity (°API at 60° F)	44.9

For gas-injection operations, all produced oil, gas, and water are separated and measured at each well. Oil and gas then are commingled and piped under pressure to a central plant where they are stage separated, the oil is stabilized, and the gas is compressed and injected into the reservoir

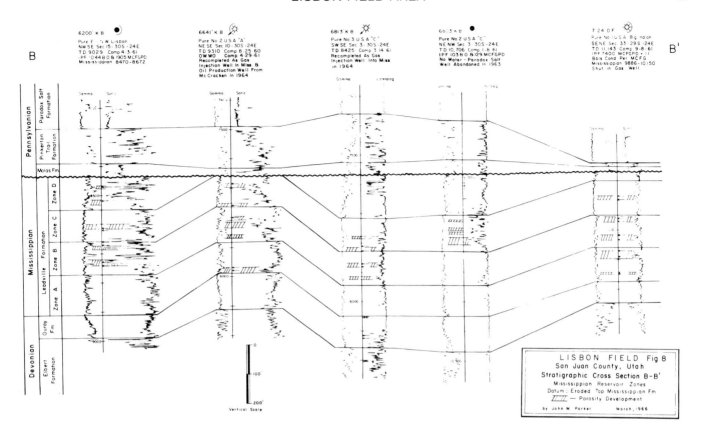

Figure 8. Stratigraphic cross section _B-B'_. Trace is line _B-B'_ on Figures 1-4.

through three injection wells at the -759, -931, and -1,018-ft levels at the top of the Mississippian (Figure 3). The dry hole in the NE ¼ NW ¼, Sec. 24, T. 30 S., R. 24 E. (datum top of Mississippian, -2,489 ft) is used as a water-disposal well; salt water produced from the Leadville Dolomite in the field is injected into the same formation in this hole. An LPG plant has recently been constructed to remove LPG products from the produced gas prior to injection of the gas.

Studies are being made to determine feasibility of a full pressure-maintenance program. With the present partial pressure-maintenance program, gas injection is to continue until 1973, at which time cumulative oil production is expected to be 27 million bbls. Reserves of oil and gas at the beginning of 1973 are expected to be approximately 14 million bbls and 240 billion cu ft, respectively, with gas sales projected to start in 1973. These reserves then would be produced through pressure depletion to a reservoir-abandonment pressure of 300 lbs, expected to be reached in 1990.

Reserves of recoverable oil and condensate are estimated to be in the range of 41-50 million bbls; reserves of gas are estimated to be approximately 240 billion cu ft. Reservoir-water constituents are tabulated in Table VII.

CHARACTER, ANALYSIS, AND DISPOSITION OF GAS

No gas is being sold. When gas injection stops and gas sales begin in 1973 (estimated), it will be necessary to remove some of the acid gas components and the liquefiable hydrocarbon gases to meet sales specifications. The analyses shown in Table V are representative of gas of the area. Gas composition varies in the Mississippian reservoir column depending on subsea datum, rate of production, and time in the life of the reservoir when the sample was taken. The complexity of the variable phase relationships of the Lisbon "gas column" is indicated by Table VIII, which shows comparative gas analyses, all taken from the same well. Gas composition also varies in the Hermosa reservoirs, both in different reservoir beds and at different elevations in an individual reservoir bed (Table V).

SHALLOWER AND DEEPER POSSIBILITIES

The Pure No. 2A (Unit D-810), NE ¼ SE ¼, Sec. 10, T. 30 S., R. 24 E., was drilled to Precambrian granite, with a total depth of 9,315 ft, without finding production below the McCracken.

Dead oil staining is present in the Aneth Formation. There are shallower possibilities for both gas and oil in the Hermosa in both the Big Indian and the Little Valley areas. There also are shallower possibilities in the thin petroleum-bearing dolomite beds of the Paradox salt unit, but because they are thin and discontinuous, they are not attractive.

TABLE IV. LISBON FIELD CUMULATIVE AND ANNUAL PRODUCTION AND INJECTION FIGURES

Year	Produced Oil (bbls)	Produced Gas (Mcf)	Produced Water (bbls)	Injected Gas (Mcf)	No. Producing Wells	No. Gas-Injection Wells
Mississippian Reservoir						
1960	210,645	425,504 (flared)	11,348		8	
1961	599,365	1,221,995 (flared)	77,584		14	
1962	1,488,290	2,956,069 (flared; stopped flaring on 7-31-62)	72,139	2,000,000 (est.)	14	
1963	3,152,901	7,349,501	64,197	7,349,501	15	
1964	3,505,285	9,002,684	81,236	9,002,684	14	3
1965[1]	2,845,044	9,990,507	194,881	9,990,507	18	
Total	11,801,530	30,946,260	501,385	28,342,692	18	3
Ouray Reservoir						
1962	17,744	32,849 (flared)	0		1	
	13,301	65,476	2,634		1	
1963	Belco Lisbon State					
	23,097	42,659	0		1	
	Calco Arnold 21-15					
	5,801	37,310	1,239		(1) temp.abn.	
1964	13,144	24,470	0		1	
1965[1]	25,934	47,974	0		1	
Total	99,011	250,738	3,873		2[2]	
McCracken Reservoir						
1962	43,770	77,451 (flared)	3,309		3	
1963	29,090	53,133	1,243		2	1 water injection
1964	23,055	43,536	0		2	(discontinued)
1965[1]	14,890	28,718	0		2	was designed for secondary recovery
Total	110,805	202,838	4,552		2	
Paradox Reservoir						
1962	3,292	5,743 (flared)	0		1	
1963	0	0	0		0 (P&A)	
Total	3,292	5,743	0		0	

[1] Through September 1965.
[2] One of the two Ouray wells was temporarily abandoned in 1963.

1981 ADDENDUM

The 1965-66 reservoir performance calculations were critical in forseeing the need for field pressure maintenance. Volume calculations were fairly good, time calculations were poor.

Current producing rates and cumulative production are listed below.

Production for December, 1980

	Month	Daily Average
Oil (bbls)	59,274	1,913
Gas (MCF)	1,650,122	53,230
Water (bbls)	115,599	3,729
Natural Gasoline (bbls)	12,499	403
Butane (bbls)	12,774	412
Propane (bbls)	19,055	615
Total Plant Liquids (bbls)	44,328	1,430
Gas sales (MCF)	0	0

Production Statistics for December, 1980

	Month	Daily Average
Gas-Oil ratio (CF/bbl)	27,878	
Gas Processed (MCF)	1,781,156	57,457
Unit Gas injected (MCF)	1,435,362	46,302
Outside Gas Injected (MCF)*	99,412	3,207
Unit Fuel used (MCF)	126,500	4,081
Outside Field Gas Used (MCF)	0	0
Non-useable acid gas flared (MCF)	10,088	325
Shrinkage (MCF)	73,323	2,365

*The unit obtains gas to inject into the Leadville reservoir from two wells in other fields; the Big Indian Unit L, Sec. 33, T. 29 S., R. 24 E., and the Mesa Federal 2-21F, Sec. 21, T. 30 S., R. 25 E.

Cumulative gas injected for the Big Indian Unit #1 is 16.17 Bcf and cumulative gas injected from the Mesa Federal 2-21F is 6.23 Bcf.

1386

JOHN M. PARKER

TABLE V. GAS COMPOSITION, UPPER HERMOSA AND MISSISSIPPIAN FORMATIONS, LISBON AREA, UTAH AND COLORADO[1]

Formation and Datum (ft) Above or Below Sea Level of Gas-Producing Unit	Well Location	Methane	Ethane	Propane	Nitrogen	Oxygen	Argon	Helium	Hydrogen	H_2S	CO_2	Btu
Upper Hermosa +3,261	Big Indian No. 4, Sec. 14, T.30S., R.25E., Utah	83.5	8.1	2.4	4.1	0.1	trace	trace	0.0	0.0	0.2	1105
Upper Hermosa +2,520	Big Indian No. 3, Sec. 10, T.30S., R.25E., Utah	59.1	21.0	10.9	2.6	trace	trace	0.010	0.1	0.0	0.1	1479
Upper Hermosa +2,135	Big Indian No. 3, Sec. 10, T.30S., R.25E., Utah	77.2	8.9	2.8	8.6	trace	trace	0.066	0.1	0.0	0.1	1093
Upper Hermosa +1,692	Big Indian No. 3, Sec. 10, T.30S., R.25E., Utah	81.4	7.8	3.1	5.0	trace	0.0	0.035	0.1	0.0	0.1	1140
Mississippian −2,200 approx.	Lisbon No. 1 USA "C," Sec. 4, T.30S., R.24E., Utah	40.1	8.5	5.2	15.5	trace	0.1	1.0	0.1	0.0	26.7	804
Mississippian −2,450	Lisbon No. 2-21-F, Sec. 21, T.30S., R.25E., Utah	61.03	5.19	1.38	13.03	not analyzed	not analyzed	not analyzed	not analyzed	2.17	15.42	799
Mississippian −2,832	Big Indian No. 1, Sec. 33, T.29S., R.24E., Utah	56.7	6.9	2.0	15.8	trace	trace	0.8	0.0	0.0	15.8	823
Mississippian −2,357	SE Lisbon No. 1, Sec. 5, T.44N., R.19W., Colorado	74.8	2.1	0.9	9.2	trace	trace	0.8	trace	0.0	9.7	929

[1] Selected constituents only.

TABLE VI. ARBITRARY ZONES, LEADVILLE DOLOMITE RESERVOIR

Zone	Fluids Produced	Producing GOR (Scf/bbl)	Depth Below Sea Level (ft)	Initial Reservoir Pressure[1] (psig)	Av. Temp. (°F)
Gas	gas, condensate	32,000	−700 to −1,800	2,800	135
Transition	gas, condensate, oil	2,400 to 8,000	−1,800 to −2,150		
Oil	oil	2,200	−2,150 to −2,570	2,945	144

[1] Measured midway from top to bottom of zone.

Cumulative Production Statistics through December, 1980
Oil (bbls)..........................42,654,516
Gas (MCF) ....363,061,668 (injected)
Liquids (bbls)* 11,357,000
*This includes natural gasoline, propane and butane.

Three wells are currently used for gas injection and one well is used for salt water disposal.

With about 43 million barrels equivalent of gas currently in the reservoir, with 42.7 million barrels of oil produced, with 11.4 million barrels of natural gasoline, propane and butane produced and with substantial producible reserves of oil and natural gas liquids remaining, Lisbon can now be put into the giant field category, over 100 million barrels.

Two new fields have been discovered in the map area of this paper since the original paper was written. One, the Hook & Ladder Field Mississippian discovery completed by Husky Oil in 1977.

The other field is the Gulf Wilson Canyon Field, completed in the Cane Creek zone of the Paradox Formation salt member in 1968. Cumulative production through October 1980 is 64,565 barrels of oil and 106,811 MCF of gas.

Cumulative production through October 1980 from the Hermosa gas well in Section 14, T. 30 S., R. 25 E., is 12,015 barrels oil and 1,561,102 MCF gas.

Cumulative production through October 1980 from the Big Indian Mississippian gas well in Section 33, T. 29 S., R. 24 E., is 141,215 barrels of oil and 19,231,789 MCF gas.

Cumulative production through October 1980 from the Hermosa well in Section 10, T. 30 S., R. 25 E., is 6,977 MCF gas.

Cumulative production through October 1980 from the Little Valley Mississippian well in Section 21, T. 30 S., R. 25 E., is 59,168 barrels oil and 5,979,106 MCF gas.

TABLE VII. ANALYSES OF WATERS ASSOCIATED WITH PRODUCING FORMATIONS, LISBON AREA, UTAH

	Basal Cutler (sand 80 ft above top Hermosa fm.) DST Sample From Interval 3,214–3,239 ft in Big Indian Unit Well No. 3 (ppm)	Mississippian DST Sample, Unit Well D-816, Interval 8,588–8,615 ft (ppm)	McCracken Production Water from NW Lisbon Well B-1 (Unit Well B-614), Sample Date 10-20-61 (ppm)
Sodium	30,925	79,253	57,793
Calcium	4,330	2,400	3,907
Magnesium	3,332	486	1,580
Sulfate	0	2,000	1,488
Chloride	65,000	122,120	99,500
Carbonate	0	0	0
Bicarbonate	122	7,320	0
Hydrogen sulfide	not analyzed	0	not analyzed
Chloride as NaCl	78,631	not analyzed	146,871
Resistivity @ 68° F, ohm-m	0.135	0.049 (at 77° F)	0.104
Total solids calculated	103,709	213,579	164,268

TABLE VIII.   COMPARATIVE GAS ANALYSES FROM ONE WELL[1] IN MISSISSIPPIAN RESERVOIR, LISBON FIELD

	3/4" Choke 8-28-60		3/4" Choke 9-6-60		26/64" Choke 9-28-60		26/64" Choke 9-28-60		31/64" Choke 11-1-60		11-22-60	
	Mol. %	GPM	Mol. %	GPM	Mol. %	GPM	Mol. %	GPM	Mol. %	GPM	Mol. %	GPM
Carbon dioxide	29.90		30.00		30.53		26.6		16.20		19.08	
Hydrogen sulfide	0.10		Trace		1.47		0.0		2.20		7.12	
Nitrogen	12.71		7.83		12.11		6.9		12.85		15.30	
Helium	—		—		—		0.3		—		—	
Methane	40.08		47.56		36.99		34.5		45.19		43.65	
Ethane	8.02		6.95		8.43		11.6		12.73		7.96	
Propane	4.26	1.169	4.11	1.127	4.89	1.341	9.8		6.94	1.904	3.90	1.070
Isobutane	0.82	0.268	0.73	0.238	0.89	0.290	1.8		1.03	0.336	0.66	0.215
N-butane	1.95	0.617	1.60	0.506	1.98	0.626	4.2		1.99	0.630	1.38	0.435
Isopentane	0.60	0.219	0.40	0.146	0.55	0.201	1.1		0.30	0.109	0.32	0.117
N-pentane	0.75	0.271	0.46	0.166	0.68	0.246	1.6		0.30	0.108	0.35	0.126
Hexane	0.81	0.353	0.36	0.157	1.48	0.644	1.3		0.27	0.118	0.28	0.122
Total	100.00	2.897	100.00	2.340	100.00	3.348			100.00	3.205	100.00	2.087
Total inerts	42.71		37.83		44.11		33.8		31.25		41.50	
Wet basis, 14.7 psi, 60° F, calc. Btu	826		822		850				976		775	
Calc. Btu/cu ft, dry @ 60° F, 30 in Hg							1,207					
Sulfur content gr/100 H₂S	66.0		1.50		921.8				1,362.5		4,478.54	
Mercaptans	—		—		—		—		—		61.4	
Specific gravity, calc. from % comp.	1.067		1.013		1.104				0.971		0.975	
CO₂ process	Orsat.		Orsat.		Orsat.		mass spectrom- eter		Orsat.		Orsat.	
H₂S process	Fluor G-6-46		Fluor G-6-46		Fluor G-6-46				cadmium chloride (field)		cadmium chloride (field)	
Bomb pressure	43		40.5		45		—		68			
Interval	DST No.2, 8,388–8,507		DST No.4, 8,609–8,712		prod. perfs. 8,550–8,672		prod. perfs. 8,550–8,672		prod. perfs. 8,550–8,672		prod. perfs. 8,550–8,672	
Analyzed by	El Paso		El Paso		El Paso		USBM		El Paso		El Paso	

[1] Pubco Lisbon Federal No. 1-12, SW ¼ sec. 12, T. 30 S., R. 24 E.

REFERENCES

Albright, J. L., 1965, Lisbon Valley anticline, Paradox basin, Utah—exploration and development, a review: presented orally before 15th Ann. Mtg., Rocky Mountain Sec., AAPG, Sept. 1965, Billings, Montana.

Baars, D. L., 1966, Pre-Pennsylvanian paleotectonics of southwestern Colorado and east central Utah: Unpub. Ph.D. thesis, Dept. Geology, Univ. Colorado.

Byerly, P. E., and Joesting, H. R., 1959, Regional geophysical investigations of the Lisbon Valley area, Utah and Colorado: U.S. Geol. Survey Prof. Paper 316-C.

Carter, W. D., and Gualtieri, J. L., 1957, Preliminary geologic map of the Mount Peale 1 SW quadrangle, San Juan County, Utah: U.S. Geol. Survey Mineral Inv. Field Studies Map MF 124.

Danes, Z. F., 1964, Mathematical formulation of salt-dome dynamics: Geophysics, v. 29, no. 3, p. 414-424.

Elston, D. P., and Shoemaker, E. M., 1963, Salt anticlines of the Paradox basin, Colorado and Utah, in Symposium on salt: Northern Ohio Geol. Soc., Inc., p. 131-146.

Fullerton, Allen (Pure Oil Co.), 1963, Operation Paradox— Northwest Lisbon field: presented at mtg. of Rocky Mountain Dist., Div. Production, API, April 1963, Paper No. 875-17-1.

Hamblin, W. K., 1965, Origin of "reverse drag" on the downthrown side of normal faults: Geol. Soc. America Bull., v. 76, p. 1145-1164.

Ohlen, H. R., and McIntyre, L. B., 1965, Stratigraphy and tectonic features of Paradox basin, Four Corners area: Am. Assoc. Petroleum Geologists Bull., v. 49, no. 11, p. 2020-2039.

Parker, J. M., 1961a, The Cambrian, Devonian and Mississippian rocks and pre-Pennsylvanian structure of southwest Colorado, and adjoining portions of Utah, Arizona and New Mexico, in Symposium on lower and middle Paleozoic rocks of Colorado: Rocky Mountain Assoc. Geologists Guidebook, 12th Ann. Field Conf., p. 59-70.

————— 1961b, The McIntyre Canyon and Lisbon oil and gas fields, San Miguel County, Colorado, and San Juan County, Utah, in Symposium on lower and middle Paleozoic rocks of Colorado: Rocky Mountain Assoc. Geologists Guidebook, 12th Ann. Field Conf., p. 163-173.

————— 1962, Pre-Pennsylvanian beds yield lion's share of oil in Lisbon area: Oil and Gas Jour., April 16, v. 60, no. 16, p. 148-154.

Picard, M. D., 1962, Occurrence and origin of Mississippian gas in Four Corners region: Am. Assoc. Petroleum Geologists Bull., v. 46, no. 9, p. 1681-1700.

Trusheim, F., 1960, Mechanism of salt migration in northern Germany: Am. Assoc. Petroleum Geologists Bull., v. 44, no. 9, p. 1519-1540.

Weir, G. W., Carter, W. D., Puffett, W. P., and Gualtieri, J. L., 1960, Preliminary geologic map and section of the Mount Peale 4 NE quadrangle, San Juan County, Utah, and Montrose and San Miguel Counties, Colorado: U.S. Geol. Survey Mineral Inv. Field Studies Map MF 150.

————— and Dodson, C. L., 1958, Preliminary geologic map of the Mount Peale 3 quadrangle, San Juan County, Utah: U.S. Geol. Survey Mineral Inv. Field Studies Map MF 145.

————— Dodson, C. L., and Puffett, W. P., 1960, Preliminary geologic map and section of the Mount Peale 2 SE quadrangle, San Juan County, Utah: U.S. Geol. Survey Mineral Inv. Field Studies Map MF 143.

————— Puffett, W. P., and Dodson, C. L., 1961, Preliminary geologic map and section of the Mount Peale 4 NW quadrangle, San Juan County, Utah: U.S. Geol. Survey Mineral Inv. Field Studies Map MF 151.

PETROLEUM GEOLOGY OF THE DEVONIAN AND MISSISSIPPIAN ROCKS OF THE FOUR CORNERS REGION

V. O. GUSTAFSON
Consulting Geologist, Littleton, Colorado

ABSTRACT

While they are still sparsely explored, the Devonian and Mississippian rocks of the Four Corners region have excellent hydrocarbon potential. The Devonian System is represented by a sequence of marine carbonates and clastics which have produced more than 500,000 barrels of oil and 500 million cubic feet of gas. The marine carbonates of the Mississippian System have produced more than 44 million barrels of oil and 350 billion cubic feet of gas. Most Devonian and Mississippian oil and gas production is from structural traps. Subsurface geology combined with improving geophysical methods should lead to significant future discoveries.

INTRODUCTION

The Devonian and Mississippian rocks of the Four Corners region have excellent hydrocarbon potential and are still sparsely explored. Production from pre-Pennsylvanian reservoirs is from structural traps. Most of the production is from Mississippian carbonates with lesser amounts from Devonian carbonates and sandstones.

The area of this discussion is bordered by the San Rafael swell on the northwest, the San Juan basin on the southeast, between the Uncompahgre uplift on the northeast, and the Black Mesa basin on the southwest.

Much of the following discussion is a concensus based on the maps and manuscripts of various authors. The most influential of these are listed as references at the end of this article.

STRATIGRAPHY

DEVONIAN

The Devonian of the Four Corners region ranges in thickness from zero at the southeast up to 800 feet at the northwest. Devonian rocks have been divided into three formations. They are, in ascending order, the Aneth Formation, the Elbert Formation and the Ouray Formation. Throughout much of the area, the Elbert is divisible into the McCracken Sandstone Member and the Upper Elbert Member.

Aneth Formation — The oldest of the Devonian formations is Frasnian in age but overlies the Cambrian without apparent angularity. It was designated the Aneth Formation by Knight and Cooper (1955, p. 58) who described it as "a dark gray siltstone and lighter dolomites." The Aneth is an entirely subsurface formation and its subsurface type locality is the Shell No. 1 Bluff Unit well in Section 32, T. 39 S., R. 23 E., San Juan County, Utah. The formation is about 200 feet thick in the area of the type section and thins to zero within 40 to 100 miles in all directions. The Aneth is recognizable where overlain by the basal McCracken Sandstone Member of the Elbert Formation, but may blend with lower Elbert beds where the McCracken is not present.

Elbert Formation — The next younger Devonian formation is the Elbert Formation of Frasnian age which conformably overlies and possibly merges with the Aneth Formation. The Elbert Formation is divided into two members. The McCracken Sandstone Member is a basal transgressive sandstone. The Upper Elbert Member consists of dolomite, green and red shale and some sandstone.

The McCracken Sandstone Member was described at its type section as consisting "predominantly of white, light gray to red sandstone, fine to medium grained, some coarse, generally poorly sorted, commonly glauconitic, with a few streaks of sandy dolomites" (Cooper, 1955, p. 63). The type section, like that of the Aneth, is the Shell No. 1 Bluff Unit well (Section 32, T. 39 S., R. 23 E.) on McCracken Mesa in San Juan County, Utah. Unlike the Aneth, the McCracken has been identified in surface sections along the Animas River in the San Juan Mountains of southwestern Colorado. The McCracken Sandstone ranges from zero to more than 100 feet in thickness underlying an area of about 25,000 square miles with the type section in the approximate center. The thickest McCracken appears to occur adjacent to a Devonian paleotectonic high area in the position of the present day Defiance uplift. McCracken sandstones grade westward into the dolomite dominated lithology of the undifferentiated Elbert Formation.

The Upper Elbert Member as originally described by Cooper (1955, p. 63) at the Shell No. 1 Bluff type locality (Section 32, T. 39 S., R. 23 E., San Juan County, Utah) "consists of thin bedded, dense to finely sucrose dolomite, locally anhydritic, commonly with floating frosted sand grains. The dolomite is associated with thin interbeds of gray-green waxy and red clayey shales generally sandy. The lower portion of the unit contains thin sandstone beds which grade downward into the underlying McCracken Sandstone." The thickness of the Upper Elbert, where recognizable, ranges from zero at the southeast to as much as 600 feet at the northwest.

Ouray Formation — The youngest of the Devonian formations is the Famennian Ouray Formation. Indeed, faunal evidence suggests that the uppermost Ouray may be Mississippian (Kinderhookian) in age. The Ouray was first mentioned in the literature by Cross and Spencer (1899) and defined and designated by Spencer (1900) for outcrops at Ouray, Colorado. The Ouray is a massive limestone and/or dolomite unit with some thin intercalated green shale. Thickness of the Ouray in the Four Corners region varies from zero at the southeast to more than 150 feet at the northwest. Thinning over positive areas suggests the subtle seafloor topography upon which the Ouray was deposited.

MISSISSIPPIAN

The Mississippian of the Four Corners is represented by a single formation. Most workers find it convenient to relate the Mississippian rocks to the well exposed Grand Canyon section and term it the Redwall Formation.

Redwall Formation — The Redwall Formation of the Four Corners region is Kinderhookian, Osagian and Meramecian in age. Meramecian rocks are limited in extent largely because of removal by late Mississippian-early Pennsylvanian erosion. If Chester series rocks were ever deposited, they suffered a similar fate. Gilbert (1875, p. 176-177) named the Redwall Limestone from outcrops in the Grand Canyon where it consists of light colored limestone and dolomite. Redwall thickness in the Four Corners region ranges from zero at the southeast to 1,000 feet at the northwest. Where Mississippian rocks are absent or thin, it is largely a result of post-Mississippian erosion. Such removal of the Mississippian is particularly evident on the Uncompahgre uplift and other sub-parallel paleotectonic positive elements in the northeastern part of the area.

OIL AND GAS

DEVONIAN

Devonian reservoirs of the Four Corners region have produced a relatively small amount of hydrocarbons. Most, if not all, production has been from structural traps; but stratigraphic trapping is an excellent possibility in a system with such varied lithology.

The Aneth Formation has been marginally productive at only one well in the Tohache Wash area of northeastern Arizona. The Texaco No. 1 Navajo Z well in Section 36, T. 41 N., R. 30 E., before abandonment, produced 764 BO from 8 feet of Aneth dolomite with fractures and 4 to 6 percent matrix porosity. The dark shales and shaly dolomites of the Aneth may provide the oil source.

The McCracken Sandstone Member of the Elbert formation is the most productive Devonian reservoir to date. McCracken production of more than 500,000 barrels of oil and 500 million cubic feet of gas comes from structural traps at the abandoned Walker Creek field in Arizona, the abandoned Akah Nez field in New Mexico, and the Lisbon field in Utah. Most of the production is from Lisbon where net pay of 25 feet of McCracken sandstone averages 8 percent porosity and permeability of 2.6 millidarcies. Where the Aneth Formation is present, it may be the source of McCracken oil, but at Lisbon, Pennsylvanian beds are a more likely source.

The Upper Elbert Member has produced a minor amount of oil from one well in New Mexico at the Tom field, discovered in 1976.

The Ouray produces from one well at the Southeast Lisbon field in Colorado where it appears to be part of a common reservoir with the overlying Mississippian Redwall Formation.

MISSISSIPPIAN

In the discussion area, Mississippian reservoirs are second only to the Pennsylvanian as a producer of oil and gas. Although some variation in porosity and permeability make stratigraphic trapping possible, all production from the Mississippian is associated with structural closure.

The Redwall Formation has produced more than 44 million barrels of oil and 350 billion cubic feet of gas from 13 fields in the Four Corners region. More than 90% of the production is from the Lisbon field in T. 39 S., R. 24 E., San Juan County, Utah. So far, Lisbon is "one of a kind", but its uniqueness is primarily one of size. Other Mississippian fields are structurally and stratigraphically similar in many ways. The

Redwall at Lisbon is generally divisible into an upper low permeability limestone, a middle permeable and porous dolomite and a lower low permeability dolomite. The dolomite porosity was probably formed by dolomitization and by selective leaching of fragments of crinoid stems and other fossil debris. A vertical fracture system is also important to permeability in Mississippian reservoirs. Porosity in dolomite of the Redwall Formation at Lisbon ranges up to 20 percent and averages about 6 percent. Highly variable permeability ranges from 0.1 to over 1100 millidarcies and averages about 20 millidarcies. The average pay thickness at Lisbon is about 200 feet. Oil gravity in the Redwall at Lisbon is 54° API. Inert gases make up about 42 percent of the 750 BTU gas produced from Lisbon Redwall. High percentages of inert gases are typical of Mississippian accumulations ranging from a low of 20 percent at Southeast Lisbon (T. 44 N., R. 19 W., San Miguel County, Colorado) to nearly 100% at several places such as McElmo field (T. 36 N., R. 18 W., Montezuma County, Colorado).

STRUCTURE OF DEVONIAN AND MISSISSIPPIAN FIELDS

Most, if not all, oil and gas production from Devonian and Mississippian reservoirs is from structural traps. The discovery and mapping of structure in pre-Pennsylvanian rocks is complicated throughout most of the region by the variable thickness of overlying Pennsylvanian salt. Although pre-Pennsylvanian structure has had a strong influence on the positioning and alignment of post-salt structure related to salt flowage, structural attitudes of Mississippian and Devonian strata are greatly different than surface structure. For example, the Lisbon field is located on a pre-salt structural element which was at least partially responsible for the positioning of the Lisbon Valley salt anticline. The high point on the Mississippian is about four miles west of the crest of the surface anticline. Geophysical methods are necessary for discovery of structural traps in Mississippian and older rocks.

Prototypal Lisbon field is a longitudinally faulted, northwest trending anticline which existed prior to deposition of the overlying Pennsylvanian beds. As much as 1,500 feet of the oldest Pennsylvanian beds that are present off-structure are absent at the crest of the structure. The major fault on the northeast flank of the structure has about 1,500 feet of vertical displacement. Structural closure is also on the order of 1,500 feet as was the original hydrocarbon column, suggesting that the structure was filled to the spill point.

SOURCE OF HYDROCARBONS

There is no general agreement on the source of the hydrocarbons in Devonian and Mississippian reservoirs of the Four Corners region. Some think the oil and gas were derived from Pennsylvanian source rocks; others believe them to be indigenous to the Mississippian and Devonian. Mississippian rocks of the region appear to be an unlikely source inasmuch as any significant hydrocarbon source material was destroyed during the long period of exposure which created the karst surface at the top of the Redwall. A Mississippian source implies long range migration in post-Mississippian time from possible source beds in western Utah. The objection to the idea that Mississippian reservoirs have been filled from Pennsylvanian source beds is based largely on the failure of destructive distillation analyses to find a satisfactory match between tested Mississippian and Pennsylvanian crude oil samples. It is probably significant, however, that most, if not all, hydrocarbon accumulations in Mississippian beds have Pennsylvanian source rocks in contact with the Mississippian reservoir.

REFERENCES

Baars, D. L., 1966, Pre-Pennsylvanian Paleotectonics — Key to Basin Evolution and Petroleum Occurrences in the Paradox Basin, Utah and Colorado: Am. Assoc. Petrol. Geol. Bull., v. 50, p. 2082-2111.

Baars, D. L., 1972, Devonian System: Geologic Atlas of the Rocky Mountain Region: Rocky Mountain Assoc. Geol., p. 90-99.

Bradley, G. A., 1975, Lisbon Field, Utah: Four Corners Geol. Soc. 8th Field Conf. Guidebook, p. 277-278.

Clark, C. R., 1978, Lisbon: Oil and Gas Fields of the Four Corners Area: Four Corners Geol. Soc., v. 1, p. 662-665.

Cooper, J. C., 1955, Cambrian, Devonian and Mississippian Rocks of the Four Corners Area: Four Corners Geol. Soc. 1st Field Conf. Guidebook, p. 59-65.

Craig, L. C., 1972, Mississippian System: Geologic Atlas of the Rocky Mountain Region: Rocky Mountain Assoc. Geol., p. 100-110.

Cross, Whitman and Spencer, A. C., 1899, La Plata: U.S. Geol. Survey Geol. Atlas Folio 60.

Gilbert, G. K., 1875, Report Upon the Geology of Portions of Nevada, Utah, California and Arizona, Examined in the Year 1871 and 1872: U.S. Geog. Geol. Surveys W. 100th Mer., pt. 3, p. 17-187.

Knight, R. L., and Cooper, J. C., 1955, Suggested Changes in Devonian Terminology of the Four Corners Area: Four Corners Geol. Soc. 1st Field Conf. Guidebook, p. 56-58.

Parker, J. M., and Roberts, J. W., 1963, Devonian and Mississippian Stratigraphy of the Central Part of the Colorado Plateau: Four Corners Geol. Soc. 4th Field Conf. Guidebook, p. 31-60.

Picard, M. D., 1960, Carbon Dioxide, Nitrogen and Helium in the Mississippian of the Four Corners Region, Preliminary Statement: Four Corners Geol. Soc. 3rd Field Conf. Guidebook, p. 138-140.

Spencer, A. C., 1900, Devonian Strata in Colorado: Am. Jour. Sci., 4th Ser., v. 9, p. 125-133.

Spencer, C. W., 1975, Petroleum Geology of East-central Utah and Suggested Approaches to Exploration: Four Corners Geol. Soc. 8th Field Conf. Guidebook, p. 263-275.

SUMMARY

The Devonian System in the Four Corners region is represented by a sequence of marine carbonates and clastics which have produced more than 500,000 barrels of oil and 500 million cubic feet of gas. The marine carbonates which characterize the Mississippian System have produced more than 44 million barrels of oil and 350 billion cubic feet of gas. Most oil and gas production from Devonian and Mississippian reservoirs is from structural traps. The variable thicknesses of overlying Pennsylvanian salt beds complicates the mapping of pre-Pennsylvanian structure, but improving geophysical methods combined with subsurface geology will lead to more oil and gas discoveries in the relatively unexplored Devonian and Mississippian reservoirs.

TABLE I. DEVONIAN PRODUCTION IN THE FOUR CORNERS REGION

State	Field	Discovery Date	Discovery Well Location	Producing Interval	Estimated Recoverable Reserves	Cumulative Production To 1-1-80
ARIZONA						
	Undesignated	7-10-60	36-41N-30E	Aneth	764 BO	764 BO (1)
	Walker Creek	5-7-63	16-41N-30E	McCracken	97,129 BO	97,129 BO (1)
COLORADO						
	SE Lisbon	8-3-71	18-44N-19W	Ouray	(Combined with Redwall)	
NEW MEXICO						
	Akah Nez	11-19-67	23-23N-20W	McCracken	17,199 BO	17,199 BO (1)
	Tom	9-12-76	33-25N-19W	Upper Elbert	2,000 BO	1,441 BO
UTAH						
	Lisbon	1-5-60	10-30S-24E	McCracken	420,000 BO 600,000 MCFG	394,233 BO 576,867 MCFG
			Total Devonian Oil		537,092 BO	510,766 BO
			Total Devonian Gas		600,000 MCFG	576,867 MCFG

(1) Abandoned

TABLE II. MISSISSIPPIAN PRODUCTION IN THE FOUR CORNERS REGION

State	Field	Discovery Date	Discovery Well Location	Producing Interval	Estimated Recoverable Reserves	Cumulative Production To 1-1-80
ARIZONA						
	Dry Mesa	6-27-59	11-40N-28E	Redwall	680,000 BO 124,000 MCFG	615,375 BO 104,585 MCFG
COLORADO						
	SE Lisbon	1-15-60	5-44N-19W	Redwall	170,000 BO 14,000,000 MCFG	122,250 BO 9,431,509 MCFG
NEW MEXICO						
	Table Mesa	1-15-51	3-27N-17W	Redwall	74,393 BO 1,193,006 MCFG	74,393 BO (1) 1,193,006 MCFG (1)
	Hogback	10-18-52	19-29N-16W	Redwall	Unknown	Small Amount
	N. Tocito Dome	7-29-63	34-27N-18W	Redwall	828 BO 1,104,668 MCFG	828 BO (1) 1,104,668 MCFG (1)
	Beautiful Mtn.	6-1-75	5-26N-19W	Redwall	9,229 BO	9,229 BO (1)
UTAH						
	Big Flat	8-16-57	14-26S-19E	Redwall	83,469 BO	83,469 BO (1)
	Lisbon	1-5-60	10-30S-24E	Redwall	45,000,000 BO 300,000,000 MCFG	41,903,443 BO 339,659,149 MCFG (2)
	Salt Wash	5-28-61	15-23S-17E	Redwall	1,270,000 BO	1,206,791 BO
	Big Indian	9-15-61	33-29S-24E	Redwall	137,000 BO 18,700,000 MCFG	135,658 BO 18,437,662 MCFG
	Little Valley	12-12-61	21-30S-25E	Redwall	100,000 BO 10,000,000 MCFG	51,387 BO 5,139,782 MCFG
	Cleft	5-19-62	19-43S-21E	Redwall	2,000 BO	2,000 BO (1)
	Hook & Ladder	4-12-77	24-29S-23E	Redwall	120,000 BO 11,000,000 MCFG	Shut in
			Total Mississippian Oil		47,646,919 BO	44,204,823 BO
			Total Mississippian Gas		356,121,674 MCFG	375,070,361 MCFG

(1) Abandoned
(2) Recycled

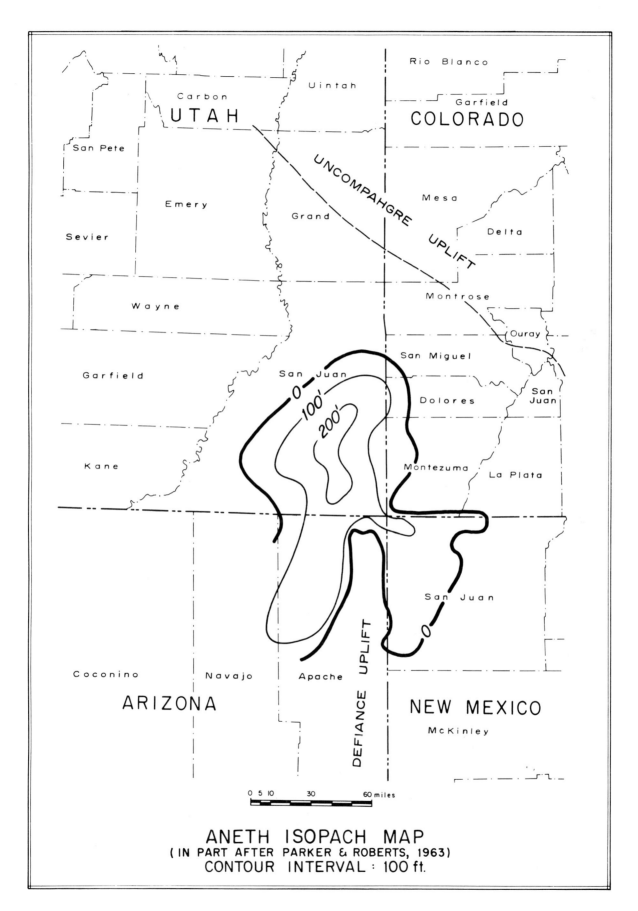

ANETH ISOPACH MAP
(IN PART AFTER PARKER & ROBERTS, 1963)
CONTOUR INTERVAL : 100 ft.

Figure 1

McCRACKEN ISOPACH MAP
(IN PART AFTER PARKER & ROBERTS, 1963)
CONTOUR INTERVAL: 50 ft.

Figure 2

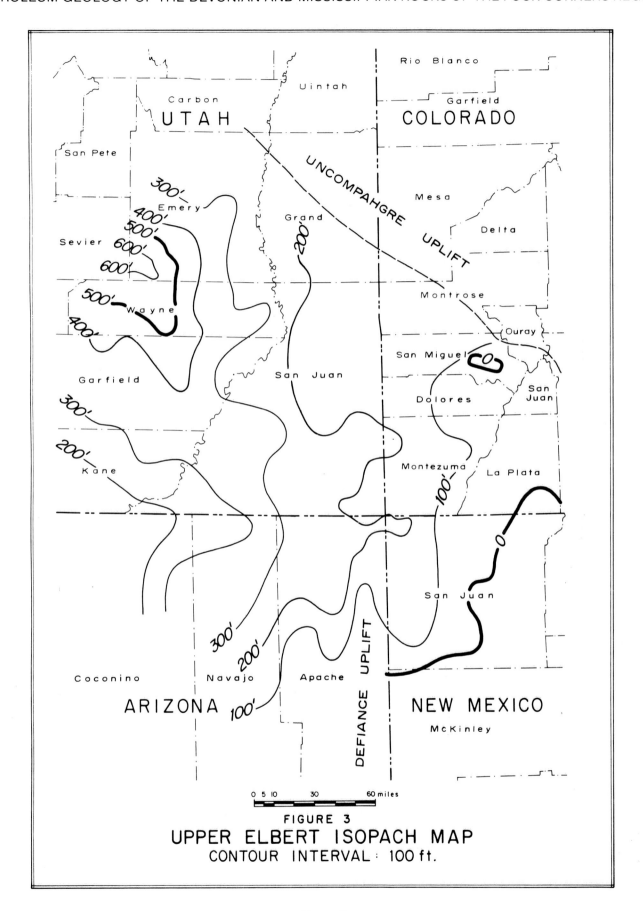

FIGURE 3
UPPER ELBERT ISOPACH MAP
CONTOUR INTERVAL: 100 ft.

Figure 3

OURAY ISOPACH MAP
(IN PART AFTER BAARS, 1972)
CONTOUR INTERVAL: 50 ft.

Figure 4

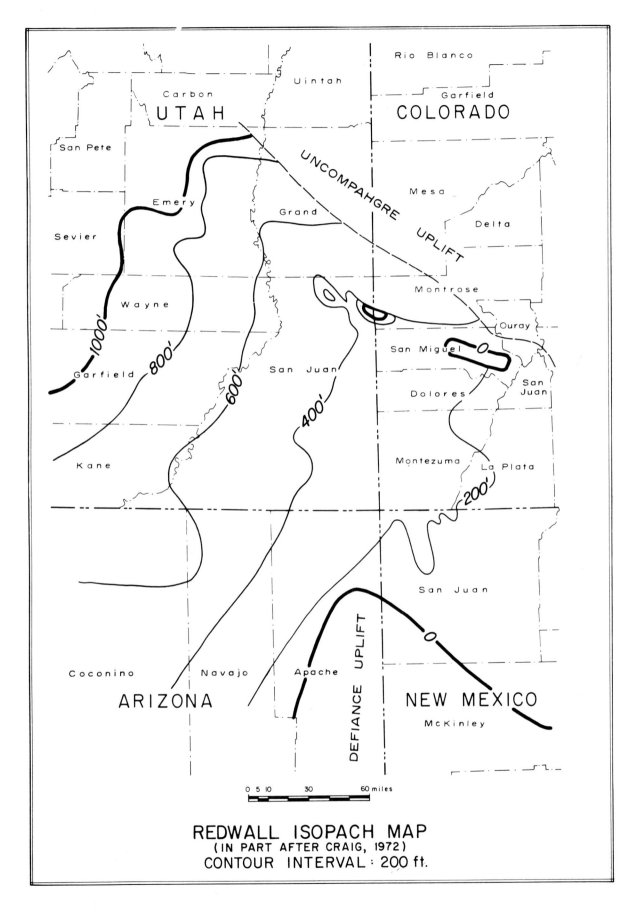

REDWALL ISOPACH MAP
(IN PART AFTER CRAIG, 1972)
CONTOUR INTERVAL: 200 ft.

Figure 5

Big Indian

FACIES RECOGNITION AND HYDROCARBON POTENTIAL OF THE PENNSYLVANIAN PARADOX FORMATION

Fred S. Reid[1] and Claude E. Berghorn[2]

INTRODUCTION

The excellent hydrocarbon potential in Pennsylvanian age rocks of the Paradox Basin is again being recognized, as evidenced by increased leasing and drilling activity. This paper will examine the present and future hydrocarbon potential of the Pennsylvanian Paradox formation and suggest areas of the basin having maximum potential.

The Paradox Basin includes parts of Arizona, Colorado, New Mexico and Utah. The basin lies east of the Cordilleran Hingeline and the Rocky Mountain Thrust Belt (Figure 1). Major tectonic and topographic features bounding the basin include the Uncompahgre-San Juan Mountain Uplift on the east, San Rafael Swell on the northwest, Monument and Defiance Uplifts on the south flank, and the Hogback Monocline on the southeast flank (Figure 2).

Sedimentary rocks ranging in age from Precambrian to Upper Cretaceous are present in the Paradox Basin. Surface outcrops throughout most of the basin are Cretaceous to Triassic in age. Permian to Precambrian rocks also crop out in the salt anticline and uplift areas. Major surface exposures of Tertiary volcanics occur in the Henry Mountains, Abajo Mountains, Ute Mountains and Navajo Mountains.

TECTONIC SETTING

From Cambrian to Mississippian time, the Paradox Basin area was part of the foreland shelf of the Cordilleran Miogeosyncline. During Mississippian Leadville time, the basin was a carbonate shelf where thick deposits of crinoidal and chalky limestone were deposited. Regional subsidence in early Pennsylvanian time created a depression extending from Utah's Oquirrh Basin on the northwest to central New Mexico on the southeast (Figure 2). In the Paradox Basin area this depression developed into a basin adjacent to the Uncompahgre and San Juan Mountain Uplifts. The Emery and Kaibab Uplifts to the west and Defiance Uplift to the south created a restricted marine environment in the basin, resulting in thick deposits of evaporites during Des Moinesian time. A carbonate shelf rimmed the evaporites on the south and southwest. Periodic Des Moinesian uplift of the Uncompaghre-San Juan Mountain Uplifts resulted in deposition of alluvial fans adjacent to the uplifts in the easternmost part of the basin.

STRUCTURE

The Paradox Basin is an asymmetric basin with a steeply dipping and faulted east flank and a relatively gently dipping west flank. Subsurface information indicates the Precambrian roots of the Uncompaghre Uplift were thrust over sedimentary Paleozoic beds in the basin. Local and subregional structures, combined with complex carbonate and clastic facies changes, have resulted in numerous stratigraphic and structural trapping conditions throughout the basin.

BASIN PRODUCTION

Oil and gas production within the Paradox Basin occurs in rocks of the Devonian, Mississippian, Pennsylvanian, Permian, Jurassic and Cretaceous systems. As indicated in Figure 3, the majority of oil and gas comes from the Pennsylvanian system.

[1]Peppard & Associates

[2]Trans Texas Energy, Inc.

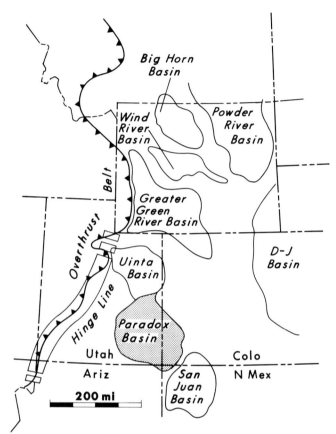

REGIONAL INDEX MAP
Figure 1

Fields producing from Pennsylvanian age rocks are illustrated in Figure 4. Although a minor amount of oil and gas is produced from stratigraphic traps in the upper Pennsylvanian Honaker Trail Formation and lower Pennsylvanian Pinkerton Trail Formation, most production is from the middle Pennsylvanian Paradox Formation of Des Moinesian age.

PARADOX FORMATION STRATIGRAPHY

The Paradox Formation evaporites have been subdivided into as many as 40 cycles of deposition based on widespread black shale on dolomite marker beds. Previous authors and industry personnel have adopted five major cycles. These are in ascending order, the Alkali Gulch, Barker Creek, Akah, Desert Creek and Ismay Zones (Figure 5). For the purposes of this paper, the Alkali Gulch was combined with the Barker Creek cycle. These hypersaline cycles were correlated laterally into equivalent carbonate shelf sediments using shale, dolomitic shale or anhydrite markers. Three major facies — marine shelf, penesaline and hypersaline — were delineated for each of the four cycles. A fourth, arkosic facies, is present adjacent to the Uncompaghre Uplift.

The marine shelf facies is composed of marine limestones, dolomites, thin black and red shales, siltstones and

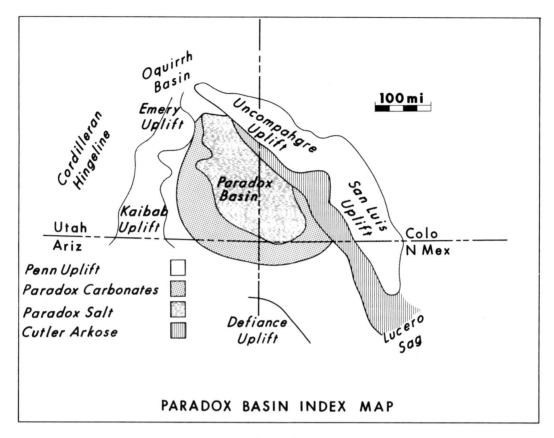

Figure 2

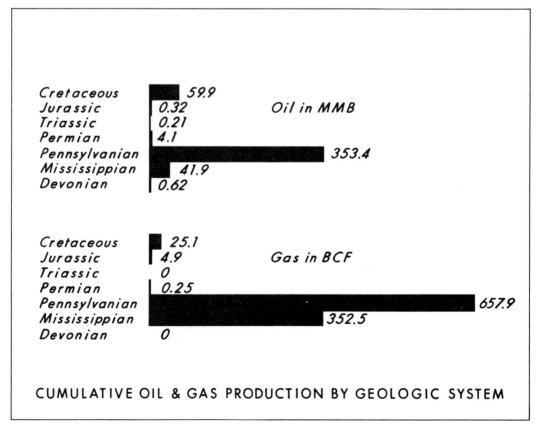

Figure 3

sandstones. This facies is also characterized by the absence of widespread evaporites. Fossiliferous and biostromal limestone units, composed of coral colonies, are found in this facies, as is algal mounding.

The penesaline facies is adjacent to and laterally equivalent to the marine shelf facies. It is a lithologic suite consisting of anhydrites, dolomites, limestones and black sapropelic shales. Previous authors have described in great detail the biogenic composition of carbonate mounds which are common in this area. The primary constituent of the mound is carbonate mud. Locally abundant bioclastic debris composed of calcified leaves of the algae *Ivanovia*, brachiopods, fusulinids, small foraminifera, crinoids and coral are also present in the mound complex. The thickest and most areally extensive mounds in the Desert Creek and Ismay cycles are close to the boundary between the marine shelf and penesaline facies. Apparently the algal colonies acted as traps for sediment and debris which was eroded and swept basinward from the marine shelf. The proximity of these colonies to the shelf edge suggests that this sediment was not transported far.

The hypersaline facies contains thick cyclic deposits of halite, anhydrite, gypsum, limestone, black shale and shaley dolomite. Halite and potash salts predominate and give rise to diapiric salt anticlines. Carbonate mounds are absent. The hypersaline facies interfingers with the penesaline facies.

The facies distribution for Ismay, Desert Creek, Akah, and Barker Creek cycles was traced throughout the basin (Figures 6A-6D).

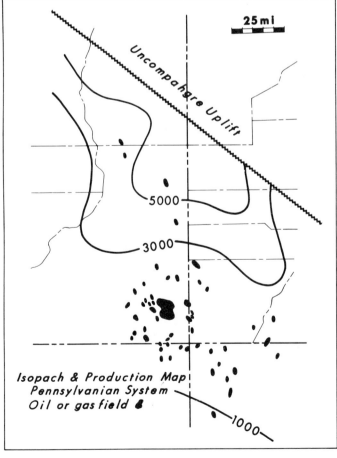

25 mi

Uncompahgre Uplift

5000

3000

Isopach & Production Map
Pennsylvanian System
Oil or gas field

1000

Figure 4

PARADOX FORMATION PRODUCTION

Most production from the Paradox Formation occurs in the penesaline and marine shelf facies. All production in the penesaline facies appears to be associated with algal mounds. There seems to be little association of production with structural anomalies. Combination structural and stratigraphic traps are present in the marine shelf facies. In fact most production in this facies, including algal mound traps, is associated or coincident with pre-Pennsylvanian structural anomalies.

Surrounding shale and evaporite beds make algal mounds more easily discernible in the penesaline facies than in the marine shelf facies. The use of sample and mechanical log data to generate various lithologic ratio maps can be a definite aid in predicting mound occurrences. In the marine shelf facies, algal mounds may be indistinguishable from shelf limestone using mechanical log data alone. Petrographic data is necessary to predict mound occurrence in this facies. Figure 7 illustrates how the lithologic character of the penesaline facies makes recognition of algal limestone build-ups easier, even when using only mechanical logs.

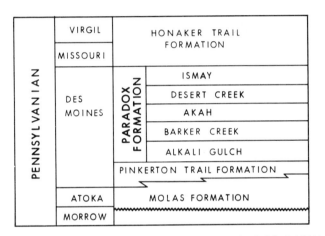

	VIRGIL	HONAKER TRAIL FORMATION	
PENNSYLVANIAN	MISSOURI		
	DES MOINES	PARADOX FORMATION	ISMAY
			DESERT CREEK
			AKAH
			BARKER CREEK
			ALKALI GULCH
		PINKERTON TRAIL FORMATION	
	ATOKA	MOLAS FORMATION	
	MORROW		

PENNSYLVANIAN STRATA OF THE PARADOX BASIN

Figure 5

BARKER CREEK ZONE

In the Barker Creek zone, a narrow band of penesaline facies separates widespread marine shelf and hypersaline facies (Figure 6A). Production in the Barker Creek zone occurs in the marine shelf and hypersaline facies and is associated with structural anomalies. There is little information about trapping conditions in the hypersaline facies, but it is believed production comes from a fractured section of thin dolomites and shales. In the marine shelf facies, significant gas production occurs at Alkali Gulch, Barker Dome and Ute Dome fields and significant oil production at Tocito Dome Field. At Dineh-Bi-Keyah Field in Arizona, a Tertiary sill in the Barker Creek zone has produced over 15 million barrels of oil. Both biostromal limestone and algal mound limestones are productive in the marine shelf facies.

An example of excellent Barker Creek production is the Tocito Dome Field, which was discovered in 1963 with the completion of a shut-in gas well. By the end of 1972, a total of 19 wells located in the western portion of the field were producing. During 1973-75, an active drilling program was completed in the eastern part of the field, raising the total number of producers to 50. With the current producing wells, development appears to be complete and cumulative

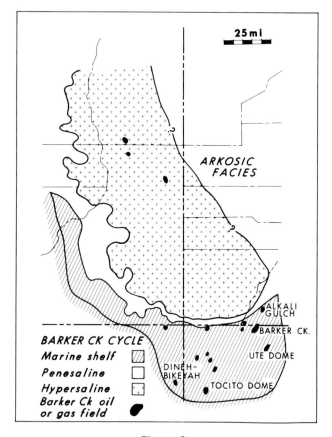

Figure 6a

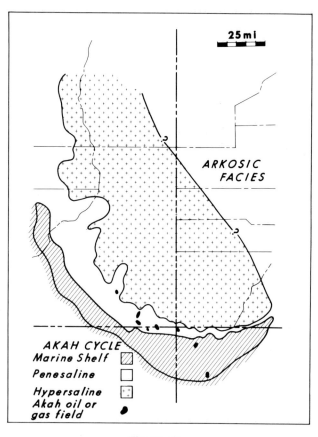

Figure 6b

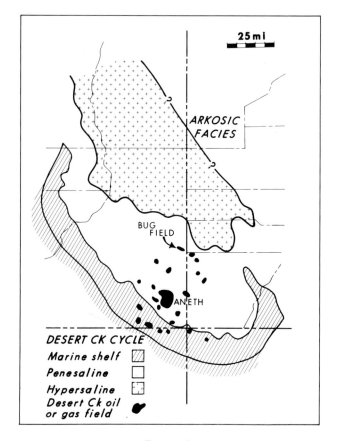

Figure 6c

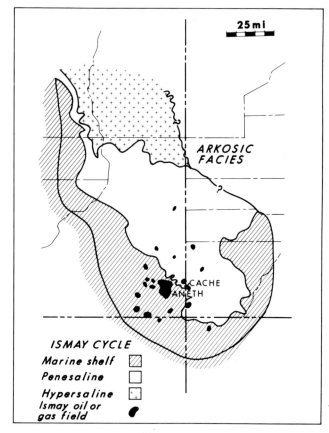

Figure 6d

production now totals over 11.5 million barrels of oil and 23 BCFG.

Figure 8 shows the structure on top of the pay zone at Tocito Dome and Figure 9 is an isopach of the net pay. Production is from what is interpreted to be an algal mound in a marine shelf environment. The mound occurs near the top of the Barker Creek zone and roughly coincides with a structural anomaly. Based on differences in reservoir and production characteristics, the field was separated into two areas for purposes of discussion. The western area has oil-water and gas-oil contacts established by DST and production data (Figure 8). The eastern area was not discovered and developed until 1973-75. Reservoir pressures encountered in these wells were 2000 psi lower than the original pressure of 3217 psi in the western part of the field. Since the pressure in the eastern part is lower than the original BHP, the two areas must be connected; however, due to differences in the apparent oil-water contacts, the communication is apparently very limited. There is no obvious discontinuity in producing zone porosity between the two areas.

AKAH ZONE

Facies distribution for the Akah zone (Figure 6B) is similar to that in the Barker Creek zone. The zones differ in that most oil and gas production from the Akah is in the penesaline facies, with only a minor part of the production occurring in the marine shelf facies. All production is coincident with multipay structural anomalies. Productive capacity of the Akah could not be determined due to the fact that the production records in the multi-pay fields are not tabulated by pay zone.

DESERT CREEK ZONE

In the Desert Creek zone (Figure 6C), the marine shelf and penesaline facies cover the majority of the basin. Most production in the Desert Creek is in the penesaline facies, as typified by the large Aneth Field. Aneth has produced nearly 300 barrels of oil since its discovery in 1956. While the discovery of another Aneth Field would be extremely desirable, current exploration programs are most likely to find fields roughly equal in size to the smaller Gothic Mesa Field. Figures 10 and 11 show the limits of the field and field structure. Limited lithographic data indicate the pay zone to be an algal mound. Entrapment is stratigraphic, with porosity development within the mound being the controlling factor in reservoir limits. Pay thickness ranges from zero to 36 feet. Cumulative production to 1979 has reached 1,556,251 barrels of oil from 18 wells. Individual well production varies from 2000 to 315,000 barrels of oil, with the average being 60,000 barrels. Ultimate recoverable reserves are estimated to be 2,100,000 barrels.

ISMAY ZONE

Most productive fields in the Ismay zone (Figure 6D) are in the marine shelf facies. There is a large area of the penesaline facies where productive potential exists. An example of the excellent quality of Ismay production to be found in the penesaline facies is Cache Field. Figure 12 shows the structure on top of the pay and Figure 13 is an

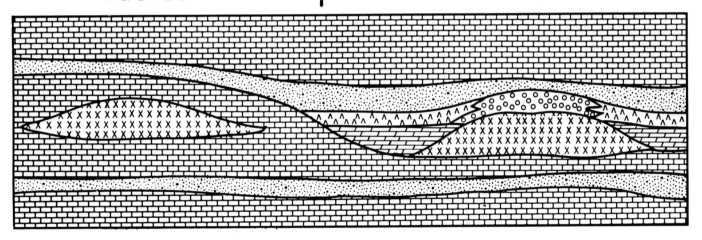

Figure 7. Marine Shelf Facies vs. Penesaline Facies Algal Mound Development

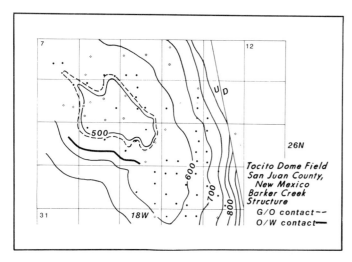

Figure 8

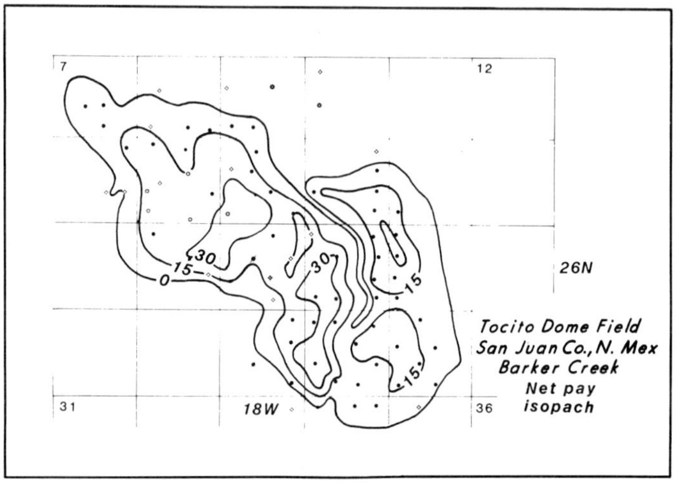

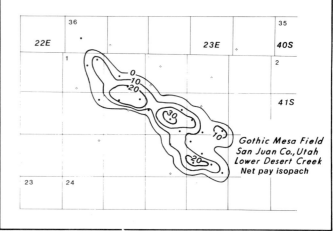

Figure 9

isopach map of the net pay. Accumulation is stratigraphic and is controlled by porosity development and an oil-water contact. The structure on top of the pay reflects a series of stacked algal mounds. The pay zone porosity is primarily in an algal calcirudite breccia; average depth of the pay is 5500 feet. Estimated ultimate production exceeds 3.3 million barrels. Maximum pay thickness is 80 feet and average thickness is 28 feet. Average per well recovery is 163,000 barrels of oil on 40 acre spacing.

EXPLORATION POTENTIAL

Exploratory drilling in the Paradox Basin has been extremely slow since the discovery of big fields such as Aneth and Lisbon in the 1950's and 1960's. Some negative factors contributing to the decline in exploration have been (1) increasing federal restrictions and strict drilling regulations, (2) large areas of federal lands that are off-limits to exploration (Figure 14), (3) lack of lease sales on Indian lands, (4) physical and legal confrontation between Indians and oil operators in the area.

In the past few years, wildcat drilling has picked up and some positive factors have occurred which should encourage a high level of future activity. These positive elements are: (1) two Desert Creek discoveries, (2) better economics due to the increase in the price of oil, (3) cutbacks in wilderness area designations which make more Federal

land available for exploration, (4) promise for seismic delineation of algal mounds as described in a recent paper (Pickett & Sherrill, 1980), (5) recent drilling for Mississippian carbon dioxide production in southwestern Colorado which should help delineate shallow Pennsylvanian prospects.

Data released on Bug Field (Desert Creek) recently discovered by Wexpro, illustrate the potential for prospecting in the Paradox Basin. Three wells have been completed in the field and subsurface data indicate potential for 10 to 12 more locations. Pay thickness in the completed oil and gas wells ranges from 15 to 20 feet at a depth of 6300 feet. If development drilling continues as predicted, cumulative field production of 2 to 4 million barrels can be expected. With present crude oil prices and drilling costs, the economic return on a field this size is quite good.

Future exploration efforts in the Paradox Basin appear to be quite promising. Those companies who use modern petrographic and seismic methods and concentrate their efforts in areas where facies studies show the best potential for algal mounding will have the best success in discovering Paradox formation oil and gas reserves.

BIBLIOGRAPHY

Fetzner, R. W., 1959, Pennsylvanian paleotectonics of the Paradox basin: Am. Assoc. Petroleum Geologists Rocky Mtn. Sec. Geol. Rec., p. 87-90.

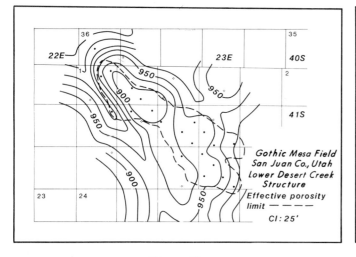

Figure 10

Figure 11

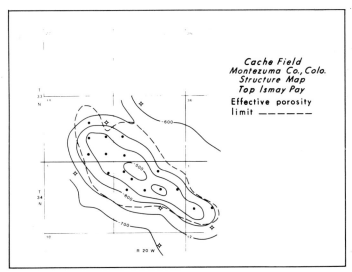

Figure 12.

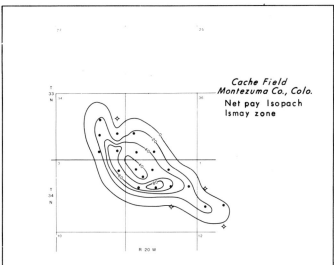

Figure 13.

Gray, R. S., 1967, Cache field — A Pennsylvanian algal reservoir in southwestern Colorado: Am. Assoc. Petroleum Geologists Bull., v. 51, no. 10, p. 1959-1978.

Hite, R. J., 1972, Pennsylvanian rocks and salt anticlines, Paradox basin: Rocky Mtn. Geol. Atlas, Rocky Mtn. Assoc. Geologists.

Kelley, V. C., 1958, Tectonics of the region of the Paradox basin: Intermtn. Assoc. Petroleum Geologists Guidebook 9th Field Conf., p. 31-38.

McKenny, J. W., and Masters, J. A., 1968, Dineh-Bi-Keyah field, Apache County, Arizona: Am. Assoc. Petroleum Geologists Bull., v. 52, no. 10, p. 2045-2057.

Peterson, J. A., 1963, Pennsylvanian shelf carbonates, Paradox basin: Four Corners Geol. Soc. Guidebook 4th Field Conf., p. 65-79.

Peterson, J. A., 1975, Stratigraphy vs. structural controls on carbonate-mound hydrocarbaon accumulation, Aneth area Paradox basin: Am. Assoc. Petroleum Geologists Rept., Ser. 15, p. 142-155.

Peterson, J. A., and Hite, R. J., 1968, Pennsylvanian evaporite-carbonate cycles and their relation to petroleum occurrence, southern Rocky Mountains, in Evaporites and petroleum: Am. Assoc. Petroleum Geologists Bull., v. 53, no. 4, p. 884-908.

Quigley, W. D., 1958, Aneth field and surrounding area (Utah): Intermtn. Assoc. Petroleum Geologists Guidebook 9th Field Conf., p. 247-253.

Reid, F. S., and Berghorn, C. E., 1980, Lower and middle Paleozoic potential of Paradox basin (abs.): Am. Assoc. of Petroleum Geologists Bull., v. 64, no. 5, p. 771.

Reid, F. S., and Stevenson, G., 1978, Gothic Mesa Field, San Juan Co., Utah: Four Corners Geological Society, Oil and Gas Fields of the Four Corners Area, p. 642-645.

Rountree, R., 1980, Wexpro wells cause new interest in Paradox basin: Western Oil Reporter, v. 37, no. 12, p. 93-94.

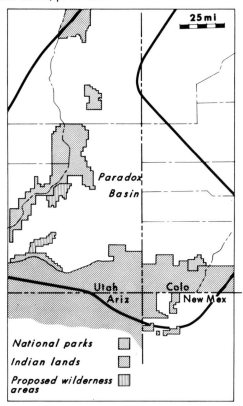

Figure 14.

"Sez here on the map "Monument Valley" . . .

MESOZOIC STRATIGRAPHY OF THE PARADOX BASIN — AN OVERVIEW

C. M. MOLENAAR
U.S. Geological Survey
Denver, Colorado

INTRODUCTION

Mesozoic rocks make up most of the surface exposures throughout the Paradox basin and adjacent areas except for the crests of the breached salt anticlines and major uplifts, and the deeper canyons of the Colorado, Green and Dolores Rivers. The magnificent exposures of these rocks, throughout most of this youthfully dissected area have made much of the Paradox basin into the scenic wonderland that it is today. These exposures are among the best in the Colorado Plateau province and have provided much of the excellent stratigraphic data on the various formations and members.

The Paradox basin is considered here to be the general area underlain by evaporites of the Pennsylvanian Paradox Member of the Hermosa Formation, and includes large parts of southeastern Utah, southwestern Colorado and small parts of northeastern Arizona and northwestern New Mexico (Figure 1).

Much has been written on the Mesozoic stratigraphy in and adjacent to the Paradox basin. This work ranges from local details described on the various 7½ minute geologic quadrangle maps to the more regional studies on specific formations or groups. Some of the more regional or recent papers on Triassic rocks include McKee and others (1959), Stewart and others (1972a), Stewart and others (1972b), Blakey (1974), and O'Sullivan and MacLachlan (1975). Papers on Jurassic rocks include Craig and others (1955), McKee and others (1956), Wright and Dickey (1963), O'Sullivan and Craig (1973) and Craig and Shawe (1975).

In some areas of the Paradox basin, suggested changes of nomenclature have not been fully accepted or incorporated on geologic maps. In addition, new information indicates a need for revisions of correlations and nomenclature. These new data have not been fully evaluated or the revisions have not been extended throughout the area. No attempt is made in this paper to favor one interpretation over another, although some of these differences will be mentioned. The primary purpose of this paper is to present an overview of the Mesozoic stratigraphy of the Paradox basin area in context with the regional relations.

Figure 2 graphically shows the regional stratigraphic relationships of most of the Mesozoic strata from northwest to southeast across the Paradox basin. Much of the Mesozoic strata are eroded along the line of section and the stratigraphy is projected from adjacent areas. The thicknesses of units on the east flank of the San Rafael Swell near Highway 1-70 are mostly from Trimble and Doelling (1978); the Shafer Trail-Moab area data are projected from outcrops in the general area; the data near Dove Creek, Colorado are from wells, principally the Continental Oil Co. Medley Scott No. 1 in section 34, T. 41 N., R. 19 W.; and the thickness data in the Durango area are from the Cayman Federal No. 1 well in section 26, T. 35 N., R. 10 W., a few miles southwest of Durango.

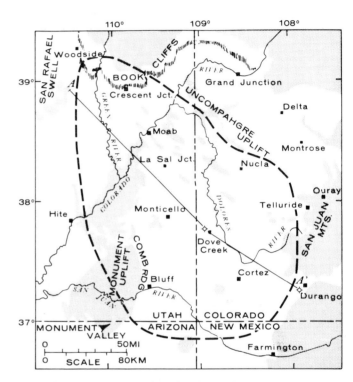

Figure 1. Index map of Paradox basin (dashed outline) and surrounding area. Mesozoic rocks are at or near surface in all areas except where shaded. A-A' is line of cross section shown in figure 2.

REGIONAL STRATIGRAPHY AND PALEOGEOGRAPHY

Based on regional paleogeography of the Colorado Plateau and adjacent areas, the Mesozoic section of the plateau can be divided into two major parts: (1) a generally pre-Nevadan part composed of the Moenkopi through Summerville Formations, Early Triassic through Middle Jurassic, when the seaway was to the west and northwest, and the fluvial clastics were derived from the east and southeast; and (2) a Nevadan-early Laramide part composed of the Morrison Formation through Mesaverde Group, Late Jurassic into Late Cretaceous, when the dominant clastic source area was to the west and southwest and the seaway was to the east and northeast. A third interval, which is of minor significance to Mesozoic deposition, is composed of uppermost Cretaceous and lower Tertiary clastics derived from local uplifts and deposited in interior basins. This part is not present in the Paradox basin.

During the deposition of the pre-Nevadan rocks, tectonic conditions were highly stable in the Colorado Plateau area. Local movements were caused by salt flowage in underlying Pennsylvanian rocks of the eastern Paradox basin. A slight increase in subsidence toward the seaway on the west is

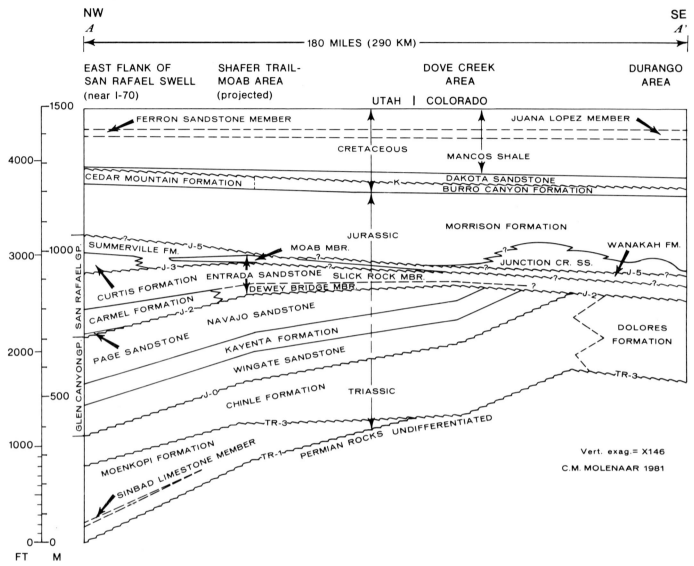

Figure 2. Cross section across Paradox basin showing generalized stratigraphic relations of Triassic, Jurassic and lower part of Cretaceous formations. Unconformities are from Pipiringos and O'Sullivan (1978). Refer to text for specific ages of formations. See figure 1 for location of cross section.

indicated by westward thickening of most of the stratigraphic units (Figure 1). Three widespread shallow marine transgressions during Moenkopi, Carmel, and Curtis times resulted in deposition of marine limestones or sandstones on the west and northwest that grade into marginal marine red siltstones and silty sandstones to the east and southeast. Separating the marine and marginal marine deposits are nonmarine deposits that generally represent a fluctuation between fluvial red bed deposits derived from mildly positive areas east, southeast or south of the Colorado Plateau, and eolian sands brought in by predominantly northwesterly winds. During this pre-Nevadan time, the red sandstones and shales were deposited that make much of the Colorado Plateau area so colorful.

Several widespread unconformities within the Mesozoic Era are present in the Western Interior. Pipiringos and O'Sullivan (1978) discussed and correlated the Triassic and Jurassic unconformities, and designated them, in ascending order, Tr-1, Tr-2, Tr-3, J-0, J-1, J-2, J-3, J-4, and J-5. Recognition of these unconformities is helpful in correlating the largely unfossiliferous strata throughout the Colorado

Plateau, and they are used in this report. Some of them have been cut out by younger unconformities and some are magnified along the flanks of the salt anticlines that were growing penecontemporaneously.

The Cordilleran seaway situated west of the Colorado Plateau started to break up during Middle or Late Triassic time. Development of a western provenance in Middle Jurassic (Callovian) time is indicated by pebbles and granules in the Curtis Formation and the Preuss Sandstone (an equivalent of the Entrada Sandstone) on the western margin of the Colorado Plateau. These early uplifts had little effect on the deposition of rocks in the Colorado Plateau, except possibly for the regional unconformities shown in Figure 2. However, pronounced uplifts starting in Late Jurassic (Kimmeridgian) time terminated any remaining vestiges of the seaway and formed the Mesocordilleran Highlands. This had a marked effect on the sedimentation patterns in the Colorado Plateau area. Not only did the source area for water-laden clastic material change, but the predominant wind direction changed from northwesterly to west and southwesterly. This shift is indicated by studies of crossbeds in eolian sandstone bodies at the base of the Morrison Formation (Upper Jurassic, Kimmeridgian) in the southern part of the Colorado Plateau.

The clastics derived from the new source area constitute the upper part of the Mesozoic sequence. These strata are mostly drab gray and buff, although the green, red and variegated shales of the Morrison Formation provide some of the color to large parts of the Paradox basin. Initially, fluvial deposition predominated during latest Jurassic and Early Cretaceous time. Later an interior seaway encroached from far to the north in Canada and finally covered much of the Colorado Plateau in Late Cretaceous time. During much of Cretaceous time, deposition alternated from open marine deposits (Mancos Shale and its tongues) as the seas transgressed from the east and northeast, to prograding shoreline and delta-plain deposits (Mesaverde Group and associated rocks).

MESOZOIC STRATA OF THE PARADOX BASIN AREA
MOENKOPI FORMATION

The Moenkopi Formation of Early and Middle(?) Triassic age unconformably overlies Permian or older rocks along the Tr-1 unconformity. The underlying Permian Cutler Formation includes the De Chelly Sandstone Member in the southern Paradox basin, the White Rim Sandstone Member in the western Paradox, and is undifferentiated in the remaining northern and eastern parts of the Paradox basin. Locally, the Moenkopi overlies Pennsylvanian rocks on the flanks and crests of some of the salt anticlines such as in a small area immediately northwest of Moab. The Moenkopi, which represents the first Mesozoic marine transgression in the Colorado Plateau, forms ledgy slopes and consists of reddish-brown, micaceous, thinly laminated siltstone and sandy siltstone, very fine grained crossbedded sandstone, and minor gypsum. Parallel and interference ripples, ripple crossbeds, and desiccation features such as mud cracks and salt casts are common.

The Moenkopi is primarily a low-energy marginal marine deposit that grades from tidal flat with some fluvial facies along the eastern part of the Paradox basin to shallow marine facies in the western Paradox basin and San Rafael Swell. Blakey (1974) recognized intertonguing deltaic and paralic marine deposits in eastern Utah, and subdivided the Moenkopi into, in ascending order, the Black Dragon, Sinbad (previously named), Torrey and Moody Canyon Members. The Sinbad is a thin tongue of marine limestone that occurs in the northwestern Paradox basin and thickens to the northwest from there.

In the northeasternmost Paradox basin, the Moenkopi has been subdivided into four members on the basis of intertonguing of coarse fluvial sandstones with finer grained facies. The coarse facies were derived from the adjacent Uncompahgre uplift, and possibly from Pennsylvanian or Permian beds exposed on the flanks of growing salt structures. In ascending order, the four units are the Tenderfoot, Ali Baba, Sewemup and Pariott Members (Shoemaker and Newman, 1959). The Tenderfoot Member may be older than the Moenkopi of the western Paradox basin.

A basal sandy unit of the Moenkopi Formation in the south and southwestern Paradox basin has been named the Hoskinnini Member or Tongue. It is well exposed in the Monument Valley area where it overlies the massive sandstone of the De Chelly and underlies the slope-forming Moenkopi shales near the top of monuments or buttes. It is a reddish-brown to reddish-orange, fine- to medium-grained sandstone with some coarse grains and minor thin siltstone

interbeds. This member can be correlated in the subsurface for several miles north and east of the Four Corners (Molenaar, 1977).

Regionally, the Moenkopi thins from about 700 ft. (213 m) in the northwestern Paradox basin to near zero on the southeastern side. However, in the salt anticline area of the northeastern Paradox basin, there are abrupt local variations because of contemporaneous salt flowage in and adjacent to the salt structures. Thicknesses here range from zero to greater than 2,500 ft. (760 m). The Moenkopi is absent on the Uncompahgre uplift to the northeast of the Paradox basin.

CHINLE FORMATION

The Chinle Formation of Late Triassic age unconformably (Tr-3 unconformity) overlies the Moenkopi Formation in most of the Paradox basin. Exceptions are the southeastern Paradox area, and locally on the flanks of some of the salt structures where it overlies Permian or older rocks. On the Uncompahgre uplift, it rests on Precambrian basement. In the San Juan Mountains, Chinle equivalent strata are included in the Dolores Formation.

Like the Moenkopi, the Chinle forms ledgy slopes, but it consists entirely of continental deposits of fluvial and lacustrine origin with a provenance far to the southeast and south. Unlike other pre-Nevadan Mesozoic formations, which thicken to the west of the Paradox basin, the Chinle thickens to the south in southwestern Utah and northeastern Arizona. In the Paradox basin, it ranges in thickness from about 1,200 ft. (365 m) in the south to 300 or 400 ft. (90 or 120 m) in the north. To the north and northeast the Chinle thins because of onlap of the lower part and internal depositional thinning of the remaining parts, especially in the salt anticline areas.

In southeastern Utah and the Monument Valley area of northeastern Arizona, the Chinle has been subdivided into six members which are, in ascending order, the Shinarump, Monitor Butte, Moss Back, Petrified Forest, Owl Rock, and Church Rock Members. The lower four members contain much bentonitic material in the finer clastics and are considered to be the lower part of the Chinle. The upper two members, which are not bentonitic, constitute the upper part of the Chinle.

The Shinarump Member is locally absent in the southern Paradox basin. To the north of the Monument uplift it thins and is overlapped by the Monitor Butte. The Shinarump is well developed in the Monument uplift and Monument Valley areas where it is a cliff-forming unit up to 200 ft. (60 m) thick. It is of fluvial origin and consists of gray to pale yellowish-orange, medium- to coarse-grained conglomeratic sandstone. Many uranium mines and prospects are present within this unit in the Monument uplift area.

The Monitor Butte Member ranges in thickness from 200 ft. (60 m) in the south to zero at its pinchout edge on the north in the central Paradox basin, where it is overlapped by the Moss Back Member. The Monitor Butte is a slope-forming unit composed of greenish-gray and minor pale reddish-brown, bentonitic claystone or clayey, fine-grained, micaceous sandstone.

The Moss Back Member is a ledge-forming fluvial channel sandstone that crops out in the northern half of the Monument uplift, the upper Canyonlands and San Rafael Swell, and in the central Paradox basin. It averages about 60 ft. (18 m) in thickness and consists of yellowish-gray and pale-orange, fine- to medium-grained, crossbedded sandstone with conglomerate lenses composed of siltstone, limestone, quartzite or chert pebbles. Carbonaceous material and silicified wood are also common. The Moss

Back was once included in the Shinarump, but later stratigraphic studies have shown that the Shinarump of the type area is older and pinches out below the Monitor Butte Member in the vicinity of Hite marina on the upper part of Lake Powell (Stewart and others, 1959). The Moss Back overlies the Monitor Butte Member in the west-central Paradox basin and becomes the basal unit of the Chinle by onlap farther north. To the south along Comb Ridge the Moss Back pinches out. Many uranium mines are present within the Moss Back in the San Rafael, Canyonlands and Lisbon Valley areas.

The Petrified Forest Member gradationally overlies the Moss Back Member and is about 250 ft. (76 m) thick in the southern Paradox basin, but loses its identity north of the Monument uplift. It typically consists of variegated bentonitic claystone, mudstone, siltstone, and some sandstone. The unit weathers to form a "frosty-surfaced" slope because of the swelling of bentonitic clay.

The Owl Rock Member, which gradationally overlies the Petrified Forest Member, typically is composed of pale red and pale reddish-brown mudstone with thin lacustrine limestone interbeds. It is about 700 ft. (213 m) thick in the southern Paradox basin, and thins to the north by facies change with underlying and overlying units owing to the pinching out of the limestone beds that define its upper and lower contacts.

The Church Rock Member is composed of reddish-brown and light-brown siltstone and very fine grained sandstone at its type locality in the Monument Valley area of northeastern Arizona. It formerly was correlated into the Paradox basin to the north, where it was thought to intertongue with the Owl Rock Member (Stewart and others, 1959). However, work by O'Sullivan (1970) indicates that the Church Rock Member of the type locality (which is equivalent to the Rock Point Member of the Wingate Sandstone to the south in Arizona) pinches out to the north along Comb Ridge.

GLEN CANYON GROUP

The Glen Canyon Group consists of two thick eolian formations separated by a fluvial formation. In ascending order these units are the Wingate Sandstone, the Kayenta Formation, and the Navajo Sandstone. In subsurface to the north and northwest of the Paradox basin, the Kayenta pinches out and the Wingate and Navajo merge to form one unit, which is referred to as the Glen Canyon Sandstone of northeastern Utah and the Nugget Sandstone of Wyoming. These relations are illustrated on cross sections of Pipiringos and O'Sullivan (1978). Marine equivalent rocks of the Glen Canyon Group and related strata are not known in the Colorado Plateau province.

The age of the Glen Canyon Group has been in doubt for years. Early workers originally placed the Triassic-Jurassic boundary at the base of the Glen Canyon Group. Later, based on a supposed Triassic dinosaur fauna found in the Kayenta, the boundary was placed in the Navajo Sandstone (Lewis and others, 1961; Galton, 1971). Recently, based on palynomorphs of supposed Early Jurassic age found in the Moenave Formation (an equivalent of part of the Wingate in north-central Arizona) it appears that the Glen Canyon Group may indeed be entirely Early Jurassic in age. Because this new evidence is still being evaluated, previous age assignments are retained by the U.S. Geological Survey. For a more detailed discussion of this problem, see Peterson and Pipiringos (1979, p. B31).

WINGATE SANDSTONE

The Wingate Sandstone is a massive, cliff-forming unit that holds up mesas and plateaus in the western Paradox basin and along the flanks of most of the salt anticlines. It is about 300 ft. (90 m) thick and consists of very pale orange and light brown, well-sorted, very fine- to fine-grained sandstone. Cliff faces commonly are dark red to black because of a veneer of desert varnish. The large-scale trough sets of crossbeds generally dip to the southeast and indicate eolian deposition with the predominant wind from the northwest. Minor horizontal bedding or small-scale crossbedding probably represents reworking of eolian deposits by water. The rather sharp contact with the underlying Chinle Formation has been interpreted as the J-0 unconformity (O'Sullivan and Green, 1973, p. 76; Pipiringos and O'Sullivan, 1978, p. A19).

KAYENTA FORMATION

The Kayenta Formation is generally a broken cliff-forming unit in the lower part and a slope-former in the upper part. It ranges from less than 100 ft. (30 m) to 250 ft. (76 m) in thickness and is composed of red and reddish-purple, very fine- to medium-grained sandstone with subordinate interbeds of red or green mudstone and lacustrine limestone. Crossbedding and lenticularity of individual sandstone units indicate a predominantly fluvial environment, probably the result of braided streams flowing to the west and southwest (Poole, 1961, p. C140). The source area was probably the ancestral Rocky Mountain uplifts in central Colorado. The Kayenta is conformable with both the underlying Wingate and overlying Navajo Sandstones. Intertonguing with the Navajo is common in southwestern Utah.

NAVAJO SANDSTONE

The Navajo Sandstone is known for its thick sets of sweeping large-scale crossbeds of eolian origin. It usually crops out in a wide belt of rounded cliffs and picturesque domes. The Navajo is about 350-450 ft. (107-137 m) thick in the western Paradox basin, but thins to zero by truncation (J-2 unconformity) that took place prior to the overlying Carmel transgression. The Navajo is composed almost entirely of buff to very pale orange, well-rounded, well-sorted, fine-grained and minor medium-grained sandstone. Very sparse thin, blue-gray, cherty, limestone beds thought to represent local playa-lake deposits within the dune complex are locally present. Although the large-scale crossbeds in the sandstone appear to dip in many directions, the foresets dip predominantly to the southeast, indicating northwesterly winds similar to those that prevailed during deposition of the Wingate and upper Paleozoic eolian sandstones (Poole, 1962, p. D149).

The Navajo Sandstone has generally been interpreted as having been deposited by eolian processes in an interior desert environment with a shoreline far beyond the present Colorado Plateau. However, there have been other interpretations. Stanley, Jordan, and Dott (1971, p. 17) suggested that the Navajo Sandstone was deposited as a shallow marine and coastal dune complex, rather than in a vast interior desert environment. Freeman and Visher (1975) suggested that the Navajo was deposited in a tide-dominated shallow marine shelf environment.

SAN RAFAEL GROUP

The San Rafael Group overlies the Navajo and older formations at the J-2 unconformity surface. The group contains units representative of the second and third Mesozoic marine transgressions in the Colorado Plateau. In the western Paradox basin, the group consists of, in ascending order, the Carmel, Entrada, Curtis, and Summerville Formations. The Carmel and Curtis Formations represent deposits of the second and third Mesozoic transgressions, respectively, In most of the other parts of the Paradox basin, the Summerville is mapped as overlying the Entrada, the underlying Curtis Formation having lost its identity owing to facies change. Recent studies, however, suggest revisions or refinements of correlations and nomenclature of the unit mapped as Summerville in much of the Paradox basin (O'Sullivan, 1980a and b). In the San Juan Mountains, Summerville-equivalent rocks are included in the Wanakah Formation.

CARMEL FORMATION

In the northern half of the Paradox basin, the Carmel Formation in this paper is restricted to areas west of the Green River. Rocks east of the Green River that were mapped as Carmel are included in the Dewey Bridge Member of the Entrada Sandstone as proposed by Wright, Shawe, and Lohman (1962, p. 2057). In the northwestern Paradox basin, the Carmel is Bajocian to early Callovian (Middle Jurassic) in age and consists of greenish-gray to red silty shale, gypsum, and thin beds of fossiliferous limestone. It thickens from slightly more than 100 ft. (30 m) near the Green River to about 280 ft. (85 m) on the east flank of the San Rafael Swell. It rests unconformably (J-2) on the Navajo Sandstone just west of the Green River, but in the San Rafael Swell area, an eolian sandstone, the Page Sandstone, separates the Carmel from the Navajo and J-2 unconformity surface. (Peterson and Pipiringos, 1979, p. B20). This sandstone was included in the Navajo prior to the recognition of the chert-pebble (J-2) unconformity at its base. It is about 100 ft. (30 m) thick on the San Rafael Swell, thins to about 15 ft. (4 m) on the east flank, and pinches out at the base of the Carmel a short distance east of there.

The Carmel nomenclature is still retained in outcrops along Comb Ridge southward from about the latitude of Monticello in the southern Paradox basin. There the Carmel ranges in thickness from about 10 to 110 ft. (3-33 m) and consists dominantly of flat-bedded to crossbedded sandstone on the north, grading to siltstone and shale to the south (O'Sullivan, 1980a). In the subsurface to the east, a 10-50 ft. (3-15 m) thick silty interval below the massive Entrada Sandstone can be traced over much of the southern Paradox basin (Molenaar, 1977). In southwesternmost Colorado and northwestern New Mexico, this silty interval has been included in the Entrada Sandstone.

ENTRADA SANDSTONE

The Entrada Sandstone of Callovian (Middle Jurassic) age conformably overlies the Carmel Formation in the western and southern Paradox basin where the Carmel is recognized. East of the Green River in the northern half of the Paradox basin, however, the Entrada was divided into three members by Wright, Shawe, and Lohman (1962, p. 2057), and the basal member overlies the J-2 unconformity surface. In ascending order, these units are the Dewey Bridge, Slick Rock and Moab Members.

The Dewey Bridge Member is largely equivalent to the Carmel Formation and apparently is a more shoreward facies of the Carmel. Lithologically, the Dewey Bridge is similar to the Entrada Sandstone of the type locality on the San Rafael Swell; it is composed of reddish-brown, horizontally bedded, poorly bedded sand siltstone and silty sandstones. It unconformably overlies the Navajo Sandstone on a sharp truncation plane (J-2). Chert pebbles reworked from the Navajo are common at the contact. Locally, as much as 30 ft. (9 m) of relief has been observed on

this surface, such as in the Seven Mile Canyon area 12 mi. (20 km) northwest of Moab (Pipiringos and O'Sullivan, 1975, p. 152). In the eastern Paradox basin, underlying formations are progressively truncated from west to east. The regional strike of the subcrops beneath the J-2 truncation surface is approximately north-south.

The Dewey Bridge Member ranges from less than 20 ft. (6 m) to more than 175 ft. (53 m) and generally weathers to form a slope, but where protected by the overlying massive Slick Rock Member, it weathers into thin rounded ledges separated by recesses. At many places, the beds have been distorted into irregular folds a few feet or more (meter or more) high that fade out laterally and vertically. Dane (1935, p. 97) interpreted the deformation to result from differential loading of the unconsolidated water-saturated sediments by the overlying thick eolian sands of the Entrada.

The Dewey Bridge is considered to have been deposited in a shallow-marine environment marginal to the Carmel seaway.

The Slick Rock Member of the Entrada Sandstone conformably overlies the Dewey Bridge Member over most of the area. Locally, probably due to salt flowage, the basal contact is erosional. The Slick Rock weathers to form slightly rounded cliffs. "Shallow holes" as much as a few feet (1 m) in diameter that weather out along horizontal layers in the massive unit are a characteristic feature of some outcrops. The magnificent arches and fins of Arches National Park are scenic examples of some of the topographic forms developed in this sandstone. In much of the northeastern Paradox basin, the Slick Rock, in combination with the Moab Member where present, is a conspicuous marker bed that is well deserving of its name.

The Slick Rock is composed of light buff to light reddish-brown or salmon, very fine- to fine-grained sandstone with scattered well-rounded, medium to coarse grains. It ranges in thickness from about 100 ft. (30 m) in the southern Paradox basin to about 350 ft. (107 m) in the Moab area. It exhibits large-scale crossbedding intermixed with zones of horizontal bedding and medium-scale crossbedding. The large-scale crossbedding has been interpreted to be of eolian origin, and the horizontal bedding to be of aqueous or shallow-marine origin. However, horizontal bedding has been observed in recent eolian sands by Glennie (1970, p. 11).

Wind patterns during Slick Rock time appear to have had a more erratic pattern than those of older eolian sandstone units. Northeast or east winds were probably dominant (Poole, 1962, p. D149).

West of the Paradox basin, the Slick Rock Member grades into horizontally bedded, silty sandstone that is considered to be of shallow marine origin.

The Moab Member is similar to the underlying Slick Rock Member, except that it is usually lighter in color and appears to lack scattered medium to coarse grains (Wright, Shawe, and Lohman, 1962, p. 2067). It is as much as 110 ft. (34 m) thick in the Moab-La Sal Junction area and thins in all directions from that area.

In the Moab-Arches area, the basal contact of the Moab Member is usually a sharp, horizontal bedding plane, marked in many places by a thin purplish-red shale. This contact may correlate with the basal Curtis J-3 unconformity to the northwest. Locally, probably due to underlying salt flowage, the contact is an angular unconformity, as displayed on the canyon walls west of Kane Springs about 16 mi. (10 km) south of Moab. The Moab Member intertongues with the Summerville Formation (of McKnight, 1940) northwest of Moab, and pinches out within the Summerville farther west toward the Green River (Wright, Shawe, and Lohman, 1962, p. 2060).

The Moab Member is interpreted to be a coastal dune complex marginal to the Curtis seaway.

CURTIS FORMATION

The Curtis Formation of Callovian (Middle Jurassic) age (Craig and Shawe, 1975, p. 160) is a white to light green, glauconitic, marine sandstone that is present in the northwestern part of the Paradox basin. It represents deposition resulting from a marine transgression that extended into the northern Paradox basin from the north and northwest. The Curtis overlies the Entrada Sandstone with a sharp, locally unconformable contact (J-3 unconformity). The Curtis is about 200 ft. (60 m) thick on the east flank of the San Rafael Swell and grades into the lower Summerville of McKnight (1940) a short distance east of the Green River.

SUMMERVILLE FORMATION

The Summerville Formation of Callovian (Middle Jurassic) age conformably overlies the Curtis Formation and is laterally equivalent to it in parts of the Paradox basin where the Curtis is absent. In those areas, the Summerville sharply overlies the Entrada Sandstone and the contact is easily defined by the contrasting deep red color of the Summerville overlying the light-colored Entrada Sandstone. The Summerville is about 25-100 ft. (8-30 m) thick in the central and eastern Paradox basin and thickens to about 200 ft. (60 m) toward the San Rafael Swell. The Summerville, as shown on most geologic maps in the Paradox basin, is composed of red, even-bedded sandy mudstone, very fine grained sandstone, and shale. Ripple marks and mudcracks are common. Scattered large spherical or elongate masses of gray-white to red chert are common in the Moab-La Sal Junction area. The Summerville is interpreted to be a marginal marine, tidal flat deposit, marginal to the Curtis seaway on the northwest.

Recent work by O'Sullivan (1980b) indicates that the upper part of the Summerville is truncated under the J-5 unconformity just east of the Green River northwest of Moab. O'Sullivan (1980a, b) considered the red beds that contain the scattered large chert nodules in the Moab-La Sal Junction area to lie above the J-5 unconformity, and hence to be a basal unit of the Morrison Formation. South of La Sal Junction, O'Sullivan (1980b) considered much of what is mapped as Summerville to be Wanakah Formation, the name applied in the San Juan Mountains to rocks overlying the Entrada Sandstone and underlying the Morrison Formation or Junction Creek Sandstone.

The Wanakah Formation of the San Juan Mountains is subdivided into three members called, in ascending order, the Pony Express, Bilk Creek Sandstone, and an unnamed upper marl member. The Pony Express correlates with the Todilto Limestone of northwestern New Mexico.

BLUFF SANDSTONE MEMBER OF THE MORRISON FORMATION AND JUNCTION CREEK SANDSTONE

The Bluff Sandstone is recognized in southeastern Utah, northeastern Arizona, and northwestern New Mexico. In southeastern Utah, it overlies the Summerville Formation or the Wanakah Formation of O'Sullivan (1980a). The Bluff was originally ranked as a member of the Morrison Formation (Baker and others, 1936, p. 15). Later, Craig and others (1955, p. 133-135) assigned the Bluff as a formation of the San Rafael Group. Recently, O'Sullivan (1980a) removed it from the San Rafael Group, reassigned it to a member of the Morrison and changed its age designation to Late Jurassic.

The Junction Creek Sandstone of southwestern Colorado overlies the Wanakah and is thought to correlate with the Bluff Sandstone.

The Bluff and Junction Creek are composed dominantly of fine- to medium-grained, gray to buff, large-scale, crossbedded eolian sandstone with some horizontally bedded units that are thought to be of aqueous origin (Craig and Cadigan, 1958, p. 184). The eolian crossbed dip directions indicate a dominant west and southwesterly wind, which is a marked change from the earlier north and northwesterly wind, which is a marked change from the earlier north and northwesterly predominating winds (Poole, 1962, p. D149). The Bluff Sandstone Member is up to 338 ft. (103 m) thick at Bluff, Utah, and pinches out at 25 mi. (40 km) north of Bluff.

The Junction Creek Sandstone is well exposed along the Animas Valley north of Durango. It is 266 ft. (81 m) thick in that area and thickens to as much as 424 ft. (129 m) along the Dolores River, 16 mi. (28 km) north of Cortez (R. A. Cadigan, personal communication, 1980).

Subsurface correlations in the southern Paradox basin show that the Bluff and Junction Creek thicken and thin at the expense of beds in the lower part of the Morrison Formation (Molenaar, 1977, figs. 10 and 12).

MORRISON FORMATION

The Morrison Formation of Late Jurassic (Kimmeridgian and Portlandian?) age marks the beginning of deposition of the upper or Nevadan-early Laramide part of the Mesozoic sequence. Fluvial clastics in the lower Morrison indicate a major change in lithology and depositional environment. In most areas, the basal contact of the Morrison is placed at (1) the base of the lowest fluvial channel sandstone, (2) the base of the lowest lacustrine limestone, or (3) at the base of lenticular mudstone, or fine-grained sandstone beds (Craig and Shawe, 1975, p. 162). Based on recognition of the J-5 unconformity, O'Sullivan (1980a) suggested that some of the beds considered to be in the Summerville should be in the Morrison. More work is required in tracing and correlating this unconformity throughout the Paradox basin. Locally, in the southern part of Gypsum Valley in southwestern Colorado, the Morrison rests on leached beds of the Paradox evaporites (Cater, 1970, p. 61).

In the southern Paradox basin, the Morrison has been divided into four members; in ascending order, these are the Salt Wash, Recapture, Westwater Canyon, and Brushy Basin Members. Over most of the Paradox basin, the Salt Wash and Brushy Basin Members comprise the entire Morrison. The Salt Wash and Westwater Canyon Members are ledgy to cliff-forming units and consist dominantly of fluvial sandstone with thinner interbedded flood-plain mudstone. The Recapture Member consists of fluvial sandstones that weather to irregular slopes and flood-plain mudstones. The Brushy Basin Member is a slope-forming unit that consists dominantly of flood-plain mudstones with minor lacustrine limestones and shales. The sandstone beds throughout the Morrison are generally light gray to buff and are fine to medium-grained, crossbedded, irregularly bedded, and lenticular. Chert pebbles are also common. The interbedded mudstones are red and green. Crossbed dip directions in the sandstone beds of the Salt Wash Member, and regional mapping indicate a provenance to the southwest, probably in west-central Arizona and southeastern California. The Recapture and Westwater Canyon Members, on the other hand, were derived from a more southerly provenance in west-central New Mexico (Craig and others, 1955, p. 150 and 156). The Morrison is about 800 ft. (245 m) thick in the southern Paradox basin and thins to the north and east from there.

Important uranium deposits occur in the Salt Wash Member in the Paradox basin, particularly in Colorado. Farther south in the Grants, New Mexico uranium district, the Westwater Canyon Member is a significant uranium producer.

CEDAR MOUNTAIN AND BURRO CANYON FORMATIONS

The Cedar Mountain and Burro Canyon Formations of Early Cretaceous age overlie the Morrison, and form either mesa-capping resistant units or ledgy outcrops above the less resistant Morrison shales. The Cedar Mountain Formation is recognized in areas west of the Colorado River, and the Burro Canyon Formation in areas to the east. Many of the mesas in the eastern and southern Paradox basin are capped by the Burro Canyon. The formation is missing owing to late Tertiary to Holocene erosion in most of the western Paradox basin. The formation is 50-200 ft. (15-60 m) thick and generally consists of two or more conglomeratic sandstone beds 10-40 ft. (3-12 m) thick separated by light green mudstone. Irregular, dense, pink to gray limestone nodules are locally present in the mudstone.

The Cedar Mountain and Burro Canyon Formations are dominantly of fluvial and flood-plain origin. According to L. C. Craig (see article. — this Guidebook), the Cedar Mountain and Burro Canyon Formations were deposited from two separate fluvial systems. The Cedar Mountain was derived from areas to the west of the Paradox basin, and the Burro Canyon was derived from a provenance south and southwest of the Paradox basin.

DAKOTA SANDSTONE

The Dakota Sandstone, of Late Cretaceous age in the Paradox basin, is a coastal-plain deposit laid down in front of the advancing Mancos sea. The Dakota consists of conglomeratic channel sandstone, dark-gray carbonaceous shale, coal, and, in places, a marine sandstone at the top. The Dakota does not generally contain mineable coal; however, one strip mine near Nucla provides the coal for a nearby power plant. There also are coal prospects in the Cortez area. The Dakota is as much as 200 ft. (60 m) thick regionally, but in the northwesternmost Paradox basin it is unusually thin, ranging from zero to 20 ft. (6 m) in thickness. It is preserved on the mesas and in the synclines in the eastern and southern Paradox basin, and has been removed by erosion in the western Paradox.

The Dakota is generally thought to disconformably overlie the Cedar Mountain or Burro Canyon Formation in the Paradox basin. Young (1960), however, stated that the Dakota intertongues with the Cedar Mountain and suggested that the Dakota be raised to group status consisting of the Cedar Mountain and the overlying Naturita Formation. To the south and southwest of the Paradox basin, the Dakota truncates progressively older formations, and in the southernmost part of the Colorado Plateau, the Dakota overlies Permian beds.

MANCOS SHALE

The Mancos Shale, a thick marine shale of Late Cretaceous age, conformably overlies the Dakota Sandstone. The Mancos was deposited in the Paradox basin area at the same time it and equivalent rocks were deposited throughout the Western Interior of the United States. The Mancos has been largely removed by erosion throughout a large part of the Paradox basin, but is partially preserved in some of the larger synclines and collapse structures in the

northeastern Paradox. The Mancos is completely preserved under the Book Cliffs in the northern Paradox basin and in the Mesa Verde area southeast of Cortez in southwestern Colorado.

The Mancos Shale is a uniform, dark gray mudstone, shale and siltstone that weathers to a drab light gray, and contains numerous zones of limestone concretions. Thin, very fine-grained sandstone interbeds are minor, except near the top where the Mancos grades into the overlying littoral sands of the Mesaverde Group. The Mancos weathers to form valleys and slopes, and bedrock outcrops support only sparse vegetation. It is about 3,500 ft. (1070 m) thick in the Book Cliffs area north of Crescent Junction, and about 2,000 ft. (610 m) thick in southwestern Colorado.

In the northern part of the Paradox basin, the Mancos includes a conspicuous marker bed recognized as the Ferron Sandstone Member of the Mancos Shale. This member is about 400 ft. (122 m) above the base of the Mancos, and forms the small cuesta that extends nearly continuously from the Grand Junction area of Colorado to the area northwest of Woodside, Utah.

This conspicuous unit contains an upper thin one- or two-foot (0.5-m) -thick, cuesta forming, sandy calcarenite bed composed of fossil fragments, and a lower unit 50-100 ft. (15-30 m) thick, consisting of fissile black shale with some calcareous siltstone interbeds. Lithologically, the unit resembles and contains a fauna (Katich, 1956) similar to the Juana Lopez Member of the Mancos Shale in the San Juan Basin. The conspicuous marker bed is undoubtedly continuous with the Juana Lopez. Molenaar (1975, p. 191) believed that it is genetically unrelated to the type Ferron Sandstone Member farther west in Utah.

MESAVERDE GROUP AND BUCK TONGUE OF THE MANCOS SHALE

The Mesaverde Group of Late Cretaceous age is partially preserved in only a few areas in the Paradox basin. However, it is fully preserved in the Book Cliffs area in the northern Paradox basin and in the Mesa Verde National Park area southeast of Cortez. The Mesaverde gradationally overlies the Mancos Shale and consists of a regressive wedge of time-transgressive shoreface sandstones, coastal or delta-plain paludal carbonaceous shale and coal with variably distributed channel sandstones, and alluvial or upper delta-plain noncarbonaceous shales and channel sandstones.

At Mesa Verde, which is the type locality of the Mesaverde, the group is divided into three formations: a lower regressive coastal barrier sandstone — the Point Lookout Sandstone; a middle thick nonmarine and paludal shale, sandstone and coal-bearing unit — the Menefee Formation; and a thick transgressive coastal barrier sandstone complex — the Cliff House Sandstone. Total thickness of the Mesaverde Group in the type locality is about 900 ft. (274 m). From the Mesa Verde area, the group thins to the northeast and thickens to the southwest.

The lower part of the Mesaverde of the Book Cliffs area north of the Paradox basin is younger than the Mesaverde of the type locality. North of the Green River-Crescent Junction area, the Mesaverde Group and the Buck Tongue of the Mancos Shale are about 2,300 ft. (700 m) thick, and, in ascending order, consists of the following units: Castlegate Sandstone, Buck Tongue of the Mancos Shale, Sego Sandstone, and Neslen, Farrer, and Tuscher Formations (Fisher and others, 1960). The Castlegate Sandstone is a regressive shoreface sandstone complex about 100 ft. (30 m) thick in the area north of Crescent Junction, and pinches out into the Mancos Shale near the Colorado-Utah border. West of the Green River, it grades into a 200-400 ft. (61-122 m) thick channel sand complex that is recognized over wide areas. The Buck Tongue is a transgressive tongue of the Mancos Shale that overlies the Castlegate and pinches out to the west near the Green River. It is about 175 ft. (53 m) thick north or Crescent Junction, and weathers to form a broad bench above the Castlegate Sandstone. The Sego Sandstone is the regressive shoreface sandstone complex above the Buck Tongue and ranges from 50 to 200 ft. (15-61 m) in thickness. Overlying the Sego is the Neslen Formation, which represents the nonmarine, paludal, coastal plain deposits behind the shoreface barrier. It is as much as 500 ft. (152 m) thick and contains much carbonaceous shale and some coal, which has been mined. The overlying Farrer Formation is about 600 ft. (180 m) thick and represents upper delta plain deposits of shale, siltstone and sandstone deposited landward from the coastal swamps. The contact with the Neslen Formation is gradational and is usually placed at the change from carbonaceous shale below to noncarbonaceous shale above. The Tuscher Formation is about 450 ft. (135 m) thick and is an alluvial-plain facies consisting dominantly of sandstone with minor amounts of shale and conglomerate.

The Mesaverde Group in the Book Cliffs is unconformably overlain by the Wasatch Formation of Tertiary (probably Paleocene-Eocene) age. A conglomerate is locally present at the contact. The degree of truncation is slight and is discernible in the outcrops, but is probably greater to the south toward the Laramide-age Monument Uplift. However, the entire Cretaceous section exposed in the Book Cliffs and Mesa Verde areas appears likely to have been present over the entire Paradox basin prior to the early Tertiary truncation.

CONCLUDING REMARKS

Approximately 8,000-10,000 ft. (2400-3000 m) of Mesozoic strata covered the Paradox basin area prior to latest Cretaceous-Tertiary erosion. Almost all are siliciclastic rocks that were deposited in diverse environments including inland desert, alluvial plain, coastal dune, marginal embayment, and shallow marine. Some of the envisioned environments have no modern analogs. Rock colors range from bright red to pastels to drab gray or buff.

The wide variety of conditions under which these rocks were deposited, and the excellent exposures make the Paradox basin and surrounding areas a natural laboratory. Where else can an individual 10 ft. (3 m) bed be traced 50 mi. (80 km) or more? Many studies have been made of these rocks, and indeed, many more will be made. There are still finer details of stratigraphy that are being unraveled. Many studies are economically oriented, such as those dealing with uranium or oil and gas exploration. Other studies may seem more academic, but data gathered here could apply to a variety of problems in other areas.

Beyond the economic needs, just the understanding of these rock sequences, the various processes, and the time involved in their deposition and subsequent erosion, provide another dimension to the appreciation of this magnificent and fascinating area.

REFERENCES CITED

Baker, A. A., Dane, C. H., and Reeside, J. B., Jr., 1936, Correlation of the Jurassic formations of parts of Utah, Arizona, New Mexico and Colorado: U.S. Geological Survey Professional Paper 183, 66 p.

Blakey, R. C., 1974, Stratigraphic and depositional analysis of the Moenkopi Formation, southeastern Utah: Utah Geological and Mineral Survey Bulletin 104, 81 p.

Cater, F. W., 1970, Geology of the salt anticline region in southwestern Colorado, with a section on Stratigraphy, by F. W. Cater and L. C. Craig: U.S. Geological Survey Professional Paper 637, 80 p.

Craig, L. C., and Cadigan, R. A., 1958, The Morrison and adjacent formations in the Four Corners area, in Intermountain Association of Petroleum Geologists Guidebook, 9th Annual Field Conference, Geology of the Paradox basin, p. 182-192.

Craig, L. C., Holmes, C. N., Cadigan, R. A., Freeman, V. L., Mullens, T. E., and Weir, G. W., 1955, Stratigraphy of the Morrison and related formations, Colorado Plateau region, a preliminary report: U.S. Geological Survey Bulletin 1009-E, p. 125-168.

Craig, L. C., and Shawe, D. R., 1975, Jurassic rocks of east-central Utah, in Four Corners Geological Society Guidebook, 8th Field Conference, Canyonlands Country, p. 157-165.

Dane, C. H., 1935, Geology of the Salt Valley anticline and adjacent areas, Grand County, Utah: U.S. Geological Survey Bulletin 863, 184 p.

Fisher, J. D., Erdmann, C. E., and Reeside, J. B., Jr., 1960, Cretaceous and Tertiary formations of the Book Cliffs, Carbon, Emery and Grand Counties, Utah, and Garfield and Mesa Counties, Colorado: U.S. Geological Survey Professional Paper 332, 80 p.

Freeman, W. E., and Visher, G. S., 1975, Stratigraphic analysis of the Navajo Sandstone: Journal of Sedimentary Petrology, v. 45, no. 3, p. 651-668.

Galton, P. M., 1971, The prosauropod dinosaur Ammosaurus, the crocodile Protosuchus, and their bearing on the age of the Navajo Sandstone of northeastern Arizona: Journal of Paleontology, v. 45, no. 5, p. 781-795.

Glennie, K. W., 1970, Desert sedimentary environments: New York, Amsterdam, Elsevier Publishing Co., Inc., 222 p.

Katich, P. J., 1956, Some notes on the Cretaceous faunas of eastern Utah and western Colorado, in Intermountain Association of Petroleum Geologists Guidebook, 7th Annual Conference, east-central Utah, p. 116-119.

Lewis, G. E., Irwin, J. H., and Wilson, R. F., 1961, Age of the Glen Canyon Group (Triassic and Jurassic) on the Colorado Plateau: Geological Society of America Bulletin, v. 70, no. 9, p. 1437-1440.

McKee, E. D., and others, 1956, Paleotectonic maps of the Jurassic System: U.S. Geological Survey Miscellaneous Geological Investigations Map I-175.

_____ and others, 1959, Paleotectonic maps of the Triassic System, U.S. Geological Survey Miscellaneous Geological Investigations Map I-300.

McKnight, E. T., 1940, Geology of area between Green and Colorado Rivers, Grand and San Juan Counties, Utah: U.S. Geological Survey Bulletin 908, 147 p.

Molenaar, C. M., 1975, Some notes on Upper Cretaceous stratigraphy of the Paradox basin, in Four Corners Geological Society Guidebook, 8th Field Conference, Canyonlands Country, p. 191-192.

_____ 1977, Mesozoic subsurface correlations in the Paradox Basin, figs. 10 and 12, in Irwin, C. D., ed.,

Subsurface cross sections of Colorado: Rocky Mountain Association of Geologists Special Publication No. 2, 39, p., 24 figs.

O'Sullivan, R. B., 1970, The upper part of the Upper Triassic Chinle Formation and related rocks, southeastern Utah and adjacent areas: U.S. Geological Survey Professional Paper 644-E, 22 p.

_____ 1980a, Stratigraphic sections of Middle Jurassic San Rafael Group from Wilson Arch to Bluff in southeastern Utah: U.S. Geological Survey Oil and Gas Investigations Chart OC-102.

_____ 1980b, Stratigraphic sections of Middle Jurassic San Rafael Group and related rocks from the Green River to the Moab area in east-central Utah: U.S. Geological Survey Miscellaneous Field Studies Map MF-1247.

O'Sullivan, R. B., and Craig, L. C., 1973, Jurassic Rocks of northeastern Arizona and adjacent areas, in New Mexico Geological Society Guidebook, 24th Field Conference, Monument Valley, p. 79-85.

O'Sullivan, R. B., and Green, M. W., 1973, Triassic rocks of northeast Arizona and adjacent areas, in New Mexico Geological Society Guidebook, 24th Field Conference, Monument Valley, p. 72-78.

O'Sullivan, R. B., and MacLachlan, M. E., 1975, Triassic rocks of the Moab-White Canyon area, southeastern Utah, in Four Corners Geological Society Guidebook, 8th Field Conference, Canyonlands Country, p. 129-141.

Peterson, Fred, and Pipiringos, G. N., 1979, Stratigraphic relations of the Navajo Sandstone to Middle Jurassic formations, southern Utah and northern Arizona: U.S. Geological Survey Professional Paper 1035-B, 43 p.

Pipiringos, G. N., and O'Sullivan, R. B., 1975, Chert pebble unconformity at the top of the Navajo Sandstone in southeastern Utah, in Four Corners Geological Socity Guidebook, 8th Field Conference, Canyonlands Country, p. 149-156.

_____ 1978, Principal unconformities in Triassic and Jurassic rocks, Western Interior United States — A preliminary survey: U.S. Geological Survey Professional Paper 1035-A, 29 p.

Poole, F. G., 1961, Stream directions in Triassic rocks of the Colorado Plateau: U.S. Geological Survey Professional Paper 424-C, p. C139-C141.

_____ 1962, Wind directions in late Paleozoic to middle Mesozoic time on the Colorado Plateau: U.S. Geological Survey Professional Paper 450-D, p. D147-D151.

Shoemaker, E. M., and Newman, W. L., 1959, Moenkopi Formation (Triassic? and Triassic) in salt anticline region, Colorado and Utah: American Association of Petroleum Geologists Bulletin, v. 43, no. 8, p. 1835-1851.

Stanley, K. O., Jordan, W. M., and Dott, R. H., Jr., 1971, Early Jurassic paleography and sediment dispersal for western United States: American Association of Petroleum Geologists Bulletin, v. 55, no. 1, p. 10-19.

Stewart, J. H., Williams, G. A., Albee, H. F., and Raup, O. B., 1959, Stratigraphy of Triassic and associated formations in part of the Colorado Plateau region: U.S. Geological Survey Bulletin 1046-Q, p. 487, 576.

Stewart, J. H., Poole, F. G., and Wilson, R. F., 1972a, Stratigraphy and origin of the Chinle Formation and related Upper Triassic strata in the Colorado Plateau region, with a section on sedimentary petrology, by R. A. Cadigan, and a section on conglomerate studies, by W.

Thorardson, H. F. Albee, and J. H. Stewart: U.S. Geological Survey Professional Paper 690, 336 p.

_____ 1972 b, Stratigraphy and origin of the Triassic Moenkopi Formation and related strata in the Colorado Plateau region, with a section on sedimentary petrology, by R. A. Cadigan: U.S. Geological Survey Professional Paper 691, 195 p.

Trimble, L. M., and Doelling, H. H., 1978, Geology and uranium-vanadium deposits of the San Rafael River mining area, Emery County, Utah: Utah Geological and Mineralogical Survey Bulletin 113, 122 p.

Wright, J. C., Shawe, D. R., and Lohman, S. W., 1962, Definition of members of Jurassic Entrada Sandstone in east-central Utah and west-central Colorado: American Association of Petroleum Geologists Bulletin, v. 46, no. 11, p. 2057-2070.

Wright, J. C., and Dickey, D. D., 1963, Block diagram of the San Rafael Group and underlying strata in Utah and part of Colorado and summary of depositional and erosional history: U.S. Geological Survey Oil and Gas Investigations Chart OC-63, 5 p.

Young, R. G., 1960, Dakota Group of Colorado Plateau: American Association of Petroleum Geologists Bulletin, v. 44, no. 2, p. 156-194.

Mitten Butte - Monument Valley (Photo by Jack Rathbone)

QUATERNARY DEPOSITS IN THE PARADOX BASIN

Norma E. Biggar, Deborah R. Harden and Mary L. Gillam
Woodward-Clyde Consultants
3 Embarcadero Center
San Francisco, CA 94111

ABSTRACT

Quaternary deposits of the Paradox Basin in southeastern Utah record several interruptions of the long-term denudation that has produced the striking erosional landforms of the area. Preliminary correlation of these scattered materials is based on the relative development of calcic soils and limited radiocarbon and paleomagnetic age control. Remnants of an early Quaternary or late Pliocene erosion surface on plateaus flanking the Green River are capped by pedogenic calcrete and underlain by deposits that display reversed magnetic polarity. The lower Harpole Mesa Formation in the La Sal Mountains and older alluvial fans flanking the Abajo Mountains display similarly well developed soils and reversed polarity, suggesting that they are of at least early Pleistocene age.

During the subsequent incision of tributary drainages, a series of gravel-capped terraces formed along streams draining the Abajo and la Sal Mountains, probably in response to major climatic oscillations. The degree of calcic soil development on the terraces suggests that they formed during middle and late Pleistocene time. A widespread hydrologic change following the last major deglaciation is indicated by the contrast between gravelly late Pleistocene terrace deposits and fine-grained Holocene terrace deposits or fills. During Holocene time, several cycles of widespread filling and erosion of fine-grained fill have occurred.

Calculated long-term incision rates for various sections of thColorado Plateau, generally ranging from 0.03 to 1 m (0.1 to 3 feet) per 1000 years, suggest that 0.25 m (0.8 feet) per 1000 years is a realistic maximum long term erosion rate for large parts of the Colorado Plateau. Data derived from this study indicate a long-term incision rate for the Green River of 0.17 m to 0.57 m (0.5 to 1.8 feet) per 1000 years.

Deformation of Quaternary deposits has been observed at several locations in the Paradox Basin. In the vicinity of the salt anticlines, Pliocene(?) and early Pleistocene fanglomerates are tilted, and alluvium of late Pleistocene age is apparently warped and perhaps locally faulted, suggesting either remobilization of the salt anticlines or dissolution of salt in the near subsurface. The significance of the anomalous local distribution of Quaternary alluvial fill adjacent to the Moab fault is presently unresolved. Subterranean alluvial deposits, emplaced along faults bounding blocks in the Grabens area near the Colorado River, are indicative of the local extensional gravity sliding that is occurring along the western limb of the Monument Upwarp.

INTRODUCTION

The Paradox Basin, located within the Colorado Plateau physiographic province, is characterized by broad upland plateaus and deeply incised canyons. Nearly horizontal sedimentary bedrock has been deformed locally by faulting, folding, and igneous intrusion. Elevations range from about 1100 m (3600 feet) along the Colorado River to more than 3590 m (13,000 feet) in the La Sal Mountains. Average annual precipitation varies from 200 mm (8 inches) in lowland areas to approximately 500 mm (20 inches) in the mountains.

Quaternary deposits and soils of the Paradox Basin in southeastern Utah are being examined to assess paleoclimatic fluctuations, tectonic stability, and rates of channel incision. Local mapping of Quaternary deposits and age dating studies presently in progress will augment existing formation on the Quaternary history of this area.

QUATERNARY DEPOSITS

Quaternary deposits of the study area reflect several environments of deposition (Figures 1 and 2). Glacial, periglacial, and landslide deposits occur in the La Sal Mountains, and periglacial deposits are present in the Abajo Mountains. Both of these domed, laccolithic ranges are flanked by extensive alluvial fans or pediments formed on radially dipping sedimentary bedrock. These upland surfaces have been incised as much as 450 m (1500 feet) by the modern drainage network. Discontinuous, gravel-capped terraces occur at several elevations along the modern channels. The lowest terraces, 10 m (30 feet) or less above the present channels, are underlain by fine-grained fill deposits. Windblown sand and silt are widespread, both as loess sheets up to 6 m (20 feet) thick on upland surfaces and as active or stabilized dunes. Talus occurs at the base of most cliffs and on hillslopes throughout the area.

Quaternary deposits in southeastern Utah are difficult to correlate and date because they are widely scattered, change facies, and contain few datable materials. Most of the preliminary correlations discussed here are based on comparative soil morphology, with limited support from radiocarbon and paleomagnetic analyses.

Because the B horizons of many soils have been removed by erosion, the morphology of carbonate-bearing horizons (Gile and others, 1966 (Gile and others, 1966; Bachman and Machette, 1977; Machette, 1978) has been used in comparing soil development. Many workers (Gardner, 1972; Lattman, 1973; Gile, 1975; Machette and others, 1976) have demonstrated that, in areas of noncalcareous bedrock, windblown dust is the principle source of pedongenic carbonate. Thus, the carbonate content of a soil reflects primarily its duration at the ground surface when the rate of carbonate influx, extent of leaching, and degree of soil erosion are relatively constant. Bachman and Machette (1977) defined the sequential stages of carbonate morphology cited in this report. These stage descriptions were further refined by Shroba (1977).

Quaternary deposits in six phsyiographic subdivisions of the Paradox Basin are discussed in the following sections.

BOOK CLIFFS AREA

The Book Cliffs extend across the northwest corner of the Paradox Basin (Figure 2). Erosional remnants of formerly

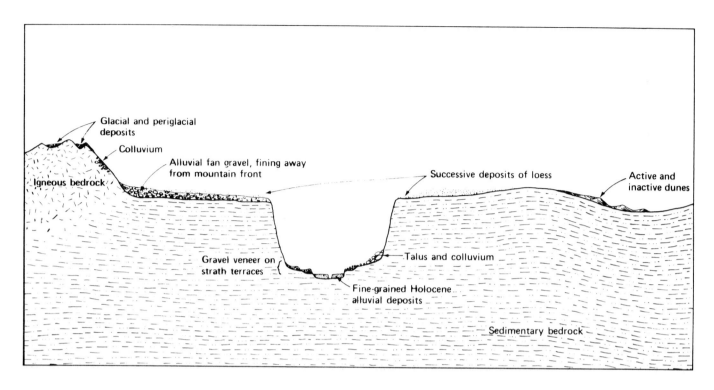

Figure 1.   Types of Quaternary deposits observed in the Paradox Basin.

extensive gravel aprons gently slope south and west from the base of the cliffs. Locally, as much as 40 m (130 feet) of gravel mantles the pediments, which are cut on the Mancos Shale (Carter, 1977). These features were originally described by Rich (1935) and Fisher (1936), who recognized three or more distinct pediment benches 15 to 60 m (50 to 200 feet) above the valley south of the cliffs. Fisher (1936) believed that the gravel benches "were formed very late in the present geomorphic cycle". However, calcareous soils have developed in the gravel at some localities, implying that the deposits are partly pre-Holocene in age. Recent studies suggest that the multiple pediment levels resulted from successive stream captures, and not from alternating episodes of pediment cutting and alluviation related to tectonic, base-level, or climatic stimuli (Carter, 1977; Godfrey, 1969).

GREEN RIVER AREA

Quaternary deposits in this area (Figure 2) include active dunes in the San Rafael Desert, mid-Pleistocene and younger alluvial gravels preserved on terraces along the Green and San Rafael rivers, and early Pleistocene or Pliocene(?) alluvial and eolian deposits locally preserved in upland areas. The alluvial deposits include both main channel (cobble gravel) and tributary (pebbly sand) facies, and fall into two major age ranges, as suggested by their topographic position and soil development.

The younger alluvial deposits form nested terraces within major river valleys. Along the Green River between the town of Green River and Tenmile Canyon, gravel-capped terraces occur at several levels up to 100 m (350 feet) above the present channel. In addition, gravelly terrace remnants occur in cutoff meanders northwest of the confluence of the Green and San Rafael rivers, at a height of approximately 135 m (450 feet) above the present channel. The soil on the latter deposits represents the maximum observed stage of development for soils on the younger terraces. This soil

displays up to 1 m (3 feet) of continuous carbonate (stage III) and is probably mid-Pleistocene in age.

Remnants of older alluvium and eolian deposits occur on the irregular plateau surface (Figure 3), into which the drainages have incised. West of the Green River, deposits 240 to 400 m (800 to 1300 feet) above the present channel consist of well-rounded cobbles or pebbly sand. Baker (1946) concluded that these deposits accumulated on Tertiary(?) and Quaternary pediments that sloped eastward from the San Rafael Reef (at the western edge of the San Rafael Desert, Figure 2). However, some of the gravels exposed near Horseshoe Canyon, 5 km (3 miles) west of the present Green River, are former channel deposits, as indicated by their coarse texture and by clasts exhibiting lithologies common to the Uinta Mountains in northeastern Utah.

East of the Green River, pebbly alluvium has been observed in the vicinity of Dubinky Wells, about 400 m (1300 feet) above the present river channel. Its texture suggests deposition by tributary streams during pedimentation.

A well developed pedogenic calcrete caps all of the older alluvium and eolian deposits east and west of the Green River. In a typical exposure just northwest of Horseshoe Canyon, approximately 400 m (1300 feet) above the present river channel, the soil has developed on 10 m (30 feet) of sand and pebbly sand (Figure 4) having reversed paleomagnetic polarity. A dense petrocalcic horizon displaying tabular structure, incipient brecciation, and an upper laminar zone (stage V) has engulfed the top 2.3 m (7.5 feet) of the deposit. Less continuous carbonate occurs to a depth of 4 m (13 feet). Similarly well developed soils have been observed at other localities west of the Green River, including on a terrace only 240 m (800 feet) above the present channel. This suggests that the carbonate in all of the older deposits accumulated after the 240 m (800 foot) terrace had been cut, or that soils of different ages have attained a steady-state carbonate morphology so that they superficially appear similar in age.

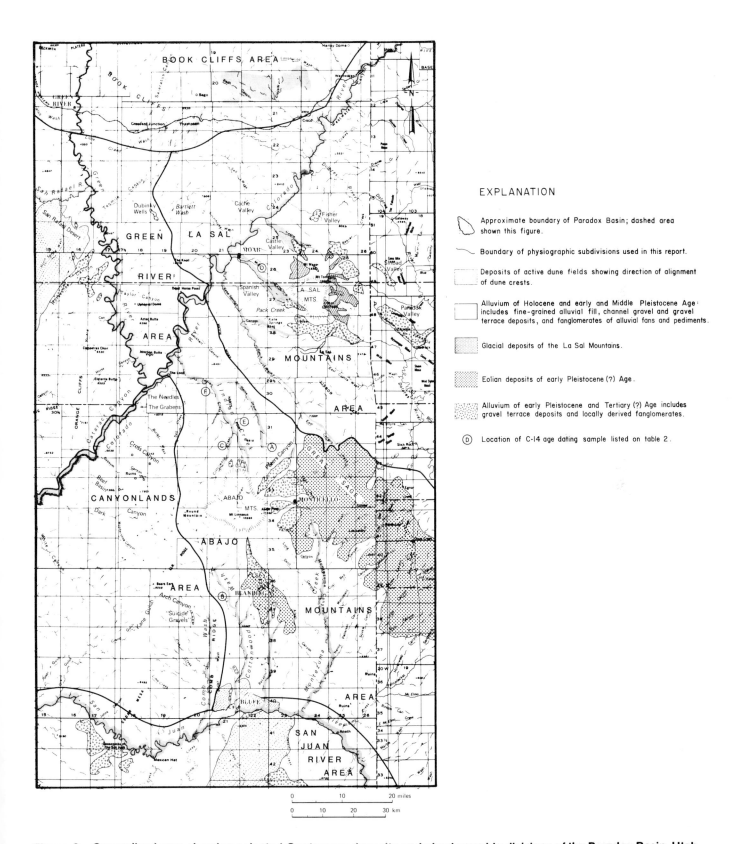

Figure 2. Generalized map showing selected Quaternary deposits and physiographic divisions of the Paradox Basin, Utah.

Figure 3.   Terrace and slope wash deposits on The Spur, near Horseshoe Canyon.

Figure 4.   Pedogenic calcrete developed on fine-grained alluvium west of Horseshoe Canyon.

CANYONLANDS AREA

The Canyonlands area extends southward from the Colorado River to the San Juan River (Figure 2). Because all of the drainages in this area originate within the sedimentary bedrock sequence, Quaternary deposits consist predominantly of fine-grained eolian and fluvial materials. Loess blankets the upland surfaces, and at least three periods of carbonate accumulation have been observed in 6-m (20-foot) thick exposures of loess on Cedar Mesa. Both active and stabilized dunes occur throughout the area on the eastern end of north-trending ridges, indicating prevailing winds from the southwest (Lewis and Campbell, 1965). Quaternary deposits up to 20 m (60 feet) thick along drainages and in the Grabens area generally consist of fine-grained, well-sorted sediments and may represent reworked eolian material that had initially collected in canyons. Closer examination of some of these deposits may reveal a complex Quaternary history of multiple fills containing debris flows and bedded alluvial deposits, such as observed by Nieuwenhuis (1975) in Gypsum Canyon.

Holocene extensional displacement on the Grabens is indicated by open holes (called "swallow holes") along the surficial projections of faults bounding the graben structures, and by unusual subsurface colluvial deposits. In Cataract Canyon of the Colorado River, alluvium-filled fractures coincide with graben-bounding faults exposed in bedrock (Figure 5). The partially cemented fracture filling contains angular blocks in a fine-grained matrix, and was probably emplaced by subsurface drainage of water and alluvium through the swallow holes. In two exposures, the colluvium is approximately 6 to 30 m (20 to 100 feet) high, 0.5 to 3 m (1 to 10 feet) thick, and fills fissures of unknown length. The thickness of the colluvium varies, indicating that spalling of the wall rock occurred while the fissure was filling with alluvium. The large volume of colluvium suggests that its emplacement followed horizontal separation of the fault blocks forming the graben structures; the swallow holes observed on the ground surface in the Grabens area indicate that this process is continuing at the present time. The separation and downward transfer of aluvium have occurred at least as deep as the present river level, or approximately 250 m (800 feet) below the plateau level in the Grabens area.

Another Quaternary(?) deposit, of interest because of its present unusual setting, occurs south of Arch Canyon, west of Blanding (Figure 2). A linear ridge underlain by cobbles and boulders up to 1 m (3 feet) in diameter rests on the Cedar

Figure 5.   Cemented colluvium filling bounding fault of a graben structure along the Colorado River.

Figure 6. Linear ridge consisting of stream channel deposits, south of Arch Canyon.

Figure 7. Fine-grained fill deposits in tributary to Comb Wash.

Mesa Sandstone, 300 m (1000 feet) above the floor of Arch Canyon (Figure 6). This gravel deposit, informally called the Suicide Gravels, is approximately 2.5 km (1.5 miles) long and contains clasts of local sedimentary lithologies. It apparently represents a former channel deposit preserved by topographic inversion. The gravel has not been dated, but its deposition preceded formation of the present drainage network and the cutting of Arch Canyon. The only other gravel deposit observed to date on the Cedar Mesa surface consists of well-round cobbles exposed in a roadcut on State Highway 261, 2 km (1.25 miles) north of Kane Gulch (Figure 2). This gravel also consists of local sedimentary lithologies.

Salkin (1975) described the lithology, molluscan fauna, and climatic implications of Holocene fill in upper Kane Gulch. The exposed fill contains two depositional units: a lower unit 4.1 m (14 feet) thick, consisting of laminated clay, silt and sand, unconformably overlain by a sand and gravel unit that is 1.3 m (4 feet) thick. A radiocarbon date of 7385 + 80 years B.P. was obtained from charcoal 1 m (3 feet) above the base of the exposure. Salkin divided the deposit into eight lithologic and molluscan zones indicating variable temperatures and precipitation, with concurrent changes in vegetation. Molluscs found in the coarser overlying unit are indicative of climatic conditions now typical of elevations 300 m (1000 feet) lower than Kane Gulch, and suggest a warmer environment than the present.

Remnants of bedded, fine-grained deposits up to 15 m (50 feet) thick are preserved in tributary canyons along the western margin of Comb Wash (Figure 7, south of Highway 95 (Figure 2). The surface of the deposits dips 3 to 5 degrees east and may grade to one of the terrace surfaces, 12 to 24 m (40 to 80 feet) above the present channel of the wash. The deposits are moderately cemented and gypsiferous in the upper meter (3 feet). Fossil snails collected here will be examined to date the deposit and investigate its depositional environment.

LA SAL MOUNTAINS AREA (OVERVIEW)

Quaternary deposits are found on the flanks of the La Sal Mountains, on strath terraces along the Colorado River, and in many stream valleys. Deposits of Quaternary and possibly Pliocene age also occur in valleys developed along the crests of salt anticlines north, east, and southeast of the La Sal Mountains (Figure 2).

A large portion of the area south of the Colorado River was studied in detail by Richmond (1962), who correlated

moraines, outwash terraces, landslides, and eolian deposits with multiple glaciations of the La Sal Mountains. On the basis of relative topographic position, lithology and texture of deposits, and degree of soil development, Richmond grouped the deposits into the Gold Basin, Beaver Basin, Placer Creek, and Harpole Mesa formations, each of which was subdivided into members and correlated with a recognized glacial cycle in the Rocky Mountain region (Table I). Richmond realized that many of the surfaces in the area are underlain by complex deposits and soils of different ages and origins. Recent work in the La Sal Mountains by Shroder and others (1980) suggests that glacial deposits are much less extensive than those mapped by Richmond and that deposition by mass movement has been widespread.

Deposits of possibly Pliocene and early Quaternary age have been used to assess the stability of the northwest-trending salt anticlines. Differential tilting of fanglomerate in Castle Valley (Hunt, 1956; Richmond, 1962), Geyser Creek (Carter and Gualtieri, 1965) and Paradox, Gypsum[1], and Sinbad valleys (Cater, 1970) is thought to reflect dissolution or migration of salt in the underlying Paradox Formation.

Volcanic ash deposits have been reported at two localities in the area of the salt anticlines. The fanglomerate in Paradox Valley is overlain unconformably by alluvium containing the early Pleistocene (0.7 million-year-old) Bishop ash (Cater, 1970), suggesting that the fanglomerate is of early

Figure 8. Pleistocene deposits in Fisher Valley.

[1]Gypsum Valley is east of Paradox Valley.

Pleistocene or Pliocene age. Two volcanic ash layers occur in alluvial deposits of the Harpole Mesa Formation in Fisher Valley (Richmond, 1962; Figure 8). These layers have been identified as the Bishop ash and the 0.6 million-year-old Pearlette "O" ash (Cater, 1970). Both layers occur in anomalously thick valley fill deposited along the axis of the underlying salt anticline.

Previously unmapped alluvial fill rests unconformably on the Summerville and Entrada formations in Barlett Wash, directly west of the Moab fault, northwest of Moab (Figure 2). The alluvium consists of at least 15 m (50 feet) of well-consolidated, alternating sandy and clayey material (Figure 9). Layers of finely bedded calcium carbonate of uncertain origin are present near the top of the section. The discovery of a mammoth(?) tusk in this area suggests that the deposits may be pre-Holocene in age, but no further age determinations have been made. The relationship between the deposits and the adjacent Moab fault is unknown.

Figure 10.   Quaternary surfaces in Upper Spanish Valley.

Figure 9.   Fine-grained fill in Bartlett Wash.

Figure 11.   Gravel-capped erosion surface on Johnson's Up-On-Top, older Harpole Mesa Formation.

SPANISH VALLEY STUDIES

Spanish Valley is a northwest-trending, structurally controlled trough on the northwest flank of the La Sal Mountains (Figure 2). Alluvium of the Harpole Mesa Formation of early to middle Pleistocene age (Richmond, 1962) occurs on the northeastern rim of the valley (Figures 10 and 11), and also underlies a southward-dipping pediment along the southern end of the valley. These relationships suggest that the valley was cut after deposition of the Harpole Mesa Formation. Late Pleistocene and Holocene alluvium covers the valley floor and forms nested terraces along Pack Creek and Mill Creek, the largest streams entering the valley.

The distribution of alluvial deposits in Spanish Valley is complex and suggests the possible concurrent influence of hydrologic factors, warping, and faulting. Large-scale landsliding has also affected some of the deposits south of the valley. Hydrologic factors are reflected in the downstream convergence of nested terrace remnants in Pack Creek Canyon in the southeastern (upper) end of Spanish Valley (Figure 10). In this part of the valley, the lower and upper Beaver Basin alluviums and the Gold Basin alluvium converge, and then form superimposed fills in the middle part of the valley.

Some factor other than hydrologic influence may be needed to explain the spatial relationship in Spanish Valley of terraces and paleosols associated with the Placer Creek

Formation. Richmond (1962) inferred the presence of the Placer Creek terrace surface beneath present stream level, between widely spaced, exposed terrace remnants that are tens of meters above present stream level. Exposures created since Richmond's (1962) study indicate that subsurface stratigraphic relations may support this inferred complexity, and reflect local warping as well as channel cut-and-fill. At the lower end of Spanish Valley, where it is traversed by the Colorado river, Holocene subsidence may be indicated by the marshes present along the river. Subsidence could be caused either by tectonism or by dissolution or migration of salt at depth.

It is not known whether Quaternary faulting has further complicated the subsurface stratigraphic relations. Huff and Lesure (1958) and Williams (1964) mapped concealed bedrock faults along the terrace risers. No direct evidence of these faults was observed during this study; however, an unusual saddle crossing the northernmost remnant of the lower Placer Creek terrace may reflect fault displacement of that surface. Several displacements of about 10 cm were observed south of Moab in deposits mapped as Placer Creek fan deposits by Richmond (1962).

Quaternary deposits and soils in the upper Spanish Valley area were examined in detail to establish a soil chronosequence. Because the deposits have been approximately dated by correlation with the Rocky Mountain glacial sequence (Richmond, 1962), rates of soil development in Spanish Valley may be used to estimate the age of soils in other parts of the Paradox Basin, particularly in the Abajo Mountains area where parent material lithology and texture are similar.

To avoid the stratigraphic and possible structural complexities mentioned previously, the soil studies were performed where successive alluvial deposits underlie vertically distinct terrace remnants. To date, soil development and rock weathering have been studied at seven test pits and one natural exposure (Figure 12). Laboratory analysis of soils and age-dating samples, geomorphic analysis of the Spanish Valley area, and correlation with Colorado River terraces are continuing.

Alluvium of the Gold Basin Formation forms low fill terraces along Pack Creek and its tributaries in upper Spanish Valley. In addition, Gold Basin deposits overlie older alluvium at other locations. The deposits are easily distinguished from older alluvium by their finer grain size; sand and silt dominate, although gravel lenses are locally present. The alluvium typically contains several weak buried A horizons overlying fresh parent material. Occasionally, minor disseminated carbonate (weak stage I) has accumulated in a thin Cca horizon. A radiocarbon date of 1280 + 55 years B.P. was obtained from charcoal found in Gold Basin deposits near the Moab Golf Course (Table II).

The older alluvial deposits consist of poorly sorted, crudely stratified, sandy cobble gravel containing a few boulders. Clasts derived from porphyritic intrusive rocks of the La Sal Mountains dominate; however, sedimentary lithologies are also common. Eolian silt and sand deposits, contining 5 to 10 percent lag gravel, overlie the Pleistocene alluvium at all the sites examined. The eolian deposits typically display a relict soil with weak cambic and calcareous horizons (stage I) and probably correlate with the Gold Basin or Beaver Basin Formation. However, older eolian deposits containing argillic and calcic horizons (stage II) overlie the older Harpole Mesa Formation.

The older alluvial deposits consist of poorly sorted, crudely stratified, sandy cobble containing a few boulders. Clasts derived from porphyritic intrusive rocks of the La Sal Mountains dominate; however, sedimentary lithologies are also common. Eolian silt and sand deposits, containing 5 to 10 percent lag gravel, overlie the Pleistocene alluvium at all the sites examined. The eolian deposits typically display a relict soil with weak cambic and calcareous horizons (stage I) and probably correlate with the Gold Basin or Beaver Basin Formation. However, older eolian deposits containing argillic and calcic horizons (stage II) overlie the older Harpole Mesa Formation.

The Cca soil horizons developed on the Beaver Basin Formation (Figure 12, sites 1 and 2) display continuous thin carbonate coats on clast tops and bottoms, and nodules and filamentous carbonate are common (stage II). Present studies support Richmond's (1962) observation that the soils in the younger and older members of the Beaver Basin Formation are not distinguishable. Calcareous soil development at these sites is roughly equivalent to that seen on Pinedale-aged deposits in similar geographic settings in the Rocky Mountain region (Birkeland, 1980, personal communication).

Deposits of the Placer Creek Formation (Figure 12, sites 3, 4 and 5) are readily separable from those of the Beaver Basin Formation on the basis of soil carbonate buildup. The calcic horizons of soils developed on Placer Creek deposits display continuous carbonate (stage III, and at one locality (Figure 12, site 5) laminar carbonate overlies a cemented horizon containing more than 50 percent carbonate (stage IV). The variability in carbonate development on the two older Placer Creek deposits (sites 4 and 5) may be partly caused by more rapid carbonate accumulation or reduced leaching at site 5 because of its lower elevation. Nevertheless, the stage of carbonate buildup at site 5 appears to be anomalously high for a Placer Creek deposit. In general, calcic soil development is equivalent to that seen on Bull Lake deposits of the Rocky Mountain region (Birkeland, 1980, personal communication).

Calcic soils observed on the middle Harpole Mesa Formation at Amasas Back (Figures 10 and 13; Figure 12, sites 6 and 7) display roughly the same thickness and stage of carbonate development as soils on Placer Creek deposits at sites 3 and 4). Laminar carbonate, present in the post-Placer Creek soil at site 5, was not observed at sites 6 and 7. Differences in elevation and local climate do not appear great enough to account for the similarity of soils on the two formations. At site 7, a buried clayey stratum 4 m (12.5 feet) thick may be an older argillic horizon, which would suggest that Amasas Back is underlain by multi-aged deposits. Complex deposition or local erosion is implied by the absence of this clayey layer at site 6. Subtle topographic features resembling landslide headscarps on the southwestern end of Amasas Back suggest that mass movement may have disrupted the deposits and complicated local patterns of erosion and deposition.

The soil observed on older Harpole Mesa alluvium at Johnsons-Up-On-Top (Figures 11, 12, and 14, site 8) displays a far greater degree of carbonate buildup than that on middle Harpole Mesa deposits. The presence of 1.5 m (5 feet) of indurated pedogenic calcrete displaying strong platey structure and laminar carbonate (stage IV to V) suggests that the deposits may be as old as early Pleistocene. This age estimate is supported by preliminary data indicating that the deposit has reversed paleomagnetic polarity.

Several factors may be responsible for the complexities in this sequence of calcareous soils. Differences in microclimate at the Placer Creek and Harpole Mesa sites may have resulted in different rates of carbonate accumulation. A single terrace or pediment surface may also have developed on deposits of different ages and origins. For example, in the middle part of Spanish Valley, where gravel pits are numerous, a complex pattern of buried soils and deposits can be observed beneath a planar depositional surface. Despite the observed complexities, the sequence of calcareous soils at the Spanish Valley sites provides a useful general framework for correlation of Quaternary deposits within the Paradox Basin and better dated sequences in the western United States.

Measurements of oxidation rinds developed on igneous cobbles collected from subsurface soil horizons exposed in the backhoe test pits revealed no consistent trends with increasing age of the deposit. Variability in lithology, spalling of the outer surfaces of clasts, and deceleration of weathering due to carbonate accumulation on the clasts are probably responsible for the lack of progressive oxidation rind development. Additionally, the variable truncation of overlying soil horizons on successive terraces makes it difficult to compare the weathering histories of buried clasts. No grusified clasts were observed on deposits of the Beaver Basin Formation, whereas older deposits generally contain 10 to 30 percent grusified clasts. No consistent increase in grusification was detected between Placer Creek and Harpole Mesa deposits.

ABAJO MOUNTAINS AREA

The Abajo Mountains area includes all drainages

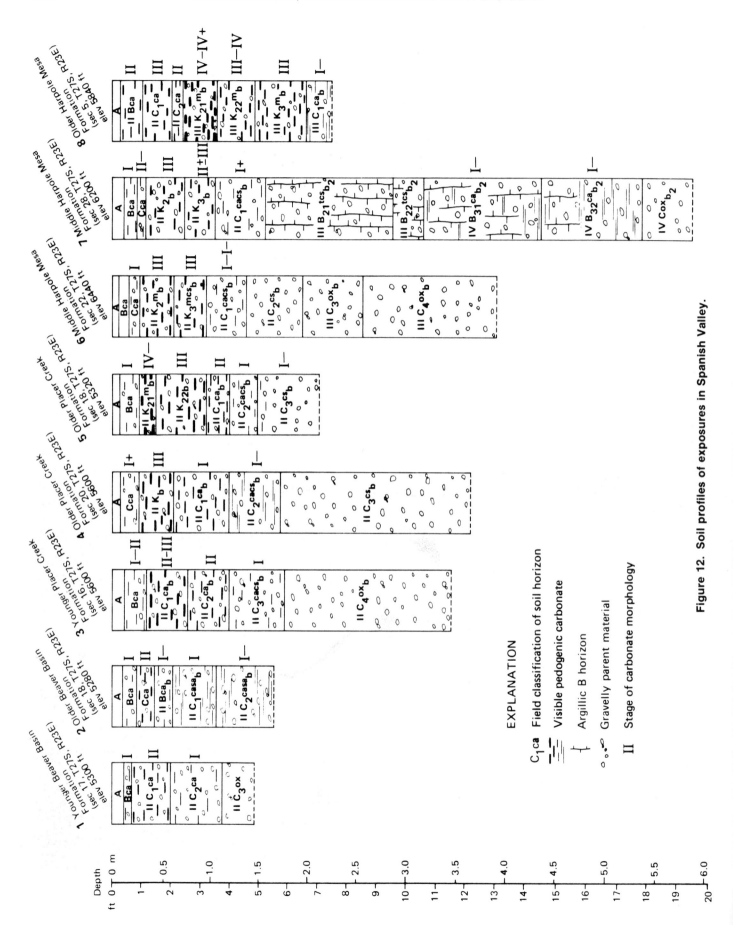

Figure 12.   Soil profiles of exposures in Spanish Valley.

Figure 13. Calcic soil developed on middle Harpole Mesa Formation at Site 7.

Figure 14. Pegogenic calcrete developed on older Harpole Mesa Formation at Site 8.

originating in the Abajo Mountains, their tributaries, and surrounding upland surfaces such as the Great Sage Plain east of Monticello (Figure 2). Quaternary deposits in this

area include periglacial rockslides and boulder fields in the Abajo Mountains (Witkind, 1964), alluvial fans flanking the north, east, and south slopes of the mountains, gravel-capped strath terraces in incised drainages, fine-grained sand and silt forming the lowest fill terraces, loess blanketing the upland, and recent eolian deposits throughout the area.

Older fan deposits flanking the Abajo Mountains (Figure 15) appear to predate stream incision in this part of the Colorado Plateau. On the north side of the mountains, coarse gravel fans appear to be displaced by the south fault of the Shay Graben (Kitcho, this volume). Deposits exposed in gravel quarries northeast of Blanding consist of poorly sorted gravel with intercalated sand lenses. The pebble and cobble gravel consists predominantly of igneous lithologies derived from the Abajo Mountains and is moderately to highly weathered; however, sedimentary clasts are also present. Locally, flat, angular clasts of indurated, white, marl-like material (altered volcanic tuff?) are common. Samples from the sand lenses have reversed paleomagnetic polarity, indicating that the deposit formed at least 700,000 years ago, and may be as old as 2.3 million years (the duration of the Matuyama reversed epoch). This age is supported by the development of as many as two buried calcic soils within the gravel unit. One of these calcic soils

Figure 15. Alluvial fans flanking the Abajo Mountains.

Figure 16. Multiple calcareous soils developed on loess deposits south of Blanding.

commonly displays stage IV carbonate morphology in gravel pits in the vicinity of Blanding and Monticello. A weaker calcareous soil (stage I) is common in the overlying loess deposits.

Hunt (1956) observed deeply weathered pre-Wisconsinan fluvial and loess deposits several feet thick south and east of the Abajo Mountains. Excellent exposures of similar materials were observed at a construction site 10 km (6 miles) south of Blanding, where the presence of multiple calcic soils (Figure 16) suggests that the lowermost deposits are definitely of pre-Wisconsinan age.

Gravel-capped terraces are numerous along streams draining the Abajo Mountains (Figure 2). These include Indian Creek (Figure 17), Harts Draw, Peters Canyon, and East Canyon Wash, which flow north from the mountains, and Cottonwood Wash (Figure 18), Montezuma Creek, and Recapture Creek, which flow south. In order to assess the relative age of terraces along these streams, several soil test pits were excavated along Indian Creek in gravel-capped strath terraces ranging from 8 to 32 m (26 to 105 feet) above present stream level. Similar studies are planned for terraces along Cottonwood Wash.

The test pits along Indian Creek exposed up to 2.3 m (7.5 feet) of sandy cobble gravel (Figure 19) composed predominantly of porphyritic igneous rock from the Abajo Mountains. Eolian deposits capping the gravel are thickest on terraces more than 12 m (40 feet) above the creek. As at

Figure 17. Gravel terrace along Indian Creek.

Figure 18. Terraces along Cottonwood Creek.

Spanish Valley, many of the soils are compound, including a younger relict profile developed on the eolian deposits and an older truncated and buried profile developed on the gravel. At sites 1, 6, 7, and 8 (Figure 19) it appears that weak argillic horizons, initially developed in the gravel, were not completely eroded and later acquired carbonate associated with the younger soil profile. At sites 2, 3, and 4, however, no B horizon is preserved in the gravels. The thick argillic horizon at site 5 suggests the development of a single relict soil that is possibly equivalent to both the buried and relict soils observed at the other test pits.

Soil morphology and grusification of clasts suggest that the lowest four terraces, 8 to 20 m (26 to 66 feet) above the present stream channel, are very close in age. Soils on these terraces display stage II carbonate morphology and clasts are not grusified. In contrast, the soil on the highest terrace, 32 m (105 feet) above present stream level, displays weak stage III carbonate morphology (Figure 20). Clasts on this terrace are slightly grusified.

Comparison of carbonate morphologies suggests that the lowest four terraces may correlate with the Beaver Basin Formation in Spanish Valley, and that the highest terrace may correlate with the upper Placer Creek Formation. However, the presence of the buried weak argillic horizons in several of the test pits implies that some of the terraces may be slightly older than suggested by carbonate alone. An older age for the 12 m (40 ft.) and higher terraces is also supported by the well developed argillic horizon observed at site 5. Laboratory data will be obtained to improve correlations between the two areas.

The thickness of oxidation rinds on igneous cobbles collected from the B or Cca soil horizons was also measured at the soil test pits along Indian Creek. Despite a general increase in rind thickness with terrace height above present stream level, the relative ages of the terraces could not be consistently defined using this technique. This difficulty may reflect the roughly equivalent ages of the deposits, as well as spalling from the clast surfaces.

Fine-grained Holocene deposits throughout the Abajo Mountains area reflect multiple episodes of channel incision and filling. The maximum thickness of fill exposed by historic gullying is 20 m (60 feet) in Cottonwood Creek (Figure 21). Recent radiocarbon dates on charcoal (Table II) and the large number of fill deposits indicate the rapidity and cyclic nature of Holocene climatic events.

SAN JUAN RIVER AREA

The San Juan River flows westward from the San Juan Mountains to the Colorado River along the southern edge of the Paradox Basin (Figure 2). Quaternary deposits of the upper San Juan River and its tributaries have been examined by Atwood and Mather (1932), Richmond (1965b), Bandoian (1968), O'Sullivan and others (1979a), and Weide and others (1979). The Animas River Valley in Colorado and New Mexico has been particularly well studied because it offers the opportunity to correlate moraines of the San Juan Mountains with numerous outwash terraces preserved in the downstream part of the valley. At least seven terraces, up to 475 m (1,550 feet) above present stream level, have been cut into the Mancos Formation along the San Juan River near Farmington, New Mexico, just below the confluence of the Animas and San Juan rivers.

Several gravel terraces are present where the San Juan River flows along the southern margin of the Paradox Basin near Bluff (Figure 22). Remnants are preserved at elevations up to 170 m (550 feet) above the present river channel. Cooley and others (1969) identified several of the terrace levels south of the river as middle and late Pleistocene. Well

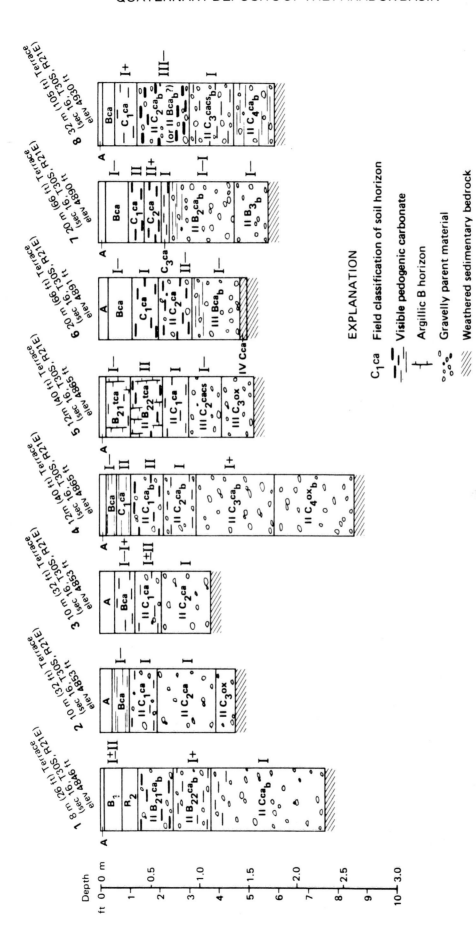

Figure 19. Soil profiles of soil test pits in Indian Creek terraces.

Figure 20. Calcic soil developed on 32 meter terrace along Indian Creek (Site 8).

Figure 21. Alluvial fill exposed in Cottonwood Creek.

Figure 22. Multiple terraces along the north side of the San Juan River.

developed calcic soils on high terrace remnants north of Bluff suggest that those deposits may be at least middle Pleistocene in age. Cooley and others also mapped remnants of an early Pleistocene erosional surface, 400 m (1300 feet) above present stream level, in the area south of Bluff and the Goosenecks of the San Juan River (Figure 2).

EROSION RATES

In response to uplift that began in mid-Tertiary time, erosion has dominated the late Tertiary and Quaternary history of the Colorado Plateau. The ancestral southwestward-flowing Colorado River had probably been established by the end of Miocene time, and during the Pliocene most major features of the present drainage system formed (Hunt, 1956). A moderately rapid long-term rate of erosion is indicated by various features of the Colorado Plateau: the great thickness (1,100 to perhaps 4,000 m, or 3,500 to perhaps 13,000 feet) of eroded Tertiary and Cretaceous rocks, meager late Tertiary and Quaternary deposits, high relief and deep, vertical-walled canyons, and the absence of significant desert varnish on many cliff faces or of talus below cliffs at several locations. This erosion was facilitated by the relatively low strength of the Tertiary and Cretaceous bedrock being eroded (Schumm and Chorley, 1966).

Long-term erosion rates for 27 areas of the Colorado Plateau were calculated from geomorphic relations discussed principally by Hunt (1969), and also by Cooley and others (1962), Hamblin and others (1975), Stokes (1964), and Lucchitta (1972). These rates, for the time period from 100,000 to 10,000,000 years ago, range from 0.03 to 1 m (0.1 to 3 feet) per 1,000 years. Approximately 65 percent of the values are less than or equal to 0.15 m (0.5 feet) per 1,000 years, and 95 percent are less than or equal to 0.25 m (0.8 feet) per 1,000 years.

Average channel incision rates may be calculated for paleomagnetically reversed fan deposits near the Green River canyon. Assuming a minimum age of 700,000 years for the deposits, the maximum long-term incision rate is 0.57 m (1.8 feet) per 1,000 years. For a maximum age of 2.3 million years, the minimum long-term incision rate is 0.17 m (0.5 feet) per 1,000 years.

Historic denudation rates based on sediment yield or reservoir sedimentation data (Brown, 1945; Hunt and others, 1953; King and Mace, 1953; Hunt, 1956; Corbel, 1959; Wolman and Miller, 1960) fall within the same range, as do very long-term erosion rates based on regional denudation since the mid-Tertiary. These erosion rates vary from low (for mountainous areas) to high (for lowland areas) in comparison with average historical erosion rates in many areas of the world (Corbel, 1959).

During late Tertiary and Quaternary time, short-term erosion rates varied considerably, as shown by pediments and terraces reflecting temporary periods of base-level stability. Part of the variation in computed erosion rates discussed above probably reflects the different time intervals used in the calculations, as well as variations in lithology, uplift rate, basin area, and runoff.

LANDFORM EVOLUTION IN THE PARADOX BASIN

Because of the paucity of datable materials, it is difficult to correlate the scattered Quaternary deposits within the Paradox Basin, or to correlate these deposits with better established stratigraphic sequences elsewhere in the West. Preliminary correlations based on relative soil development, together with limited radiocarbon and paleomagnetic age control, are shown in Table I.

Remnants of a formerly extensive Miocene erosion surface are present in northern Arizona (Cooley and others, 1969). A similar, early Quaternary or late Pliocene erosion surface is partially preserved on uplands flanking the Green River; paleomagnetic data suggest that it may correlate with a second surface in northern Arizona (described by Cooley an others, 1969), with the surface developed on the older Harpole Mesa Formation in the La Sal Mountains, and with some of the older alluvial fans flanking the Abajo Mountains. Only the major rivers were apparently incised at this time. Later, the larger tributaries cut their present canyons, and a series of gravel-capped terraces formed along streams draining the Abajo and La Sal mountains. It is likely that periods of downcutting and terrace formation were climatically controlled (Cooley and others, 1969). Deposition probably occurred during early or middle glacial stages along streams heading in glaciated or periglacial regions, and during late glacial or early interglacial stages along tributaries heading in arid, unglaciated regions (Schumm, 1977).

A major change in the hydrologic regime of tributaries in the area is indicated by the contrast between Pleistocene gravel deposits and fine-grained Holocene fill deposits (Figure 23). Dating control is not yet adequate to establish the synchroneity of this change throughout the area. Since deposition of the Holocene fills, little or no bedrock incision has occurred. However, abundant evidence for repeated accumulation and flushing of fine-grained sediment exists here and throughout the southwest (Haynes, 1968). Comparison of Holocene and modern channel deposits of tributary streams in the area suggest that the present streams are transporting somewhat coarser sediments than those seen in the typical Holocene section.

In the absence of sufficient "absolute" dates, soil development provides the best relative means for local and long-distance correlation of Quaternary deposits. However, this method is subject to several complications in the Paradox Basin, in addition to the standard restrictions on variability of soil parent material, climate, vegetation, and topography (Birkeland, 1974). Partial erosion of many buried and relict soils has removed their original B horizons, forcing stronger reliance on the characteristics of Cca or K horizons, which may also have been eroded to an unknown extent. Whereas the morphology of younger calcareous soils usually changes progressively with age, data from the upper Spanish Valley and Green River areas indicate that the trend

is less consistent in early Wisconsinan and pre-Wisconsinan soils; in soils of early Pleistocene age, carbonate morphology may reach a steady state and cease to alter perceptibly with increasing soil age.

Further work to improve correlations between varied deposits in the La Sal and Abajo mountains, terraces along the San Juan and Colorado rivers, and moraines in the San Juan Mountains will aid in developing the Quaternary history of the Paradox Basin. "Absolute" ages must also be established for definite correlations between these and other areas. Several dating methods are being tested: carbon-14 dating, paleomagnetic analysis, uranium isotope and thermoluminescence dating of soil carbonate, amino acid racemization in soils, and extent of clay and carbonate accumulation in soils (as determined by laboratory analysis).

ACKNOWLEDGEMENTS

This report presents the results to date of the Quaternary studies element of an overall geologic evaluation of the Paradox Basin in Utah. The investigation is being conducted by Woodward-Clyde Consultants (WCC) for the Office of Nuclear Wast Isolation (ONWI), Battelle Memorial Institute, Columbus, Ohio, under the direction of Fred Conwell, WCC's project manager. In addition to the authors, other personnel from Woodward-Clyde Consultants participated in the Quaternary studies. Kathryn Hanson, Roy McKinney, and Robert Harpster helped with mapping and soil descriptions. Richard Ely originally identified some of the deposits and erosion surfaces and critically reviewed the manuscript.

The carbon-14 analyses were done by Irene Stehli at the Dicarb Radioisotope Company; Irene provided many helpful suggestions for the collection of suitable carbon samples, and comments on the quality of the analyses. The paleomagnetic analyses were made by the Woodward-Clyde facility in Oakland, California, under the direction of Duane Packer. Jeff Johnson assisted in collecting samples for paleomagnetic dating. Peter W. Birkeland of the University of Colorado reviewed the interpretation of soil test pits in the Spanish Valley area. N. A. Frazier and S. Kowall (ONWI) and F. H. Swan III (WCC) reviewed the manuscript, and critiqued the field studies and overall objectives of the study.

REFERENCES

Atwood, W. W., and Mather, K. F., 1932, Physiography and Quaternary geology of the San Juan Mountains, Colorado: U.S. Geological Survey Professional Paper 166, 176 p.

Bachman, G. O., and Machette, M. N., 1977, Calcic soils and calcretes in the southwestern United States: U.S. Geological Survey Open-File Report 77-794, 163 p.

Baker, A. A., 1946, Geology of the Green River desert — Cataract Canyon region, Utah: U.S. Geological Survey Bulletin 951, 122 p.

Bandoian, C. A., 1968, Fluvioglacial features of the Animas River Valley, Colorado and New Mexico: New Mexico Geological Society, 19th Field Conference Guidebook, p. 28-32.

Birkeland, P. W., 1974, Pedology, Weathering, and Geomorphological Research: Oxford University Press, New York, 285 p.

Bloom, A. L., 1978, Geomorphology: Prentice-Hall, Inc., Englewood Cliffs, New Jersey, p. 407-408, 419.

Bowen, D. Q., 1978, Quaternary Geology: Oxford Pergamon Press, 211 p.

Figure 23. Fine-grained Gold Basin deposits overlying gravel of the Beaver Basin Formation in channel of Pack Creek.

TABLE I. CORRELATION OF QUATERNARY DEPOSITS IN THE PARADOX BASIN AND ADJACENT AREAS

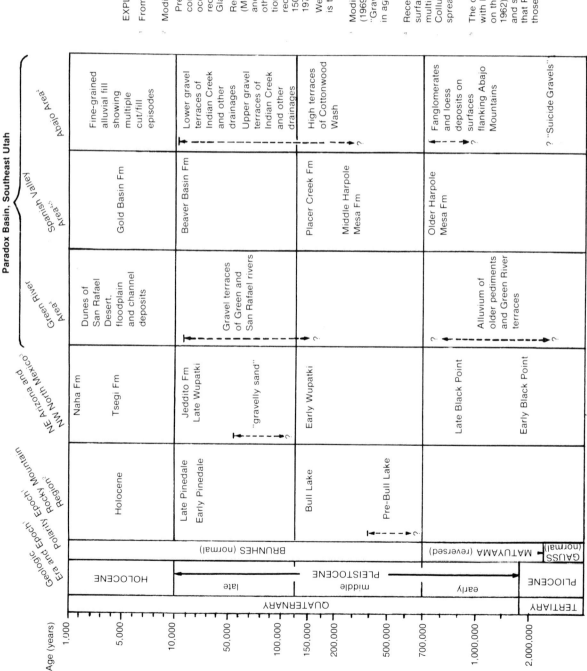

EXPLANATION

[1] From Bloom (1978) and Bowen (1978)

[2] Modified from Meierding and Birkeland (1980)

Previous workers (Richmond, 1965a, for example) considered the Bull Lake Glaciation to have occurred after about 100,000 years B.P. More recently (Richmond, 1970), the early Bull Lake Glaciation was placed before 100,000 years B.P.

Recent evidence provided by relative dating data (Meierding, 1977; Madole and Shroba, 1979) and by obsidian hydration dating (Pierce and others, 1976) suggests that the Bull Lake Glaciation correlates with a worldwide climatic event recorded in deep-sea cores about 130,000 to 150,000 years B.P. (Shackleton and Opdyke, 1973).

We are aware that the chronology shown here is the subject of ongoing debate.

[3] Modified from Hack (1942), Cooley and others (1969) and O'Sullivan and others (1979). "Gravelly sand" is thought to be "pre-Pinedale" in age (O'Sullivan and others, 1979).

[4] Recent and older eolian deposits blanket most surfaces in the Paradox Basin. At several localities, multiple episodes of deposition have occurred. Colluvial deposits of varying ages are also widespread on slopes of the area.

[5] The correlation of the La Sal Mountain deposits with Rocky Mountain glacial deposits was made on the basis of the earlier chronology (Richmond, 1962). Based on observations of rock weathering and soil development in Spanish Valley, it appears that Placer Creek deposits significantly predate those of the Beaver Basin Formation.

TABLE II.

RADIOCARBON DATES OBTAINED FROM QUATERNARY DEPOSITS IN THE PARADOX BASIN

Location*, Lab No.	C-14 Date (yr. B.P.)	Comments
A. Sec. 7, T32S, R23E (DIC-1548)	5160 + 55	Harts Draw, near base of 5 m (15 ft) exposure
B. Sec. 3, T37S, R21E (DIC-1550)	3070 + 325	Cottonwood Wash, near base of 9 m (27 ft) exposure
(DIC-1549)	1750 + 60	Charcoal collected 4 m (13 ft) from top of same 9 m (27 ft) exposure
C. Sec. 10, T32S, R21E (DIC-1493)	1600 + 100	Cottonwood Creek, at base of 20 m (60 ft) fill terrace
(DIC-1547)	1270 + 100	Near top of same 20 m (60 ft) fill terrace
(DIC-1495)	720 + 550	Indicator age only; extremely small sample taken from base of 12-m (38-ft) thick, cut and fill structure in same 20 m (60 ft) terrace. The date is not considered as reliable.
D. Sec. 22, T26S, R22E (DIC-1544)	1280 + 55	From Gold Basin Formation in Spanish Valley, near Moab Golf Course
E. Sec. 11, T31S, R21E (DIC-1893)	430 + 110	Charcoal layer buried by 0.5 m (1.5 ft) of loess on top of 45-m (150-ft) terrace
F. Sec. 8, T30S, R21E (DIC-1546)	"Modern"	Indian Creek, burn layer near ground surface

*Locations are shown on Figure 2.

Brown, C. B., 1945, Rates of sediment production in southwestern United States: U.S. Soil Conservation Service Technical Publication 58, 40 p.

Carter, T. E., 1977, Pediment development along the Book Cliffs, Utah and Colorado (abstract): Geological Society of America, Abstracts with Programs, v. 9, no. 6, p. 714.

Carter, W. D., and Gualtieri, J. L., 1965, Geyser Creek fanglomerate (Tertiary), La Sal Mountains, eastern Utah: U.S. Geological Survey Bulletin 1224-E, p. E1-E11.

Cater, F. W., 1970, Geology of the Salt Anticline region in southwestern Colorado: U.S. Geological Survey Professional Paper 637, 80 p.

Cooley, M. E., Harshbarger, J. W., Aikers, J. P., and Hardt, W. F., 1969, Regional hydrogeology of the Navajo and Hopi Indian Reservations, Arizona, New Mexico, and Utah: U.S. Indian Reservations, Arizona, New Mexico, and Utah: U.S. Geological Survey Professional Paper 521-A, 61 p.

Corbel, J., 1959, Vitesse de l'erosion: Zeitschrift fur Geomorphologie, v. 3, p. 1-28.

Fisher, D. L., 1936, The Book Cliffs coal field in Emery and Grand counties, Utah: U.S. Geological Survey Bulletin 852, 104 p.

Gardner, L. R., 1972, Origin of the Mormon Mesa claiche: Geological Society of America Bulletin, v. 83, p. 143-156.

Gile, L. H., 1975, Holocene soils and soil-geomorphic relations in an arid region of southern New Mexico: Quaternary Research, v. 5, no. 3, p. 321-360.

Gile, L. H., Peterson, F. F., and Grossman, R. B., 1966, Morphological and genetic sequences of carbonate accumulation in desert soils: Soil Science, v. 101, no. 5, p. 347-360.

Godfrey, G. A., 1969, Geologic history and processes of fan and pediment development in the northern Henry Mountains Piedmont, Utah: unpublished Ph.D. thesis, John Hopkins University, 98 p.

Hack, J. T., 1942, The changing environment of the Hopi Indians of Arizona: Harvard University, Peabody Museum of American Archaeology and Ethnology, Papers, v. 35, no. 1, 85 p.

Hamblin, W. K., Damon, P. E., and Shafiqullah, M., 1975, Rates of erosion in the Virgin River drainage basin in southern Utah and northern Arizona (abstract): Geological Society of American, Abstracts with Programs, v. 7, no. 7, p. 1097-1098.

Haynes, C. V., Jr., 1968, Geochronology of the late Quaternary alluvium, in Morrison, R. B. and Wright, H. E., Jr., eds., Means of Correlation of Quaternary Successions: INQUA VII Congress, Proceedings, v. 8, p. 591-631, Utah Press, Salt Lake City University.

Huff, L. C., and Lesure, F. G., 1958, Preliminary geologic map of the Verdure 3 SE quadrangle San Juan County, Utah: U.S. Geological Survey Mineral Investigation Field Studies Map, MF-167.

Hunt, C. B., 1956, Cenozoic geology of the Colorado Plateau: U.S. Geological Survey Professional Paper 279, 99 p.

Hunt, C. B., 1969, Geologic history of the Colorado River: U.S. Geological Survey Professional Paper 669-C, p. 59-130.

Hunt, C. B., Avirett, P., and Miller, R. L., 1953, Geology and geography of the Henry Mountains region, Utah: U.S. Geological Survey Professional paper 228, 234 p.

King, N. J., and Mace, M. M., 1953, Sedimentation in small

reservoirs on the San Rafael Swell, Utah: U.S. Geological Survey Circular 256, 21 p.

Lattman, L. H., 1973, Calcium carbonate cementation of alluvial fans in southern Nevada: Geological Society of America Bulletin, v. 84, p. 3013-3028.

Lewis, R. Q., and Campbell, R. H., 1965, Geology and uranium deposits of Elk Ridge and vicinity, San Juan County, Utah: U.S. Geological Survey Professional Paper 474-B, p. B1-B69.

Lucchitta, I., 1972, Early history of the Colorado River in the Basin and Range province: Geological Society of America Bulletin, v. 83, p. 1933-1948.

Machette, M. N., 1978, Dating Quaternary faults in the southwestern United States by using buried calcic paleosols: U.S. Geological Survey Journal of Research, v. 6, no. 3, p. 369-381.

Machette, M. N., Birkeland, P. W., Markos, G., and Guccione, M. J., 1976, Soil development in Quaternary deposits in the Golden-Boulder portion of the Colorado Piedmont, in Epis, R. C., and Weimer, R. J., eds.: Studies in Colorado Field Geology, Colorado School of Mines Professional Contributions, no. 8, p. 339-357.

Madole, R. F., and Shroba, R. R., 1979, Till sequence and soil development in the north St. Vrain drainage basin, east slope, Front Range, Colorado, in Ethridge, F. G., ed., Field guide, northern Front Range and northwest Denver basin, Colorado: Rocky Mountain Section, Geological Society of America, p. 123-178.

Meierding, T. C., 1977, Age differentiation of till and gravel deposits in the upper Colorado River basin: unpublished Ph.D. thesis, University of Colorado, 235 p.

Meierding, T. C., and Birkeland, P. W., 1980, Quaternary glaciation of Colorado, in Kent, H. C., and Porter, K. W., eds., Colorado Geology: Rocky Mountain Association of Geologists, 1980 Symposium, p. 165-173.

Nieuwenhuis, C., 1975, Alluvial history of Gypsum Canyon, Utah: unpublished M.S. thesis, University of California, Berkeley, 38 p.

O'Sullivan, R. B., Scott, G. R., and Heller, J. S., 1979a, Preliminary geologic map of the Hogback south quadrangle, San Juan County, New Mexico: U.S. Geological Survey Miscellaneous Field Studies Map MF-1093.

O'Sullivan, R. B., Scott, G. R., and Weide, D. L., 1979b, Preliminary geologic map of the Kin Klizhin Ruin quadrangle, San Juan and McKinley counties, New Mexico: U.S. Geological Survey Miscellaneous Field Studies Map, MF-1094.

Pierce, K. L., Obradovich, J. D., and Friedman, I., 1976, Obsidian hydration dating and correlations of Bull Lake and Pinedale glaciations near West Yellowstone, Montana: Geological Society of America Bulletin, v. 87, no. 703-710.

Rich, J. L., 1935, Origin and evolution of rock fans and pediments: Geological Society of America Bulletin, v. 316, p. 302-320.

Richmond, G. M., 1962, Quaternary stratigraphy of the La Sal Mountains, Utah: U.S. Geological Survey Professional Paper 324, 135 p.

Richmond, G. M., 1965a, Glaciation of the Rocky Mountains, in Wright, H. E., Jr., and Frey, D. G., eds., The Quaternary of the United States: Princeton University Press, Princeton, New Jersey, p. 217-230.

Richmond, G. M., 1965b, Quaternary stratigraphy of the

Durango area, San Juan Mountains, Colorado, *in* Geological Survey Research, 1965: U.S. Geological Survey Professional Paper 525-C, p. C137-C143.

Richmond, G. M., 1970, Comparison of the Quaternary stratigraphy of the Alps and Rocky Mountains: Quaternary Research, v. 1, p. 3-28.

Salkin, P. H., 1975, The malacology of the Kane Springs column and the paleocology of Cedar Mesa, southeastern Utah, *in* Fassett, J. E., ed., Canyonlands Country: Four Corners Geological Society, 8th Field Conference, Guidebook, p. 73-79.

Schumm, S. A., 1977, The fluvial system: New York, John Wiley and Sons, 338 p.

Schumm, S. A., and Chorley, R. J., 1966, Talus weathering and scarp recession in the Colorado Plateau: Zeitschrift fur Geomorphologie, v. 10, no. 1, p. 1-36.

Shackleton, N. J., and Opdyke, N. D., 1973, Oxygen isotope and paleomagnetic stratigraphy of Equatorial Pacific core v28-238: oxygen isotope temperatures and ice volumes on a 105 year and 106 year scale: Quaternary Research, v. 3, p. 39-55.

Shroba, R. R., 1977, Soil development in Quaternary tills, rock-glacier deposits and taluses, southern and central Rocky Mountains: unpublished Ph.D. thesis, University of Colorado, 424 p.

Shroder, J. F., Jr., Giardino, J. R., and Sewell, R. E., 1980, Tree-ring and multi-criteria, relative-age-dating of mass movement and glacial phenomena, La Sal Mountains, Utah (abstract): American Quaternary Association, Abstracts and Programs, Sixth Biennial Meeting, p. 175.

Stokes, W. L., 1964, Incised, wind-alligned stream patterns of the Colorado Plateau: American Journal of Science, v. 262, p. 808-816.

Weide, D. L., O'Sullivan, R. B., and Heller, J. S., 1979, Preliminary geologic map of the Fruitland quadrangle, San Juan County, New Mexico: U.S. Geological Survey Miscellaneous Field Studies Map MF-1089.

Williams, P. L., 1964, Geology, structure, and uranium deposits of the Moab quadrangle, Colorado and Utah: U.S. Geological Survey Map I-360.

Witkind, I. J., 1964, Geology of the Abajo Mountains area, San Juan County, Utah: U.S. Geological Survey Professional Paper 453, 110 p.

Wolman, M. G., and Miller, J. P., 1960, Magnitude and frequency of forces in geomorphic processes: Journal of Geology, v. 68, p. 57-74.

Woodward-Clyde Consultants, 1980, Regional overview of the geology of the Paradox Basin Region, November 1980: Battelle Memorial Institute/Office of Nuclear Waste Isolation, Report No. 92, Columbus, Ohio, 165 p., (draft).

STRATIGRAPHIC CORRELATIONS, FACIES CONCEPTS, AND CYCLICITY IN PENNSYLVANIAN ROCKS OF THE PARADOX BASIN

R.J. Hite[1] and D.H. Buckner[2]

ABSTRACT

Pennsylvanian rocks in the Paradox Basin of southwest Colorado and southeast Utah are dominated by evaporite-carbonate cycles of the Paradox Member of the Hermosa Formation. Black shales in this sequence are easily correlated from evaporite facies to carbonate facies and as a result have frequently been used improperly as formation boundaries. This has led to some confusing stratigraphic nomenclature.

Since the discovery of petroleum in these cycles, much progress has been made concerning the understanding of the genesis of these rocks. However, a prerequisite of facies analysis is the detailed study of intimate relationships between the deeper, basin evaporite faces and the dominantly carbonate facies of the shallower southwestern shelf. These relationships reveal that the economically important algal carbonate reservoir facies was deposited during phases of lowering sea level. Correlating exposure surfaces in algal mounds with solution disconformities at the top of halite beds in time equivalent evaporite cycles shows that the mounds' exposure and leaching and some deposition, may be contemporaneous with the halite. Also indicated is optimum algal growth during periods of increasing salinities in the basin.

Another facies in the Paradox cycles which has been largely unrecognized are the turbidites of the deeper basin. Studies of cores from Salt Valley, Utah document the presence of sandstones with many features associated with turbidite deposition. This, and other reports of turbidite facies in this part of the basin, suggests that an area along the steep Uncompaghre Front was favorable for this facies development and might offer a new potential for pertroleum exploration.

Because the Paradox evaporite cycles record a very complete history of sedimentation, they afford an excellent opportunity to relate cyclicity to geologic time. Rates of sedimentation calculated for the rock types in cycle 2 (Upper Ismay) suggests that deposition of this cycle took about 110,000 years.

Theories advanced to explain the cause of strong cyclicity in Middle Pennsylvanian rocks include control by sedimentation rates, tectonics, eustacy, and climate. The recognition of world wide cyclic deposition in the Middle Pennyslvanian is strong evidence for eustatic control. Also, the apparent geologic time represented by each of the Paradox cycles and their asymmetry conform to the proposed glacio-eustatic theory.

INTRODUCTION

During Pennsylvanian time a thick wedge of principally marine sediments, which is dominated by evaporites, filled a depositional basin in southeast Utah and southwest Colorado which is now known as the Paradox Basin (Fig. 1). Thinner sequences of correlative strata extend southwest and southeast beyond the basin margins that are generally defined by the lateral extent of the evaporites. The thickest accumulation of evaporites lies in a deep trough bordering the ancestral Uncompahgre Uplift on the northeast flank of the basin (Fig.1). Leached residues of these evaporites crop out in the valleys of the breached diapiric salt anticlines located in the trough. One of the largest of these diapirs is the Paradox Valley anticline (Fig. 1). This valley was so named by the early Mormon settlers because of the paradoxical course of the Dolores River, flowing directly across, instead of parallel to the valley. Excellent exposures of the Pennsylvanian evaporite sequence, from which all the halite has been leached, can be observed in the southwestern part of the valley. It is from these outcrops that the Paradox Basin derived its name.

Through a period of about 75 years the Pennsylvanian sequence in this basin has been studied by a large number of geologists that have steadily advanced the state of knowledge concerning its stratigraphy and facies analyses. Major discoveries of petroleum in these strata in the 1950's greatly accelerated these investigations. Consequently, there is an abundance of literature available concerning the Pennsylvanian rocks of the Paradox Basin. Therefore, we

[1]U.S. Geological Survey, Denver, Colorado
[2]McAdams, Roux, O'Connor Associates, Inc., Denver, Colorado

will confine our discussion to an investigation of problems relating to stratigraphic nomenclature and regional correlations, the genesis of two economically important facies, and the factors controlling cyclicity. We will also limit our discussion to rocks principally of Middle Pennsylvanian age which includes all of the Paradox evaporite-carbonate cycles.

STRATIGRAPHIC NOMENCLATURE AND REGIONAL CORRELATIONS

Throughout most of the Paradox Basin rocks of Pennsylvanian age are buried from 2,000 to 10,000 feet (600 to 3,000 m). Outcrops are present only in the La Plata and San Miguel Mountains to the southeast, basin edge, in deeply incised canyons of the Colorado and San Juan Rivers on the west and southwest, and in the cores and flanks of salt anticlines located in the northeast (Fig. 1).

STRATIGRAPHIC NOMENCLATURE

The development of the stratigraphic nomenclature for Pennsylvanian rocks in the Paradox Basin began when Cross and Spencer (1899) applied the name Hermosa Formation to a sequence of limestones, sandstones, shales and evaporites exposed along Hermosa Creek about eight miles (13 km.) north of Durango, Colorado. Baker (1933), on the basis of conodont fauna, assigned a Pennsylvanian age to the highly contorted black shales, dolomites and gypsum beds that crop out in Paradox Valley, Colorado, and named these beds the Paradox Formation. Later it was recognized by Bass (1944) that the Paradox Formation was a facies within the main body of the Hermosa Formation, and he assigned it Member rank. As the result of detailed studies of

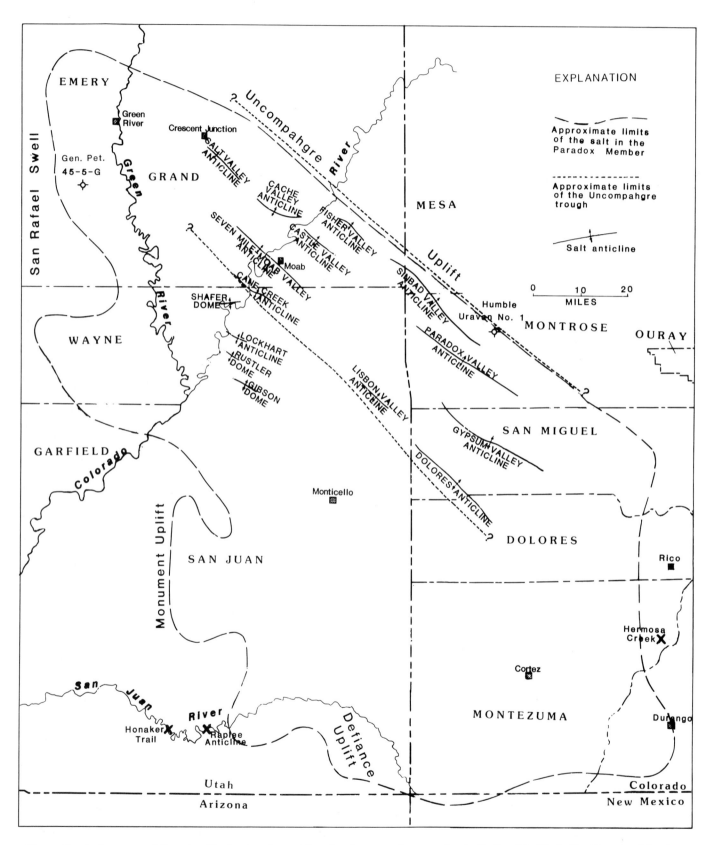

Figure 1.   Index map of Paradox Basin showing major structures and approximate limits of halite in the Paradox Member (short-dashed line).

Pennsylvanian rocks at the San Juan River and Durango localities, Wengerd (notably Wengerd and Matheny, 1958) renamed the Lower and Upper Members of the Hermosa Formation the Pinkerton Trail and Honaker Trail Formations, respectively. When petroleum discoveries were made in the Four Corners area, it was convenient for geologists to apply names to certain intervals in the Pennsylvanian sequence which contained important reservoir rocks. These informal designations, from older to younger, include the Barker Creek, Akah, Desert Creek, and Ismay intervals (Baars, et al., 1967). The stratigraphy of the strongly cyclical deeper basin evaporite sequence was studied by Hite (1960) who gave an informal numerical designation to each cycle, and showed these cycles to be correlative across the basin into the shelf carbonate facies.

Regional correlations of black shales, which are time-rock units, can easily be made throughout most of the Paradox Basin. Unfortunately, because these time units are so easily mappable a confusing stratigraphic terminology developed. The black shales can be correlated from an evaporite facies, consisting of 70 to 80 percent halite, into a carbonate facies which is 70 to 80 percent limestone. Because certain intervals in the carbonate facies are bounded by these mappable time planes there has been a tendency for some stratigraphers to give these intervals formation names and then extend the formation into a totally different facies. This practice is contrary to the Code of Stratigraphic Nomenclature (see AAPG Bull. v. 45, p. 645-665). Those parts of the code which have been ignored are as follows: "Article 5.

b) Key beds used for boundaries. —Key beds may be used as boundaries for formal rock-stratigraphic units over an area where the internal *lithologic characterists of the units remain relatively constant.* Even though key beds may be traceable beyond the area of the diagnostic over-all lithology, an extension of the potential boundary markers does not alone justify geographic extension of a rock-stratigraphic unit. Where the rock between key beds becomes drastically different from that of the type locality a new unit should be recognized, even though key beds are continuous."

"Article 6.

The formation is the fundamental unit in rock stratigraphic classification. A formation is a body of rock characterized by *lithologic homogeneity;*[1] it is prevailing but not necessarily tabular and is mappable at the earth's surface or traceable in the subsurface."

At the type locality of the Honaker Trail Formation (as defined by Wengerd and Matheny, 1958) the sequence consists primarily of carbonate rock. There are no evaporites present at this locality. Although there are mappable time-rock units (black shales) present, there is no over-all vertical change in lithologic homogeneity in all of the sequence originally included in the Hermosa Formation as described by Misner (1924) in his work in the canyon of the San Juan River. According to the above definitions of the Code of Stratigraphic Nomenclature there is no justification for dividing the Hermosa sequence at the Honaker Trail locality into four different formations in the manner proposed by Wengerd (1973), which, from older to younger, includes the Lime Ridge, Pinkerton Trail, Paradox, and Honaker Trail Formations. The use of Pinkerton Trail (carbonate facies) and Honaker Trail (carbonate facies) would be appropriate only where the two units are separated by the distinctly different Paradox facies (evaporites); otherwise, the name

[1]Emphasis added by authors

"Hermosa Formation" should be used. Furthermore, it would be inconsistent with the "Code" to define the boundaries of the "Paradox Formation" at the Honaker Trail locality where no evaporites are present. To extend time-rock boundaries into the main body of evaporites would force at least three salt beds, younger than Wengerd's upper boundary of the Paradox Member, into the "Honaker Trail Formation." Because of these problems concerning the more recent stratigraphic nomenclature, we will use the older terminology of Bass (1944) along with certain informal terms for key intervals or cycles (see Fig. 2).

Regional Correlations

The Middle Pennsylvanian strata of the Paradox Basin include numerous time-rock units (black shales) which allow rather precise correlation throughout most of the basin. Subsurface units can be correlated with outcrop units exposed at the San Juan River, Utah, localities and also at Hermosa Creek, north of Durango, Colorado (Fig. 1). Correlation is essentially impossible in the structurally complex cores of the diapiric salt anticlines in the deepest part of the basin, and is difficult on southeastern shelf of the basin near Rico, Colorado where drilling density is low.

Some of the early regional correlations in the basin were based primarily on fusulinid control (Welsh, 1958 and 1963) and led to errors which must be corrected for the benefit of newcomers to the area. At the Honaker Trail locality (Fig. 3) a stratigraphic interval which includes almost all the Middle Pennsylvanian is well exposed. A prominent limestone ledge near the middle of this sequence has been informally called the "Horn Point Limestone" (Misner, 1924). The top of this unit was considered by Welsh to be the top of the Desert Creek interval (Fig. 4) as defined in the subsurface about 25 miles (40 km) east of Honaker Trail. Welsh also correlated a thin limestone bed, about 170 feet (52 m) stratigraphically above the Horn Point, with the top of the Ismay interval defined in wells east of the locality. These correlations were used for many years by numerous authors, notably Wengerd (1962, 1963), and Wengerd and Szabo, (1968).

In 1971, the senior author restudied the Honaker Trail and Raplee Anticline sections and found it possible to correlate surface units with units defined on radioactivity logs from nearby drill holes. The correlations (Fig. 4) show a dark silty, thin-bedded, cherty dolomite above the top of the Horn Point to be the outcrop equivalent of a subsurface black shale near the middle of the Upper Ismay interval.[2] In the subsurface these black shales may consist of as much as 15 percent organic carbon and 20 to 30 percent carbonate. The remainder of the rock is clay to silt sized detritus consisting of various clay minerals, quartz, and feldspar. Outcrops of these units at Honaker Trail and Raplee Anticline consist of dark, silty dolomites, characterized by thinly laminated, nodular, black chert. The presence of chert on the outcrop and its absence in the subsurface suggests the reorganization of silica by weathering processes. On the basis of the restudy, and using disconformities as cycle boundaries, the "Horn Point Limestone" is the Upper Ismay interval, rather than the Upper Desert Creek interval as reported by Welsh (1958). Recently, Wengerd (1973), following the advice of D. Irwin and D. Baars, also recognized this early miscorrelation.

Excellent correlation between units in the Honaker Trail section and the nearby Texaco Inc. Johns Canyon No. 1 well, located in Sec. 6, T41S, R18E (Figs. 3 & 4), shows that the oldest rocks exposed at river level are about 250 feet (76 m) stratigraphically above the top of the Molas Formation.

[2]Common usage by the petroleum industry is to pick the top of intervals or cycles at the base of the black shale. In this study cycle boundaries are based on disconformities which separate eustatic cycles as shown on figure 7.

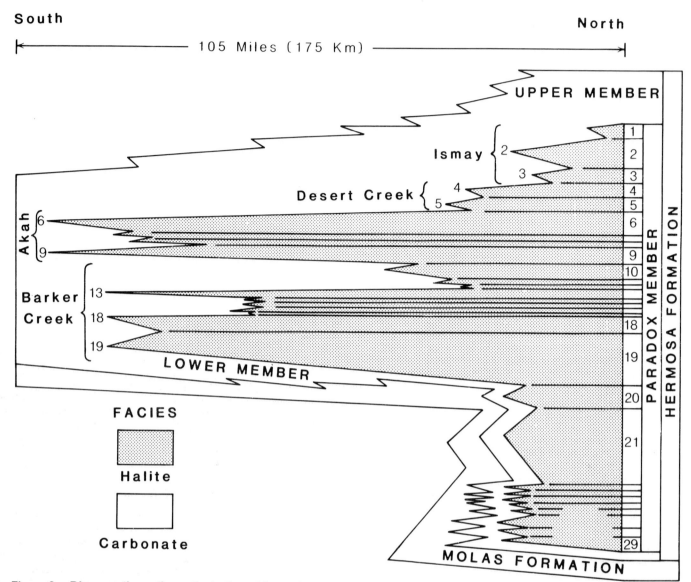

Figure 2.   Diagramatic north-south stratigraphic section across the Paradox Basin showing the stratigraphic nomenclature of the Hermosa Formation of Middle Pennsylvanian age as used in this report. Numbered units are evaporite cycles of the Paradox Member which consist primarily of halite. Note that the maximum extent of evaporite conditions came during cycles 6, 9, 13, 18 and 19.

Although there are no evaporites present at Honaker Trail and the sequence is considerably thinner, there is good lateral continuity with many lithologic units in the Raplee Anticline section (Fig. 4) located about eight miles (13 km) east. At the latter locality the oldest rocks exposed include gypsum beds and solution breccias which are stratigraphically equivalent to the lower part of the Akah interval or evaporite cycle 9 (Fig. 4). In the subsurface about four miles (6 km) east of this locality, the gypsum beds undergo transition to halite in evaporite cycles 6, 7, 8, and 9 (Fig. 3).

There are two additional regional correlations in the literature requiring significant change. At Gibson Dome (Fig. 1), where the Paradox Member consists of about 3,000 feet (915 m) of a halite-bearing evaporite sequence, Welsh (1963) reported the top of the Upper Ismay and Upper Desert Creek intervals at about 1,630 and 1,790 feet, respectively, in the Reynolds Mining Corp. Gibson Dome No. 1 well located in Sec. 35, T29 ½S, R20E. These correlation points should be 1,950 feet and 2,165 feet, respectively. Another correlation change should be noted in the General Petroleum Corp. No. 45-5-G well located in Sec. 5, T24S, R15E. This well, located

along the northwest edge of the Paradox Basin, was a very important stratigraphic test because almost all the Middle Pennsylvanian sequence was cored. Wengerd and Matheny (1958) reported their "P" datum at 3,982 feet in this well. They defined the "P" datum as the top of the "Horn Point Limestone" at the Honaker Trail locality which, as explained previously, is in the Upper Ismay interval. The top of the "Horn Point Limestone" in this well is actually 1,268 feet lower than reported, or at a depth of 5,250 feet.

FACIES CONCEPTS

As first noted in the work of Herman and Sharps (1956) and Herman and Barkell (1957), Middle Pennsylvanian rocks in the Paradox Basin are strongly cyclical and characterized by classic lateral and vertical facies changes. Since that time much has been written concerning descriptions of the cycles and the genesis of the various facies involved. On the southern and southwestern shelf of the Paradox Basin, the cyclic sequence is predominantly carbonate and contains important petroleum reservoirs. For this reason, much of the literature describing Paradox cycles and their genesis is derived from this portion of the basin. We are concerned that

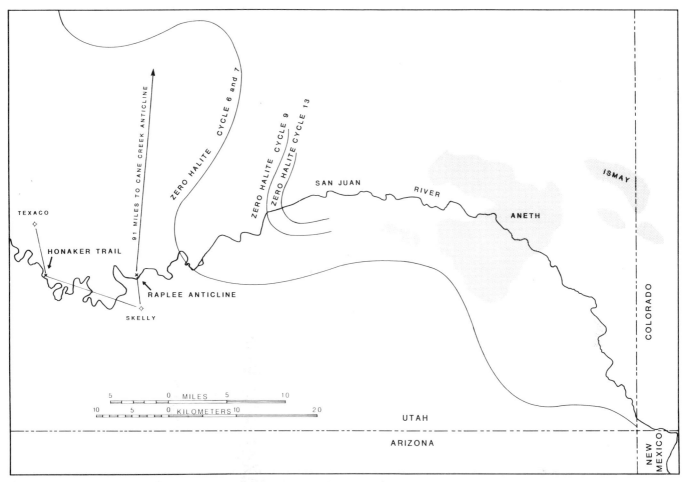

Figure 3.   Index map showing the location of the Honaker Trail and Raplee Anticline sections and line of section in figure 4. Also shown are the approximate limits of halite in the evaporite cycles 6, 7, 9 and 13. The stippled pattern shows approximate boundaries of oil and gas fields producing from Pennsylvanian carbonate cycles.

analyses of these cycles should be more regional in scope to include the predominantly evaporitic facies of the basin deep. We believe this to be justified because in the evaporite basin, the specific response of the chemical facies to salinity change can be easily demonstrated by the solubility order of the various salts involved. In contrast, the effect of salinity changes on the carbonate facies of the adjacent shelf is not understood as well, primarily because it involves changes in the biologic community, and methods of interpreting the ecology of a biofacies are not as precise. In addition, the deeper, more stable environment of the evaporite basin probably preserves a more complete depositional record than does the shallower shelf. Because evaporite deposition is such a sensitive record of salinity, it follows that these chemical sediments are also the best record of sea level change. Therefore, in the Paradox Basin where evaporites are associated with shelf carbonates, it may be possible to use the evaporites as the key to deciphering the complex depositional history of the carbonates.

Our objectives in this paper include describing two economically important facies that form elements of certain Paradox cycles and relating them in a regional to a generalized depositional model. These facies are the *Ivanovia* dominated carbonates of the basin shelf and the local turbidities in the ubiquitous clastic facies.

Ivanovia Facies

Banks or mounds of porous algal carbonates of Middle

Pennsylvanian age form important petroleum reservoirs in three depositional cycles along the shallow southwestern shelf of the Paradox Basin. These cycles, from older to younger, include cycle 5 (Lower Desert Creek), cycle 3 (Lower Ismay), and cycle 2 (Upper Ismay) (Fig. 2). Other cycles may contain this facies, but this has not been convincingly documented. Petroleum was discovered in this facies in 1954, but it wasn't until 1960 that the rock builder was identified as the calcareous phylloid alga *Ivanovia* (Murray, 1960, p. 66). In 1963, the Four Corners Geological Society published a concise and informative volume entitled *Shelf Carbonates of the Paradox Basin* containing several papers which contributed greatly to the understanding of this facies.

The largest known development of *Ivanovia* facies in the Paradox Basin is in the Lower Desert Creek (cycle 5) in the Aneth Field (Fig. 5). This particular bank or mound covers an area of more than 100 square miles (260 square km) and is locally as much as 150 feet (46 m) thick (Peterson and Ohlen, 1963, p. 74). Other Desert Creek mounds have been found basinward from Aneth; however, in all cases, they have proven to be much more areally restricted. Algal mound development is also well known in the Ismay intervals particularly in the Ismay Field (Fig. 6). Although Ismay mounds are not known to reach the size of those in the Desert Creek, they nevertheless have a broader regional distribution. This is particularly true for the Lower Ismay (cycle 3) (Fig. 6). The geometry of mound development in

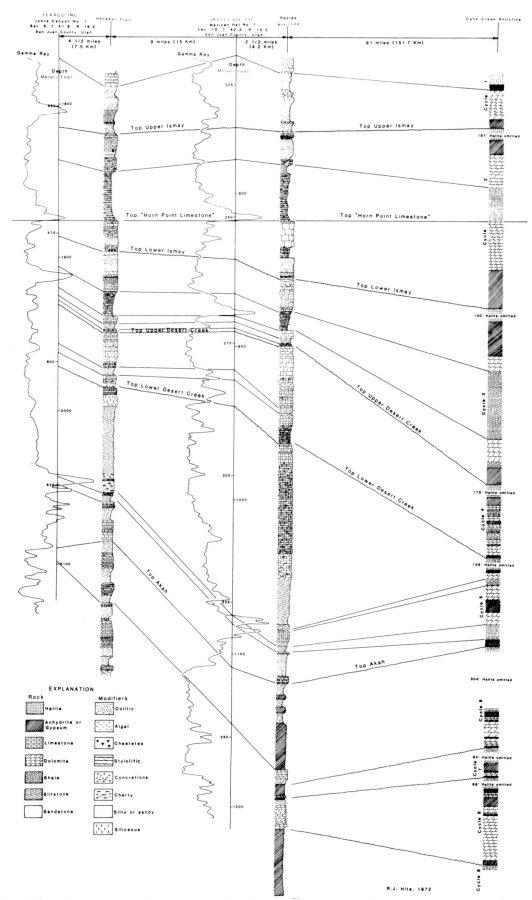

Figure 4.   Correlation of measured sections of part of the Hermosa Formation at Honaker Trail and Raplee Anticline in San Juan River Canyon with gamma ray logs from nearby drill holes. Lithologies of the evaporite cycles are from a potash core hole located in Section 32, T26S, R20E, Grand County, Utah, on the Cane Creek anticline.

both the Upper (cycle 2) and Lower (cycle 3) Ismay has been described in great detail by Choquette and Traut (1963) and Elias (1963) in the Ismay Field. At this locality the *Ivanovia* facies developed in three separate, but overlapping intervals. This "stacked" occurrence involves one interval in the Lower Ismay (cycle 3) and two intervals in the Upper Ismay (cycle 2). Collectively, these mounds cover an area of about 12 square miles (31 square km). According to Choquette and Traut (1963, p. 157), individual buildups are generally elongated northeast to southwest, appear to be flat bottomed, and can be several thousand feet in width, at least 10,000 feet (3,050 m) in length, and up to 40 feet (12 m) thick. Collectively the mounds form a trend oriented northwest to southeast.

Additional observations pertaining to the geometry of *Ivanovia* mounds can be made from the exposures in the Lower Ismay at the Honaker Trail and Raplee Anticline localities. Here the buildups of the *Ivanovia* facies have a conspicuous wave-like distribution. Maximum thickness at the crests of the buildups may reach 30 feet (9 m) and thin nearly to zero in the trough areas. The buildup period ranges from about 50 to 350 feet (15 to 107 m). These small mounds seem linear, but, because only two dimensions are usually displayed on vertical canyon walls, it is difficult to assign a dominant direction. Pray and Wray (1963, p. 225) suggest that mound trends at Honaker Trail are east to west or east-northeast to west-southwest. Similar trends seem to be present at Raplee Anticline. At both localities the base of the mounds is flat.

When considering the origin of the *Ivanovia* facies, one must consider the vertical position it occupies in the depositional cycles of the shelf carbonate facies. Descriptions by different authors of facies which comprise the shelf carbonate cycles vary considerably in terminology; however, it is possible to equate each author's terminology with a common lithofacies (Hite, 1970, Table 1). Using a synthesis of these descriptions, the following vertical sequence of lithofacies represents the simplified or idealized (*Ivanovia*-bearing) shelf carbonate cycle.

Cap facies	Next cycle
Buildup facies (algal limestone)	
Intermediate facies (Silty dolomite and limestone)	
Euxinic facies (black, argillaceous, calcareous shale)	
Intermediate facies (siltstone and sandstone or very silty dolomite)	
Cap facies (pelletal-foraminiferal limestone)	

Buildup facies	Next cycle

To gain an understanding of the genesis of the *Ivanovia* facies, we believe it is important to relate all of the facies in the "idealized" cycle to sea level fluctuations. There is considerable disagreement in the literature concerning this subject. One method to resolve these differences is to apply the sea level relationships established for elements of the evaporite cycles to the carbonate cycles. The evaporite cycles consist primarily of chemical facies, which record a complete and rather sensitive response to changes in sea level. An "idealized" evaporite cycle consists of the following vertical sequence.

C	Anhydrite	Next Cycle
D	Halite (may contain potash near top)	
C	Anhydrite (transitional with overlying halite)	
B	Dolomite (slightly silty)	
A	Black shale (20 to 30 percent carbonate)	
B	Dolomite (very silty)	

C	Anydrite (sharp contact with underlying halite)	
D	Halite	Next Cycle

Detailed descriptions of evaporite cycles can be found in Peterson and Hite (1969) and Hite (1970). It is established that the sequence in which rock-forming minerals precipitate from evaporating sea water is 1) carbonate, 2) calcium sulfate, 3) halite, and 4) potash. When this sequential order is applied to a Paradox evaporite cycle a curve representing conditions of paleosalinity can be drawn (Fig. 7). The one element of the cycle which cannot be related directly to salinity is the black shale facies (A) which consists of greater than 50 percent non-evaporitic material. However, when the position of this facies in the cycle is considered (salinity decreasing up to the shale and increasing above), it can be assumed that the shale represents lowest salinities, and correspondingly, the highest sea level. The reversal in the cycle from the transgressive phase (rising sea level and decreasing salinity) to the regressive phase (falling sea level and increasing salinity) should take place sometime during the deposition of the black shale (point Y, Fig. 7). There is a second reversal (point X, Fig. 7) in the cycle between the halite unit (D) and the overlying transgressive anhydrite (C). This represents an abrupt rise in sea level with an attendant decrease in salinity. This cycle reversal is particularly significant when attempting to decipher the genesis of the various elements of the carbonate cycle.

The same framework of salinity and sea level conditions established for the various elements of the evaporite cycles can also be applied to the carbonate cycles because certain elements are common to both types; for example, the black shale (A), and the regressive and transgressive silty dolomites (B), are probably synchronous, or nearly so, between the evaporite facies and the carbonate facies and are connected by solid lines on Fig. 7. An additional tie point between the two cycles is the cycle reversal (point X) which in the evaporite cycle is represented by a solution surface or disconformity. We believe that this reversal is represented in the carbonate cycle by the contact between the algal facies and the overlying pelletal-foraminiferal limestone. Our interpretation is based on 1) the abrupt contact between these two facies, 2) the fact that locally the pelletal-foraminiferal limestone fills in and obliterates the relief created by the mound, and 3) the evidence of the emergence of the algal facies prior to being covered by a rising sea and subsequent deposition of the pelletal-foraminiferal limestone. From these observations, we conclude that the *Ivanovia* facies was deposited during a lowering of sea level. From the position of the algal facies in Fig. 7 there is some justification to assume that at least its exposure and leaching and possibly some of its deposition may be contemporaneous with the halite facies of the evaporite cycle. However, it should be remembered that the interval of geologic time represented by the halite facies may be inadequate to account for some of the thick buildups of the *Ivanovia* facies as well as their subsequent leaching.

The *Ivanovia* facies in the Paradox Basin shows great selectivity in its stratigraphic occurrence. As we have previously stated this facies has only been identified in three of the Paradox evaporite-carbonate cycles. In addition there are no known occurrences of this facies in the Upper Member of the Hermosa Formation in rocks younger than the Upper Ismay, even though this interval includes as much as 1,000 feet (300 m) of cyclical marine carbonates in the deep part of the basin.

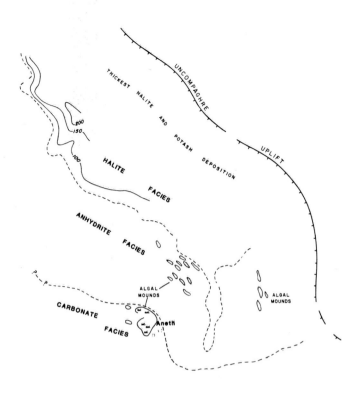

DHB 4/76

Figure 5.   Generalized map showing the distribution of evaporite - carbonate facies for cycle 5. (Lower Desert Creek) with the location of known algal mounds.

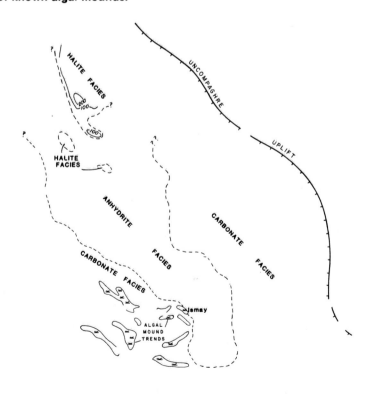

DHB 4/76

Figure 6.   Generalized map showing the distribution of evaporite-carbonate facies for cycle 3 (Lower Ismay) with the location of known algal mound trends.

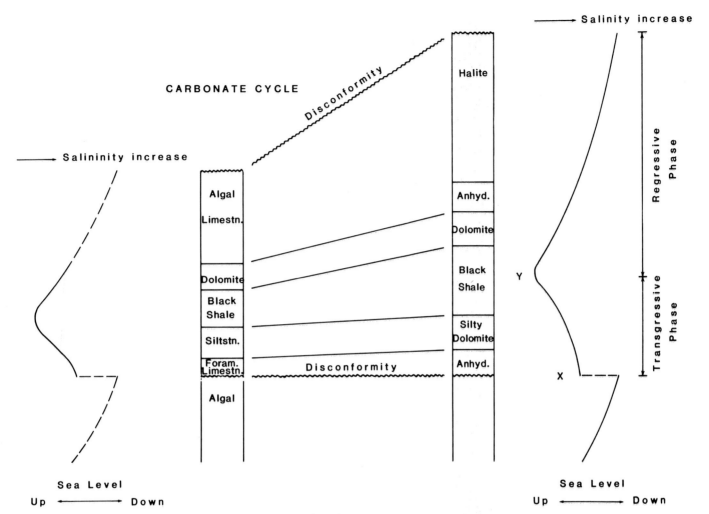

Figure 7.   Diagramatic correlations of facies in "idealized" evaporite and carbonate cycles of the Paradox Member. Curves show relative sea level and salinity conditions during the deposition of each facies. The letters X and Y are referred to in the text as cycle reversals.

Many factors such as bathymetry, water temperature, sunlight and continuous circulation of nutrient and calcium bicarbonate-bearing water were probably important in promoting the development of the *Ivanovia* facies. There is strong evidence that salinity was perhaps the dominant control and that optimum conditions were at or near saturation for calcium sulfate. Our conclusions are based on the following observations:

1. The *Ivanovia* facies is limited to carbonate cycles which are contemporaneous with halite-bearing evaporite cycles.
2. Cycles containing the *Ivanovia* facies also reach highest salinities (potash or high bromine halite).
3. The position of the *Ivanovia* facies in the carbonate cycle is strongly regressive (low sea level and high salinities).
4. The *Ivanovia* facies occurs either in close proximity to or within the area of an anhydrite facies.

CLASTIC FACIES

The exotic element in the Paradox evaporite-carbonate cycles is their clastic component because it usually occupies

a precise position in the cycles and yet it is difficult to relate its sedimentation to sea level change. The clastics in the shelf carbonate cycles include black shales, dolomitic siltstones, and fine-to-medium-grained sandstones (Fig. 4). All of these rocks occupy precise positions in the cycles and can be traced throughout most of the shelf. In addition, a few small isolated lenses of sandstone can be seen in cycles 6 and 7 (upper part of the Akah) at Raplee Anticline. The dolomitic siltstones and sandstones of the transgressive phase of the cycles on the shelf grade basinward into silty dolomites. These beds are characterized by almost perfect sorting and show a pronounced decrease in grain size from the shelf to the basin deep (Hite, 1969). The black shales show very little regional change except that they thicken in some cycles along the southeast shelf and in the basin interior.

In the deeper basin, clastics include a facies additional to those described on the shelf. In recent drilling at Salt Valley anticline (Department of Energy, Salt Valley No. 3, Sec. 5, T23N, R20E, Grand County, Utah) about 4,000 feet (1,220 m) of the evaporites of the Paradox Member have been sampled by continuous coring. Several intervals in the corehole were found to include fine to medium-grained laminated sandstones which have many thin layers (0.39 in. to 3.94 in. or 10 to 100 mm thick) characterized by graded bedding, poor sorting, small-scale cross-laminations, sole marks and other features that are associated with turbidite deposition. The cross laminations are accentuated by concentrations of clay rather than heavy minerals. Macerated remains of vascular plants and thin clasts of gray shale are scattered thoughout most of the sequence. Similar sandstones have been noted in cores from the Paradox Member in the Humble Oil Company Urvan No. 1 located in Sec. 26, T48N, R17W, San Miguel County, Colorado (oral communication, C.M. Molenaar, 1981). In the Salt Valley cores, sandstones with turbidite characteristics are found in at least four separate intervals, but some of these intervals may be repeated by folding and faulting. Penetration thicknesses of these units range from 30 feet (10 M) to 100 feet (30 M). Most of these sandstone intervals appear to be part of evaporite cycles because they are associated with sequences containing anhydrite and dolomite beds. However, one 41 foot (12.5 m) thick interval (penetration thickness) is entirely clastic. The bottom[3] half of this unit consists of small-scale, cross-laminated, medium-grained sandstone in sharp contact with an underlying halite unit.

The origin of the described clastic facies is complex. Unquestionably, there were two main sources of clastics for the Paradox Basin during this period, the Uncompahgre Uplift and the southwest shelf. However, the complete explanation of facies genesis is difficult because clastics from these different sources were apparently deposited synchronously and are an integral part of many of the Paradox cycles. Thus, some sort of basin-wide mechanism involving eustatic control is probably required.

It has been noted that the transgressive phase of the Paradox cycles contains a much greater volume of silt or sand-size detritus than the regressive phase (Hite, 1970, p. 55). This can be explained as the result of a transgressive sea churning up source sediments covering low-lying land areas and transporting them into the basin, perhaps as turbid but light (clay and silt-size particles only) density layers riding into the basin *over* heavy evaporite brines. These silts and sands are very well sorted and increase in grain size toward source areas on the southwest and southeast basin margins.

The proposed turbidite facies of the Uncompahgre Trough (Fig. 1) does not fit the grain-size distribution expected if these clastics were also derived from sources to the southwest and southeast. This facies includes poorly sorted medium-grained sandstones in juxtaposition with well sorted, silt-size detritus from southern source areas. Consequently, this identifies the source of the turbidite clastics as the nearby Uncompahgre Uplift. A high sea level stage may also have been responsible for transporting sediment along this northeast basin margin (oral communication, O.B. Raup, 1970). Some of the turbidite facies could have been deposited at this time when the transgressive sea triggered the slumping of fan deltas along the deep and steeply sloping Uncompahgre Front (Fig. 8). In this case the turbidity currents contained large particles and had greater density than the brine.

This mechanism could explain the contemporaneity between some of the turbidites and clastics from the southwest source, and the repeated positioning of these facies in the transgressive phase of the Paradox cycles. However, some of the turbidites may have resulted from floods, storms, or earthquakes, and would occupy an unpredictable stratigraphic position in the evaporite facies.

[3]Because of structural complexities due to salt flowage the depositional top or bottom of this bed is interpretive.

The recognition of a turbidite facies along the Uncompahgre Front could be highly significant to petroleum exploration. Turbidites with potentially favorable reservoir qualities extending downdip into the rich source rocks of the evaporite sequence could offer an interesting new dimension to exploration in the Paradox Basin.

CYCLICITY

DEPOSITIONAL RATES AND GEOLOGIC TIME

The Paradox carbonate-evaporite cycles are superimposed on a major marine transgression that includes all of the Middle Pennsylvanian. According to Van Eysinga (1975) the Middle Pennsylvanian is represented on the geologic time scale by a period of about 10 million years. The time of strongest cyclicity includes most of the Atoka and Des Moines. Because the Paradox evaporite cycles probably record a very complete history of sedimentation they afford an excellent opportunity to relate cyclicity to a geologic time scale. In addition the cycles primarily consist of chemical precipitates which have much more predictable rates of sedimentation than other rock types.

The easiest unit in the evaporite cycle to assign a sedimentation rate for is halite rock. This can be done by counting bands or laminae of anhydrite which bound individual layers of halite. Each anhydrite band is considered to represent the end or beginning of one season; however, the reader should be aware that not all "evaporite geologists" agree with this interpretation. Band counts which have been made for the halite rock in a large number of Paradox cycles show average sedimentation rates of about 1.57 in. (40 mm) per year.

The average halite rock in the Paradox cycles contains about 2 weight percent anhydrite. This material includes laminae as well as small crystals of anhydrite disseminated in the halite between the laminae. The calculated rate of anhydrite sedimentation, which can be obtained by multiplying the halite sedimentation rate (1.57 in. or 40 m m) by 2 percent, is 0.035 in. (0.80 m m) per year.

The rate of dolomite sedimentation can be calculated by assuming that seawater flowing into the basin, was at or near saturation for calcium bicarbonate. If we also assume a high rate of evaporation with a loss of about 13 feet (4 m) of water per year, and that loss is constantly replenished by influx, a sedimentation rate of 0.0067 in. (0.17 m m) per year can be expected. Kirkland and Evans (1981, p. 189) arrived at a similar figure (0.0059 in. or 0.15 mm/year). For the transgressive phase of a Paradox cycle the rate increases to 0.0079 in. (0.20 mm) per year due to the addition of clastics (quartz silt).

The most difficult element of the cycle to evaluate in terms of its sedimentation rate is the black shale, because it contains constituents that are clastic, chemical, and organic in origin. One possible solution to the problem is to apply knowledge of high yearly rates of organic carbon production in marine environments to the amounts of organic carbon found in these black shales. For example, the modern ocean is known to produce as much as 100 g/m³/y to 300 g/g/m³/y (Tissot and Welte, 1978, p. 30) in certain areas of high productivity, particularly upwelling localities. The evaporite basin is now known to be one of the most productive environments (Kirkland and Evans, 1981) and is probably capable of producing even more bio-mass than upwelling. The Paradox black shales have average densities of about 1.8 and contain an average of about 8 weight percent organic carbon. Therefore each m³ of shale contains about 144,000 g. of organic carbon. This value divided by the above rates of productivity, gives a depositional rate of 0.027 in. or 0.69 mm

Southwest

Northeast

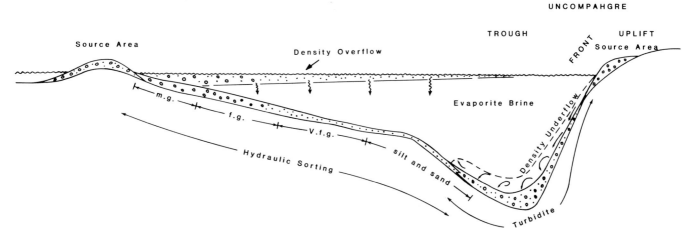

Figure 8. Depositional model for the clastic facies in the Paradox evaporite-carbonate cycles. Overflow of lighter seawater carrying fine-grained sediment derived from a southwest source deposits hydraulically sorted sediment. Underflow (turbidity current) of brine with coarse particles derived from fan deltas along the shore of the Uncampahgre Uplift deposits turbidite contemporaneously with the other clastic component.

and 0.082 in. or 2.08 mm per year respectively, for black shale.

These rates of sedimentation applied (see Table 1) to the sequence of rock types in Cycle 2 (Upper Ismay) suggests a depositional time span for this cycle of about 104,000 to 111,000 years. Note that if we assume the cycle reversal is at the mid-point of the black shale, then the transgressive phase is about 10,000 years longer than the regressive phase. This relationship is not necessarily the same in all the cycles.

Paradox cycles are markedly asymmetric (Hite, 1970). This is manifested by sharp disconformities at the top of each halite unit, the fact that most postash deposits are positioned at the top of halite units, and the presence of much more clastic material in the transgressive phase of the cycles. Although the transgressive phase occupies a greater interval of geologic time, it is represented by a thinner sequence because the thick, rapidly deposited halite unit is in the regressive phase.

MECHANISMS CAUSING CYCLICITY

Mechanisms controlling cyclicity can involve sedimentary, tectonic, eustatic and/or climatic controls (Duff et al., 1967). The strong differential in rates of sedimentation in evaporite basins such as the Paradox (Table 1) and the German Zechstein has led Brongersma-Sanders (1971) to propose a new and intriguing theory in which cyclicity is controlled by sedimentation. This theory calls for a constant rate of basin subsidence which is intermediate between the slowest and fastest rates of sedimentation. Accordingly, basin depths will increase during the slow phases of sedimentation (anhydrite-dolomite) and shoal during rapid sedimentation (halite). As basin depths change, the pattern of water circulation between basin and the sea will alternate from quasi-estuarine to estuarine and back. These changes in circulation will in turn control the type of sediment deposited in the basin. This theory has its merits, but it may be unrealistic as the sole explanation because subsidence would have to persist through millions of years at a specific and uniform rate.

Strong arguments can be made for tectonic controls of Paradox cyclicity. The Uncompahgre Uplift was mildly positive during the deposition of the Paradox cycles and, as we have noted, it was the source of some clastic material

TABLE 1
ESTIMATED RATES OF SEDIMENTATION
FOR PARADOX CYCLE 2 (UPPER ISMAY)

	UNIT	THICKNESS		YEARLY RATE	YEARS
		Ft.	M	m m	
Regressive	Halite	172	52.43	40.00	1,300
Phase	Anhydrite	10	3.05	.80	3,800
	Dolomite	21	6.40	.17	37,600
- - - - - - - - - - - -	Black shale	22	6.82	.69 to 2.08	9,900 to 3,300
Transgressive	Dolomite	32	9.76	.20	48,800
Phase	Anhydrite	25	7.62	.80	9,100
	Totals	282	86.08		110,500 or 103,900

Note: Thicknesses from Delhi-Taylor Oil Corporation Cane Creek No. 1, Sec. 36, T26S, R20E, Grand County, Utah.

found in the cycles. Furthermore, the presence of clastics in each Paradox cycle might also suggest that a tectonic pulse was involved. For example, the black shales associated with both the Lower and Upper Ismay cycles (3 and 2) are significantly thicker in local areas of basin subsidence than in other cycles. However, it is difficult to see how the tectonics of the Uncompahgre alone could control evaporite deposition. Tectonic control of evaporite deposition would be effective only if the tectonic element was in the path of seawater access to the basin.

Cycle control by eustatic changes can be either tectono-eustatic or glacio-eustatic. The first is the result of epeirogenic movements of the sea floor which change the capacity of the ocean basins, and the latter is the result of withdrawal or addition of water by either withdrawal, increase, or melting of glacial ice. Duff, et al. (1967, p. 247) proposes that eustacy provides the best mechanism to explain major evaporite cycles and that sea level changes of only a few meters might have been sufficient to cause cycle changes. They also suggested that eustatic controls provide the most logical explanation for the asymmetry of the various types of cycles. Peterson and Ohlen (1963, p. 79) related the origin of Paradox cyclicity to sea level changes caused by Carboniferous glaciation in the southern hemisphere. The marine accessways of the Paradox Basin appear to have been broad shelves rather than narrow channels. Consequently, a sea level change of only 6 to 10 feet (2 to 3 m m) would be sufficient to cause significant changes in chemical sedimentation inside the basin. It has been noted by Hollin (1969, p. 905) that many of the eustatic theories do not account for the apparent speed of a transgression. Hollin suggests that rapid rise accompanied by slow fall of sea level might be explained by rapid surges of continental ice sheets into the sea. A surge would cause sea level to rise through a period of 100 years or less which would be followed by a slow fall in sea level as the ice sheet built up again (Hollin, 1969, p. 904). The period of surges is thought to be about 100,000 years (J.T. Hollin, oral communication, 1976). The ice sheet surge hypothesis does appear to fit some of the characteristics of Paradox cycles such as the asymmetry and cycle period. The recognition of cyclic deposition in many Middle Pennsylvanian rocks worldwide is also compelling evidence for glacial control of cyclicity. However, as previously shown on table 1, for the Paradox cycles, the transgressive phase apparently occupies more time than the regressive phase, even though it began abruptly.

The last control of cyclicity to be considered is climate. The association of evaporites with certain climatic conditions such as aridity is well known. Furthermore, it has been suggested that some of the "seasonal" banding in evaporite rocks is the result of small scale climatic variation. Whether climate could have had long term effects on cyclic deposition is debatable. In large evaporite basins it would be quite possible for climatic change to have some influence on chemical and clastic sedimentation. For example, if the flow capacity of a basin's accessway remains constant and a climatic change causes a drastic increase in evaporation, then the basin salinities will increase just as they would respond to a lowering of sea level. However, cyclic sedimentation controlled by climate should show evidence of terrestrial contributions; both clastic and chemical. In the Paradox cycles it is doubtful that the clastics are land derived and related to climate control since the evaporite mineral suite does not include sodium sulfate minerals which are the best indicators of fluviatile contribution.

Before drawing any conclusions regarding the principal control of Paradox cyclicity, the reader should be aware that not all the Paradox cycles are as perfect as the example

(cycle 2) described in this paper. Many cycles show that there were numerous fluctuations in sea level in the transgressive phase before the smooth and more or less continuous fall during the regressive phase. The responsible control must relate to both asymmetry and the period (± 100,000 years) of these cycles, and would have to be superimposed on a major marine transgression which lasted about 10 million years. We conclude that eustatic changes in sea level, or more specifically glacio-eustatic control, would be the best means of deriving the patterns of cyclicity observed in the Pennyslvanian evaporite-carbonate facies in the Paradox Basin.

REFERENCES

American Association of Petroleum Geologists, 1961, Code of stratigraphic nomenclature: v. 45, no. 5, p. 645-665.

Baars, D.L., Parker, J.W., and Chronic, John, 1967, Revised stratigraphic nomenclature of Pennsylvanian System, Paradox basin. Am. Assoc. Petroleum Geologists Bull., v. 51, no. 3, p. 393-403.

Baker, A.A., 1933, Geology and oil possibilities of the Moab district, Grand and San Juan Counties, Utah: U.S. Geol. Survey Bull. 841, 95 p., 11 pls.

Bass, N.W., 1944, Paleozoic stratigraphy as revealed by deep wells in parts of southwestern Colorado, northwestern New Mexico, northeastern Arizona, and southeastern Utah: U.S. Geol. Survey Oil and Gas Inv. Prelim. Chart 7, with accompanying test.

Brongersma-Sanders, M., 1971, Origin of major cyclicity of evaporites and bituminous rocks: An acualistic model: Marine Geol., v. 11, p. 123-144.

Choquette, P.W., and Traut, J.D., 1963, Pennsylvanian carbonate reservoirs, Ismay Field, Utah and Colorado, in Four Corners Geol. Soc. 4th Field Conf. Guidebook, Symposium on shelf carbonates of the Paradox basin, 1963: p. 157-184.

Cross, C.W., and Spencer, A.C., 1899, U.S. Geological Survey La Plata Folio, 60.

Duff, P.M.D., Hallan, A., and Walton, E.K., 1967, Developments in sedimentology - v. 10, Cyclic sedimentation: New York, Elsevier Publishing Co., 280 p.

Elias, G.K., 1963, Habitat of Pennsylvanian algal bioherms, Four Corners area, in Four Corners Geol. Soc. 4th Field Conf. Guidebook, Symposium on shelf carbonates of the Paradox basin, 1963: p. 185-203.

Herman, G. and Barkell, C.A., 1957, Pennsylvanian stratigraphy and productive zones, Paradox Salt basin: Am. Assoc. Petroleum Geologists Bull., v. 41, No. , p. 861-881.

Herman, G., and Sharps, S.L., 1956, Pennsylvanian and Permian stratigraphy of the Paradox Salt Embayment, in Intermountain Assoc. Petroleum Geologists 7th Ann. Field Conf., 1956: p. 77-84.

Hite, R.J., 1960, Stratigraphy of the saline facies of the Paradox Member of the Hermosa Formation of southeastern Utah and southwestern Colorado, in Four Corners Geol. Soc. 3rd Field Conf. Guidebook, Geology of the Paradox fold and fault belt, 1960: p. 86-89.

_____, 1970, Shelf carbonate sedimentation controlled by salinity in the Paradox basin, southeast Utah, in Ran, J.L., and Dellwig, L.F., eds., Third symposium on salt: Northern Ohio Geol. Soc., v. 1, p. 48-66.

Hollin, J.T., 1969, Ice-sheet surges and the geological record: Canadian Jour. of Earth Sciences, v. 6, no. 4, p. 903-910.

Kirkland, D.W. and Evans, R., 1981, Source rock potential of the evaporitic environment: Am. Assoc. Petroleum Geologists Bull., v. 65-2, p. 181-190.

Misner, H.D., 1924, Geologic structure of the San Juan Canyon and adjacent country, Utah: U.S. Geol. Survey Bull. 751-9, p. 115-155.

Murray, R.C., 1960, Origin of porosity in carbonate rocks: Jour. Sedimentary Petrology, v. 30, p. 59-84.

Peterson, J.A. and Hite, R.J., 1969, Pennsylvanian evaporite-carbonate cycles and their relation to petroleum occurrence, southern Rocky Mountains: Am. Assoc. Petroleum Geologists Bull., v. 53, no. 4, p. 884-908.

Peterson, J.A., and Ohlen, H.R., 1963, Pennsylvanian shelf carbonates, Paradox basin, in Four Corners Geol. Soc. 4th Field Conf. Guidebook, Symposium on shelf carbonates of the Paradox basin, 1963: p. 65-79.

Pray, L.C., and Wray, J.L., 1963, Porous algal facies (Pennsylvanian), Honaker Trail, San Juan Canyon, Utah, in Four Corners Geol. Soc. 4th Ann. Field Conf. Guidebook, Symposium on shelf carbonates of the Paradox basin, 1963: p. 204-234.

Tissot, B.P. and Welte, D.H., 1978, Petroleum formation and occurrence: Berlin, Heidelberg, New York, Springer-Verlag, 538 p.

Van Eysinga, F.W.B., 1975, Geological time table (3rd ed.): Amsterdam, Elsevier.

Welsh, J.E., 1958 Faunizones of the Pennsylvanian and Permian rocks in the Paradox basin, in Intermountain Assoc. Petroleum Geologists 9th Ann. Field Conf. Guidebook Geology of the Paradox basin, p. 153-162.

_____, 1963, Paradox basin salt disconformities (and their relationship to oil production), in Oil and gas possibilities in Utah, re-evaluated: Utah Geol. and Minerological Survey Bull. 54, p. 487-494.

Wengerd, S.A., 1962, Pennsylvanian sedimentation in Paradox basin, in Branson, C.C., ed., Pennsylvanian System in the United States - a symposium: Am. Assoc. Petroleum Geologists, p. 264-330.

_____, 1963, Stratigraphic section at Honaker Trail, San Juan Canyon San Juan County, Utah, in Four Corners Geol. Soc. 4th Ann. Field Conf. Guidebook, Symposium on shelf carbonates of the Paradox basin, 1963: pp. 235-243.

_____, 1973, Regional stratigraphic control of the search for Pennsylvanian petroleum, southern Monument Upwarp southeastern, Utah, in New Mexico Geol. Soc. 24th Field Conf. Guidebook of Monument Valley and vicinity, Arizona and Utah: p. 122-138.

Wengerd, S.A., and Matheny, M.L., 1958, Pennsylvanian system of the Four Corners region: Am. Assoc. Petroleum Geologists Bull., v. 42, no. 9, pp. 2048-2106.

Wengerd, S.A., and Szabo, E., 1968, Pennsylvanian correlations in southwestern Colorado, in New Mexico Geol. Soc. Guidebook of San Juan - San Miguel - La Plata Region: p. 159-164.

The Three Sisters - Monument Valley (Photo by Jack Rathbone)

SEISMIC SURVEYING SALT ANTICLINE REGION PARADOX BASIN

G. L. Scott and Sharon Klipping
North American Exploration Company, Inc.

INTRODUCTION

The Salt Anticlines in Southwestern Colorado and Southeastern Utah, lie in the deepest portion of the evaporite facies of the Paradox Basin, in an area known as the Uncompaghre Trough. They cover an area approximately 30 miles wide and 100 miles long and trend in a Northwest-Southeast direction, parallel to the Uncompaghre Uplift (See Figure 1).

North American Exploration developed an interest in this area due to an obvious lack of CDP seismic data available to the industry. A study was undertaken in the summer of 1977 to determine the feasibility of a speculative seismic survey. This study included an investigation of published geological literature and well data, as well as an investigation to determine the optimum seismic data acquisition parameters and procedures. On the basis of this investigation, a seismic program was proposed to the industry. Sufficient support was received and the program commenced in the fall of 1977. Over 280 miles of seismic data were acquired in Mesa, Montrose and San Miguel Counties, Colorado, and San Juan County, Utah. The location of this seismic control is illustrated in Figure 1.

SEISMIC DATA ACQUISITION

The seismic program was intended for reconnaissance purposes in order to gain regional control and generate local leads. It was designed so as to take advantage of the roads and trails that exist in the area. Additional program to develop the leads would probably require a portable seismic crew because of topographic conditions and/or U.S. Forest Service regulations.

Initially, the survey was conducted using shot hole dynamite as the energy source. The quality of the data was good but the cost of the shot hole drilling was as high as $5000 per mile in portions of the area. For this reason the energy source was changed to Vibroseis. Costs were reduced without a reduction in quality.

Data acquisition parameters for the dynamite and the Vibroseis data are listed below. A typical data processing sequence can be seen on the Exhibits.

Dynamite Data Field Parameters

CDP Stack:	600%
Shotpoint interval:	880 feet
Group interval:	220 feet — 24 phones/Group
Energy Source:	Dynamite
Depth of shot:	60 foot holes (3 hole patterns)
Recording:	DFS V — 48 channels

Vibroseis Data Field Parameters

CDP Stack:	1200%
Group interval:	220 feet
V.P. interval:	440 feet
Near offset:	1155 feet
Far offset:	8745 feet

Number of traces:	48
Geophones per trace:	24
Recording filter:	8-62
Sample rate:	4 mils.
Record length:	19 seconds
Sweep length:	14 seconds
Sweep frequency:	10-40
Number of sweeps:	16 per Vibrator point

To illustrate the quality of data that was acquired with the above data acquisition and processing parameters, three exhibits are included.

Exhibit (A) — A large salt pillow with major geological changes is noted as follows:
1. Large normal fault on the flank of the pillow.
2. Major depositional changes throughout the entire section from one flank of the pillow to the other.
3. Onlap pattern on the north flank of the pillow.

Exhibit (B) — This illustrates the loss of data across a salt anticline. A major unconformity is also noted on this section.

Exhibit (C) — Apparently this line of control is on the flank of a salt anticline because the deep data is preserved. A salt pillow is also indicated just above the Mississippian.

It is noted on the Exhibits that data is destroyed where the salt anticlines outcrop. It may be possible to solve this problem by designing a program to shoot normal to the anticline using a long in line offset and keeping both the source and receivers off the salt outcrop. This could eliminate noise generated by the salt.

GEOLOGICAL REASONS FOR OIL EXPLORATION

The area of investigation contains many intriguing possibilities for the trapping and accumulation of hydrocarbons. Known traps in the area are both structural and stratigraphic. The known structural traps are anticlinal closures, faulted anticlines, and drape folding in association with block faulting. The stratigraphic traps include pinchouts of sandstone lenses, algal mound build-ups (southern part of the area) and unconformity traps. The area in and around the salt anticlines themselves provides a wide variety of trapping situations. These are due to the unique depositional features that are associated with flowage and deformation of salt.

A system of faults probably developed in Pre-Cambrian time and was repeatedly rejuvenated throughout Paleozoic time (Baars, 1966). Flowage of the Pennsylvanian Paradox Salt began when the overlying Honaker Trail formation was preferentially eroded along basement fault trends. The salt continued to flow due to increased overburden as a result of rapid Permian (Upper Cutler) sedimentation. This rapid

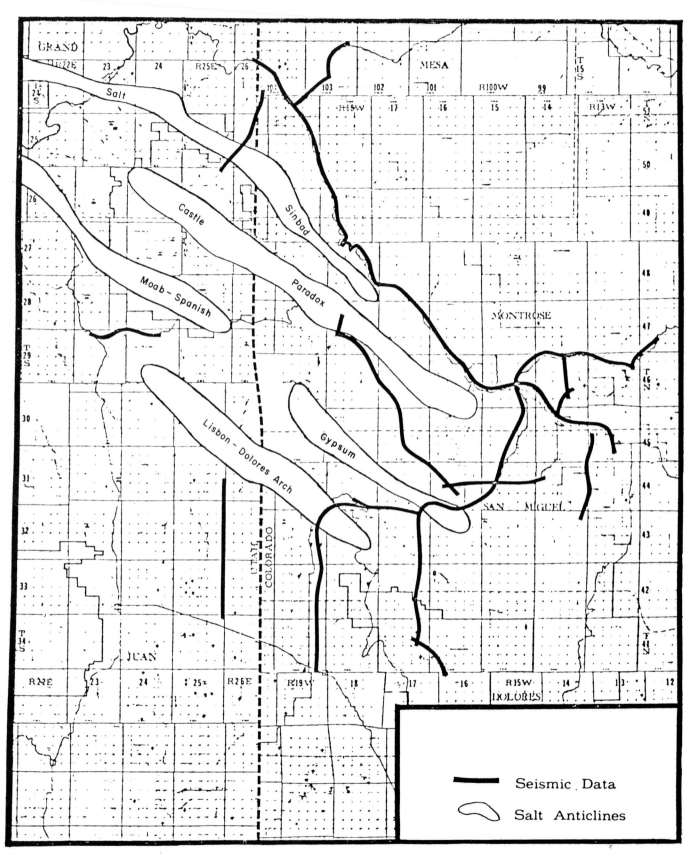

Figure 1

deposition of Upper Cutler sediments caused upwelling of the salt into areas which are now the present day salt anticlines. Lower Cutler beds were upwarped by this flowage along the flanks of the anticlines. Upper Cutler beds, however, are flat lying and therefore, angular unconformities exist between the Upper and the Lower Cutler beds. Flowage continued until late Jurassic and locally there are areas where no salt remains. In these areas the Pinkerton Trail formation (Lower Pennsylvanian Hermosa) is directly overlain by the Ismay (Upper Pennsylvanian Paradox). The upward movement of the salt caused thinning and in some instances, non-deposition of later sediments over the axis and flanks of the Salt Anticlines.

Later regional modifications occurred as a result of compression during the Laramide Orogeny and by normal faulting on the flanks of the Anticlines as the Colorado Plateau was uplifted.

EXPLORATION AND PRODUCTION

Early exploration in the area centered around the obvious surface structures with little success. Due to the masking effect of the mobile salt section or modification of the structures by later uplifts, the subsurface structures rarely coincide with surface structures. The elusive nature of the subsurface structures requires the use of seismic exploration. Modern CDP data is of utmost value as an exploration tool.

Table I shows a list of discoveries in the subject area. The wells are listed by state in chronological order, showing operator, date of discovery, location, producing formation, type of trap and method of exploration leading to the discovery. As can be seen in Table I, the majority of discoveries were found through seismic exploration. Even in the very early days of 100% analog seismic data, stratigraphic as well as structural anomalies were mapped and successfully drilled. Advancements in seismic technology, including digital seismic recording and common depth point stacking, yield data with far better resolution of seismic reflectors. This enables the geophysicist to explore for the more subtle traps.

CONCLUSION

Successful exploration in the Salt Anticline Area is increasing significantly due to advancements in technology in the recording and processing of seismic data. Today's technology enables the explorationist to locate structural and stratigraphic traps that could not have been discovered in the past. Further improvements should prove to be even more effective in locating traps favorable for hydrocarbon accumulation.

REFERENCES CITED

Baars, R. L., "Pre-Pennsylvanian Paleotectonics of Southwestern Colorado and East Central Utah", unpublished thesis, Dept. of Geology, University of Colorado, 492-841, 1966.

Cater, F. W. and D. P. Elston, "Structural Development of San Juan Basins". *Four Corners Field Conference Guidebook,* Four Corners Geological Society, 125-131, 1955.

Cater, F. W., and D. P. Elston, "Structural Development of Salt Anticlines of Colorado and Utah", *Backbone of the Americas,* AAPG Memoir #2, 152-159, 1963.

Elston, D. P., and E.M. Shoemaker, "Late Paleozoic and Early Mesozoic Structural History of the Uncompahgre Front", *Four Corners Geological Society Guidebook,* 47-55, 1960.

Hite, Robert J. and F. W. Cater, "Pennsylvanian Rock and Salt Anticlines, Paradox Basin, Utah and Colorado", *Geologic Atlas of the Rocky Mountain Region,* Rocky Mountain Assoc. Geol., Denver, 1972.

Maret, Raymond Eldon, "Geology of Sinbad Valley Anticline", *Geology of the Paradox Basin Fold and Fault Belt, Third Field Conference Guidebook,* Four Corners Geological Society, 43-46, 1960.

Parker, John M., "Lisbon Field Area, San Juan Co., Utah", AAPG Memoir #9, *Natural Gases of North America, Vol. 2,* 1371-1388, 1968.

Shoemaker, Eugene M., J. E. Case and D. P. Elston, "Salt Anticlines of the Paradox Basin", *Guidebook to the Geology of the Paradox Basin,* Ninth Annual Field Conference, Intermt. Assoc. Pet. Geol., Salt Lake City, Utah, 1958.

Acknowledgements go to Dennis Bodenchuk and Joan Klipping for their help.

TABLE I

Oil and Gas Fields in
THE SALT ANTICLINE AREA

NAME OF FIELD AND DISCOVERY DATE & OPERATOR	LOCATION OF DISCOVERY WELL	PRODUCING FORMATION	TYPE OF TRAP	EXPLORATION TECHNIQUE LEADING TO DISCOVERY
SOUTHWEST COLORADO				
Dove Creek 1948 - Western Natural Gas Co.	NE NW Sec. 3, T38N-R19W Montezuma Co., Colorado	Pennsylvanian, Lower Desert Creek, Member of Paradox Formation	Stratigraphic Structural	Surface Mapping
Montrose Dome 1958 - Kirby Petroleum	SW SW (530' FSL and 950' FWL) Sec. 4, T45N-R16W Montrose County, Colo.	Permian, Lower Cutler Group & Pennsylvanian Upper Honaker Trail Formation	Structural and Stratigraphic	Seismic, subsurface, and surface geology
Lisbon S.E. 1960 - Pure Oil Co. *1972 Deeper Pool	NE NW (712' FNL and 1921' FWL) Sec. 5 T44N-R19W, San Miguel County, Colorado	Mississippian, Leadville, Limestone	Anticlinal Structure	Seismic & Subsurface Geology

TABLE I (Cont'd.)

Egnar 1961 - (Combined with Lisbon S.E.)	T44N-R19W - *see #3 Lisbon S.E.			
House Creek 1961 - The California Company	SW SW (725' FSL & 510' FWL) Sec. 20, T38N-R15W Montezuma County, Colo.	Permian, Cutler Formation	Pinchout of Sandstone Lense	Seismic & Subsurface Geology
Andy's Mesa 1967 - Union Oil	NW SE (2121' FSL & 1839' FEL) - Sec. 34, T44N-R16W, San Miguel County, Colorado	Permian, Cutler Formation and Pennsylvanian, Honaker Trail Formation	Stratigraphic & Structural	Seismic & Stratigraphic
Papoose Canyon 1970 - Cherokee & Pittsburg Coal & Mining	NE NE (660' FNL & 660' FEL) - Sec. 31, T39N-R19W, Dolores County, Colorado	Pennsylvanian, Desert Creek Zone, Paradox Formation	Stratigraphic, algal mound "Buildup"	Subsurface geology & Seismic
Slickrock 1972 - Read & Stevens, Inc.	NE SE - Sec. 8, T43N-R17W	Pennsylvanian, Ismay Member of Paradox Formation	Stratigraphic, Fractures	Subsurface Geology & Seismic
Undesignated (combined with Papoose Canyon)	*See #7 Papoose Canyon			
Undesignated 1975 Grynberg	SE NE Sec. 24, T46N-R18W	Cutler		
Hamilton Creek 1976 Beaver Mesa Explor.	NW NW (1350' FWL & 900' FWL) - Sec. 16 T44N-R14W, San Miguel County, Colorado	Pennsylvanian, Honaker Trail Formation	Stratigraphic	Subsurface Geology
Shell Oil 1978 #1 Federal	NE NW Sec. 8, T40N-R16W, Dolores County, Colorado	Mississippian, Leadville		
SOUTHEAST UTAH				
Coalbed Canyon 1956 Gulf	SE SE Sec. 15, T35S-R25E, San Juan County, Utah	Pennsylvanian, Desert Creek, Member of Paradox Formation	Stratigraphic (small but highly permeable reservoir)	Surface Geology & Seismic
Lisbon 1960 Pure Oil	NE NW Sec. 10, T30S-R24E, San Juan County, Utah	Dev. McCracken SS. Member of Elbert Fm.; Mississippian, Redwall Lm.	Faulted anticline	Seismic & Subsurface Geology
Big Indian Field 1961 Pure	SE NE Sec. 33, T29S-R24E, San Juan County, Utah	Mississippian, Leadville Lm.	Faulted anticline	Seismic
Little Valley 1961 Pubco	SE NW Sec. 21, T30S-R25E, San Juan County, Utah	Mississippian, Leadville Lm.	Faulted anticline	Surface Geology & Seismic
Big Indian Undesignated 1963 Pure	NE SW Sec. 10, T30S-R25E	Pennsylvanian, Upper Hermosa	Stratigraphic	Surface Geology & Seismic
Alkali Canyon 1965 Conoco	NE SE Sec. 15, T37S-R23E, San Juan County, Utah	Penn., Middle Ismay Member of Paradox Formation	Stratigraphic	Seismic

TABLE I (Cont'd.)

Wilson Canyon 1968 Gulf	SE NE Sec. 24, T29S-R23E, San Juan County, Utah	Penn., Cane Creek Zone, Paradox Formation	Stratigraphic with Struc. implications	Seismic
Piute Knoll 1973 Mountain Fuel	NE SW Sec. 26, T33S-R25E, San Juan County, Utah	Penn., U. of Ismay of the Paradox Formation	Stratigraphic	Subsurface geology
Undesignated 1976 Mountain Fuel	SW SW Sec. 32, T33N-R26E	Pennsylvanian		
Hook & Ladder 1977 Husky	SW SE Sec. 25, T29S-R23E	Mississippian, Leadville Lm.	Anticlinal folding assoc. with Block Faulting	Seismic & Subsurface Geology

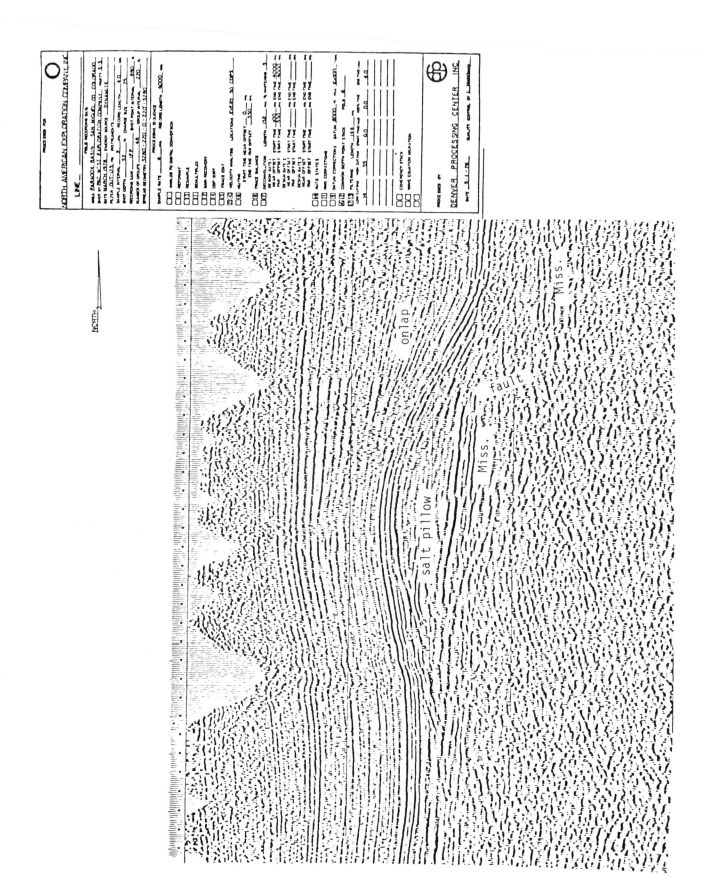

EXHIBIT A

EXHIBIT B

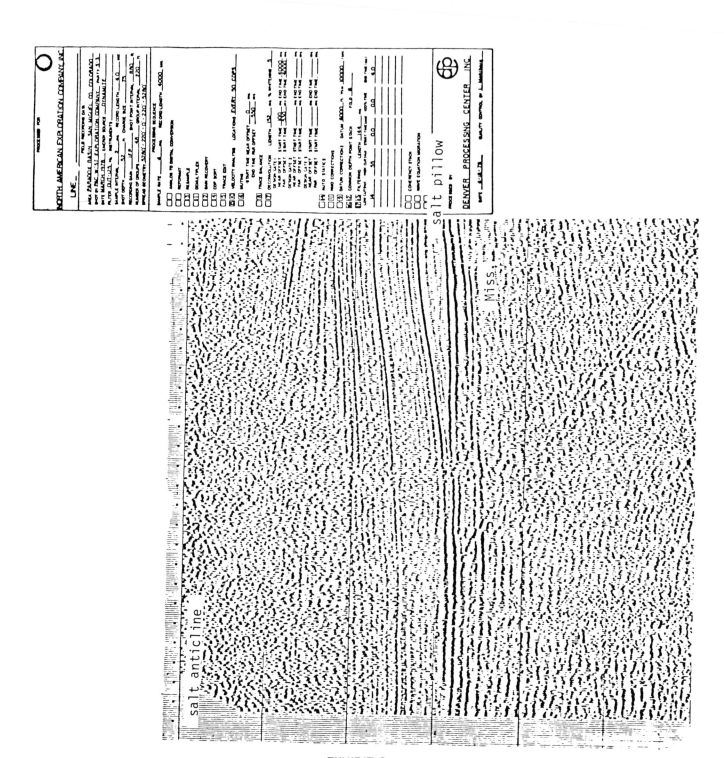

EXHIBIT C

LOW-LEVEL HISTORICAL AND CONTEMPORARY SEISMICITY IN THE PARADOX BASIN, UTAH AND ITS TECTONIC IMPLICATIONS

Ivan G. Wong and Ruth B. Simon

ABSTRACT

The level of seismicity within the Paradox Basin of southeastern Utah and southwestern Colorado appears to be very low relative to regions outside the interior of the Colorado Plateau. However, this assessment is based primarily upon a historical record of seismicity that is most likely incomplete and limited in its time span. Of the 22 events recorded in the Paradox Basin in the last 126 years, 10 are distributed diffusely throughout the basin and 12 events are located in the northwestern portion of the basin near the Book Cliffs. These latter earthquakes are probably induced events attributable to underground coal extraction.

In order to assess the contemporary seismicity in the Paradox Basin, an extensive program of microearthquake monitoring was initiated in the summer of 1979. In the ensuing 15 months, approximately 230 microearthquakes ranging from M_L -1.0 to 2.4 were detected; 95 percent were observed along a 35 km long section of the Colorado River north of its confluence with the Green River. The apparent northern extent of this microseismicity coincides with an approximate 20 degree change in the river's direction near Moab. Focal depths of events range from 2 km, the top of the Precambrian basement, to approximately 10 km. Fault plane solutions exhibit strike-slip faulting with minor components of reverse motion, and maximum horizontal compressive stress in an approximate east-west direction. This is consistent with other observations for the Colorado Plateau interior. Each solution possesses a right-slip nodal plane trending in an approximate northeast direction parallel with the river. These observations are consistent with the suggestion by several authors that this portion of the Colorado River is underlain by a Precambrian basement wrench fault(s).

Present observations also suggest that the annual ten-fold increase and decrease in the river discharge and corresponding change in the river stage may influence the occurrence of microseismicity along the river.

The microearthquake activity observed in other portions of the basin is diffusely distributed. Events were generally shallow (less than 15 km); one notable microearthquake was located at a focal depth of 38 km, near the crust-upper mantle boundary.

INTRODUCTION

The Paradox Basin of southeastern Utah and southwestern Colorado is located in the interior of the Colorado Plateau. The plateau is a geomorphic and tectonic province that is generally considered to be relatively tectonically stable. Consistent with this view, the historical record of seismicity in the Paradox Basin indicates a very low level of seismicity. However, this may not be a completely accurate assessment because: (1) the historical record is very short relative to a geologic time scale; (2) the pre-instrumental earthquake record, which dates back to the 1850s, is dependent upon population density and distribution for felt reports and southeastern Utah has remained sparsely populated since the arrival of the first pioneer settlers; and (3) adequate regional seismographic coverage has only been in existence since 1962.

As part of a geological program designed to identify a potential site for an underground, high-level nuclear waste repository, studies into the historical and contemporary seismicity of the Paradox Basin were undertaken by Woodward-Clyde Consultants (WCC) under contract to the Office of Nuclear Waste Isolation, Battelle Memorial Institute. The objectives of the seismology program are twofold. The first objective is to define the seismic environment of the basin by identifying and characterizing source areas of seismic activity and correlating such activity with geologic structures. This knowledge provides baseline information for evaluating historical, contemporary, and possibly future earthquake activity. The second objective is to identify potential seismic hazards that could impact the installation and operation of an underground repository located in the Paradox Formation.

HISTORICAL SEISMICITY

Figures 1 and 2 show the epicenters of historical earthquakes of approximate Richter magnitude (M_L) 1.0 or greater within the Paradox Basin and surrounding region (Four Corners) for the periods 1853 through 1961, and 1962 to 30 June 1979, respectively. The primary source for this data base is the University of Utah Seismographic Stations (Arabasz and others, 1979). Other data sources are the National Oceanic and Atmospheric Administration Hypocenter Data File, Cash and others (1978), Docekal (1970), Jaksha and Locke (1978), Newton and others (1976), Northrop (1976), Northrop and Sanford (1972), Sanford (1978), and Slemmons (1975). For the period before 1962, locations are based primarily on felt reports and are assigned the location of the maximum reported intensity (Figure 1). For the period after 1962, locations are determined instrumentally (Figure 2). The great majority of recorded historical seismicity is in this latter period.

The accuracy of epicentral locations based on felt reports is a function of population size and density. In regions of low population density, such as the Paradox Basin, an earthquake may occur a considerable distance from the nearest location reporting the event. In many cases an historical earthquake may be associated with a particular town because the felt report from that town was the only one available. When detailed descriptions of effects from many locations are available, an isoseismal map can be constructed and a more accurate epicentral location can be estimated.

The detection level and completeness of the pre-1962 record is therefore a function of changing population size and density. Although a seismographic station was

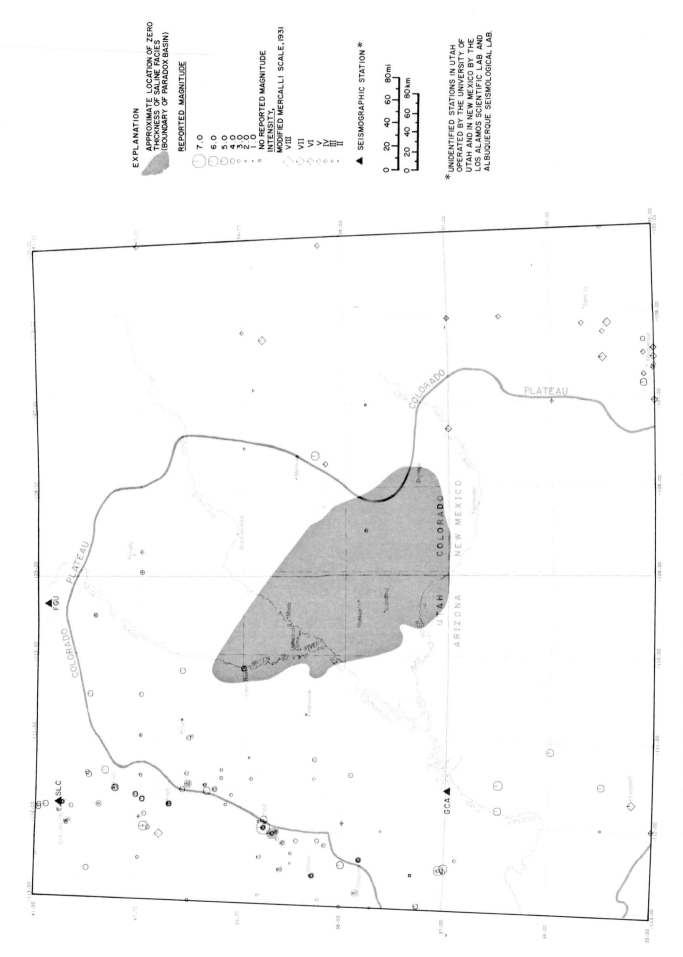

Figure 1. Preinstrumental historical earthquake epicenters of the Paradox Basin and Four Corners Region, 1853 through 1961

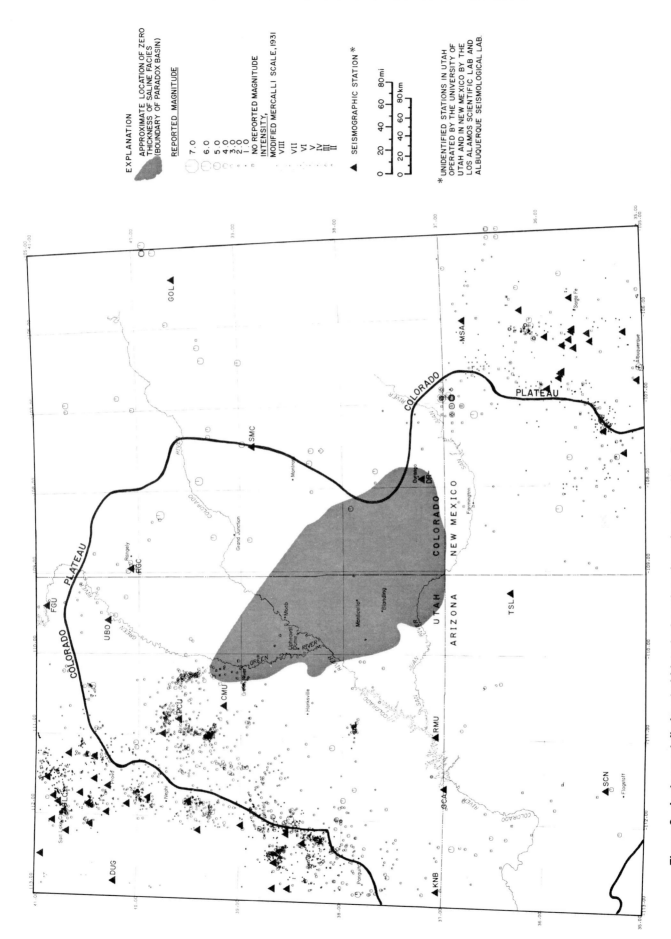

Figure 2. Instrumentally located historical earthquake epicenters of the Paradox Basin and Four Corners Region, 1962 to 30 June 1979

established in the Intermountain region in Salt Lake City in 1909, there were not enough stations in the Intermountain states prior to approximately 1962 to accurately locate an earthquake less than M_L 4.5 in the Paradox Basin.

To locate an earthquake instrumentally, at least three seismographs at separate locations must record the event. The calculation of the epicenter or hypocenter is based on mathematical procedures of triangulation and on a knowledge of the seismic wave velocities along the travel path from source to recording station (Richter, 1958). Four location parameters of an earthquake are routinely calculated using seismic wave arrival times: origin time, latitude, longitude, and focal depth of the earthquake. Focal depth is usually the least well determined parameter because stations are generally too widely spread to provide well-constrained data. To calculate accurate focal depths, an arrival time from at least one station having an epicentral distance equal to or less than the focal depth of the earthquake is required.

DETECTION LEVELS AND LOCATION UNCERTAINTY

Based on population density and distribution data (Figure 3) and on a history of seismographic station coverage in the region, detection levels and location uncertainty can be estimated for historical earthquakes occurring in the Paradox Basin and surrounding region for the period 1850 to 1979. The term "detection level" is defined as the minimum magnitude (M_L) or minimum epicentral intensity (Modified Mercalli, MM) of an earthquake that can be located instrumentally or based on felt reports. Location uncertainty is stated in terms of a radius of estimated average uncertainty of a reported epicenter.

1850 TO 1890

The Settlement of Utah began in the Salt Lake Valley in 1847 with the arrival of Mormon pioneers led by Brigham Young. The population slowly increased in north-central Utah; southeastern Utah remained relatively unpopulated (Figure 3). By 1890, the population of southeastern Utah approached 10,000. More than half of this population was centered in Emery County and was associated with the growth of the coal mining industry. For southeastern Utah and the Four Corners region, only very large earthquakes (MM intensity IX or greater) are likely to have been reported during this time period. No such events were reported. A smaller earthquake might have been reported if it had occurred close to one of the widely scattered population centers. The location uncertainty is estimated to be as much as 160 km.

1890 TO 1950

During this period the population of southeastern Utah doubled. However, most of the increase for southeastern Utah was in and around population centers and not in the rural areas. For southeastern Utah, northwestern New Mexico, and northeastern Arizona, the record is estimated to be complete for earthquakes of MM intensity VI or greater. The location uncertainty is estimated to be 80 km. For much of western Colorado, with its greater relative population, earthquakes of MM intensity V or greater are estimated to have been detected with a location uncertainty of better than 40 km.

During this period, seismographic stations were established in Salt Lake City (1909), Logan, Utah (1933), and Boulder Dam, Arizona (1941). These stations, however, were intended for studying local seismicity and were not routinely used for locating regional earthquakes.

1950 TO 1962

This period represents a transition during which earthquakes in the Intermountain states began to be located instrumentally. In some cases, events in Utah were located instrumentally if they were large enough to be recorded at seismographic stations outside the Intermountain states. In 1950, the U.S. Coast and Geodetic Survey also began coordinating, collecting and publishing information on earthquakes occurring throughout the United States.

In 1959, a station was installed at Glen Canyon, Arizona. This station would later become one of the most important stations for studies of Four Corners seismicity. However, for this time period, the Four Corners region had an instrumental detection level of about M_L 4.0 to 4.5 and a location uncertainty of 50 km.

1962 TO 1974

As a result of nuclear test ban discussions in 1958, the United States Coast and Geodetic Survey, under the U.S. Department of Commerce, embarked upon an extensive global seismic monitoring program called the Worldwide Standardized Seismograph Network (WWSSN). In 1962, a significant increase in the number of seismographic stations occurred in the Intermountain states. WWSSN stations were installed at Price, Uinta Basin, and Dugway, Utah; Albuquerque, New Mexico; and Golden, Colorado. These additional installations provided the capability to locate all moderate-sized earthquakes occurring within the region. For the Four Corners region, the detection level decreased to about M_L 3.0 to 3.5 and the location uncertainty decreased to 20 km.

1974 TO 1979

In 1974, the University of Utah Seismograph Stations (UUSS) initiated an extensive program of seismic monitoring in north-central and south-central Utah. Approximately 50 high-gain stations are currently in operation; the heaviest station concentration is along the Wasatch fault zone in north-central Utah. This program vastly improved the detection of earthquakes in northern and central Utah. However, only a single UUSS station was installed in southeastern Utah: northwest of the Green River[1]. Even with the installation of the Rainbow Monument station in 1976 (now out of operation) by the U.S. Bureau of Reclamation, the detection level and location uncertainty improved only slightly for the Four Corners region, possibly to M_L 2.5 to 3.0 and 10 to 20 km, respectively.

HISTORICAL SEISMICITY OF THE FOUR CORNERS REGION

The region shown on the map of historical epicenters (Figures 1 and 2) includes three physiographic and tectonic provinces: (1) the block-faulted Basin and Range; (2) the Colorado Plateau; and (3) the middle and southern Rocky Mountains. Most of the instrumentally located earthquakes (Figure 2) are located along (1) the Intermountain Seismic Belt, which coincides with the boundary between the Basin and Range province and the Colorado Plateau-middle Rocky Mountains (Smith and Sbar, 1974); and (2) the Rio Grande rift zone in north-central New Mexico.

Nonuniform seismographic coverage (stations are concentrated along the Intermountain Seismic Belt and the Rio Grande rift) may partially account for the uneven distribution of seismic activity shown on Figure 2. Nevertheless, the dominant source of seismicity in the Intermountain region is the Intermountain Seismic Belt, which extends north from Arizona through Utah to northwestern Montana. In Utah, the belt is defined by the

[1]A station has recently been installed near Capitol Reef.

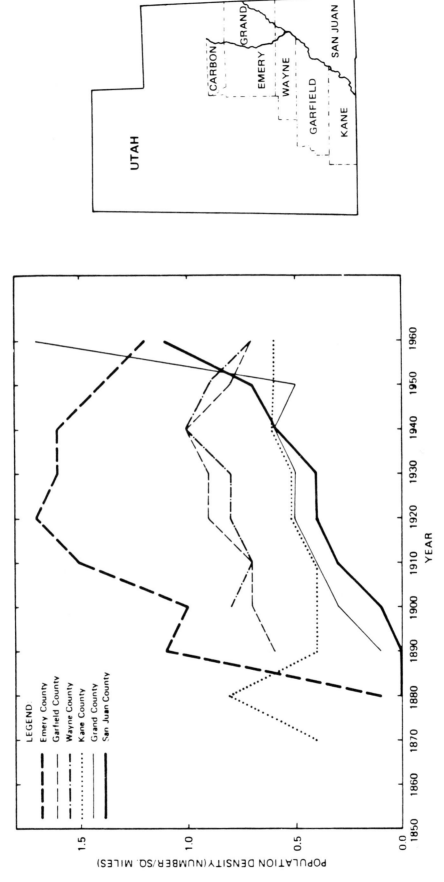

Figure 3. Population growth of southeastern Utah based on U.S. Census Records

East Cache and Wasatch fault zones in the north-central portion of the state, and by the Sevier, Tushar, and Hurricane fault zones in the south-central portion. The belt is interpreted to be a zone of extension developed along an intraplate boundary (Smith and Sbar, 1974).

A notable feature of New Mexico seismicity (Figure 2) is a cluster of moderate-magnitude epicenters on the Colorado-New Mexico border, composed principally of the 22 January 1966 M_L 5.5 Dulce earthquake and its aftershocks.

HISTORICAL SEISMICITY OF THE PARADOX BASIN

OVERVIEW

For the period 1853 to June 30, 1979, 22 seismic events with M_L approximately greater than 3.0 have been located within the Paradox Basin. Because the Paradox Basin has been an area of very active mining, the term "seismic event" is used here because some of the events may have been explosions. Discrimination between earthquakes and blasts from a simple examination of the seismic signature is difficult, particularly at regional distances. However, it is likely that only a few blasts were mistaken as earthquakes, because the sources of large, frequent blasting in Utah have been known to seismic monitoring agencies such as UUSS.

Of the 22 recorded historical events in the Paradox Basin, 12 occurred in the extreme northwestern area where the basin extends for a short distance beneath the Book Cliffs. A horseshoe-shaped distribution of epicenters (Figure 2) defines the extent of the Book Cliffs in the vicinity of Price and Green River. Studies by the U.S. Bureau of Mines, the U.S. Geological Survey (USGS), and the University of Utah in the Sunnyside coal-mining district (18 km north of the Paradox Basin) indicate that this local seismicity is induced by underground coal extraction.

The remaining 10 events recorded in the Paradox Basin are widely scattered. The only reported felt event in the historical record was a Modified Mercalli intensity V event west of Green River on 30 July 1953 (Figure 1). This event is located in the zone of seismicity defining the Book Cliffs (Figure 2) and so may be a mining-induced event.

The largest magnitude-determined event in the Paradox Basin was a m_b^2 3.8 event on 1 February 1967 located near Upheaval Dome (Figure 2). This event may have been slightly mislocated; it is possibly associated with microearthquake activity near the Colorado River northeast of its confluence with the Green River.

INDUCED SEISMICITY

Induced seismicity is defined as the man-related occurrence of earthquakes, usually triggered by mine excavations, reservoir impoundment, fluid injection, and underground explosions. In all cases, the local area must be pre-stressed to a substantial fraction of the stresses necessary for failure in order for seismicity to be induced (Kisslinger, 1976). Stress concentrations caused either by the presence of faults or by inhomogenities in material properties play an important role in localized induced seismicity (Kisslinger, 1976). Two examples of induced seismicity by fluid injection occurred at the Rangely, Colorado oil field at the northern perimeter of the Colorado Plateau (Raleigh and others, 1972) and the Rocky Mountain arsenal waste disposal well in Denver (Major and Simon, 1968) (Figure 2).

A mining-induced earthquake is sometimes manifested by a rock-burst (or bump when it occurs in coal), which is a sudden and often violent failure of masses of rock in quarries, tunnels and mines associated with the free face exposed by excavation (Osterwald, 1970). In the summer of

1970, Smith and others (1974) conducted detailed microearthquake and associated acoustical monitoring in the Sunnyside district. The zone of greatest activity was found to be located 1 km beneath a mine that exhibited floor and roof failures. The fault directions deduced from seismic records were in general agreement with the stress pattern attributed to the tectonic development of the nearby San Rafael Swell. This pattern suggests that the main earthquake energy was derived from regional tectonic stress (Smith and others, 1974). Seismic monitoring by the USGS (Dunrud and Osterwald, 1965) also revealed seismic activity extending to 2.4 km below the mine. Another case of mine-induced seismicity in the region has been observed at the coal mines near Somerset, Colorado on the eastern perimeter of the Colorado Plateau (Osterwald and others, 1972).

CONTEMPORARY SEISMICITY BASED ON MICROEARTHQUAKE DATA

MICROEARTHQUAKE MONITORING

An accurate assessment of the seismic environment of the Paradox Basin cannot be made solely on the basis of the historical record. The limited time span of the record, its incompleteness, the variation of the detection levels as a function of time and the possibly large location errors (which do not permit correlation with geologic structures) are major difficulties. Areas of low-level seismicity must always be considered cautiously in light of possibly long recurrence intervals (between large earthquakes) relative to the length of the historical record.

In order to define the present-day seismic environment, an extensive program of microearthquake monitoring was initiated in the summer of 1979. Because microearthquakes (events less than M_L 3.0) occur with greater frequency than large events, much can be learned from their occurrence: spatial and temporal characteristics, geologic associations, style and orientation of causative faults, recurrence rates, and regional tectonic stress field characterization. The study of microearthquakes is thus an important element in many modern seismic hazard investigations.

The microearthquake monitoring program consists of three phases: (1) a 6-month, 24-station monitoring of an oval-shaped area approximately 130 km long and 70 km wide extending from Moab, Utah south to the San Juan River, and from Highway 163 west to the Colorado River which began in late July 1979 (Figure 4); (2) a long-term monitoring by two subnetworks beginning in February 1980 and totaling 12 seismographic stations selected from the 24-station network of an area extending from Potash along the Colorado River through Moab northeast to Fisher Tower, including Salt Valley which began in late August 1980 (Figure 6).

SEISMOGRAPH STATION SITE SELECTION

The configurations of the microearthquake networks were selected to allow the identification of active earthquake sources within specific portions of the Paradox Basin at a detection threshold of approximately M_L 0.0. Stations were installed 10 to 20 km apart, providing good focal depth control (except possibly for events less than approximately 5 km deep). This station density also provided some redundancy in seismographic coverage in case of station malfunction or disruptions in scheduled maintenance and record-changing, a likely event given the rugged terrain and severe winter conditions in the Paradox Basin. Many of the stations located in the more rugged and less accessible areas of the networks were equipped with radio transmitters to provide FM telemetry to stations where the data could be more easily retrieved and recorded.

Body-wave magnitude

INSTRUMENTATION

Two types of microearthquake recording instruments are being used in the Paradox Basin microearthquake networks: a battery-powered, 48-hour smoked paper drum recorder and a digital event recorder. The drum recorder records continuously; the event recorder records on magnetic cassette tape only when it detects a signal that it identifies as an earthquake according to internally programmed criteria. The internal clocks of both instruments are synchronized to an external reference clock calibrated to the international radio time standard, station WWV. This allows timing accuracy to a few hundredths of a second. The sensors used are vertical component, short period (1 second) seismometers. Some of the long-term and Salt Valley stations telemeter their data into a recording center in Moab, where they are recorded on 16-mm photographic film and 24-hour pen-and-ink drum recorders.

SEISMIC EVENT LOCATIONS, VELOCITY MODEL AND MAGNITUDES

Hypocentral locations are calculated employing the computer program HYPOELLIPSE (Lahr, 1979). The inputs to the program are station locations, a crustal velocity model, and P and S arrival times. The origin time, latitude, longitude, focal depth and location statistics (standard errors, rms error, etc.) of the seismic event are calculated from these data.

The local crustal velocity model adopted for this study is modified from a regional model[3] presently employed by the University of Utah Seismographic Stations in their location of earthquakes in the Colorado Plateau portion of Utah. The top layer of the UUSS model has been changed from 1.5 km thick with a P-wave velocity of 3.0 km/sec to 2.0 km thick and a 4.3 km/sec P-wave velocity, based on WCC borehole velocity measurements. S-wave velocities were calculated by assuming a V_p/V_s ratio of 1.74 corresponding to a Poisson's ratio of 0.25. The model adopted for this study is as follows:

P-wave Velocity (km/sec)	S-wave Velocity (km/sec)	Depth (km)
4.3	2.47	0.0 - 2.0
6.2	3.56	2.0 - 27.5
6.8	3.91	27.5 - 40.0
7.8	4.48	40.0 and greater

Richter magnitudes or equivalent Richter magnitudes were obtained from the University of Utah for those seismic events within the Paradox Basin that were recorded at stations in their regional network. Otherwise, equivalent Richter magnitudes were calculated on the basis of a coda duration formula devised by Griscom and Arabasz (1979) for use by the University of Utah. Their estimated standard error for such magnitude determinations is ± 0.27.

FAULT PLANE SOLUTIONS

Fault plane solutions were produced by plotting first motion data on a lower hemisphere stereographic projection utilizing the computer program HYPOELLIPSE (Lahr, 1979). The distribution of the first P-wave motions of an earthquake recorded at seismographic stations can provide information on the orientation and style of faulting and the directions of the principal stresses. Whenever possible, fault plane solutions are prepared for single earthquakes. However, if not enough first motions are available to provide a well-constrained solution, either because the event is too small or because seismographic coverage is too sparse, several

events can be plotted on a single projection. A composite solution assumes that the orientation and style of faulting is the same for all the composited events.

BLASTING IDENTIFICATION

Because the Paradox Basin is a region of extensive mineral exploration, mining, oil and gas activities, a detailed investigation into sources of blasting was conducted to aid in earthquake-blast discrimination. Repetitive blasts at the same location produce similar seismograms, so blasting operations can be identified if they are conducted regularly at about the same time. Most suspected blasts occur during daylight hours, although some mining operations in the Paradox operate 24 hours a day.

Typically many events in this study were recorded on a single station and could not be located because of their small size and rapid loss of propagated seismic energy (identified as near surface source). However, many events exhibited signal characteristics generally displayed by blasts: compressive P-wave first motions, low frequency S-waves, and/or multiple phases. Together with the knowledge of nearby blasting locations and measured S-P arrival times to provide distances, it was usually possible to determine at least whether these events were blasts.

OBSERVATIONS AND RESULTS

Beginning 24 July 1979, when the first seismographic station was installed in the 24-station network, through 1 November 1980, approximately 500 seismic events (M_L -1.0) were detected in the Paradox Basin. Of these, 54 microearthquakes, 26 suspected blasts, and 10 events of unknown origin were recorded on a sufficient number of stations to be located (Figures 4, 5, and 6). Of the remaining 410 events that were too small to be located, approximately 170 were determined to be microearthquakes; the remainder were possible blasts or events of unknown origin.

Soon after the installation of the Grand View Point station on 29 July 1979, a microearthquake swarm (a sequence of events occurring close together in time and space but without a distinct mainshock) was observed in an area along the Colorado River approximately 10 km northeast of the Confluence. During the next 15 months of seismic monitoring, approximately 200 microearthquakes were detected in this area and along the 35-km long section of the river between the Confluence and Moab. This stretch of the Colorado River is the most active source of seismicity observed in the monitored portions of the Paradox Basin.

Figures 4, 5, and 6 show the spatial distribution of 47 located epicenters (M_L greater than approximately -1.0) in the vicinity of the Colorado River through 1 November 1980. Because of the variation in factors that govern the accuracy of an epicenter, the events shown have a varied degree of accuracy, estimated to be from 1 to 5 km. This variation is illustrated by the locations of the two northwestern epicenters shown near the Green River (Figure 4). Because a nearby station in the network was out of operation, these events are probably mislocated to the northwest by 5 to 10 km. Figure 7 shows a typical seismogram of two microearthquakes from this source area.

The majority of epicenters exhibit a slightly broad linear trend in a north-northeast direction coincident with the Colorado River. As Figure 6 illustrates, it appears that the northern extent of the microseismicity may be in the vicinity of Moab. This truncation of activity may be related to the approximate 20° change from the Colorado River's north-northeast direction south of Moab to a northeast course north of Moab.

[3]The UUSS model was adopted from a seismic refraction profile across the Colorado Plateau from Hanksville, Utah to Chinle, Arizona (Roller, 1965).

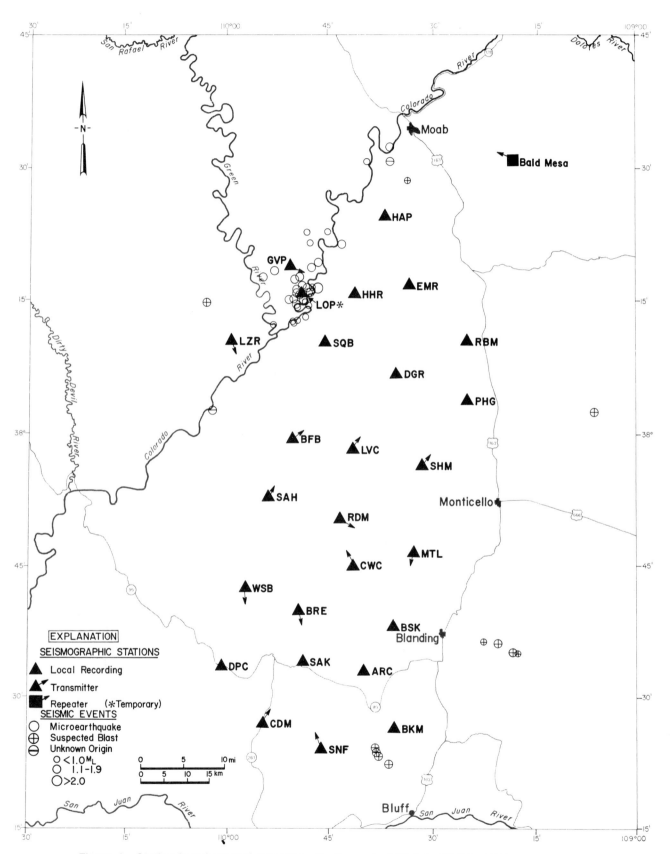

Figure 4.   Station locations and epicenters for the period 29 July 1979 to 15 February 1980

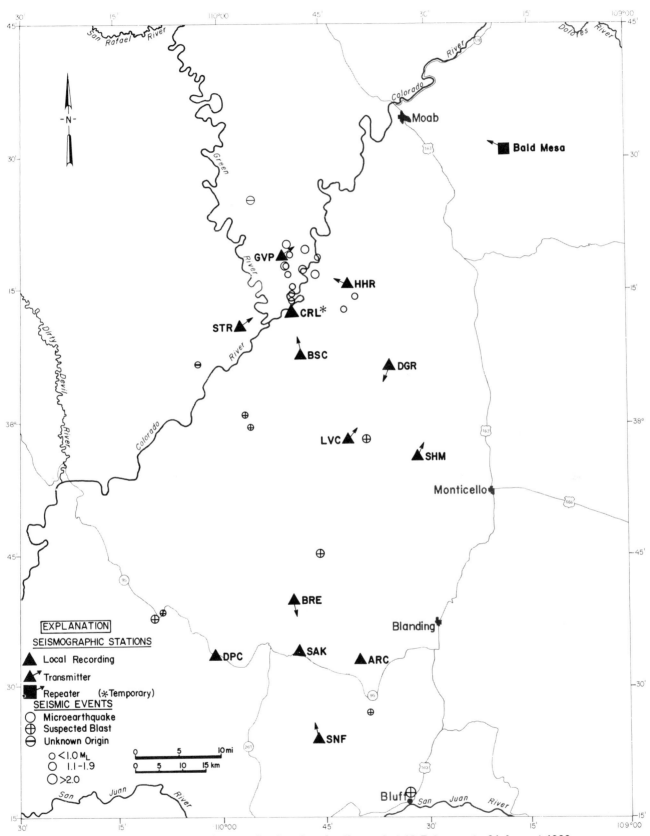

Figure 5. Station locations and epicenters for the period 16 February to 21 August 1980

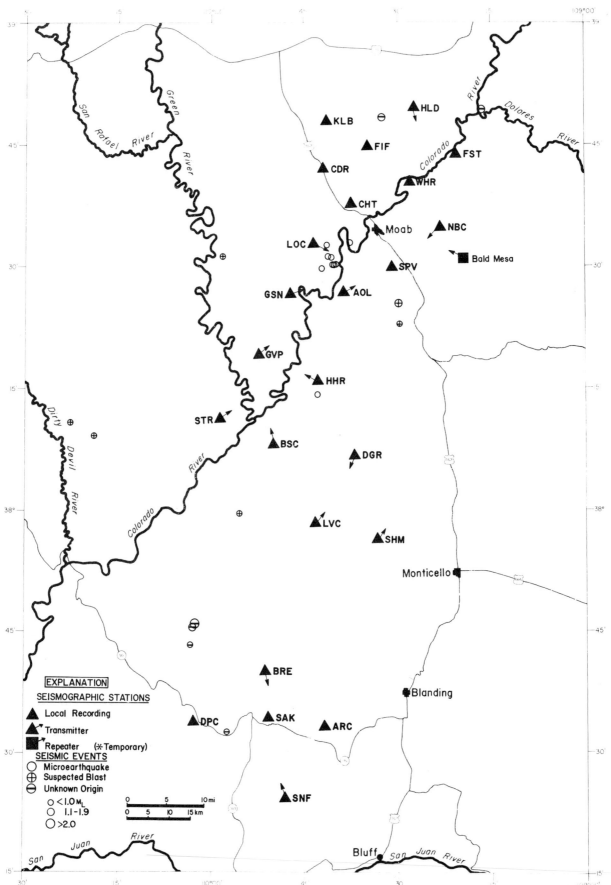

Figure 6. Station locations and epicenters for the period 22 August to 1 November 1980

The largest microearthquake observed to date in the vicinity of the river and the study area was a M_L 2.4 event on 10 September 1979 at 1221 Universal Coordinated Time (UCT). This event appeared to be preceded by one foreshock and was followed by approximately 25 aftershocks.

One other notable area of microseismicity is located approximately 3 km south of station HHR (Figures 5 and 6). Only three events have been located in this area; however, a M_L 0.5 event occurred there at 0809 UCT on October 12, 1980 with a focal depth of 38 km (the remaining two events had focal depths of 11 and 13 km). This anomalous focal depth would locate the microearthquake near the crust-upper mantle boundary. Although other deep intraplate earthquakes have been observed elsewhere in the world (a M_L 3.6 earthquake was located at approximately 90 km in northeast Utah on February 24, 1979; Zandt and Richins, 1980), they are poorly understood.

EVENT RELOCATIONS AND GEOLOGIC IMPLICATIONS

Many of the epicenters shown on Figure 4 occurred on the perimeter of the 24-station network, and were located with less than optimal azimuthal station coverage. In an attempt to improve the locations and possibly reveal a spatial pattern of the hypocenters, a relocation technique called Master Event was applied to the 18 largest microearthquakes observed during the period 24 July 1979 to 15 February 1980.

The Master Event method consists of relocating events utilizing station corrections calculated from a single "best located" event. This method provides a high level of relative accuracy for the hypocenters and an absolute accuracy dependent upon the master event. The master event used in this case was a well-recorded M_L 1.9 event that occurred at 0054 UCT on 27 August 1979.

Figure 8 shows the epicenters that were relocated by Master Event (circle size is dependent upon M_L; see Figure 4). They exhibit a tighter clustering of epicenters and a slightly more linear trend parallel to the Colorado River than was indicated by the single event locations. Profile views of the same events are also shown on Figure 8. Hypocenters are distributed between the approximate depths of 2 and 7 km, with an estimated accuracy of ± 1 to 2 km. These shallow focal depths are typical of the Intermountain area, where earthquakes seldom occur below 15 km and are usually less than 10 km. The 2-kilometer depth corresponds with the top of the Precambrian basement; therefore microseismicity appears to be occurring in crystalline rock rather than in sedimentary strata. No linear spatial trends indicative of faulting are evident in the profiles, although if the causative fault is assumed to strike in a northeast direction, the northeast view would show a seismogenic zone 5 km wide.

COMPOSITE FAULT PLANE SOLUTIONS

Figure 9 shows composite fault plane solutions for two series of events near the Colorado River: (1) four events of a possible foreshock-mainshock-aftershock sequence that occurred on 10 September 1979, including the largest event observed to date, a M_L 2.4; and (2) three events in mid-May 1980. Additional first motion data for the 10 September 1979 mainshock were obtained from the UUSS.

The solutions show fair constraint on the nodal planes, which exhibit strike-slip faulting with possible minor components of reverse motion on either an approximate northeast or northwest trending plane. The north-northeast striking nodal plane of the May 1980 solution agrees with the trend of this section of the Colorado River. The nodal plane trends of both solutions generally agree with the regional structural grain, which is composed dominantly of both northwest and northeast striking features. Both solutions exhibit east-west horizontal maximum compression as well as north-south minimum compression for the principal stress directions. These solutions agree well with a composite fault plane solution for several events in the Sunnyside coal mining district (Smith and others, 1974) and a fault plane solution for the fluid-induced seismicity at Rangely, Colorado (Raleigh and others, 1972), both of which also exhibit east-west maximum compression.

TEMPORAL BEHAVIOR

A remarkable aspect of the microseismicity observed during the 15 months of monitoring is the temporal behavior of the activity along the Colorado River, as shown on Figure 10. The level of activity was quite high in August 1979 (approximately 3 events per day), and then declined to essentially no events per day at the end of October. Thereafter, for a period of six months, only four microearthquakes above M_L -1.0 were detected in this area.

Activity resumed in mid-May 1980, lasted for one month, and ceased until the middle of September, except for three events on 19 July. This activity was confined to the area just south of Moab; no microearthquakes were observed in the Grand View Point area (Figure 6). Seismic monitoring of the upper portion of the Colorado River near Moab was not initiated until August 1980.

The Colorado River shows large oscillatory changes during a dramatic annual rise and decline in discharge during the spring and summer months (USGS, 1980). Because of the close spatial relationship of the microearthquake activity with the Colorado River, and its unusual temporal pattern, a possible relationship between seismicity and the discharge of the river was investigated. As Figure 10 illustrates, the events appear to occur after rapid declines; it also appears that the number of events is grossly related to the amount of decline in the river discharge. The high level of microearthquake activity in late July to August 1979 followed a relatively rapid and sharp decline (16,600 ft^3/sec) that began on 3 July and ended on 8 August.

The activity in mid-September 1979 followed a small peak in river discharge in the last half of August (Figure 10). Activity in mid-May and early June 1980 followed two sharp drops in river discharge during the general increase in discharge caused by spring runoff. During the period from November 1979 through April 1980, when seismic activity was almost nonexistent, two of the four detected microearthquakes followed small peaks in river discharge.

These observations suggest that a rapid drop in river discharge, and more specifically the corresponding drop in river stage, triggers microearthquake activity along a pre-existing fault or fault zone in the underlying Precambrian basement. The possible mechanism for such triggering may be similar to a few observed cases of reservoir-induced seismicity where instantaneous crustal weakening occurs because of excess pore pressure caused by rapid unloading (Bell and Nur, 1978).

Ninety-five percent of the microearthquakes occurring in the Paradox Basin are confined to the Colorado River. Although other northeast trending faults may exist elsewhere in the Precambrian basement (Hite, 1975), the concentration of activity along the river suggests that the river has a seismically triggering influence on the release of stress on fractures in the underlying basement (fault or fault zone).

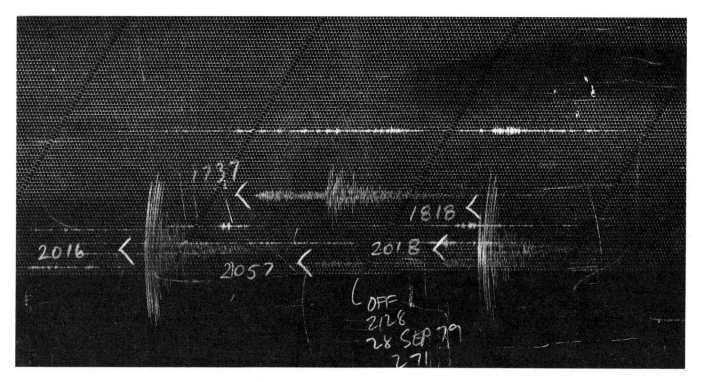

Figure 7. Portion of a smoked paper seismogram showing two microearthquakes recorded at the Grand View Point station. From left to right, the events are M_L 1.6 and 1.3. Both events occurred along the section of the Colorado River northeast of the Confluence.

TECTONIC IMPLICATIONS

NORTHEAST-TRENDING FEATURES AND THE COLORADO LINEAMENT

Hite (1975) suggested that many of the northeast trending features in the Paradox Basin, including the Colorado River below Moab, Utah, may be structurally controlled by basement shear zones or wrench faults. Hite noted that (1) many of the northeast-trending lineaments indicate left-lateral displacement of basement features; and (2) it is not well understood whether the basement structure is a wide shear zone, a single wrench fault, or a series of an echelon wrench faults. Hite also suggested that the northeast-trending structures in the Paradox Basin are probably only a small segment of a more extensive system. Warner (1978) assigned the name Colorado Lineament to this more extensive system of northeast-trending Precambrian faults, which traverses the Rocky Mountains of Colorado and the Colorado Plateau and is followed along much of its trend by the Colorado River. Warner suggested that this wrench fault system formed adjacent to the southeastern margin of the ancestral North American continent in connection with the Penokean orogeny 2000 to 1700 m.y. B.P.

The existence of a basement wrench fault or fault zone along at least 35 km stretch of the Colorado River southwest of Moab, as suggested by Hite (1975) and Warner (1978), is consistent with the following observations of microearthquake activity: (1) the apparent alignment of epicenters along the river; (2) the distribution of hypocenters extending from the top of the Precambrian basement to depths of approximately 10 km; and (3) the fault plane solutions, which exhibit dominantly strike-slip faulting along northeast trends. However, because of limited geological data, the existence of these northeast trending basement structures is speculative.

Although the fault plane solutions in this study exhibit right-slip faulting on the northeast trending plane, this does not necessarily conflict with Hite's suggestion of predominantly left-slip faulting, because slip direction on an active fault zone is determined by the contemporary regional stress field. An appropriate rotation in the stress field can reverse the sense of slip on a well established fault zone. En echelon faulting suggested by Hite could also account for these observations. Stone (1969) suggested that many northeast trending wrench faults in the Rocky Mountain region could be right-slip in character.

COMPARISON TO MIDCONTINENT SEISMICITY

In general, the seismicity of the Paradox Basin and the Colorado Plateau interior is more analogous to the seismicity of the mid-continent United States than of the western United States. The moderate to high level of seismicity in the western United States (which can be subdivided into a number of tectonic regions) is dominated by the San Andreas fault system, the Basin and Range province, and the Intermountain Seismic Belt. By contrast, the interior of both the Colorado Plateau and the midcontinent exhibit a diffuse pattern of low-level seismicity with few zones of concentrated activity. The similarity between the Colorado Plateau and the midcontinent may be related in large part to similar tectonic stress fields and crustal evolutions and properties (e.g., thickness, heat flow). The Paradox Basin and the Colorado Plateau interior appear to be subject to maximum horizontal compression in a general east-west direction, as exhibited by several fault plane solutions. The east-west compression of the plateau interior may be influenced by Basin and Range crustal extension to the west and extension of the Rio Grande rift to the east and southeast (Smith and Sbar, 1974). Much of the eastern United States is also characterized by predominantly compressional tectonism (which favors both thrust and strike-slip faulting) (Zoback and Zoback, 1980). Sbar and Sykes (1973) suggested that earthquake zones in the eastern United States are controlled by the existence of unhealed fault zones that are subject to high deviatoric stresses.

Hinz and others (1980), in their research on midcontinent tectonic models, devised the term "resurgent tectonics," believing that much contemporary tectonic activity is controlled by pre-existing geological features. Such models suggest that crustal rifts, zones of weakness and crustal boundaries and local crustal inhomogeneities passively localize the deformation resulting from stresses generated by a variety of tectonic forces.

CONCLUSIONS

Based on a limited historical record, the seismicity of the Paradox Basin has been and continues to be at a very low level. This observation is consistent with the view that there has been an absence of major crustal deformation in the interior of the Colorado Plateau since the Laramide orogeny, 40 m.y. B.P. The results of WCC's microearthquake monitoring program, showing a general low level of microseismicity within the Paradox Basin, support this theory.

The view that the seismicity along the Colorado River is possibly triggered by rapid declines in discharge and corresponding declines in river stage is consistent with the observation that within the interior of the Colorado Plateau, the few areas exhibiting relatively high levels of seismicity are related to some external influence, i.e., the mine-induced seismicity in the Book Cliffs and near Somerset, Colorado, and the fluid-induced seismicity at Rangely, Colorado. The tectonic stresses within the Plateau, at least in several localized areas, appear to be at sufficiently near-critical levels to provide the strain energy accumulation needed to produce earthquakes along possibly pre-existing zones of weakness. Local external changes in the stress field over a relatively short time period, when added to this tectonic stress, appear to be capable of triggering the seismic release of stored strain energy.

ACKNOWLEDGEMENTS

This research was sponsored by the Office of Nuclear Waste Isolation of Battelle Memorial Institute, Columbus, Ohio under contract to the U.S. Department of Energy. We wish to acknowledge the assistance of N. A. Frazier, ONWI Project Manager, Steve Kowall, ONWI Assistant Project Manager, and Fred Conwell, WCC Project Manager. We are indebted to the staff of WCC for their assistance and contributions: Barbara Munden, Jim Cullen, Jim Humphrey, Jean Briggs, Steve Kocherhans, Elizabeth Grace, Dick Thompson, Dave Marks, V-Anne Chernock, and Janet Adams. Critical review by Woody Savage, Tom Rogers, Terry Grant and Richard Ely is appreciated.

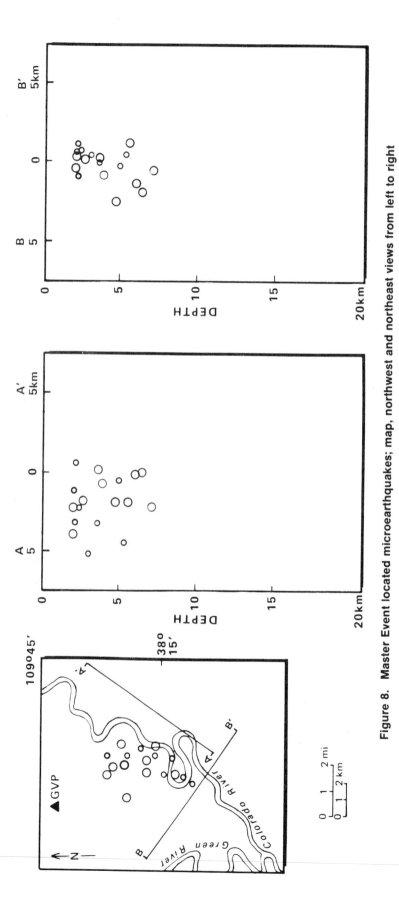

Figure 8.   Master Event located microearthquakes; map, northwest and northeast views from left to right

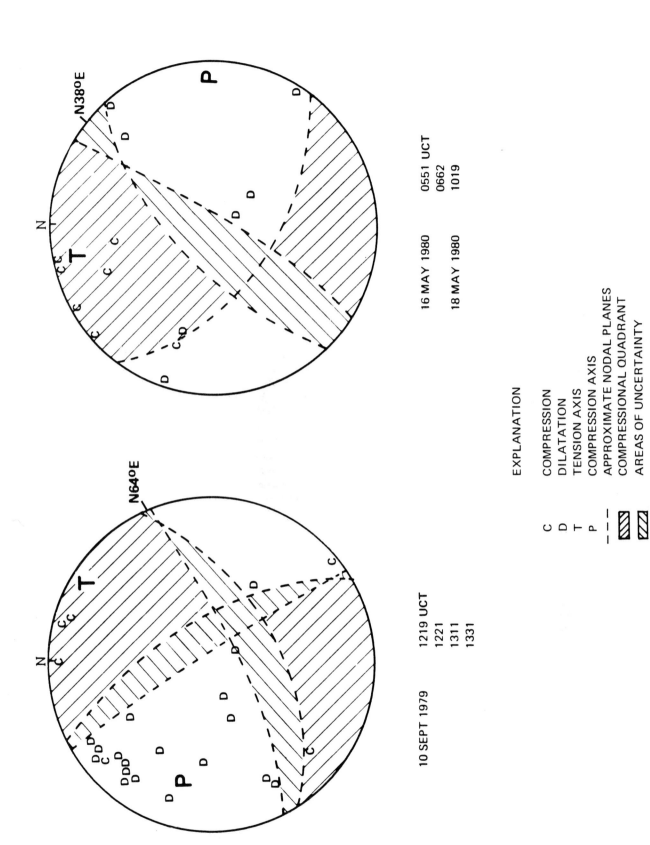

Figure 9. Composite fault plane solutions

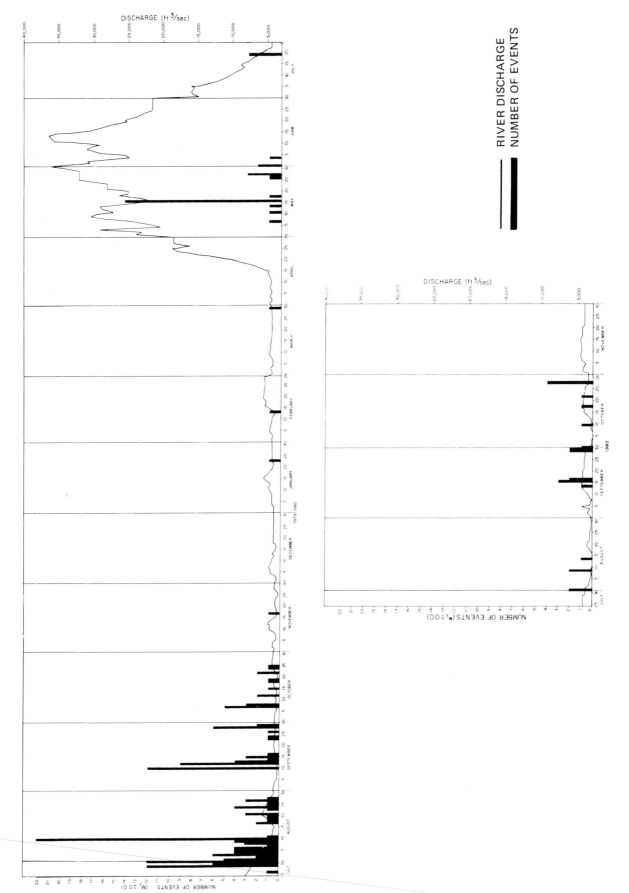

Figure 10. Histogram of events along the Colorado River and daily river discharge at the USGS Cisco, Utah monitoring station

REFERENCES

Arabasz, W. J., Smith, R. B. and Richins, W. D., 1979, Earthquake studies in Utah, 1850-1978, University of Utah Seismograph Stations, p. 57-251.

Bell, J. L., and Nur, A., 1978, Strength changes due to reservoir-induced pore pressure and stresses and application to Lake Oroville: Journal of Geophysical Research, v. 83, no. B9, p. 4469-4483.

Cash, D. J., McFarland, N. J., and Heady, J. J., 1978, Seismicity of northern New Mexico, 1973-1978: Los Alamos Scientific Laboratory Informal Report LA-1978.

Docekal, J., 1970, Earthquakes of the stable interior, with emphasis on the mid-continent, 2 volumes: Ph.D. dissertation, University of Nebraska, Lincoln, Nebraska.

Dunrud, C. R., and Osterwald, F. W., 1965, Seismic study of coal mine bumps, Carbon and Emery Counties, Utah, Society of Mining Engineers Transactions, v. 232, no. 2, p. 174-182.

Griscom, M. and Arabasz, W. J., 1979, Local magnitude (M_L) in the Wasatch Front and Utah Region: Wood-Anderson calibration, coda duration estimates of M_L and M_L versus m_b, in Earthquake studies in Utah, 1850 to 1978, edited by W. J. Arabasz, R. B. Smith and W. D. Richins, University of Utah Seismograph Stations, p. 433-443.

Hinze, W. J., Braile, L. W., Keller, G. R., and Lidiak, E. G., 1980, Models for Midcontinent Tectonism, in Continental Tectonics, National Academy of Sciences, p. 73-83.

Hite, R. J., 1975, An unusual northeast-trending fracture zone and its relation to basement wrench faulting in northern Paradox Basin, Utah and Colorado: Four Corners Geological Society 8th Field Conference Guidebook, p. 217-224.

Jaksha, L. H., and Locke, J., 1978, Seismicity near Albuquerque, New Mexico, 1976-1977: U.S. Geological Survey Open File Report 78-1054, 22 p.

Kisslinger, C., 1976, A review of theories of mechanisms of induced seismicity: Engineering Geology, v. 10, no. 2-4, p. 85-98.

Lahr, J. C., 1979, HYPOELLIPSE: A computer program for determining local earthquake hypocentral parameters, magnitude and first motion patterns: U.S. Geological Survey Open File Report 79-43, 58 p.

Major, M. and Simon, R., 1968, Seismic study of Denver (Derby) Earthquakes Quarterly, Colorado School of Mines, v. 63, no. 1, p. 9-65.

Newton, C. A., Cash, D. J., Olsen, K. H., and Homuth, E. F., 1976, LASL seismic programs in the vicinity of Los Alamos, New Mexico: Los Alamos Laboratories, Los Alamos, New Mexico, Informal Report LA 6406 MS, 42 p.

Northrop, S. A., 1976, New Mexico's earthquake history, 1849-1975: New Mexico Geological Society Special Publication No. 6, p. 77-87.

Northrop, S. A., and Sanford, A. R., 1972, Earthquakes of northeastern New Mexico and the Texas Panhandle: New Mexico Geological Society, Annual Field Conference Guidebook No. 23, p. 148-160.

Osterwald, F. W., 1970, Comments on rockbursts, outbursts and earthquake prediction, Seismological Society of America Bulletin, v. 60, no. 6, p. 2083-2085.

Osterwald, F. W., Dunrund, C. R., Bennetti, J. B., and Maberry, J. D., 1972, Instrumentation studies of earth tremors related to geology and to mining at the Somerset Coal Mine, Colorado, U.S. Geological Survey Professional Paper 762, 27 p.

Raleigh, C. B., Healy, J. H., and Bredehoeft, J. D., 1972, An experiment in earthquake control at Rangeley, Colorado, Science, 191, p. 1230-1237.

Richter, C. F., 1958, Elementary Seismology, W. H. Freeman and Company, 768 p.

Roller, J. C., 1965, Crustal structure in the eastern Colorado Plateaus Province from seismic-refraction measurements, Seismological Society of America Bulletin, v. 55, no. 1, p. 107-119.

Sanford, A. R., 1978, Earthquake activity in New Mexico (1849 through 1977): Geophysical Open File Report 26, Geoscience Department and Geophysical Research Institute, New Mexico Technical, Socorro, New Mexico, 23 p.

Sbar, M. L., and Sykes, 1973, Contemporary compressive stress and seismicity in eastern North America, an example of intraplate tectonics, Geological Society of America Bulletin, 84, p. 1861-1882.

Slemmons, D. B., 1975, Fault activity and seismicity near the Los Alamos Scientific Laboratory geothermal test site, Jamez Mountains, New Mexico: Los Alamos Scientific Laboratory, Los Alamos, New Mexico, Informal report LA-5911-MS, 26 p.

Smith, R. B., and Sbar, M. L., 1974, Contemporary tectonics and seismicity of the western United States with emphasis on the Intermountain Seismic Belt: Geological Society of America Bulletin, v. 85, p. 1205-1218.

Smith, R. B., Winkler, P. L., Anderson, J. G., and Scholz, C. H., 1974, Source Mechanisms of Microearthquakes Associated with Underground Mines in Eastern Utah, Seismological Society of America Bulletin, v. 64, no. 4, p. 1295-1317.

Stone, D. S., 1969, Wrench faulting and Rocky Mountain tectonics, The Mountain Geologist, v. 6, no. 2, p. 67-69.

U.S. Geological Survey, 1980, Colorado River Discharge data at Cisco, Utah Water Resources Division, unpublished data.

Warner, L. A., 1978, The Colorado Lineament: A middle Precambrian wrench fault system: Geological Society of America Bulletin, v. 89, p. 161-171.

Zandt, G., and Richins, W. D., 1980, An upper mantle earthquake beneath the Middle Rocky Mountains in NE Utah, (abs), Earthquake Notes, v. 50, no. 4, p. 69-70.

Zoback, M. L., and Zoback, M., 1980, State of stress in the conterminous United States, Journal of Geophysical Research, v. 85, no. B11, p. 6113-6156.

"Don't worry - it's a typical field trip —
one outcrop, two geologists and three interpretations!"

URANIUM MINERALIZATION AND DEPOSITIONAL FACIES IN THE PERMIAN ROCKS OF THE NORTHERN PARADOX BASIN, UTAH AND COLORADO

John A. Campbell
Department of Geology
Fort Lewis College
Durango, CO 81301

and

U.S. Geological Survey
Box 25046, DFC, MS 916
Denver, CO 80225

ABSTRACT

Depositional-system studies of the Permian Cutler Formation in the Paradox (Uncompahgre) Basin have identified five fluvial and two marine facies, and associated eolian deposits. The fluvial facies, from northeast to southwest, are proximal braided, medial braided, distal braided, 50 percent meandering, 50 percent distal braided, and 100 percent meandering. The braided facies outline a large (60 km^2) fluvial or wet fan. The sediments change from distal braided to coarse-grained meandering at the toe of the fan which originally was near sea level. Seaward from the toe meandering is more common. A marine transgression occurred early during fan development resulting in the deposition of the limestones and shales of the Rico Formation, or Elephant Canyon Formation of Baars. Later, a marine invasion from the southwest deposited limestones, sandstones, and shales which are lateral equivalents of the Cedar Mesa Sandstone Member of the Cutler Formation. The eolian rocks are closely related to the marine facies and are considered to be coastal dune-field deposits. The maximum clast size as observed on outcrop, the maximum clast size as observed in thin section, and the mean grain size determined from thin sections all decrease from the proximl to the distal part of the fan system. The amount of shale, the degree of sorting and total quartz increase distally, whereas the amount of rock fragments and mica decrease distally. The amount of feldspar remains relatively unchanged from the proximal to the distal part of the system.

Uranium is located in the extreme distal part of the system, where streams close to sea level were meandering. Uranium occurrence is most favorable between the marine facies to the west and the distal braided fluvial facies to the east, in the zone of fluvial and marine intertonguing. The uranium occurs in arkosic, fluvial sandstones deposited in a meandering distributary environment. These sandstones are similar to other fluvial sandstones, but are slightly coarser grained and contain less calcite cement and more clay matrix. Uranium minerals are finely disseminated and difficult to identify but appear to include uraninite, coffinite, uranophane, and carnotite. Much of the uranium is associated with (1) iron oxide grain coatings and (2) disseminated within the matrix. Significant organic carbon was not found in the ore zone. Uranium was introduced after oxidation had formed hematite, and ore formation has not significantly modified the host sandstones. Formation of these orebodies has occurred without any obvious reductant. Perhaps sorption of uranyl ions by hematite was the concentrating mechanism.

INTRODUCTION

The thick sequences of arkosic sediment that accumulated in the Paradox Basin during Permian time have long been an intriguing target for uranium exploration. Early mining and exploration in the Lisbon Valley district of eastern Utah focused on the Permian Cutler Formation. Drilling by Charles A. Steen, which led to the discovery of high grade uranium ore in the Moss Back Member of the Triassic Chinle Formation, was for prospects in the Cutler. Several uranium occurrences are known in the area extending from the Green and Colorado Rivers eastward to the vicinity of Moab and Lisbon Valley, Utah (Figure 1), but few are known elsewhere in Permian age rocks in the Paradox basin. Production from the Lisbon Valley district totalled about 2.4 million pounds of U_3O_8 by 1975 (Chenoweth, 1975, p. 256), and mining continued through 1979.

A regional study of major Permian depositional basins in the southwestern United States by Campbell and Steele (1976) indicated that the Paradox Basin, had the greatest potential for significant uranium deposits. Factors considered included the sediment source, the potential uranium source, sediment dispersal, depositional environments, basin geometry, lithology (including organic content), sand-shale ratios, thickness of the Permian sequence, regional unconformities, and known uranium occurrences. Data for this study were obtained from the literature, principally the U.S. Geological Survey paleotectonic map series (McKee and others, 1967).

The potential for finding additional uranium in the Permian of the Paradox Basin has initiated a detailed study of host rock depositional environments (Campbell, 1979, 1980) and characteristics of major ore deposits (Campbell and Steele-Mallory, 1979a, b). This report summarizes the findings of these studies and adds new data concerning mineralogic and texture trends related to depositional facies and uranium

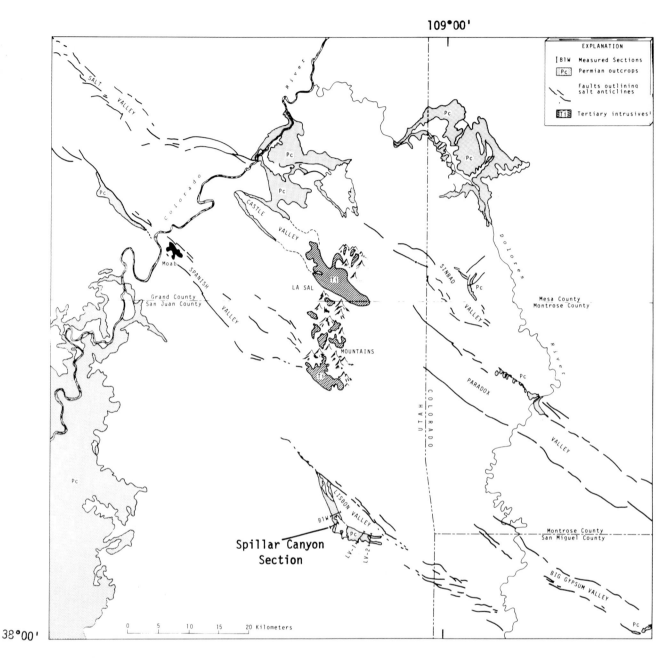

Figure 1. Index map showing Permian outcrops in the study area and locations of measured sections. Base map from Moab 1° × 2° quadrangle.

occurrences. The new data will aid in the formulation of a hypothesis concerning the origin of the Permian uranium deposits.

The area discussed in this report includes most of the central and western portion of the Moab 1° x 2° NTMS quadrangle, west and southwest of the Uncompahgre Plateau (Figure 1). This area includes the northern part of San Juan, and the southern part of Grand Counties, Utah, and western Mesa, Montrose, and San Miguel Counties, Colorado. While the entire Paradox Basin has been studied (Campbell, 1980), the northern part of the basin is emphasized report.

GEOLOGIC SETTING

Figure 1 shows Permian outcrops and major structural elements. The structural features are the northwest-

southeast trending anticlines and associated faults that mainly are of diapiric origin. Permian rocks crop out along the flanks of these anticlines. The wide outcrop belt in the western part of the area, along the east side of the Colorado River, is exposed along the plunging nose of the Monument upwarp, modified by smaller anticlines probably of diapiric origin. The outcrops along the Dolores River at Gateway, Colorado, are on the flanks of the northwest-southeast-trending Uncompahgre Plateau. In the center of the study area, the sedimentary sequence has been intruded by diorite porphyry stocks and laccoliths of Cretaceous or Tertiary age forming the La Sal Mountains.

The stratigraphic sequence exposed in the area ranges from Precambrian to Tertiary in age, exclusive of the lower and middle Paleozoic. The oldest formations exposed in the center of the anticlines are of Pennsylvanian age. In the

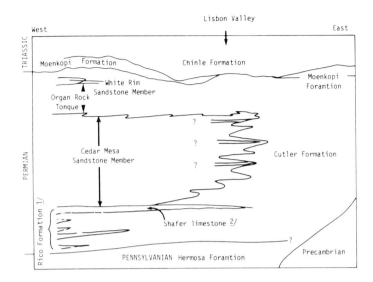

Figure 2. Schematic cross section of Lower Permian stratigraphic units, southern part of the study area. (1) Elephant Canyon Formation of Baars, 1962; (2) informal name.

Gateway area the Lower Permian is in depositional contact with the Precambrian. However, older Paleozoic rocks have been encountered in oil wells in the area. The stratigraphic terminology and correlations used in this report are shown on Figure 2. This regional stratigraphic terminology is the same used by Baars (1962, p. 154), and by McKee and others (1967, Table 1). The age of the Permian sequences as determined by Baars (1962, p. 168) is mainly Wolfcampian; only the White Rim Sandstone Member of the Cutler Formation and equivalents are early Leonardian.

DEPOSITIONAL FACIES

The Permian rocks throughout the study area were (Figure 1) deposited in varied environments. Fluvial environments predominated in the east and central part of the study area (Figure 3). In the western part marine, eolian and meandering fluvial sequences are present.

BRAIDED-STREAM DEPOSITS

The fluvial sequences in the eastern part of the study area, adjacent to the Uncompahgre Plateau, are braided stream deposits. Three gradational facies of these deposits have been recognized: proximal, medial, and distal (Campbell, 1980). The proximal braided deposits are found in an area extending from Gateway, Colorado, 20 to 30 km to the southwest (Figure 3). These deposits consist of granule to boulder size conglomerates and commonly have a very coarse grained sand to granule size matrix, and a clast-support texture. Boulders average about 1 m across; however, the largest measured was 2 x 3 x 4 m. Boulders are rounded, often water polished, and probably were deposited by a very high energy stream. Some matrix-support texture boulder conglomerates are present and probably were deposited as debris flows. Interbedded with these coarse boulder conglomerates are granule to pebble size conglomerates, coarse-grained conglomeratic sandstones,

and minor amounts of shaly siltstones and fine- to coarse-grained sandstones. These finer grained, proximal sediments were deposited by lower energy streams which built the main body of the fan.

TABLE I.

CORRELATION COEFFICIENTS FOR TEXTURAL PARAMETERS
[All are significant at the 5 percent level]

	1	2	3	4	5
1. Maximum clast size—outcrop	0	0.63	0.60	0.66	0.80
2. Maximum grain size—thin section		0	.87	.91	.70
3. Mean grain size—thin section			0	.93	.77
4. Standard deviation				0	.78
5. Sandstone/shale ratio					0

Sedimentary structures present in the proximal braided deposits range from massive-bedded units that fill prominent scours, to horizontal bedding. Trough crossbedding, ripple marks and horizontal laminations occasionally were found in the finer grained rocks. Abrupt changes in sedimentary structure are common.

The characteristics of the medial-braided facies include a less coarse conglomerate grain size and more sandstone, siltstone, and shale than is present in the proximal-braided deposits. Horizontal stratification and laminations are the most common sedimentary structures, but trough crossbeds also are present. Some tabular-planar crossbeds were found, and more ripples and ripple laminations were noted in the finer grained rocks than in those of the proximal-braided deposits.

The distal-braided sequences consist of medium- to very coarse-grained sandstone that contains as much as 40 percent granules, pebbles, and cobbles. The conglomeratic material is found at the base of scours as lenses and as clasts suspended in a sand-grain matrix. Although 1-7 cm clasts are most common the maximum clast size is about 20 cm. The sandstone grain size averages about 0.5 mm. Rocks consisting of fine- to very fine-grained sandstone, siltstone, and shale comprise from 15 to 50 percent of the sequence.

MEANDERING-STREAM DEPOSITS

Two types of meandering-stream deposits have been recognized in the study area (Campbell, 1980). They are coarse-grained and fine-grained meandering sequences and are very similar in textural features but differ in characteristics of sedimentary structures. Both are composed of sandstones deposited in channels, and siltstone, shale or mudstone, and fine-grained sandstones deposited as overbank sediments in adjacent flood-plain areas. The amount of overbank material varies from about 50 to 85 percent of the sequence. The sandstones predominantly are medium-grained but range from fine to very coarse. Granules, pebbles, and a few cobbles that range from 2 to 80 mm are present at the base of many channel sequences. The coarsest materials at the base of channel sequences are clay or siltstone clasts probably deposited by bank-caving processes. Grain size in some of the coarse-grained meandering channel sequences grades to finer upward; in others there is little grain-size change upward, and some channel deposits coarsen upward. Typically, fine-

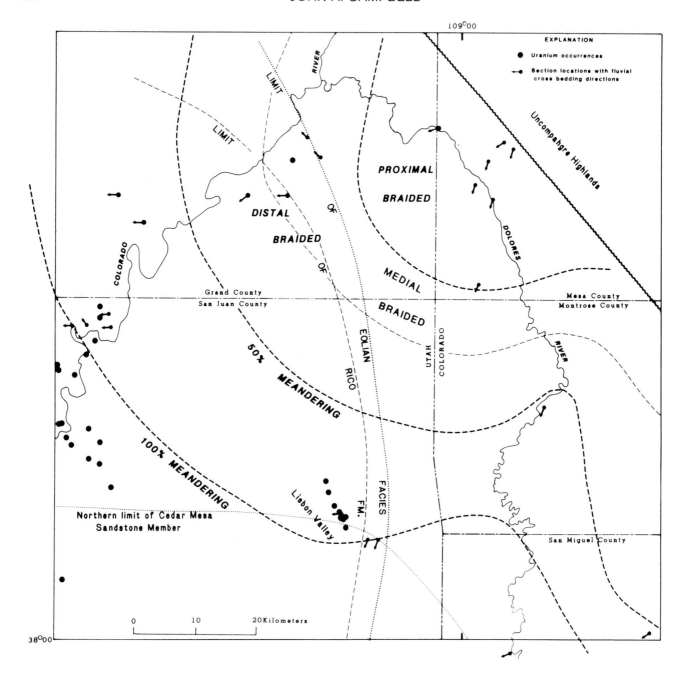

Figure 3. Map showing distribution of facies on the northern part of the Paradox Basin.

grained meandering channel sequences coarsen toward the base and fine upward.

The sedimentary structures in both types of meandering sequences predominantly are trough crossbeds, with lesser amounts of horizontal stratification and laminations, or tabular-planar crossbeds. In some of the coarse-grained meandering channel sequences the largest trough crossbeds are near the base of the deposit and the smallest are at the top. Some sequences have large troughs in the middle or near the top, others show little vertical variation in trough size. Fine-grained meandering-channel deposits show a more consistent change from large-scale to small-scale trough crossbedding from the base to the top. Fine-grained sequences contain more ripples and ripple laminations at or near the top of the channel deposits. Shale beds or partings are also present in the middle and top of the

fine-grained channel deposits; these probably are mud-drapes marking epsilon-crossbedding (Allen, 1963).

MARINE DEPOSITS

Two marine sequences of Permian age are present in the Cutler in the northern part of the Paradox Basin (Campbell, 1979, 1980). The lower marine sequence of limestone and shale is found between Moab and the northern part of Lisbon Valley and usually is mapped (Figures 2 and 3) as the Rico Formation or as the Elephant Canyon Formation of Baars (1962). The upper marine sequence occurs in the southern part of the Lisbon Valley and contains limestones, sandstones and shales. This sequence is more than 100 m above the highest Rico limestones and are considered to be lateral equivalents of the Cedar Mesa Sandstone Member of the Cutler Formation (Campbell and Steele-Mallory, 1979a and b; and, Campbell, 1979, 1980).

EOLIAN DEPOSITS

Sandstone beds of eolian origin are interbedded with both fluvial and marine rocks in the northern part of the area, and their number and thickness decrease to the south and southeast. Only a few eolian sandstone beds are present at Lisbon Valley and none were to be found south or east. These sandstones contain a wide variety of sedimentary structures indicative of eolian deposits (Campbell, 1979, 1980). At several localities the upper surface of eolian sandstones have been scoured and filled with fluvial sediments. These channels and the presence of slump structures in the eolian sandstones suggest that these sands were water saturated shortly after deposition (Campbell, 1979, 1980).

Stratigraphically and geographically the eolian sandstones are closely associated with the marine rocks (Figure 3). This spatial relationship and the presence of features suggesting water saturation have led to the interpretation that they are mainly coastal in origin (Campbell, 1979).

DEPOSITIONAL SYSTEM

The overall depositional system suggested by the various environments and their geographic distribution (Figure 3) is that of a large fluvial fan (Schumm, 1977) or fan delta that built southwestwardly into the basin, and has been termed the Gateway fan. Three large fans filled the Paradox basin during Early Permian time (Campbell, 1980). Key characteristics of a fluvial (wet) fan that distinguish it from an alluvial (dry) fan are (1) very large size, commonly at least twice as large as an alluvial fan; (2) low gradient profiles; and (3) predominantly fluvial deposits with only minor amounts of interbedded ephemeral stream, mud-flow, and debris-flow deposits (Schumm, 1977). Modern equivalents are the Kosi River fan in India (Gole and Chitale, 1966), and the Yallaks fan delta in Jamaica (Wescott and Ethridge, 1980). Examples of ancient deposits having similar characteristics include the Precambrian Van Horn Sandstone of Texas (McGowen and Groat, 1971), and Precambrian fans deposited in the Witwatersrand Basin in South Africa (Pretorius, 1974).

The toe of the Gateway fluvial fan was close to sea level throughout its history (Figure 3). Streams crossing the fan changed from proximal, to medial, to distal-braided, and then to low-sinuosity, mixed-load streams (Schumm, 1972), probably similar to the coarse-grained meandering streams described by McGowen and Garner (1975). As the streams flowed across the coastal plain, meandering increased. Two marine invasions occurred: initially from the west during the early development of the fan, and later from the southwest. Coastal dune fields shifted in belts parallel to the fluctuating shoreline.

TEXTURAL AND MINERALOGICAL CHARACTERISTICS OF THE GATEWAY FAN

Down-fan changes in a variety of textural parameters and detrital mineralogy are shown in Figures 4, 5, 6, and 7. Changes in texture and mineralogy of fluvial channel sequences are plotted against the distance from the head of the Gateway fan. The maximum clast size observed on the outcrop (Figure 4), the maximum clast size observed in thin sections, and the mean grain size determined from thin sections (Figure 5) all decrease from the proximal to the distal end of the system. The sandstone-shale ratio (Figure 4) decreases as the amount of shale increases, and the

standard deviation of grain size (Figure 5) (a measure of sorting) decreases as the sorting increases distally. The surprise in the textural data is the very strong correlations between the various parameters presented in Table 1. This strong correlation between parameters measured by different methods must reflect a consistency in the fluvial processes that deposited the sediment. The down-fan mineralogical changes are much more variable than the textural changes due to diagensis. The amount of quartz (Figure 6) increases distally, probably at the expense of both igneous and metamorphic rock fragments (Figure 7), which decrease distally as larger rock fragments weather into component grains. Both muscovite and biotite mica decrease distally, probably due to sorting. The distal channel deposits are well sorted, and mica has been deposited with the finer overbank deposits. The amounts of potassium and plagioclase feldspar scarcely vary distally (Figure 6). The feldspars appear to have been relatively stable in this fluvial system. Calcite, as a cementing agent, increases distally, perhaps in respone to the presence of marine units at the toe of the fan (Figure 7).

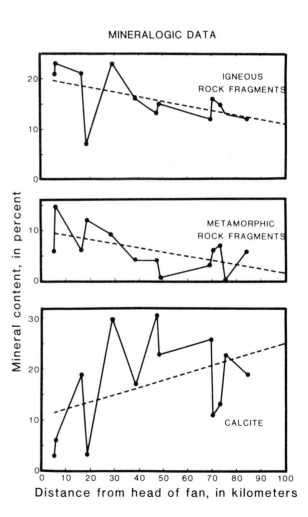

Figure 4. Maximum clast size as measured on the outcrop and the sandstone/shale ratio vs. the distance from the head of the Gateway fan. Dashed line is the linear best fit for the data.

TEXTURE DATA

Thin section

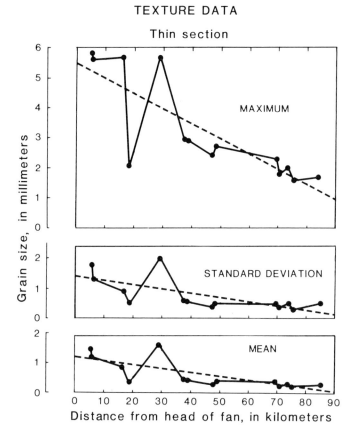

Figure 5. Maximum grain size, mean grain size, and standard deviation as determined from thin sections vs. the distance from the head of the Gateway fan. Dashed line is linear best fit for the data.

URANIUM IN THE DEPOSITIONAL SYSTEM

Figure 3 shows the relationship of the various facies boundaries and known uranium occurrences. Whereas some occurrences have been developed, many are small, and only those in Lisbon Valley have been mined. The uranium is located in the extreme distal part of the system, where the streams were meandering close to sea level. The most favorable area for uranium is between the more marine facies to the west and the distal braided fluvial facies to the east, in the zone of fluvial and marine intertonguing. The stratigraphic horizons in this zone are the Rico Formation, or Elephant Canyon Formation of Baars (1962), in the northern and central part of the area, and the Cedar Mesa Sandstone Member of the Cutler Formation in the southern part.

The Lisbon Valley uranium deposits are in the upper part of the Cutler Formation in the fluvial-marine transition zone. of the Cedar Mesa Sandstone Member. The ore occurs in bleached, fluvial, arkosic sandstones interbedded with marine and eolian sandstones (Figure 8). This association and the sedimentary structures in the sandstones suggest a fluvial-distributary origin (Campbell and Steele-Mallory, 1979a). The ore is in discontinuous tabular zones near the base, near the top, or close to pinchouts of the sandstone bodies. Ore grade decreases toward the middle of the sandstone bodies. Vertical joints that intersect ore and surrounding country rock are also mineralized. A study of thin sections from ore and non-ore sandstones shows that ore sandstones contain less carbonate cement, more clay matrix and slightly coarser grains than the average fluvial

sandstones that distance (70 km) from the head of the depositional system.

Uranium minerals from Lisbon Valley, identified by X-ray methods, include uraninite, coffinite, uranophane, and carnotite. X-ray peaks were very weak for all minerals except uranophane. The highest alpha count from separates of each ore sample emanated from the light weight, fine fraction, suggesting the uranium is finely disseminated therein Fission-track maps show uranium to be most commonly located within the iron oxide coatings surrounding detrital grains, in the matrix, and within biotite flakes altering to hematite (Campbell and Steele-Mallory, 1979b). Chemical analyses of selected samples for organic carbon did not show any relationship between the presence of organic carbon and ore. Ore samples averaged 0.009 percent organic carbon and non-ore samples averaged 0.21 percent organic carbon (Campbell and Steele-Mallory, 1979b).

The characteristics of the ore found in the Permian deposits are different from those found in other uranium deposits in the same area (Campbell and Steele-Mallory, 1979b). Ore formation in the Cutler has had little effect on host rock mineralogy and texture, whereas changes in both have been noted in the Jurassic Salt Wash Member of the Morrison Formation in the La Sal mine (Brooks and Campbell, 1976) and in the Chinle Formation in the Mi Vida

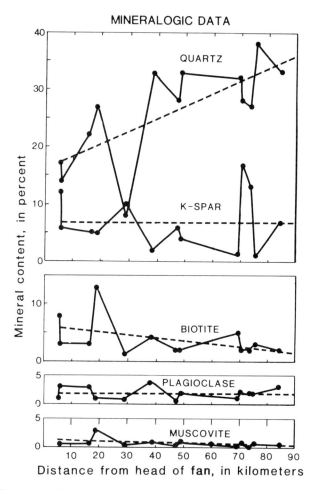

Figure 6. Mineralogical changes within the Gateway fan vs. the distance from head of the fan. Dashed lines is the linear best fit for the data.

TEXTURE DATA

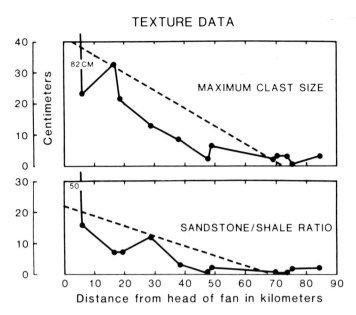

Figure 7. Mineralogical changes down fan on the Gateway fan. Dashed line is the linear best fit.

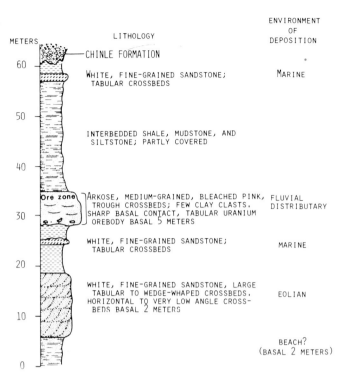

Figure 8. Stratigraphic section of the upper part of the Permian Cutler, and the basal Triassic Chinle, Formations in Spillar Canyon, Lisbon Valley, Utah. See Figure 1 for location.

mine (Gross, 1956). Also, ore formed later during diagenesis in the Cutler, and elemental variation across Cutler ore is not systematic as it is in other uranium deposits (Campbell and Steele-Mallory, 1979b).

The formation of the Cutler uranium deposits appears to have followed a different sequence than that of many other uranium deposits. The source for the uranium could have been the granites in the Uncompahgre highland, detritus within the Cutler, or the overlying Chinle Formation. Transport of the uranium probably was by ground water. Deposition occurred without the obvious reductants, perhaps by sorption of uranyl ions by the hematite present in the host rocks. Such processes have been described by Van der Weijden, Arthur, and Langmuir (1976). This process occurred after the sediment was oxidized but before the carbonate cement was added. The formation of the calcite cement from carbonate-rich ground water removed uranium from the centers of the sandstone channel deposits, leaving only the base, top, and pinchout edges mineralized.

The understanding of the chronlogy of the formation of the uranium deposits is important for a complete grasp of their formation and future exploration modelling. The restriction of ore to distributary-like channel deposits and the geographic distribution of occurrences in the depositional system suggest facies control and thus an early age of ore formation shortly after deposition of the system. The diagenetic sequence and the close association of uranium with iron oxide suggest events after deposition and diagensis of the sediments and thus a later age of ore formation. Work is in progress that should aid in resolving the age problem.

REFERENCES CITED

Allen, J. R. L., 1963, The classification of cross-stratified units, with notes on their origin: Sedimentology, v. 2, p. 93-114.

Baars, D. L., 1962, Permian System of the Colorado Plateau: American Association of Petroleum Geologists Bulletin, v. 46, no. 2, p. 149-218.

Brooks, R. A., and Campbell, J. A., 1976, Preliminary investigation of the elemental variation and diagenesis of a tabular uranium deposit, La Sal mine, San Juan County, Utah: U.S. Geological Survey Open-File Report 76-287, 30 p.

Campbell, J. A., 1979, Lower Permian depositional system, northern Uncompahgre Basin, in D. L. Baars, ed., Four Corners Geological Society Guidebook, 9th Field Conference, Permianland, p. 13-21.

_____ 1980, Lower Permian depositional systems and Wolfcampian paleogeography, Uncompahgre Basin, eastern Utah and southwestern Colorado, in T. D. Fouch and E. R. Magathan, eds., Paleozoic paleogeography of west-central United States: Rocky Mountain Section, Society of Economic Paleontologists and Mineralogists, Rocky Mountain Section, Paleogeography Symposium 1, p. 327-340.

Campbell, J. A., and Steele, B. A., 1976, Uranium potential of Permian rocks in the southwestern United States: U.S. Geological Survey Open-File Report 76-529, 26 p.

Campbell, J. A., and Steele-Mallory, B. A., 1979a, Depositional environments of the uranium-bearing Cutler Formation, Lisbon Valley, Utah: U.S. Geological Survey Open-File Report 79-994, 35 p.

_____ 1979b, Uranium in the Cutler Formation Lisbon Valley, Utah, in D. L. Baars, ed., Four Corners Geological Socicty Guidebook, 9th Field Conference, Permianland, p. 23-32.

Chenoweth, W. L., 1975, Uranium deposits of the Canyonlands area; in J. E. Fassett, ed., Four Corners Geological Society Guidebook, 8th Field Conference, Canyonlands, p. 253-260.

Gole, C. V., and Chitale, S. V., 1966, Inland delta building activity of Kosi River: American Society Civil Engineers Proceedings, Journal Hydraulics Division, HY-2, p. 111-126.

Gross, E. B., 1956, Mineralogy and paragenesis of the uranium ore, Mi Vida Mine, San Juan County, Utah: Economic Geology, v. 51, no. 7, p. 632-648.

McGowen, J. H., and Groat, C. G., 1971, Van Horn Sandstone, West Texas: an alluvial fan model for mineral exploration: Texas University Bureau of Economic Geology Rep. of Invest. 72, 57 p.

McGowen, J. H., and Garner, L. E., 1975, Physiographic features and stratification types of coarse-grained point bars: modern and ancient examples: Texas University Bureau of Economic Geology Geologic Circular 75-9, 27 p.

McKee, E. D., Oriel, S. S., and others, 1967, Paleotectonic investigations of the Permian System in the United States: U.S. Geological Survey Professional Paper 515, 271 p.

Pretorius, D. A., 1974, The nature of the Witwatersrand gold-uranium deposits: University of Witwatersrand Economic Geology Research Unit Information Circular 86, 50 p.

Schumm, S. A., 1972, Fluvial paleochannels, in J. Keith Rigby and Wm. Kenneth Hamblin, eds., Recognition of ancient sedimentary environments: Society of Economic Paleontologists and Mineralogists Special Publication 16, p. 98-107.

_____ 1977, The fluvial system: John Wiley and Sons, New York, 338 p.

Van der Weijden, C. H., Arthur, R. C., and Langmuir, D., 1976, Sorption of uranyl by hematite: theoretical and geochemical implications: Geological Society of America Abstracts with Programs, v. 8, no. 6, p. 1152.

Wescott, W. A., and Ethridge, F. G., 1980, Fan-delta sedimentology and tectonic setting — Yallahs Fan Delta, southeast Jamaica: American Association of Petroleum Geologists, v. 64, no. 3, p. 374-399.

Spud Mtn.

LOWER CRETACEOUS ROCKS, SOUTHWESTERN COLORADO AND SOUTHEASTERN UTAH

LAWRENCE C. CRAIG[1]

ABSTRACT

The Burro Canyon Formation of Early Cretaceous age overlies the Morrison Formation of Late Jurassic age and underlies the Dakota Sandstone of Late Cretaceous age over much of southeastern Utah and southwestern Colorado. It consists mainly of alternating beds of fluvial sandstone and overbank mudstone with sandstone dominating in the lower part of the formation and mudstone in the upper part. To the west and north the stratigraphically equivalent Cedar Mountain Formation is present in south-central and northeastern Utah and northwestern Colorado and consists mainly of swelling mudstone and lesser amounts of fluvial sandstone.

Based on thickness, percent-sandstone, pebble-size, and limited paleocurrent-direction studies, the Burro Canyon and Cedar Mountain are interpreted as two alluvial systems deposited across a broad, even surface on top of the Morrison Formation. The major source for the Burro Canyon was southwest of the Four Corners area, perhaps in southern Arizona. Burro Canyon sediments were spread northward and eastward from a major depositional axis along the southern part of the Utah-Colorado State line. The source for the Cedar Mountain Formation was somewhere west of the High Plateaus in central Utah; Cedar Mountain deposits were spread eastward from this area. The two formations merge or interfinger laterally along a zone that parallels the Colorado River in Utah and trends northeasterly into northwestern Colorado.

INTRODUCTION

The Lower Cretaceous rocks as discussed here consist of two stratigraphically equivalent lithofacies, the Burro Canyon Formation (Stokes and Phoenix, 1948) in southeastern Utah and adjacent Colorado, and the Cedar Mountain Formation (Stokes, 1944, 1952) in east-central and northeastern Utah and northwestern Colorado.[2]

The Burro Canyon Formation is present in a broad area in southeastern Utah and southwestern Colorado. It consists of alternating lenticular beds of conglomeratic sandstone and layers of dominantly greenish mudstone. Sandstone generally dominates in the lower part and mudstone in the upper part of the formation. The Burro Canyon overlies the Upper Jurassic Morrison Formation and underlies the Upper Cretaceous Dakota Sandstone. To the west in Utah, the Burro Canyon Formation grades laterally into the Cedar Mountain Formation. The Cedar Mountain consists of a relatively thin basal conglomeratic unit, the Buckhorn Conglomerate Member, and a relatively thick upper shale unit, the shale member.

This paper is based on material and data gathered in a study of the Morrison Formation by the author and others of the U.S. Geological Survey on behalf of the U.S. Atomic Energy Commission in the early 1950's (Craig and others, 1955, 1959); it draws heavily on a study by Donald G. McCubbin for his Ph.D. thesis at Harvard University (1961) and a published report by Robert G. Young (1960). A minimal amount of field work during the summers of 1974 through 1976 was undertaken to develop and check concepts expressed in the report.

DEFINITION AND DISTINGUISHING CHARACTERISTICS

The Burro Canyon Formation as defined by Stokes and

Phoenix (1948) is a sequence of lenticular conglomeratic sandstone and variegated mudstone that intervenes between the Brush Basin member of the Morrison Formation and the Dakota Sandstone. The type locality for the Burro Canyon is in Burro Canyon near Slick Rock in western San Miguel County, Colorado.

The formation is distinguished from the underlying Brushy Basin Member in that it consists of course, generally conglomeratic sandstone and interbedded generally non-swelling mudstone of dominantly greenish gray color. The Brushy Basin contains only a few conglomeratic sandstone beds, particularly in its upper part, and is dominantly composed of alternating red, green, and gray swelling mudstones that generally form distinctly color banded outcrops. The Burro Canyon Formation is distinguished from the overlying Dakota Sandstone by the greenish mudstone and by the absence of carbonaceous material and organic-rich shale, lignite, or coal. The Dakota consists of interbedded sandstone and carbonaceous shale; the sandstone is in part conglomeratic and generally contains carbonaceous debris and impressions of twigs, stems, and branches.

The Cedar Mountain Formation as defined by Stokes (1944, 1952) consists of the basal Buckhorn Conglomerate Member and an informal upper shale member. The Buckhorn is a broadly lenticular, yellowish-gray, scour-fill sandstone that contains granule- to cobble-sized conglomeratic material. The relatively thick upper shale member consists of pastel-colored swelling claystone and mudstone but also may contain a few yellowish-gray, scour-fill sandstone beds.

Unlike the Burro Canyon, the informal upper shale member of the Cedar Mountain Formation consists of pastel-colored swelling clays, including purple and red, as well as green, and generally contains an abundance of limestone nodules that cover the weatherd slopes. The upper shale member of the Ceder Mountain Formation also differs from the underlying Brushy Basin Member of the Morrison Formation in that it lacks the brilliant colors of the Brushy Basin, it lacks the distinct color banding, and it has abundant limestone nodules. The Cedar Mountain is distinguished from the overlying Dakota Sandstone by the absence of carbonaceous gray to black mudstone.

[1] U.S. Geological Survey, Box 25046, MS 916, Denver Federal Center, Denver, CO 80225.

[2] In 1960 R. G. Young proposed to abandon the name Burro Canyon and extend the name Cedar Mountain to these beds. This action certainly acknowledges the generally accepted equivalency of these beds but does not preserve the recognition of the general lithic differences between them. In this report the author has chosen to preserve the two names simply to emphasize those differences. At the same time, Young proposed to raise the term Dakota to group status, to redefine its lower contact to include the Burro Canyon, and to replace the name Dakota Sandstone with the name Naturita Formation. Although this has merit in that it makes terminology parallel with the Front Range terminology, it is not followed herc because of the marked lithologic contrast between the Burro Canyon-Cedar Mountain and the Dakota Sandstone. Also, the addition of the Burro Canyon to the Dakota would be a major, and perhaps undesirable, redefinition of the Dakota (American Commission on Stratigraphic Nomenclature, 1970, art. 14).

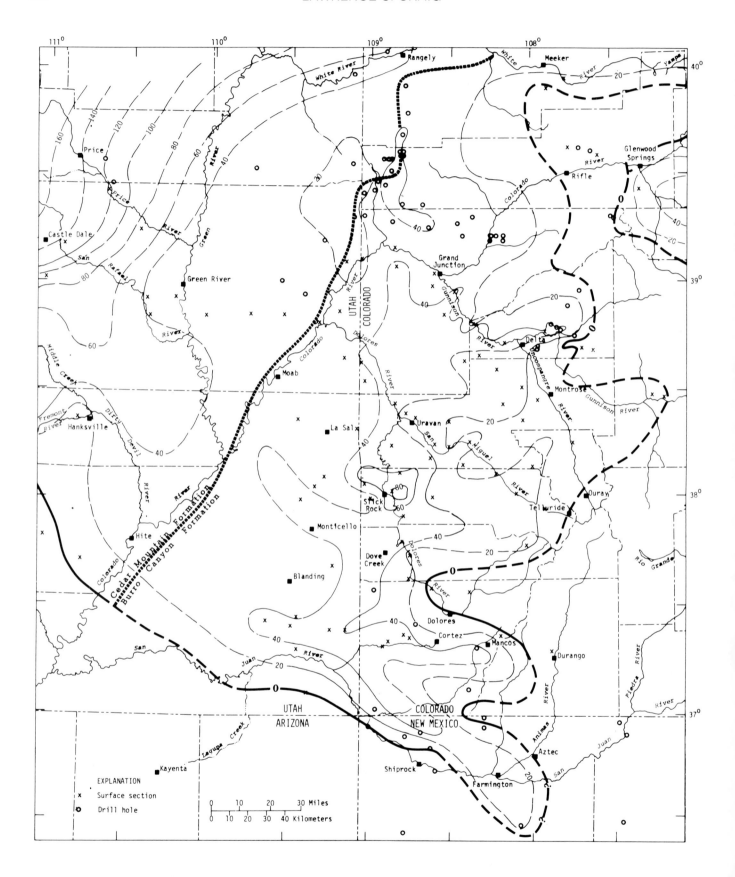

Figure 1. Isopach map of Burro Canyon and Cedar Mountain Formations in southeastern Utah and southwestern Colorado. Contour interval 20 m. Isopach lines are dashed where uncertain. Heavy zero line marks pinchout of Burro Canyon and Cedar Mountain. Heavy dotted line is arbitrary boundary separating areas in which Burro Canyon and Cedar Mountain Formations are recognized.

DISTRIBUTION AND STRATIGRAPHIC RELATIONS

The Burro Canyon Formation is recognized over a broad area in southeastern Utah and western Colorado; recently the name has been extended to similar rocks occupying a similar stratigraphic position in the Chama basin of north-central New Mexico (Saucier, 1974).

The southern limit of the Burro Canyon (fig. 1) is an erosional limit where the Burro Canyon is cut out by the regional unconformity at the base of the overlying Dakota Sandstone. This limit is along a northwest-trending line that passes near the Four Corners area. South of this limit the pre-Dakota unconformity progressively bevels Morrison and older formations.

To the east, beds equivalent to Burro Canyon are believed to be present in eastern Colorado (Lytle Formation of Dakota Group along the Front Range foothills) and (Lytle Sandstone Member of Purgatoire Formation in southeast Colorado). However, the Burro Canyon itself reaches a poorly known pinchout along an irregular north-south line extending from the eastern part of the Piceance basin in northwestern Colorado to the northern part of the San Juan Basin in northwestern New Mexico (fig. 1). The nature of this pinchout is uncertain. In part it is probably the result of pre-Dakota erosion, but in part it also may be due to depositional thinning of the formation. In the poor exposures along the few outcrop belts that cross the feather edge, the sandstone beds in the Burro Canyon appear to thin as the pinchout is approached. However, pre-Dakota erosion seems the most important factor in the pinchout of the formation, because beds as much as 69 m thick (fig. 1) have been mapped as Burro Canyon to the east in the Aspen area of central Colorado (Freeman, 1972), and further to the south the beds called Burro Canyon in the Chama Basin imply initial continuity of the formation across the region.

The Cedar Mountain Formation is recognized over much of south-central and northeastern Utah and northwestern Colorado. The southern limit is south of the Henry Mountains (Utah) and is an erosional limit along which the Cedar Mountain is cut out by the erosional unconformity at the base of the Dakota. The western limit is poorly known but it extends beneath the High Plateaus of central Utah. To the north the formation is identified as far as the Wyoming State line in both northeastern Utah and northwestern Colorado.

The boundary between the Burro Canyon Formation and the Cedar Mountain Formation is placed arbitrarily along the Colorado River in Utah (Stokes, 1952, p. 1774), although for a distance of approximately 40 km west of the river the characteristics of the two formations intermingle.

To the north in Colorado the Burro Canyon Formation grades laterally into the Cedar Mountain Formation. In this area north of the Colorado River, the line of demarcation between the Burro Canyon and Cedar Mountain is placed where Burro Canyon characteristics give way to Cedar Mountain characteristics in the subsurface as interpreted from drill hole logs.

ROCK TYPES

Sandstone and mudstone are the dominant rocks in both the Burro Canyon and the Cedar Mountain although the proportions are different in the two formations. Over most of its extent the Burro Canyon consists of more than 50 percent sandstone, whereas the Cedar Mountain contains more than 30 percent sandstone in only a few places. Chert and limestone are minor rock types in both formations.

Sandstone units are generally more abundant in the lower part of the Burro Canyon, although thin beds of sandstone may occur in the upper part. Sandstone may form a single thick unit at the base of the formation, but commonly sandstone is separated into units by one or more thin mudstone beds; as many as four thick sandstone units may be present in the formation.

The sandstone units are light colored; very pale orange to yellowish gray in weathered outcrop, but almost white on fresh surfaces. As reported by D. R. Shawe (1968, table 2, and p. B25), the sandstone of the Burro Canyon Formation is highly quartzose (83 percent) and contains less chert (3 percent) and feldspar (1.5 percent) than either the sandstone of the Morrison or the Dakota. Other detrital minerals are quite minor constituents (3 percent or less) and calcite cement is also present in minor amounts (6 percent).

In the outcrop the sandstone units form ledges and vertical cliffs in contrast to gentle to steep slopes formed by the mudstone units. Many of the sandstone units show a crude sedimentation cycle that starts at the base with an irregular scour surface: Scour depressions on this surface generally are filled with relatively coarse, poorly sorted sandstone and conglomeratic sandstone in trough cross-stratified sets which are commonly thickest at the base and thin upwards. This coarse, trough cross-stratified unit passes upwards into finer grained, better sorted sandstone that is planar cross-stratified to parallel bedded and laminated which may show parting lineations, rib and furrow structures, and current ripple marks. Commonly the cycle is interrupted and the upper planar beds are missing either because they never formed, or because they were removed by scour when the next stream or flood cycle began.

In the conglomeratic sets of the sandstone units, pebbles occur in layers and stringers, and usually are concentrated immediately above the basal scour surface. Based on two pebble counts made by P. J. Katich, Jr., (written commun., 1951) the rock fragments of the Burro Canyon are chert (57 percent), silicified limestone (38 percent), quartzite (5 percent), and quartz (1 percent). The largest clasts in the Burro Canyon have been found near Blanding in southeastern Utah where a maximum diameter of 13 cm (boulder size) was recorded. To the north and east, maximum diameters are smaller.

The mudstone of the Burro Canyon Formation ranges from almost pure claystone to siltstone, but most is silty to sandy mudstone. The mudstones are predominantly pale greenish yellow to grayish yellow green. In a few places thin units of pale-reddish-brown to grayish-red mudstone are preserved. They appear to be relicts of a former more widespread red coloration that in some manner was protected from alteration to green (Shawe, 1976, p. D23). Much less common than the relict red mudstone units are rare carbonaceous mudstone beds. These range from light gray to grayish black and are considered as unaltered relicts of beds originally deposited under reducing conditions. Based on a few analyses by W. D. Keller (1962, p. 64-83) the dominant clay mineral in Burro Canyon mudstone is illite and mixed-layer illite-chlorite, which probably accounts for the generally nonswelling properties of the mudstone on outcrop.

Limestone and chert are minor rock types in the Burro Canyon Formation and are generally restricted to the upper part. The limestone is generally a light-gray micrite which forms beds as much as 50 cm thick that are local in extent but when present usually form a conspicuous ledge in a mudstone slope. Chert is thought to be mainly secondary, partially or completely replacing limestone beds, and forms outcrops similar to the limestone.

The Cedar Mountain Formation is dominantly silty to sandy mudstone in pastel shades of greenish gray, lavender, and pink to red. The colors form broad zones in contrast to the thin and distinct banding of colors in the underlying Brushy Basin Member. Like the Brushy Basin and unlike the Burro Canyon, the clay in the mudstone is dominantly montmorillonite and shows considerable swelling on weathered outcrop (Keller, 1962, p. 64). In contrast to both the Brushy Basin and Burro Canyon the mudstone of the Cedar Mountain contains abundant limestone nodules and in some zones the nodules cover the weathered mudstone slopes.

Sandstone in the Cedar Mountain Formation, including the basal Buckhorn Conglomerate Member, is light gray to light greenish gray and moderate orange pink, fine to medium grained, and composed mainly of clear quartz grains and minor accessory minerals. Many sandstone units are conglomeratic, particularly at their base and the sedimentary structure distribution within the units is similar to those noted in the sandstone beds of the Burro Canyon; however, the sandstone units in the Cedar Mountain are rarely more than 10 m thick and for the most part are only 2 or 3 m thick. Pebbles consist of gray chert (47 percent), silicified limestone (34 percent), quartz (9 percent), and quartzite mostly gray (10 percent); a maximum clast dimension of 18 cm was recorded at two localities between Green River and Castle Dale, Utah (P. J. Katich, written commun., 1951).

In addition to the limestone nodules in the mudstone of the Cedar Mountain, the upper shale member locally contains light-gray, commonly brown weathering, aphanitic to fine-grained limestone in beds as much as 1 m thick. Chert is a minor secondary component and occurs mainly as fracture fillings in limestone or as irregular replacement bodies in limestone.

THICKNESS

The Lower Cretaceous rocks differ markedly in thickness over relatively short distances and thus yield a rather complicated isopach map (fig. 1). This irregularity is thought to be the result of initial depositional differences, pre-Dakota erosion, and probably compactional differences related to the sandstone-mudstone ratio.

The Burro Canyon Formation thins to the southwest from more than 50 m in southeastern Utah and southwestern Colorado to an erosional pinchout that extends from southern Utah into northwestern New Mexico. The formation has a maximum thickness of more than 90 m in a drill hole in Disappointment Valley in southwestern Colorado (D. R. Shawe, 1975, written commun.). Some of the irregularities of isopachs (fig. 1) in this salt anticline area result from depositional thinning and thickening because of subsidence of synclines and irregular uplift of the salt anticline as a result of salt flowage during deposition of the Burro Canyon (Cater, 1970, p. 64-67). However, Shawe (1970, p. C15) reports that much of the thinning of the Burro Canyon along the anticlines is the result of pre-Dakota erosion.

In spite of these irregularities an axis of thick (40 m or more) Burro Canyon (fig. 1) extends in a north-northeast direction along the Utah-Colorado State line from near the Four Corners area to west of Grand Junction. To the east of this axis, the formation thins to an irregular zero line that suggests a series of lobes extending southeastward and eastward from the thick area. To the west the Burro Canyon thins and grades laterally into the Cedar Mountain Formation which in turn gradually thickens westward toward central Utah where it attains a thickness of more than 170 m. To the north in northeastern Utah and northwestern Colorado, the Burro Canyon also grades into Cedar Mountain, but control in this area is sparse. The erratic

thickening of the Lower Cretaceous rocks in the subsurface along the Douglas Creek arch north of Grand Junction is poorly understood, but they appear as an extension of the northerly trending axis of thick Burro Canyon.

Total thickness of sandstone, regardless of the number of units, in the Burro Canyon and Cedar Mountain Formations has a distribution similar to the total isopach map. As on the total isopach map, the Burro Canyon shows an axis of thick sandstones extending north-northeastward from southeastern Utah to near Grand Junction, Colorado. Along this axis, the cumulative thickness of sandstone exceeds 30 m. As on the total isopach map, irregularities occur in the salt anticline region of western Colorado and eastern Utah. These irregularities are considered to be the result of greater deposition in the subsiding synclines as a result of deep salt flowage from the synclines to the anticlines.

The Burro Canyon sandstone thins west and north of the depositional thick. In these areas the total sandstone thickness of the Cedar Mountain Formation is quite thin as compared to that of the Burro Canyon. The total sandstone in the Cedar Mountain does increase westward and in central Utah attains a maximum thickness of more than 20 m.

DIRECTIONS OF TRANSPORT AND SOURCE

A few studies of crossbedding orientations from the Burro Canyon Formation and the Buckhorn Conglomerate Member of the Cedar Mountain Formation are summarized on figure 2. The sedimentary structures in the Buckhorn Conglomerate in central Utah show an eastward direction of transport and imply a source area to the west. Crossbedding in the Burro Canyon Formation in southwestern Colorado and southeastern Utah indicates a dominantly northward direction of transport and implies a source area to the south.

In the area surrounding Grand Junction, Colorado and extending from Green River, Utah, to Delta, Colorado, the direction of transport fans through an arc of about 100 degrees, from north-northwest to due east. This fanning of transport directions is thought to result, primarily, from a radiating stream pattern in the Burro Canyon, and secondarily, from the merging of sediments from two major source areas, one to the west (Cedar Mountain) and one to the south (Burro Canyon).

Petrographic studies by D. R. Shawe (1968, p. B7) indicate that typical sandstone of the Burro Canyon Formation is dominantly quartzose and contains less chert and feldspar than does the sandstone of the underlying Morrison Formation (Shawe, 1968, p. B25). This grain composition seems to indicate that the source terrane was an area dominated by quartzose sedimentary rocks. The composition of the finer grained components in the Burro Canyon also are compatible with this type of source terrane.

The conglomerate and sandstone beds in the Cedar Mountain Formation are quartzose and also were derived from a dominantly sedimentary terrane. However, the mudstone component of the Cedar Mountain contains large amounts of swelling montmorillonitic clay (Keller, 1962, p. 64) that was derived from volcanic ash. Airborn ash was probably deposited on the source terrane and the depositional area simultaneously. It was then transported and reworked by streams.

AGE

The age of the Burro Canyon and Cedar Mountain Formations is not well documented. Fossil remains are sparse and most have been found near the top of the formations. They include fragments of dinosaurs, a few plants, including calcareous algae (charophytes), and a few fresh water invertebrates (gastropods, pelecypods, and

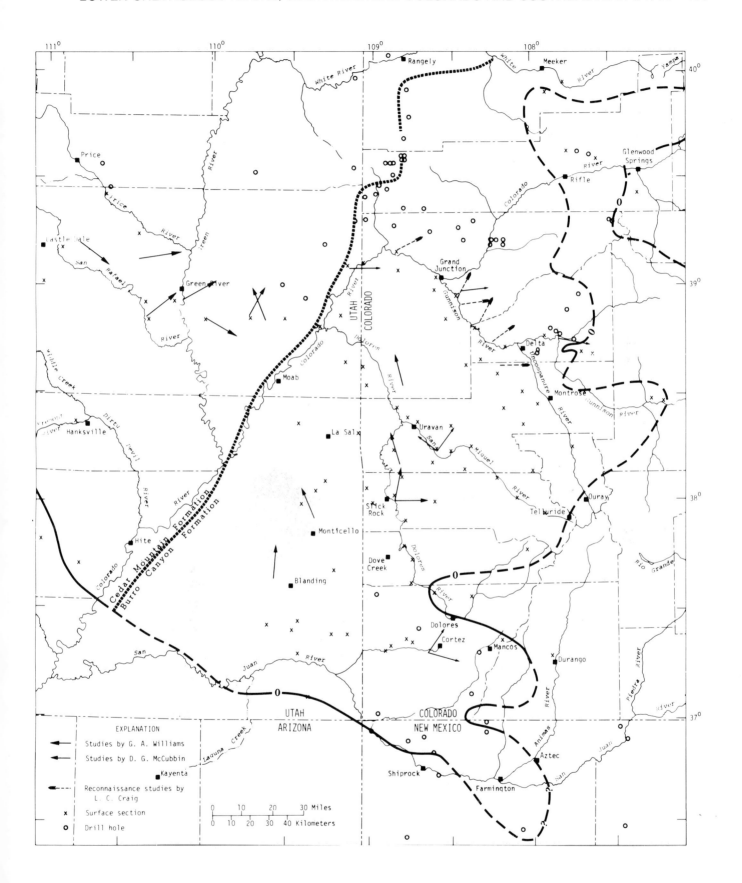

Figure 2. Resultant dip directions of cross laminae in sandstone units of the Burro Canyon and Cedar Mountain Formations. Heavy zero line (dashed where uncertain) marks pinchout of Burro Canyon and Cedar Mountain. Heavy dotted line is arbitrary boundary separating areas in which Burro Canyon and Cedar Mountain Formations are recognized.

ostracodes). Young (1960, p. 180-181) has summarized the known fossil occurances up to 1960. One plant, one gastropod, and two pelecypods seem to fix the age as definitely Early Cretaceous. Reeside (in Simmons, 1957, p. 2526) is cited as indicating that two pelecypods are "widespread [middle] Early Cretaceous (Aptian) species." The fossils in the Burro Canyon and Cedar Mountain are commonly compared to similar forms in the Kootenai Formation, Cloverly Formation, and Gannett Group of the northwestern United States.

Recently, palynomorphs have been recovered from samples, collected by R. H. and B. D. Tschudy, of dark carbonaceous mudstone near the top of both the Burro Canyon and the Cedar Mountain Formations. The Tschudys (written commun., 1981) report that the Cedar Mountain collection is late or latest Early Cretaceous (post-mid-Albian) and the Burro Canyon collections are middle to late Early Cretaceous (Aptian to early Albian) with a possibility that early Early Cretaceous (late Barremian) is represented.

Thus it seems possible that these formations represent much of early Cretaceous time. Only the earliest part of the Early Cretaceous remains unrepresented by fossil control. The author thinks it might be represented in the unfossiliferous lower parts of the Burro Canyon and Cedar Mountain and/or possibly in the upper part of underlying Brushy Basin Member of the Morrison Formation.

ENVIRONMENT OF DEPOSITION AND TECTONIC RELATIONS

The Burro Canyon and Cedar Mountain Formations are interpreted as two alluvial systems deposited across a broad, relatively even surface on top of the Morrison Formation. In many respects, the formations appear to represent a continuation of Morrison deposition. The sandstone and conglomeratic sandstone in both formations were deposited from a relatively high energy transport medium and are distinctly fluvial deposits formed by meandering or sinuous streams. Mudstones are largely overbank deposits formed in interfluve areas. These interfluve areas also were the site of deposition of limestone, probably in ephemeral fresh-water lakes.

The climate is visualized as warm and relatively humid with adequate moisture to support a moderate vegetation on the interfluve areas and a modest population of dinosaurs. Rainfall was probably cyclic and allowed the wetting and drying of the interfluve areas and resulted in the oxidation and destruction of much of the organic material.

Much volcanic ash was contributed to the Cedar Mountain and probably was transported in part as airborne ash falls. This pumiceous material doubtless clogged the streams and was reworked and intermixed with clastic debris derived from the source area to the west. No discrete ash beds have been reported, or observed by the author in the Cedar Mountain Formation.

Stream deposits dominate at the base of both the Cedar Mountain and Burro Canyon Formations. In the Cedar Mountain Formation, the Buckhorn Conglomerate Member is a high-energy deposit and forms a widespread lenticular layer. The unnamed shale member, which appears to be a dominantly low energy deposit, composes most of the formation, although other lensing fluvial sandstone units occur higher in the formation. The Burro Canyon Formation, on the other hand, consists of 50 percent or more sandstone over much of its extent. Higher energy conditions prevailed through much of Burro Canyon deposition. Although overbank, low-energy deposits occur interbedded with the sandstone, they are dominant only in the upper third of the formation.

These parallel changes in the two formations may represent a major cycle of tectonism and sedimentation. The high-energy deposits at the bottom of both formations may reflect a distinct period of uplift in the source areas and may have been accompanied by slight increase in gradients across the depositional plain. This period of uplift was followed by a period of tectonic quiescence in which low-energy deposits became dominant.

REFERENCES

American Commission on Stratigraphic Nomenclature, 1970, Code of stratigraphic nomenclature: Tulsa, Okla., American Association of Petroleum Geologists, 21 p.

Cater, F. W., 1970, Geology of the salt anticline region in southwestern Colorado: U.S. Geological Survey Professional Paper 637, 80 p.

Craig, L. C., Holmes, C. N., Cadigan, R. A., Freeman, V. L., Mullens, T. E., and Weir, G. W., 1955, Stratigraphy of the Morrison and related formations, Colorado Plateau region, a preliminary report: U.S. Geological Survey Bulletin 1009-E, p. 125-168.

Craig, L. C., Holmes, C. N., Freeman, V. L., Mullens, T. E., and others, 1959, Measured sections of the Morrison and adjacent formations: U.S. Geological Survey Open-File Report 485, approx. 700 p.

Freeman, V. L., 1972, Geologic map of the Woody Creek Quadrangle, Pitkin and Eagle Counties, Colorado: U.S. Geological Survey Geologic Quadrangle Map GQ-967.

Keller, W. D., 1962, Clay minerals in the Morrison Formation of the Colorado Plateau: U.S. Geological Survey Bulletin 1150, 90 p.

McCubbin, D. G., 1961, Basal Cretaceous of southwestern Colorado and southeastern Utah: Harvard University, Ph.D. Thesis, 172 p.

Saucier, A. E., 1974, Stratigraphy and uranium potential of the Burro Canyon Formation in the southern chama Basin, New Mexico, in Guidebook of central-northern New Mexico, New Mexico Geological Society, 25th Field Conference: p. 211-217.

Shawe, D. R., 1968, Petrography of sedimentary rocks in the Slick Rock district, San Miguel and Dolores Counties, Colorado: U.S. Geological Survey Professional Paper 576-B, 34 p.

_____, 1970, Structure of the Slick Rock district and vicinity, San Miguel and Dolores Counties, Colorado: U.S. Geological Survey Professional paper 576-C, 18 p.

_____, 1976, Sedimentary rock alteration in the Slick Rock district, San Miguel and Dolores Counties, Colorado: U.S. Geological Survey Professional Paper 576-D, 51 p.

Simmons, G. C., 1957, Contact of the Burro Canyon Formation with the Dakota Sandstone, Slick Rock district, Colorado, and correlation of Burro Canyon Formation: American Association of Petroleum Geologists Bulletin, v. 41, p. 2519-2529.

Stokes, W. L., 1944, Morrison and related deposits in and adjacent to the Colorado Plateau: Geological Society of America Bulletin, v. 55, p. 951-992.

_____, 1952, Lower Cretaceous in Colorado Plateau: American Association of Petroleum Geologists Bulletin, v. 36, no. 9, pp. 1766-1776.

Stokes, W. L., and Phoenix, D. A., 1948, Geology of the Egnar-Gypsum Valley area, San Miguel and Montrose Counties, Colorado: U.S. Geological Survey Oil and Gas Investigations, Preliminary Map 93.

Young, R. G., 1960, Dakota Group of Colorado Plateau: American Association of Petroleum Geologists Bulletin, v. 44, no. 2, p. 156-194.

GROUND-WATER CIRCULATION IN THE WESTERN PARADOX BASIN, UTAH

John W. Thackston, Bryan L. McCulley, and Lynne M. Preslo

ABSTRACT

The primary focus of this study is to describe the ground-water flow systems in and around the bedded salt areas of the Paradox Basin, Utah. Potentiometric and hydrogeochemical data were collected and analyzed. Using these data, the upper Paleozoic section was divided into three hydrostratigraphic units. Ground-water flow in the upper hydrostratigraphic unit, which lies above the Paradox Formation, appears to be controlled mainly by topography. Although this flow system is composed generally of a calcium-magnesium-bicarbonate water, another significant component of the water is sodium-chloride. The saline facies strata which comprise the middle hydrostratigraphic unit are generally typical of aquitards, although in some localities, zones of high pressure and permeability exist. Water with variable chemical composition occurs as a result of there being no interconnected ground-water flow system within this middle unit. Stratigraphically below the Paradox Formation, the lower hydrostratigraphic unit contains a regionally extensive flow system, the Mississippian Leadville Limestone. In general, the flow of ground water in this lower unit is toward the southwest. The lower unit contains water which is typically high in total dissolved solids (TDS), particularly sodium-chloride, where its strata are overlain by the Paradox salt. Lower salinity waters are found in the lower unit to the west, outside of the basin proper, where salt beds do not exist in the Paradox Formation. The occurrence of the high-TDS water may be explained by downward cross-formational flow from the Paradox Formation in areas where the normal, low permeability stratigraphic sequence has been structurally disrupted to provide more permeable flow paths.

INTRODUCTION

In 1969, Hanshaw and Hill published the most extensive discussion to date of the hydrogeology of the Paradox Basin region. Their study was based primarily on a compilation of drill-stem test results and other data analyses performed prior to 1961. At that time the major interest in ground-water circulation within deep Paleozoic formations was related to the exploration for hydrocarbons. Although the quest for oil and gas continues, a new interest in deciphering the deep ground-water movement patterns has arisen: underground storage of high-level nuclear waste.

Work performed on the Paradox Basin Project, a feasibility and siting study for a high-level nuclear waste respository in the Utah portion of the Paradox Basin, has resulted in the compilation of data presented and discussed herein. This project, part of the Department of Energy National Waste Terminal Storage Program, is being conducted by Woodward-Clyde Consultants under subcontract to Battelle Memorial Institute, Office of Nuclear Waste Isolation. The primary area of focus for the hydrogeologic discussions in this report is the bedded salt areas in and adjacent to the Monument Upwarp, as shown on Figure 1.

Of particular importance to this study is an understanding of the regional ground-water circulation rates and directions within the Paleozoic formations, especially in those strata surrounding the Paradox Formation salt bodies. Although the project is not complete at this time, data have been obtained that advance the state of knowledge in some areas beyond the pioneering work of Hanshaw and Hill.

PREVIOUS STUDIES

Numerous authors have provided information on the hydrogeology of the Paradox Basin Region. However, most of these studies have been limited to near-surface formations, and were considered potentially worthwhile for water supply development or uranium exploration. Jobin (1962) provided regional isotransmissivity and isopermeability maps for Permian and younger sedimentary rock formations of the Colorado Plateau. To derive maps of the transmissive character of the rocks, Jobin performed a statistical analysis on data from numerous laboratory permeability tests and thin sections of rock samples collected from outcrops in the region. Pre-Permian formations were not studied in his investigation.

Feltis (1966) compiled most of the data presently available relating to the ground-water quality of springs and water wells, and also data from deep formations encountered in oil/gas drilling. However, his paper did not discuss or advance hypotheses from the basic data that he presented. Irwin (1966) compiled data for the purpose of identifying potential sources of water supply for the residents of Ute Mountain Indian Reservation in southwestern Colorado. Cooley and others (1969) identified present and potential sources of water supply within the Navajo and Hopi reservations that are located along the southern margin of the Paradox Basin. Ritzma and Doelling (1969) compiled the ground-water data available for the southern part of the Paradox Basin. Huntoon (1977, 1979a,b) and Richter (1980) compiled and analyzed data for the purpose of identifying potential sources of ground-water in the Canyonlands National Park for the National Park Service. Huntoon and Richter (1979) discussed ground-water circulation and dissolution of salt in the Lockhart Basin area.

Except for the previously mentioned work by Hanshaw and Hill (1969), little is available in the literature regarding the ground-water hydrology of the Paleozoic formations associated with the Paradox Formation salt. The report by Hanshaw and Hill (1969) is particularly relevant to this current study because, in addition to the presentation of basic information, hypotheses on ground-water flow conditions in the Paleozoic formations were included. Hanshaw and Hill delineated five aquifers and presented a potentiometric map of each based on hundreds of drill-stem test analyses. From the potentiometric maps and trends observed in water chemistry data (gathered largely from Feltis, 1966), inferences were drawn regarding the flow patterns, including recharge and discharge areas, of the deep ground-water system.

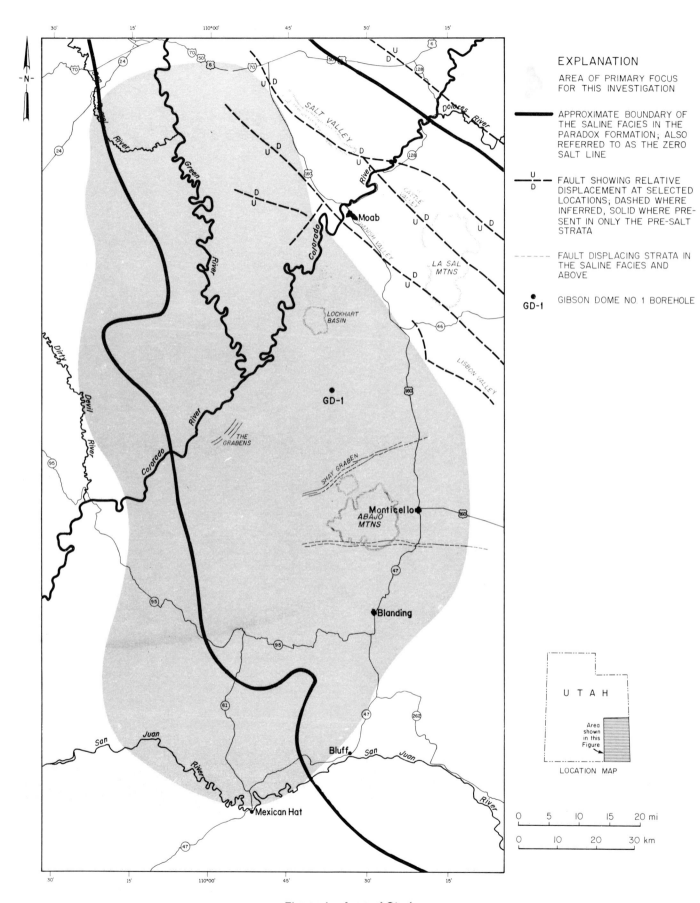

Figure 1. Area of Study

GEOLOGIC SETTING

The Paradox Basin is a northwest-trending asymmetric depositional trough. Limits of the basin coincide with the maximum areal extent of the Paradox Formation salt deposits (termed herein the zero-salt line). Figure 1 shows the principal area of focus for the investigation and the major tectonic and topographic features of interest.

The Paradox Formation is of Pennsylvanian age, and contains up to 29 cycles of deposits composed of limestone, silty dolomite, anhydrite, calcareous shale, and halite (some potash salts are also present at some localities). The total thickness and number of cyclic deposits within the saline facies of the Paradox Formation lessen toward the basin margins and grade laterally into contemporaneously deposited carbonate rocks (Hite, 1968).

Marine carbonates overlie and underlie the Paradox Formation. Intertonguing continental and marine sediments of Permian age unconformably overlie the Pennsylvanian marine carbonates and evaporites. Figure 2 is a generalized stratigraphic column developed for the study region based upon the work of Hintze (1973), Molenaar (1975a, 1975b), Baars and Seager (1970), Baars and others (1967) and Baars (1962).

The following brief geologic history of the upper Paleozoic strata within the region is summarized from the work of Wengerd and Matheny (1958). In Mississippian and early Pennsylvanian time the region now known as the Paradox Basin was part of a cratonic shelf that existed east of the Cordilleran miogeosyncline. During the early Pennsylvanian a marine regression occurred that resulted in development of a regolithic and in some places karstic terrain on the preexisting Mississippian carbonate formations.

Subsidence of the Paradox Basin began in the middle Pennsylvanian, allowing marine deposition. Periodic changes in the rate of influx of saline waters into the basin resulted from sea level fluctuations and created the remarkably cyclical pattern of saline facies deposition within the Paradox Formation (Hite, 1970). During the Permian, clastic sediments began to invade the basin at a much greater rate because of tectonic activation of the Uncompahgre Uplift on the northeast side of the basin.

Structurally the region is characterized as a broad homocline with strata generally dipping at low angles toward the northeast and terminating against the Uncompahgre Uplift. Abrupt anticlines, monoclines, and igneous intrusives occur locally within the homocline. Many faults in the region are associated with the anticlines, which were created as a result of salt flowage. Other faults are associated with igneous intrusives in the Abajo and La Sal mountains. Figure 3 shows the generalized structural map of the region. It is noteworthy that faults in the formations lying stratigraphically below the salt cannot be traced directly into the strata within and above the salt deposits (Jones, 1959). However, faults exposed along the margins of several diapiric salt anticlines such as Spanish Valley, Lisbon Valley, and Paradox Valley coincide vertically with major faults offsetting the strata that predate salt deposition. Periodic reactivation of the pre-salt faults has been suggested as providing impetus for the salt diapirism (Baars, 1972; Hite and Lohman, 1973).

Topography within the area is characterized by deeply-incised canyons along the Green, San Juan, and Colorado rivers. Along these major canyons are many rugged side canyons containing dry washes or perennial streams. Elevations range from approximately 3500 feet in canyon bottoms in the western part of the region to over 13,000 feet

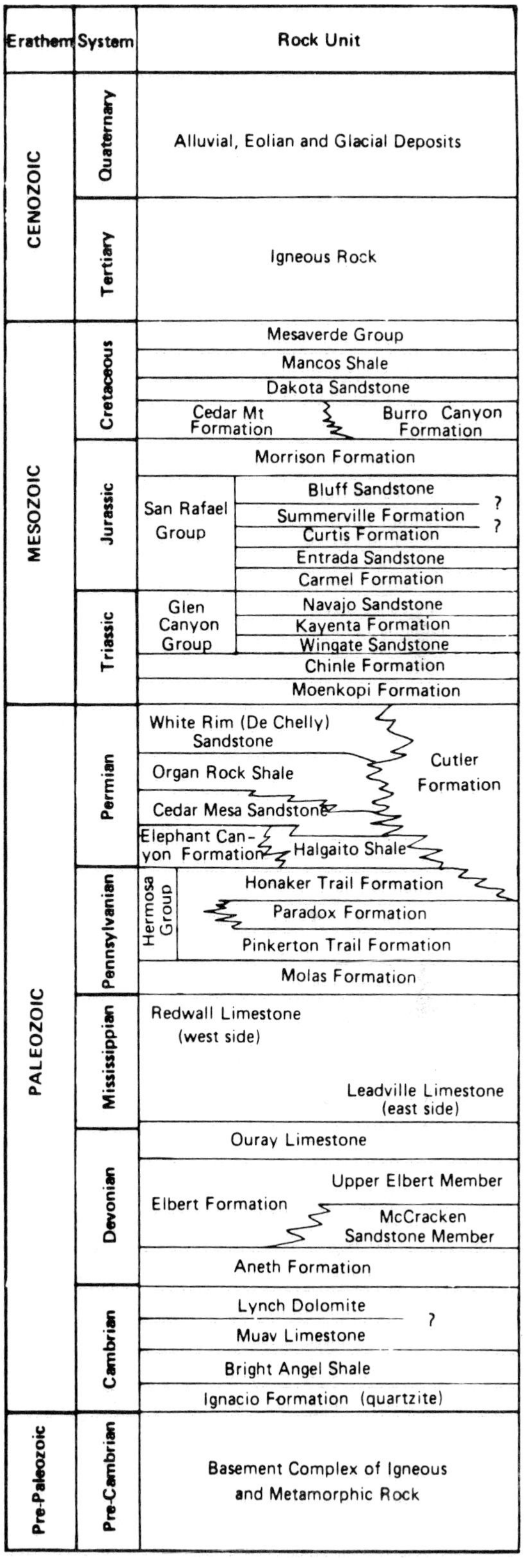

Erathem	System	Rock Unit		
CENOZOIC	Quaternary	Alluvial, Eolian and Glacial Deposits		
	Tertiary	Igneous Rock		
MESOZOIC	Cretaceous	Mesaverde Group		
		Mancos Shale		
		Dakota Sandstone		
		Cedar Mt Formation	Burro Canyon Formation	
	Jurassic	Morrison Formation		
		San Rafael Group	Bluff Sandstone	?
			Summerville Formation	?
			Curtis Formation	
			Entrada Sandstone	
			Carmel Formation	
	Triassic	Glen Canyon Group	Navajo Sandstone	
			Kayenta Formation	
			Wingate Sandstone	
		Chinle Formation		
		Moenkopi Formation		
PALEOZOIC	Permian	White Rim (De Chelly) Sandstone	Cutler Formation	
		Organ Rock Shale		
		Cedar Mesa Sandstone		
		Elephant Canyon Formation	Halgaito Shale	
	Pennsylvanian	Hermosa Group	Honaker Trail Formation	
			Paradox Formation	
			Pinkerton Trail Formation	
		Molas Formation		
	Mississippian	Redwall Limestone (west side)	Leadville Limestone (east side)	
	Devonian	Ouray Limestone		
		Elbert Formation	Upper Elbert Member	
			McCracken Sandstone Member	
		Aneth Formation		
	Cambrian	Lynch Dolomite	?	
		Muav Limestone		
		Bright Angel Shale		
		Ignacio Formation (quartzite)		
Pre-Paleozoic	Pre-Cambrian	Basement Complex of Igneous and Metamorphic Rock		

Figure 2. Generalized Composite Stratigraphic Column for the Paradox Basin

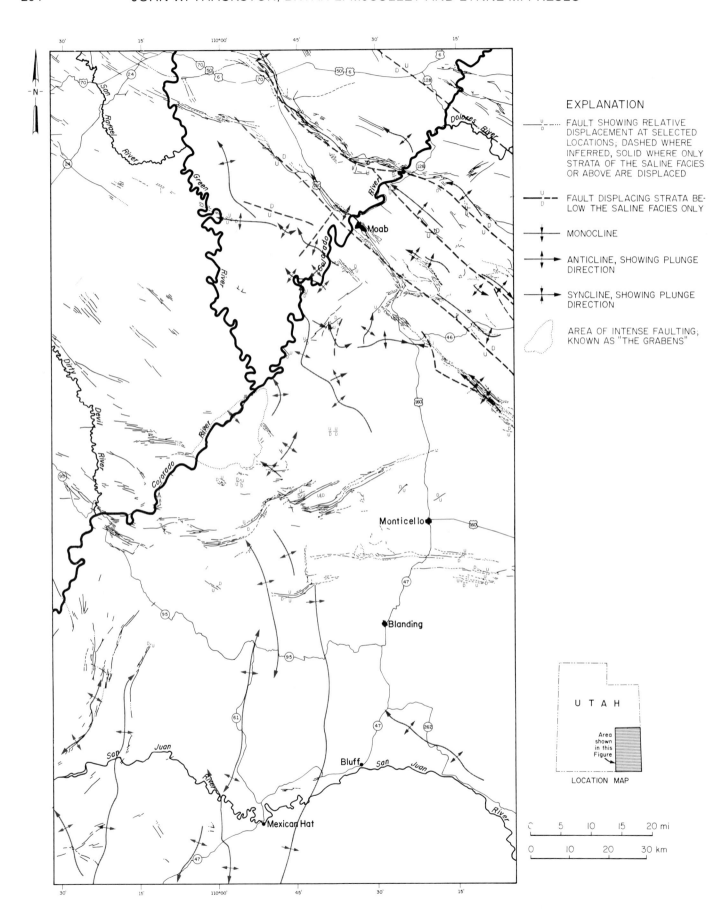

EXPLANATION

FAULT SHOWING RELATIVE DISPLACEMENT AT SELECTED LOCATIONS; DASHED WHERE INFERRED, SOLID WHERE ONLY STRATA OF THE SALINE FACIES OR ABOVE ARE DISPLACED

FAULT DISPLACING STRATA BELOW THE SALINE FACIES ONLY

MONOCLINE

ANTICLINE, SHOWING PLUNGE DIRECTION

SYNCLINE, SHOWING PLUNGE DIRECTION

AREA OF INTENSE FAULTING; KNOWN AS "THE GRABENS"

UTAH

Area shown in this Figure

LOCATION MAP

Figure 3. Structural Features

in the mountains. Relatively flat plains are found between the highland areas of the Abajo, La Sal, and Henry mountains, covered by sparse vegetation typical of arid and semi-arid climates. Along major monoclines such as Comb Ridge and along the margin of the Salt anticlines, barren cuesta and hogback ridges occur. In the highest mountain areas precipitation averages more than 32 inches per year, whereas in the lower plains and canyons 8 to 12 inches or less per year is typical.

HYDROSTRATIGRAPHIC UNITS

In this study the concept of hydrostratigraphic units is used to facilitate description of the ground-water flow system, rather than the subdivision of the stratigraphic section into a series of aquifers as proposed by Hanshaw and Hill (1969). Maxey (1964) defined hydrostratigraphic units as "bodies of rock with considerable lateral extent that compose a geologic framework for a reasonably distinct hydrologic system". Using this concept, an aquifer, a confining unit, or a combination of both may be contained within a hydrostratigraphic unit.

Data were collected for this study through literature searches, the sampling and chemical analysis of springs, and the interpretation of numerous drill-stem tests conducted throughout the region. Precise site-specific data were also collected during hydrologic tests in the Gibson Dome No. 1 (GD-1) borehole (T. 30 S., R. 21 E., Sec. 21), drilled for the Paradox Basin Project. Based on these data, we subdivide the upper Paleozoic section (Figure 2) of the bedded salt areas of the western Paradox Basin into three hydrostratigraphic units. Stratigraphic intervals that possess similar hydrogeological characteristics form the units. The upper hydrostratigraphic unit includes strata of the Permian and extends downward to approximately the lower third of the Pennsylvanian Honaker Trail Formation or the top of the Paradox Formation. Underlying strata to the bottom of the Paradox Formation comprise the middle hydrostratigraphic unit. Included within the lower hydrostratigraphic unit are the Pennsylvanian Pinkerton Trail Formation and Mississippian Molas Formation and Leadville Limestone. A paucity of data from below the Leadville Limestone creates uncertainty regarding the lowermost extent of this unit. However, the unit extends at least to the base of the Leadville Limestone, the most permeable and extensive Paleozoic aquifer identified to date in the region.

UPPER HYDROSTRATIGRAPHIC UNIT

Characteristics of the Permian and upper Honaker Trail strata show similarities that indicate a single hydrostratigraphic unit. At well GD-1 the hydrostatic pressure gradient through this section (Figure 4) increases steadily with depth. The trend of increasing pressure is consistent with the density and weight of the pore fluids. This pressure increase with depth indicates that hydrologic continuity exists within this section.

Hanshaw and Hill (1969) referred to the Permian formations and the Honaker Trail Formation as separate aquifers. Clearly this is not the case in the bedded salt areas at the GD-1 location. With the exception of one zone in the Elephant Canyon Formation, the most productive aquifer encountered in the section, and two zones in the upper Honaker Trail, the strata are too tight to yield detectable quantities of water both during air drilling and subsequent hydrologic testing. Only a few zones of limited vertical extent yielded water to the drillhole; nevertheless the entire thickness of the hydrostratigraphic unit proved to be saturated. Drilling through tight lithologic intervals such as

these, with no water production while drilling with compressed air or air-mist, often gives misleading impressions. Drillers, geologists and hydrogeologists in the field frequently assume that "dry" strata are being penetrated.

The sparse occurrence and limited vertical extent of aquifers within the unit are strongly controlled by porosity distributions related to depositional facies trends and fractures associated with faults, igneous intrusions, and salt flowage. Despite the large contrast in hydraulic conductivities of the few thin aquifers and the intervening tight fine-grained strata, the unit probably acts in general as a single flow unit under steady-state conditions.

Potentiometric levels in the unit and the locations of springs in the area indicate that topography strongly controls the ground-water flow of the upper hydrostratigraphic unit (Figure 5). The high elevations, high precipitation, and structures in the mountainous areas influence the regional flow pattern. There are at present no human activities such as ground-water pumping or injection that might significantly interrupt the natural gravity-driven flow pattern.

Hydrogeologic cross sections through the Abajo highlands, canyonlands, and Elk Ridge areas (Figures 6, 7, and 8) illustrate the relative simplicity of stratigraphic relationships and igneous intrusives. In the mountainous areas the upper hydrostratigraphic unit is overlain by fractured, sedimentary rocks of Mesozoic age, and Quaternary alluvial and glacial deposits. Snow-melt waters that recharge these surficial deposits provide a potential source of ground water to percolate downward into the Permian rocks and below. The presence of suitable pathways of vertical hydraulic continuity would enable this percolation to occur.

Continuous zones of effective porosity are evident in outcrop areas along the periphery of the highlands, and probably extend to great depths below the weathered zone. Contact zones between the laccoliths and the weakened country rock that they intrude exhibit minor faulting, fracturing and brecciation at ground surface. Stresses induced during post-emplacement cooling produced the volumetric shrinkage that caused these deformations. In addition to contact zone porosity, several fault zones surround the mountains. Extensive graben systems such as the Shay, Verdure and Hammond grabens nearly surround the Abajo Mountains. Field observations of chemical alteration and mineralization along these fault zones strongly suggest past ground water movement (Kitcho, this volume). Streams entrenched in alluvium crossing these fault zones are potentially good areas for recharge to the unit.

Discharge from the upper hydrostratigraphic unit is apparently quite small. Only scattered springs emanate from the Permian formations in the canyonlands area lying topographically below the broad plains that surround the highlands. Even fewer springs were found flowing from the Honaker Trail Formation, despite an extensive areal reconnaissance conducted specifically to locate and sample all springs that might represent discharge from the Honaker Trail and Paradox Formations. In the Cataract Canyon area, no more than seven Honaker Trail springs were found above low river stage, each with a very small discharge rate (less than 5 gallons per minute). A profile of salinity in the Colorado River between Potash and Lake Powell (Figure 9), conducted for the purpose of detecting saline ground water discharge at or below river level, detected no anomalies that might indicate major saline inflows. No perennial Honaker

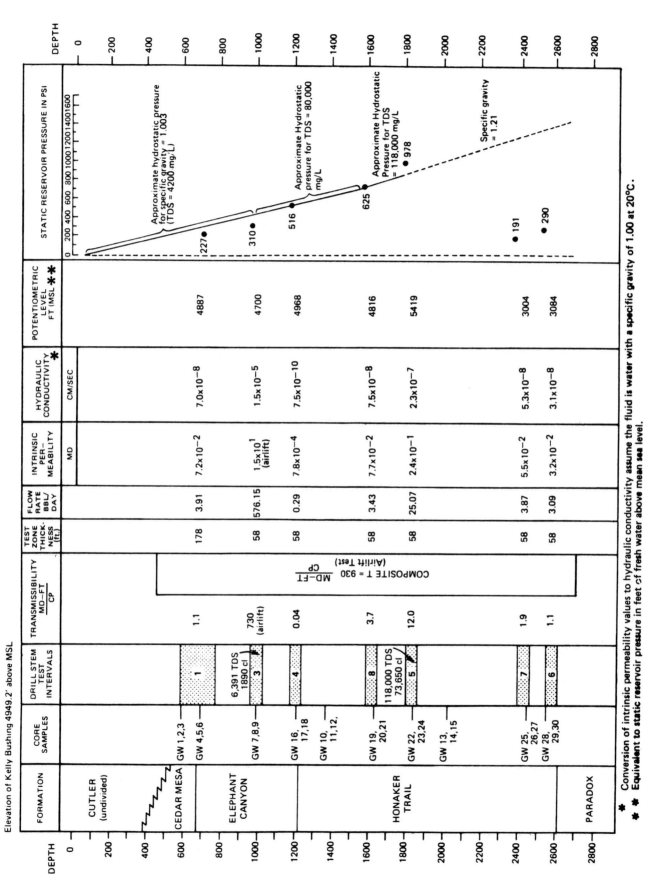

Figure 4.   Preliminary Hydrogeologic Results from Gibson Dome No. 1 Borehole

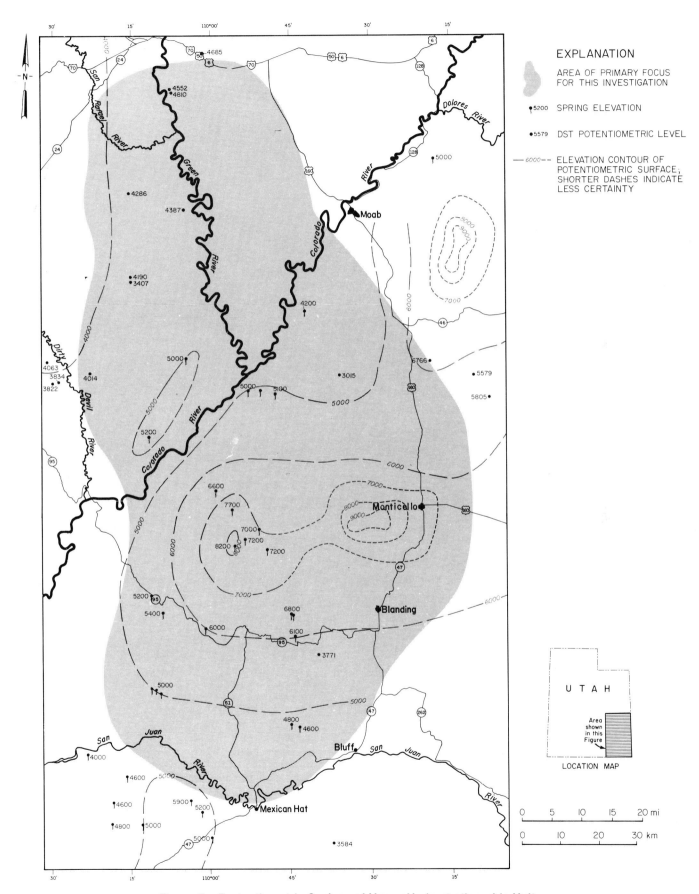

Figure 5. Portentiometric Surface of Upper Hydrostratigraphic Unit

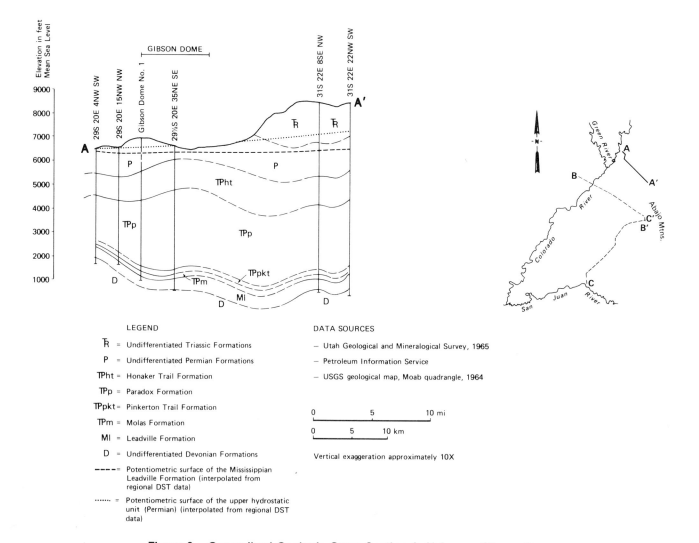

Figure 6. Generalized Geologic Cross Section A-A' Across Gibson Dome

Trail springs were detected along the San Juan River.

A large emphasis has been placed on compiling and interpreting hydrochemistry data for this study. While a hydrostratigraphic unit is pictured as a stratigraphic section containing a reasonably continuous ground-water body or flow system, there may be several hydrochemical facies within each hydrostratigraphic unit. As summarized by Back (1966, p. A-11), hydrochemical facies "reflect the effects of chemical processes occurring between the minerals within the lithologic framework and the ground water."

Any hypothesis regarding the chemical evolution of ground water requires an assumption about the direction, and often the rate, of ground-water flow. Such an assumption can then be compared against the gradients derived from potentiometric maps, and vice versa. If the hydrogeologic system of a particular area is to be completely understood, both the chemical and potentiometric data must be consistent.

Water chemistry data available in the literature and from various governmental agencies, and those collected in the field for this study were evaluated using contour maps of dissolved solids, trilinear diagrams, Stiff diagrams, and ionic ratios. Water-mineral analyses have not yet been completed.

Numerous workers have investigated the chemical evolution of ground water (e.g., Back, 1966; Chebotarev, 1955; Foster, 1950; Freeze and Cherry, 1979; Galloway,

Kreitler and McGowen, 1978; Hanshaw and Back, 1979; White, 1965). Some, for example, have reported the change from a calcium-bicarbonate water type near the recharge area to a sodium-chloride water type down-gradient. This type of evolution has been attributed to dissolution and cation exchange.

As shown on Figure 10, the upper hydrostratigraphic unit is composed of a spectrum of relatively dilute, calcium-bicarbonate ($Ca-HCO_3$) to more concentrated sodium-chloride (Na-Cl) waters (Figure 10). Most of the Na-Cl waters occur in the Honaker Trail Limestone. While lack of data makes it difficult to describe the exact phenomena responsible for the range of water chemistry in this unit, it appears that at least two types of hydrochemical facies and attendant mixing are occurring within this unit.

At one extreme, the calcium-bicarbonate waters probably represent shallow flow systems with short residence times. This $Ca-HCO_3$ water type is caused by percolation through a calcareous soil zone and through a stratigraphic section containing abundant calcium carbonate. The extensive jointing and the deeply dissected topography occurring in this hydrostratigraphic unit over much of the Paradox Basin allows the formation of steep gradients between upland recharge areas and discharge zones in the incised canyons. The incised topography, coupled with the short-circuiting effect of the abundant jointing and fracturing within these

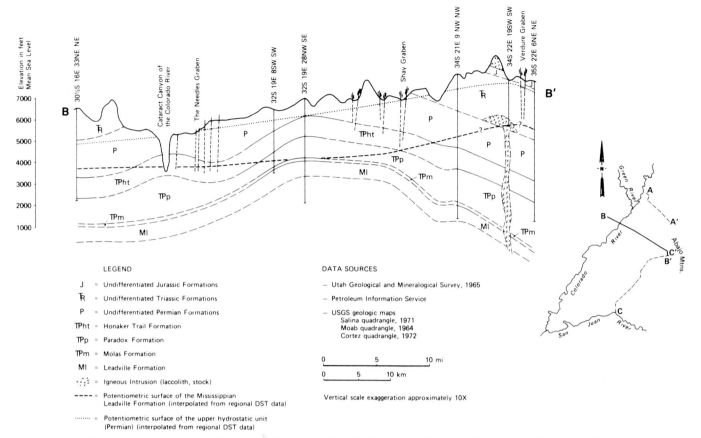

Figure 7.   Generalized Geologic Cross Section B-B' Across Cataract Canyon of Colorado River

formations, provides the hydrogeologic setting for shorter travel paths and residence times for the ground water than would normally occur in an undissected basin of similar size. As a result of these shorter travel times, ionic exchange of calcium for sodium on clay particles is curtailed, and less chloride is dissolved from the aquifer matrix. Therefore, calcium-bicarbonate water with a low total dissolved solids (TDS) content is found in some areas of this unit.

At the other end of the water quality spectrum, sodium-chloride (Na-Cl) waters with high TDS values are also present in the upper hydrostratigraphic unit (Figure 10). These Na-Cl waters could represent several processes: an end member in the chemical evolution of younger, active ground-water flow systems; an older connate ground water; a water of salt dissolution; or a combination of these three processes.

Predicting the final chemical composition of ground water recharged to the upper hydrostratigraphic unit is a difficult task because of the lack of chemical data and the multitude of lithologies present along the flow path. It appears reasonable, however, to assume that the final chemistry of ground water involved in the dynamic part of the flow system in the upper hydrostratigraphic unit could be of the sodium-chloride type. If sufficient clay minerals are present, calcium and magnesium ions may exchange for sodium ions, enriching the ground water in sodium. Chloride ions tend not to become involved in precipitation or reduction reactions, as do bicarbonate and sulfate ions. In an aquifer matrix containing chloride ions, the concentration of chloride ions in the water will be directly proportional to the length of the flow path.

A relict marine water would also be Na-Cl rich, although it could have shifted significantly in composition during diagenesis or mixing with other waters. As proposed by Lane (1908), connate water would have been buried with the rocks in which it occurs, retaining its chemical composition. White (1965) pointed out that such water probably does not exist, and proposed the following redefinition:

> Connate water . . . generally is similar in age or somewhat younger, since last direct contact with the atmosphere, than the age of its associated rocks.

The exact age of the older saline water is not relevant to this study; the term connate is instead used in this paper to distinguish qualitatively between actively circulating ground water and extremely sluggish, possibly static flow regimes. Such a distinction has relevance both to the Paradox Basin Project as well as to the migration of hydrocarbons.

The third process, a water involved in the dissolution of halite, would clearly produce a sodium-chloride composition. If a meteoric water comes in contact with halite, it would contain little other than sodium and chloride ions in solution.

One method that researchers have used to determine the origin of saline waters involves the use of chloride/bromide ratios (Rittenhouse, 1967; Carpenter, 1978; White, 1965). This method assumes that, as sea water is evaporated, chloride and bromide are concentrated in the same proportion. Once halite begins to precipitate, however, much more chloride than bromide is lost to the crystalline salt matrix.

The ratio of chloride to bromide in sea water during evaporation is shown by the solid line on Figure 11. The change in slope of the solid line is the point at which halite begins to precipitate. When the halite is subsequently dissolved by a relatively low TDS water (e.g., meteoric

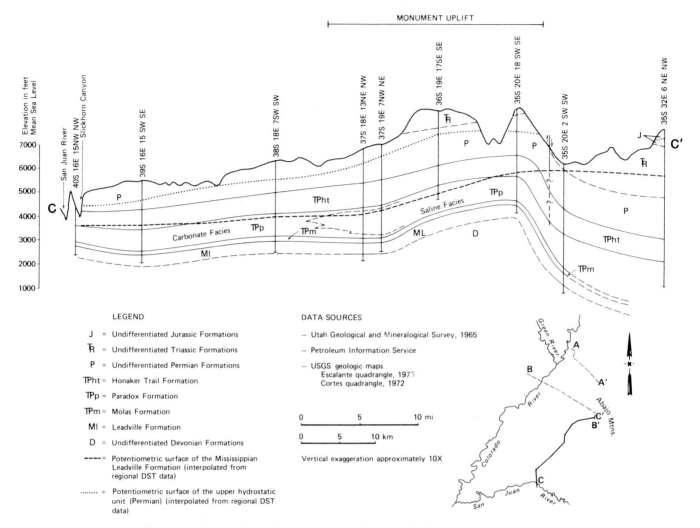

Figure 8.   Generalized Geologic Cross Section C-C' Across Elk Ridge Area

water), the ratio of chloride to bromide in the resultant saline water will reflect the ion ratio within the halite crystal. As a result, the saline water or brine produced by the dissolution of halite will plot to the left of the solid line shown on Figure 11. Cl/Br ratios then could be assumed to distinguish between saline connate water and saline water produced by halite dissolution.

Most of the hydrochemical analyses from the Paradox Basin in the literature do not include bromide values. However, water samples collected during drill-stem testing at GD-1 were analyzed for bromide. The ratio of chloride to bromide in these water samples is shown on Figure 11. All values of the Cl/Br ratio from GD-1 plot close to the trend of evaporating seawater (the solid line). These data imply that the water in the Elephant Canyon and Honaker Trail formations in the Gibson Dome area is largely an older connate ground water and is not affected by salt dissolution. Some of the Elephant Canyon samples are less saline than sea water, but have a Cl/Br ratio similar to sea water (i.e., they plot on the straight line). These data imply that the samples have been diluted by a relatively fresh meteoric water rather than water of dissolution, with no significant components of chloride or bromide.

As shown on Figure 11, however, some springs emanating from the Honaker Trail Limestone have Cl/Br ratios that plot

to the left of the sea water evaporation trend, implying an origin related to salt dissolution. These springs, in the Cataract Canyon of the Colorado River near the Grabens (Needles fault zone), occur within a 1- to 2-foot range of the river's low water stage, and are therefore submerged much of the year. Unlike samples taken at depth, these springs probably represent discharge from the more short-circuited flow systems prevalent in the upper hydrostratigraphic unit. Shallow flow systems such as this are heavily influenced by meteoric water.

Gaping crevasses filled with alluvium are common in the Grabens area (Biggar and others, this volume), and act as effective recharge areas during periods of heavy rains. Extensive fracturing in the Grabens area is thought to extend downward to or into the Paradox salt (McGill and Stromquist, 1975). Pathways in the fracture zones would allow for fresh water to dissolve Paradox salt and eventually discharge to the river from springs emanating from the fractured Honaker Trail.

A trend similar to the one shown on Figure 11 could be produced by dilution of a connate water with another water containing chloride ions. Moreover, if a bromine source or sink such as organic matter or clay adsorption of bromine exists in the system (Collins, 1975; Valyashko, 1956), the origin of the saline water becomes more obscure, and must be substantiated by other methods.

An evaluation of the ratio of sodium to chloride (Na/Cl) supports conclusions drawn from Cl/Br data. The dissolution of halite by a relatively fresh water produces a sodium-chloride water with a Na/Cl ratio of approximately 0.65 on a weight basis. If this ratio in a sodium-chloride water significantly deviates from 0.65, some process other than or in addition to salt dissolution is controlling the concentration of sodium and chloride. For example, empirical observation has shown that connate oil field waters in the Permian Basin characteristically have Na/Cl ratios of 0.55 or less (Johnson, 1980, personal communication). Water samples from the Elephant Canyon and Honaker Trail formations at GD-1 have Na/Cl ratios ranging from 0.42 to 0.46. This suggests an origin unrelated to salt dissolution. Water samples from the springs in Cataract Canyon, however, have Na/Cl ratios that range from 0.58 to 0.70, and average 0.64, which is typical of a water that has dissolved halite.

Water samples from the upper hydrostratigraphic unit elsewhere in the Paradox Basin show a more variable but generally higher range of Na/Cl ratio. Because few processes remove chloride from solutions in the subsurface, it is assumed another mechanism besides salt dissolution is probably operating as a source of sodium in the upper hydrostratigraphic unit. No trona deposits or other non-chloride, sodium-rich evaporites have been reported in this unit. Possible sources of sodium include ion exchange in clay-rich strata and alteration of plagioclase. Further evaluations of ions and mineral equilibria are being conducted to investigate this sodium enrichment process.

MIDDLE HYDROSTRATIGRAPHIC UNIT

Lower Honaker Trail and Paradox rocks of the middle hydrostratigraphic unit generally show characteristics of aquitards in the area of this report. Most drill-stem test records in the region indicate low production rates, low permeabilities, and limited reservoir conditions. Typically, pressure buildups during the shut-in portions of drill-stem tests in this formation are commonly slow. The final shut-in pressures are often below normal hydrostatic pressure for the test depth. On the other hand, in the salt anticline areas and a few other scattered localities, abnormally high shut-in pressures are sometimes encountered; small quantities of oil, gas and brine have been reported from a few of these tests. In most of the high pressure cases, however, the return of fluid pressure is slow after the initial pressure release. This phenomenon is indicative of extremely limited zones of effective porosity and permeability. Abnormally pressured zones such as these are most readily explained as the result of salt flowage and deformation within interbeds where part of the lithostatic loading is transferred to the pore fluids.

Drill-stem test (DST) data from the GD-1 borehole provide the most definitive values of permeabilities and potentiometric levels for the tight interbeds of the saline facies of any data available in the area. The GD-1 tests were performed on interbeds in the Paradox Formation that appeared, on the basis of core inspection and geophysical logs, to contain the highest relative transmissivity. Production rates for each of the tests were less than 10 barrels per day during the initial flow periods, diminishing in the second flow period. Some flow tests yielded only a fraction of a barrel per day for the entire zone tested. Test interval thickness ranged from approximately 50 to 200 feet. All zones tested contained abnormally low fluid pressures and potentiometric levels. Standard analyses of DST data (Horner, 1951; Earlougher, 1977) provided values of permeability of less than 10 millidarcies, although actual permeability values are likely to be considerably lower.

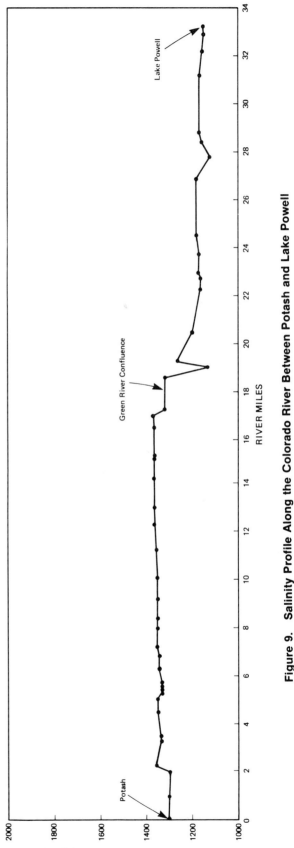

Figure 9. Salinity Profile Along the Colorado River Between Potash and Lake Powell

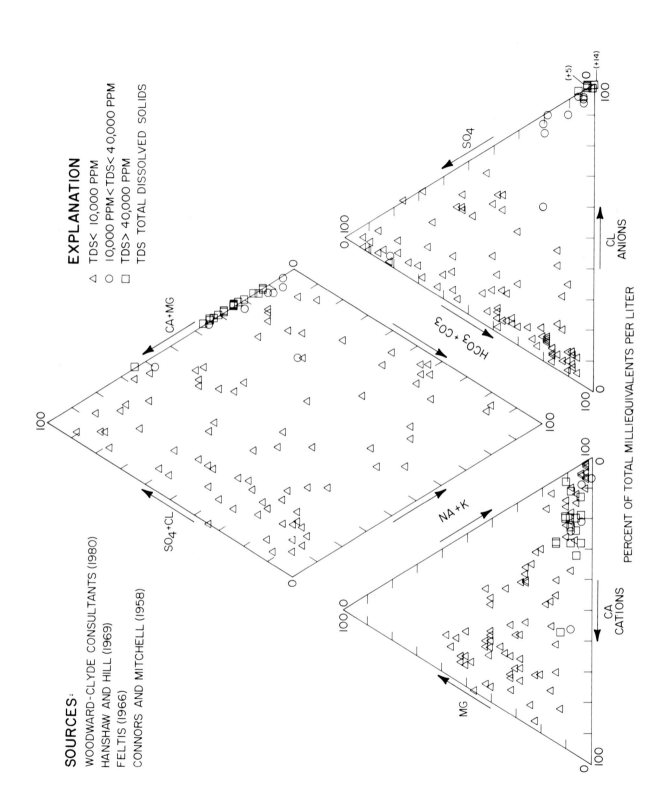

Figure 10.   Trilinear Diagram of Water Analyses, Upper Hydrostratigraphic Unit

Complications exist in the analysis of some of these drill-stem tests. Extremely low productivities and pressure heads, combined with an unusual borehole deformation, resulted in abnormal shut-in data. The initial rate of shut-in pressure buildup was abnormally diminished, possibly as a result of flow into the test interval after the shut-in valve was closed downhole. This afterflow can be attributed to fluid compressibility and system elasticity, in addition to low pore pressure and flow rates.

Another problem encountered in GD-1 tests was borehole squeeze. The squeeze was caused by deformation of the salt strata, and possibly shale beds in some cases. This squeeze caused an abnormally steep pressure buildup during the latter portions of the shut-in periods. This effect was particularly pronounced at depths greater than about 3500 feet. Once understood, effects such as these may be accounted for in the analyses. Despite the resultant uncertainties in the quantitative values, the basic conclusion still holds: Paradox Formation interbeds have very low permeabilities and transmissivities in the vicinity of the GD-1 borehole. Extensive review of DST results throughout the region show that this characteristic is common in the bedded salt areas of the western basin.

Elsewhere in the region there are a few exceptional flow conditions within the saline facies. For example, interbeds within the Paradox Formation have been reported on drilling logs as producing concentrated brine in the Big Flat area near Dead Horse Point. Both interbeds and salt beds in the Paradox Formation have produced brine in the Lisbon Valley area (Hite, 1978). In addition, strata within the upper Paradox have yielded commercially significant volumes of oil in the Hatch Point area.

Unusual hydrologic conditions also exist in Lockhart Basin where the salt beds within the Paradox have been totally removed by dissolution. Only insoluble residue, presumably from the interbeds, remains at one test well location in Lockhart Basin. This dissolution collapse feature is discussed in more detail in a later part of this paper and by Huntoon and Richter (1979). Sugiura and Kitcho (this volume) describe the breccia pipe structures in Lockhart Basin and other similar features.

A discussion of the middle hydrostratigraphic unit must address the question of whether an osmotic flow system exists. Berry and Hanshaw (1964) described osmotic flow systems in other areas in which potentiometric levels increase below a semipermeable membrane of shale, but decrease in the strata above. This phenomenon, they explained, results from the salinity gradient between waters separated by the membrane. Hanshaw and Hill (1969) speculated that such an osmotic flow system may exist in the Paradox Basin, albeit of limited extent. As evidence of osmotic gradients causing downward flow into the saline facies, they cited an apparent low area in the potentiometric surface of the Permian aquifer map in the Aneth oil and gas field area. Regional potentiometric data and the results of the GD-1 tests show no evidence of an osmotic flow system in the bedded salt area of this study.

There is no interconnected aquifer flow system within the middle hydrostratigraphic unit. Many unusually low and abnormally high potentiometric levels exist (Figure 12), and do not form a consistent pattern in the bedded salt area of the western Paradox Basin. For this reason contouring of the data points has not been attempted. Many of the tests that produced very little fluid and small pressure buildup could not be successfully analyzed using the standard Horner technique. These tests are labeled with a "T" (tight) on the

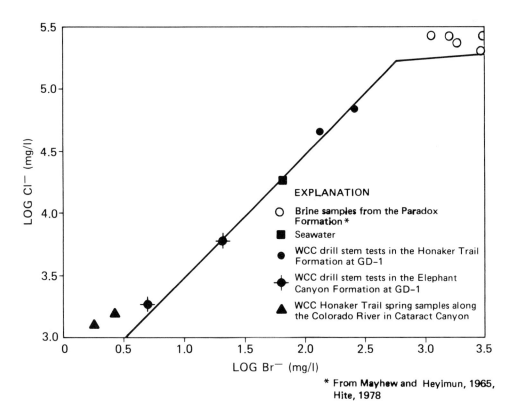

Figure 11.   Relationship of Chloride to Bromide for Selected Water Analysis

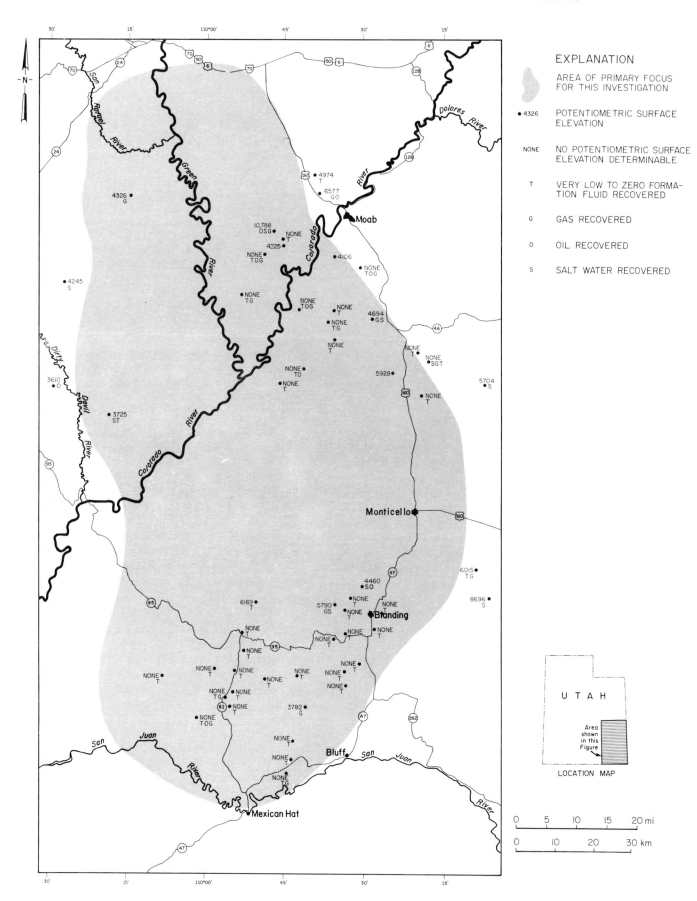

Figure 12. Potentiometric Levels of the Middle Hydrostratigraphic Unit

map (Figure 12), indicating that these zones have low permeabilities.

Hydrochemical data are an additional basis for the interpretation provided by DST data, although some of the water chemistry data from samples in this unit may represent drilling fluid contamination. Most wells are drilled through the Paradox Formation with a Na-Cl saturated brine. Without a tracer in the drilling fluid, or successive sampling of fluid produced in the drill-stem test as the test string is brought out of the hole, it is generally difficult to ascertain how much drilling fluid contamination is present in a particular water sample.

A drilling fluid tracer program is being conducted at GD-1. The validity of the existing chemical data will be evaluated with the results of the tracer program. Until this evaluation is completed, and more data are collected, the available chemical data discussed in this section are assumed to be representative of formation water in the middle hydrostratigraphic unit.

Water within this unit is predominantly a high TDS, sodium-potassium-calcium-chloride water, although locally magnesium is an important constituent (Figures 13, 14, and 15). The trilinear diagram (Figure 13) illustrates a linear trend extending from Na-Cl type water towards Ca-Cl-SO$_4$ type water. As discussed by Piper (1944), such linear trends suggest mixing of two water types along a flow path with compositions defined by the coordinates at either end of the trend. However, the presence of two geographically distinct bodies of water representing the end members of this trend, separated by an attendant mixing zone, is not evident in the Stiff diagram (Figure 14). The absence of such a trend suggests that there is not an active interconnected flow system in the middle unit.

Concentrations of TDS also do not explain the linear trend evident on the trilinear diagram (Figure 13). If a lower TDS, Ca-Cl-SO$_4$ water were to mix with a higher TDS, Na-Cl water or come in contact with halite, a similar compositional trend would be observed, and values of TDS would increase towards the Na-Cl end member. However, as shown on Figure 13, there is no consistent increase in TDS from one end of the trend to the other. In addition, the map of TDS values (Figure 15) shows no geographically consistent trends, which is similar to the interpretation of the Stiff diagrams (Figure 14). The interpretation that an inactive, non-interconnected flow system exists in this unit is again supported by these data.

The lack of any geographic trends in the chemical data indicating transport along a flow path suggests that water in much of the middle hydrostratigraphic unit is connate water, largely isolated from a currently active flow system. The compositional variations of Na, Mg, Cl, Ca and SO$_4$ evident on the trilinear diagram are probably caused by varying amounts of dolomitization and anhydrite formation during deposition and diagenesis, as well as possible expulsion of interstitial fluids from the Paradox salt into interbeds during compaction (see Carpenter, 1978 and Hite, 1978 for further discussion). The linear trend on the trilinear diagram (Figure 13), according to this hypothesis, would represent different stages of brine evolution in the geologic past without significant mixing of water in a currently active flow system.

When all water-mineral equilibria analyses are complete, the information gained is expected to clarify the compositional trends evident on Figure 13 and their associated mineralogical controls. This evaluation will also assess the chemistry of potassium in solution, because potassium is not separated from sodium or trilinear and Stiff diagrams.

A connate origin for the brine in the Paradox Basin is also suggested by the sparse Cl/Br data available for the middle hydrostratigraphic unit. These data, plotted on Figure 11, were published in reports by Hite (1978) and Mayhew and Heylmun (1965). Many of the water analyses in Mayhew and Heylmun (1965) either do not include values for bromide, or have significant charge balance errors, suggesting that analytical results may not be reliable. Those values with less than 5 percent charge balance error are plotted on Figure 11. These data cluster near the trend of evaporating sea water, and do not indicate salt dissolution.

LOWER HYDROSTRATIGRAPHIC UNIT

Because of its great depth, the vertical boundaries of this unit are probably less well defined than either of the other two units previously described. However, the unit contains a regionally extensive flow system. The most widespread and transmissive aquifer in the region is the Mississippian Leadville Limestone, which occurs within this unit. Transmissibility values from drill-stem tests in the western Paradox Basin range from less than 5.6 to more than 21,154 millidarcy-feet per centipoise. Tests in the GD-1 borehole show transmissibilities which range from approximately 200 to 9800 millidarcy-feet per centipoise. A stratigraphic equivalent of the Redwall Limestone, which crops out in the Grand Canyon, the Leadville Limestone is a common target of oil and gas exploration in the Paradox Basin. Strata of the Pinkerton Trail and Molas formations are also included within the lower hydrostratigraphic unit. Even though test data from these formations are extremely scarce in the area covered by this report, elsewhere in the basin they appear to be hydrologically interconnected to some extent with the Leadville Limestone. The Molas and Pinkerton Trail formations probably serve as aquitards in much of the structurally undisturbed bedded salt areas of the western basin.

A map of potentiometric level contours, based on drill-stem test results, is shown on Figure 16. In all cases the final shut-in pressures were extrapolated into the apparent static reservoir pressure. This value was then translated into the equivalent potentiometric level for fresh water with a specific gravity of 1.00. The density of fresh water is often used by hydrologists because of a lack of good salinity data in an area. However, large density variations may alter the apparent flow pattern indicated by a potentiometric map, particularly in steeply-dipping aquifers. To correct for density variations, a computer program was developed that calculates flow direction vectors. This program is currently being tested on existing data sets.

Despite the uncertainties that may result from density variations, several interesting patterns are evident on the map of the potentiometric surface (Figure 16). Although the general trend in ground-water movement in the lower hydrostratigraphic unit is toward the southwest, a large mound in the potentiometric surface appears in the area of the Abajo highlands. Recharge along the laccolithic contact zone or along the nearby graben systems may explain this mound. Suggestions that similar mounds may exist in the areas of the La Sal Mountains, Lisbon Valley, and the Henry Mountains are consistent with observed patterns, although all these areas are on the fringe of the region of good data coverage. Additional recharge areas identified by Hanshaw and Hill (1969) occur along the western flank of the Uncompahgre Uplift (on the northeast boundary of the Paradox Basin) and along the outcrops of the Mississippian

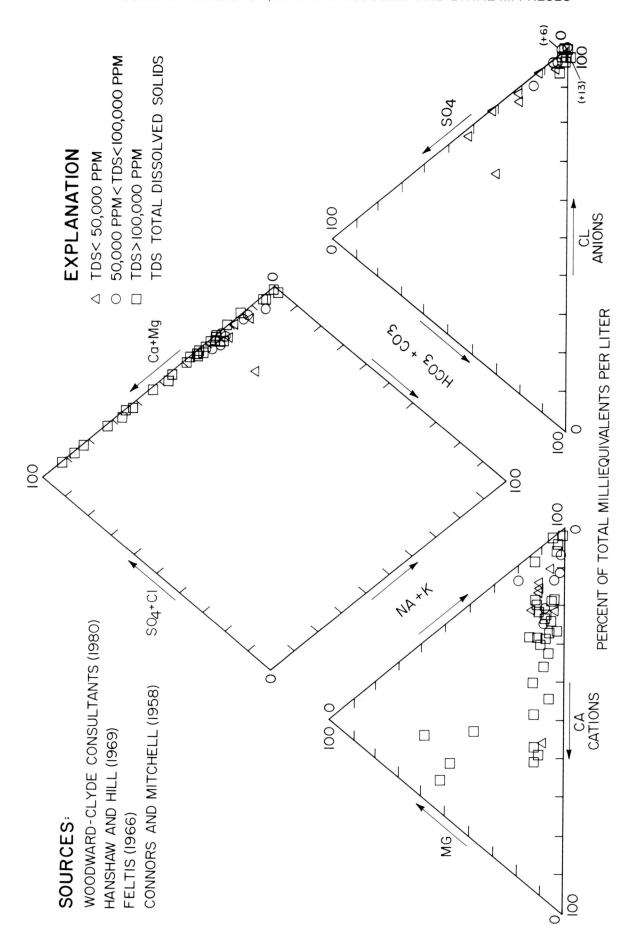

Figure 13. Trilinear Diagram of Water Analysis, Middle Hydrostratigraphic Unit

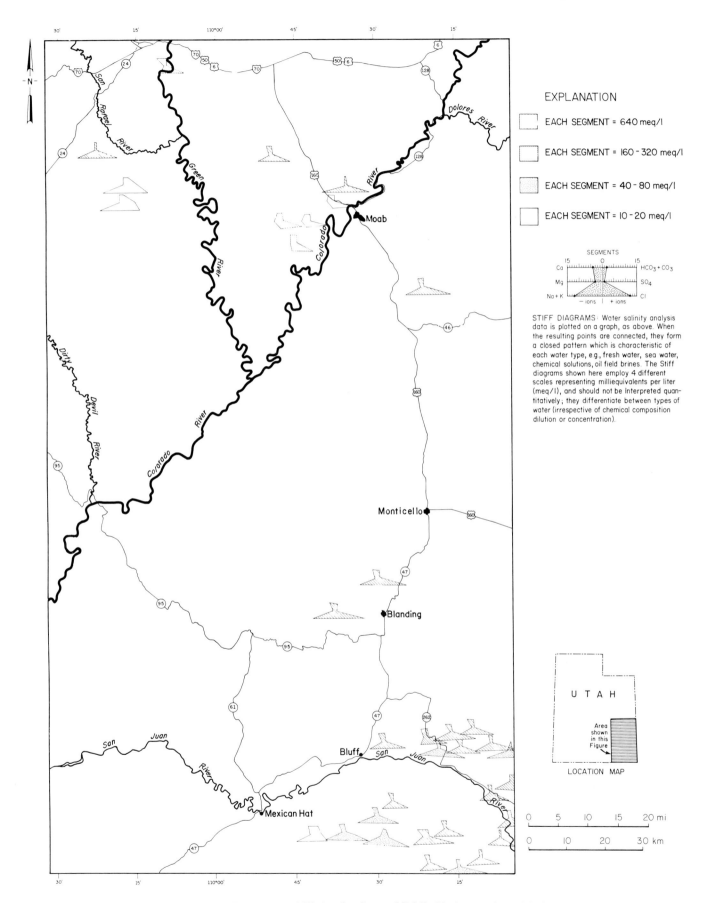

Figure 14. Stiff Diagrams of Water Analyses, Middle Hydrostratigraphic Unit

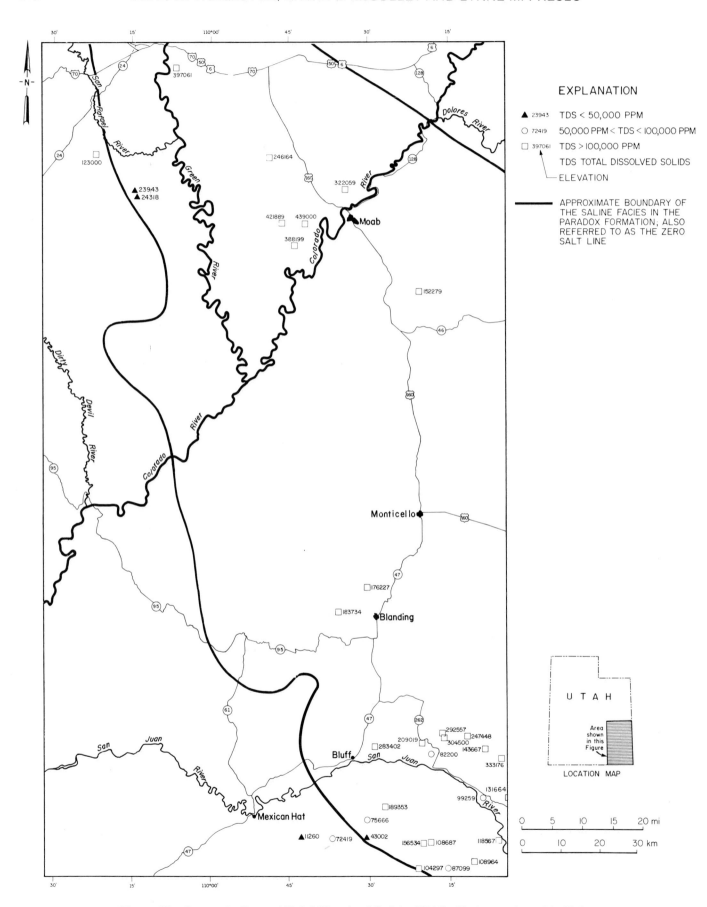

Figure 15.   Concentrations of Total Dissolved Solids, Middle Hydrostratigraphic Unit

carbonates in the San Juan Mountains, farther to the east. Recharge from these highland areas accounts for the observed convergence of flow paths in the vicinity of the Colorado River.

Ground water from the valley fill aquifer in Spanish Valley may percolate downward along the Moab fault, which abuts the valley on the southwest, thus providing another source of recharge to the lower unit. The valley fill aquifer contains an estimated 200,000 acre-feet of storage. Ground-water level contours from wells in the valley show that recharge is supplied continuously from streams originating in the La Sal Mountains. Flow is to the northwest within the valley, toward discharge areas along the Colorado River (Sumsion, 1969). If suitable pathways exist along the Moab fault to permit deep percolation, then recharge could occur to the units surrounding the salt, along the margins of the anticline. The potentiometric level in the valley fill aquifer is similar to that of the lower unit at this location, therby suggesting hydraulic interconnection, but additional data are not available to verify this concept.

Discharge of ground water from the lower unit to the surface has not been detected anywhere in the study area. The nearest area where saline springs emanate from the unit are those that flow from the Redwall Limestone into the Marble and Little Colorado river canyons, at an estimated total discharge of 220 cubic feet per second (Cooley and others, 1969). The water in these springs is much lower in salinity than test data indicate for the water in Mississippian strata underlying the Paradox Basin bedded salt. Huntoon (1981), based on geochemical studies of these springs, suggested that the recharge areas lie to northwest, including the Marble Platform and probably the Kaiparowits Basin of southern Utah.

Chemical data from the lower hydrostratigraphic unit are not uniformly distributed over the Paradox Basin, but some trends are evident. This unit generally contains a high TDS, sodium-chloride type water where it is overlain by the Paradox saline facies. Specific gravity values of the samples suggest a range of TDS content of 66,000 to 82,000 ppm. Lower TDS waters with significant amounts of calcium and sulfate in addition to sodium and chloride are generally found to the west of the zero-salt line (Figures 17, 18, and 19). Drilling fluid contamination may not be a significant problem with existing Mississippian water quality data. The water samples recovered from this unit during drill stem tests at GD-1 contained less than five percent drilling fluid contamination based on detection of drilling fluid tracer concentrations.

Hanshaw and Hill (1969) attributed the fresher water in the western margin of the Paradox Basin to the absence of saline facies in the overlying Paradox Formation and the convergence of flow paths. Ground water flowing southward in this area would keep saline water to the east, a trend that would be accentuated by the recharge of fresh water on the western side of the Monument Upwarp. The scarcity of sodium-chloride water in the fresher, western edge of the unit supports this hypothesis, and probably represents water recharged in the San Rafael Swell, Waterpocket Fold, and the Henry Mountains. However, at scattered locations some sodium-chloride type water is also found in the western margin of the basin (Figure 18). The presence of such water in this area is not completely understood at present, but may be related to residual connate water, as may be some of the sodium-chloride water to the east.

The presence of sodium chloride water in Leadville strata, which lie below the saline facies of the Paradox, was suggested by Hanshaw and Hill (1969) as being the result of

downward cross-formational flow of saline water from the Paradox Formation. The trilinear and Stiff diagrams for both the middle and lower hydrostratigraphic units appear similar (Figures 13, 14, 17, and 18), and thus support this suggestion. Because of the extremely low permeability of the salt beds, however, cross-formational flow could only occur where the normal stratigraphic sequence has been disrupted. The conduits of these flows might be caused by faulting or folding in areas such as the Lisbon Fault and the Shay and Verdue grabens, or by diapirism-induced pinchouts of the salt adjacent to salt anticlines. These structurally related pathways, if permeable, would allow water to flow past and dissolve the Paradox salt, then flow downward into the Mississippian carbonates. This flow path would also allow migration of Paradox connate water, water of hydration, or possibly hydrocarbons into the Mississippian carbonates.

HYDROGEOLOGICAL ASPECTS OF SALT DISSOLUTION FEATURES

The study of dissolution features is significant to the study of the present hydrogeologic flow system, and may provide insights regarding the paleohydrology of a region such as the Paradox Basin.

Lockhart Basin is perhaps the best known and certainly one of the most remarkable dissolution collapse features in the Paradox Basin. It is located approximately 18 miles southwest of Moab and 10 miles northeast of Gibson Dome. Strongly down-folded beds of the Moss Back Member of the Chinle Formation are visible on the ground surface. Well logs in the area show a circular zone of dissolution, which is responsible for the collapse feature seen at ground surface. In the center of the feature, a mass of insoluble residue remains where approximately 2,500 feet of Paradox Formation strata were once present. Overlying a pronounced structural high in the Leadville Limestone, the dissolution zone decreases in thickness outward from the center of the basin. Based on seismic interpretations, the elevated Mississippian surface is probably related to structural uplift.

Huntoon and Richter (1979) described the structure of the Lockhart Basin in detail and proposed that dissolution occurred by downward percolation along a northeast-trending fault zone that transects the basin. However, the hydraulic gradient in the Leadville Limestone could have been one of the important factors initiating the dissolution.

In many areas of the Paradox Basin, the potentiometric surface of the Mississippian carbonates is elevated above the top of the Paradox Formation. This upward gradient would provide an alternate mechanism to the one advanced by Huntoon and Richter (1979). With the significant potential for upward flow in Lockhart Basin, it is easy to envision a density-driven flow system as described by Anderson and Kirkland (1980). If interformational flow pathways were established between the Leadville Limestone and the lowest salt beds, a density convection cell could form. Such pathways could have formed by faulting or by stratigraphic pinchout of the Molas and Pinkerton Trail aquitards in Lockhart Basin.

Once the density convection cell formed, it would be self-perpetuating as less saline water would rise from below to dissolve the salt along some pathways, while other pathways would allow downward percolation of the more saline waters of dissolution. Geochemical data gathered and evaluated for the Paradox Basin Project may clarify this question.

Other dissolution features are found in most of the salt anticlines of the Paradox Basin. Many valley floors are

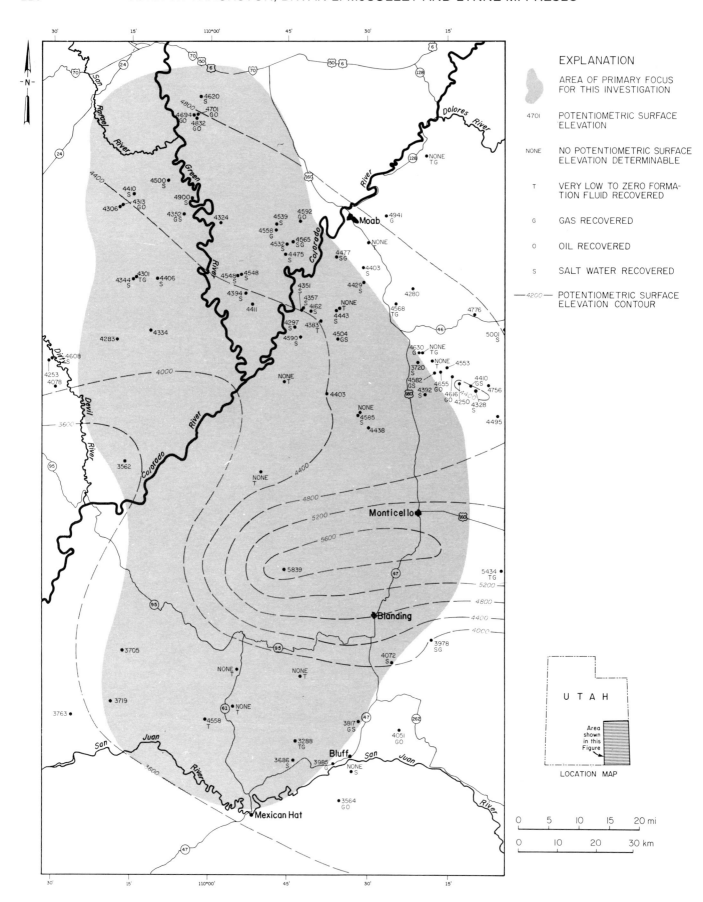

Figure 16. Potentiometric Surface of Lower Hydrostratigraphic Unit

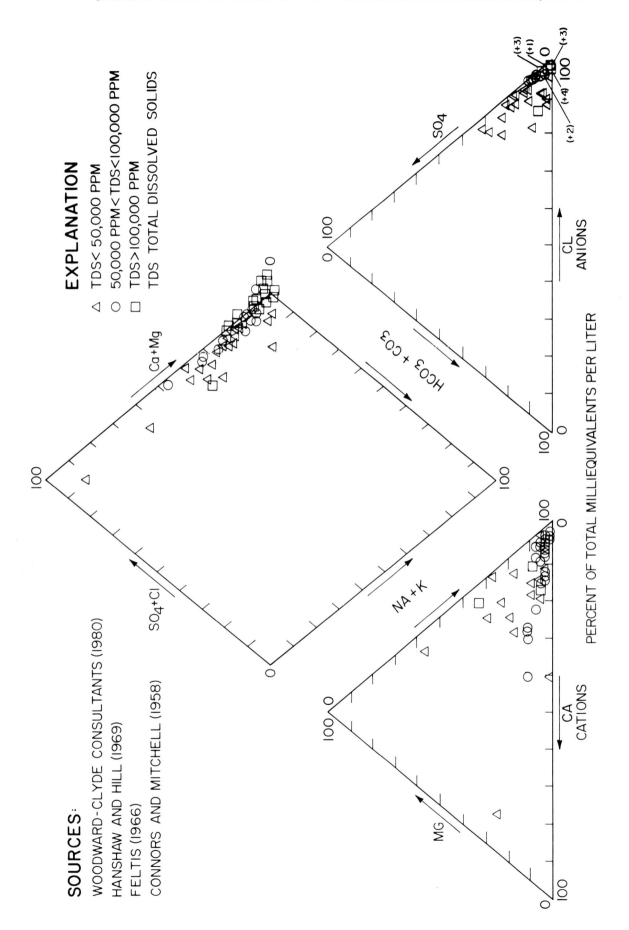

Figure 17. Trilinear Diagram of Water Analyses, Lower Hydrostratigraphic Unit

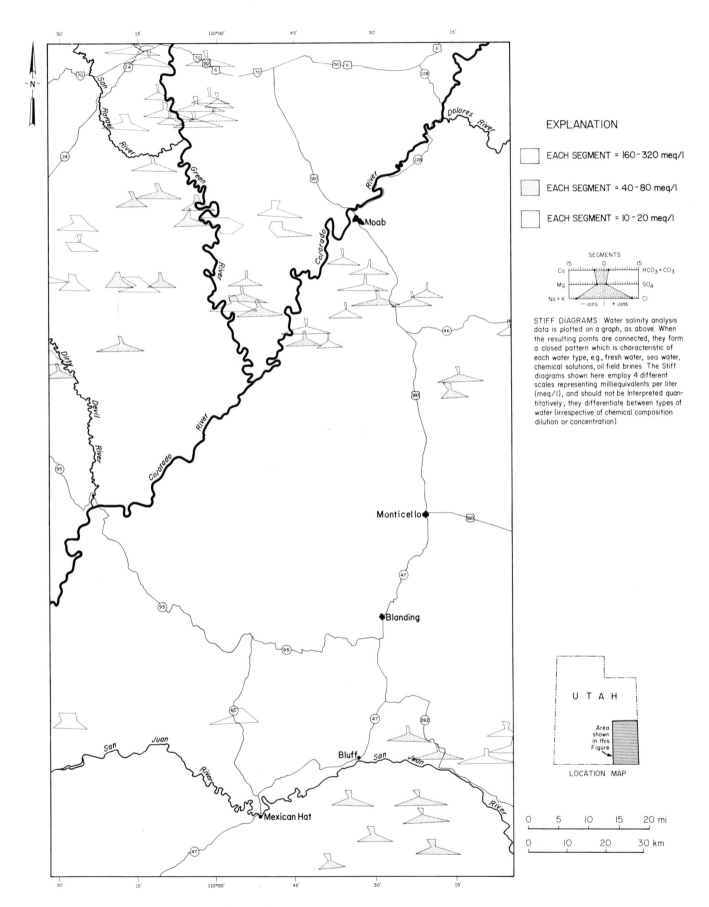

Figure 18. Stiff Diagrams of Water Analyses, Lower Hydrostratigraphic Unit

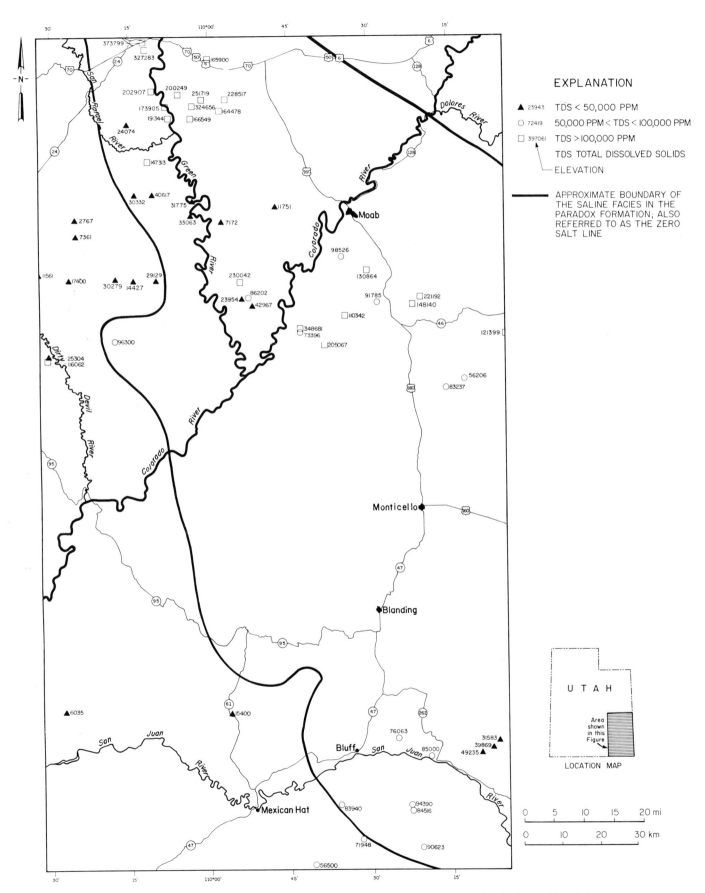

Figure 19.   Concentrations of Total Dissolved Solids, Lower Hydrostratigraphic Unit

underlain by caprock composed largely of insoluble residue from dissolution of salt. Spanish Valley, for example, contains a circulating ground-water system overlying the caprock (Sumsion, 1969), whereby continued dissolution of salt at the top of the anticline core is indicated.

Paradox Valley, located to the southeast of the La Sal Mountains, has a similar circulating ground-water system. As a result, there are many saline seeps along the Dolores River where it crosses Paradox Valley. The U.S. Water and Power Resources Service is currently conducting a program to reduce saline discharge in this part of the Colorado River drainage system.

CONCLUSIONS

Based upon available drill-stem test records and hydrochemistry data, the saline facies of the Paradox Formation are generally isolated from the flow systems in the overlying and underlying hydrostratigraphic units, although some interconnection may exist. The Paradox Formation contains beds of very low permeability strata over much of the western part of the Paradox Basin. Higher permeability reservoirs that sometimes contain oil, gas and brine occur in the Paradox Formation in some areas, but are generally of limited extent. Igneous intrusions, salt diapirs and salt-dissolution collapse structures in the study area that may provide vertical flow conduits include Lockhart Basin, the La Sal and Abajo laccoliths, and some of the salt anticlines.

Ground-water flow in the hydrostratigraphic units above and below the salt is generally controlled by topography and structure. Recharge waters that enter the ground-water system in the Abajo and La Sal highlands, move down-gradient toward the major river canyons. These flow paths merge with ground water flows that originate in highlands just outside the perimeter of the basin; such highlands include the Uncompahgre Uplift, the San Juan Mountains, the Henry Mountains and the Waterpocket fold.

Minor springs discharge from the upper hydrostratigraphic unit in the Colorado River Canyon. No ground-water discharge has been detected from the lower unit within the Paradox Basin or immediately down the apparent flow path to the southwest of the basin. However, further downstream along the Colorado River, in the Marble Canyon of Arizona, large slightly saline springs flow from the Redwall Limestone, a stratigraphic equivalent of the Leadville Limestone. Possible hydraulic interconnection of these springs with the Paradox Basin Leadville aquifer remains uncertain and requires further investigation.

ACKNOWLEDGEMENTS

The authors wish to acknowledge their appreciation to the many people who have generously contributed to this report. Mr. N. A. Frazier and Dr. S. Kowall of Battelle Memorial Institute, Office of Nuclear Waste Isolation, provided support and review of the manuscript. Roger Hoeger and Harvey Merrell, consulting geologists, kindly assisted with drill-stem test data collection. Robert Hite and Bruce Hanshaw of the U.S. Geological Survey and Alden Carpenter of the Department of Geology, University of Missouri at Columbia, provided thought-provoking discussions regarding geochemistry of saline waters. Peter Huntoon and Henry Richter of the University of Wyoming introduced us to a number of remarkable hydrogeologic features in the region.

The fundamental ingredients of this paper are the result of the diligent efforts of many Woodward-Clyde Consultants staff. Fred Conwell, David Stephenson, and Ben Lofgren critically reviewed and provided valuable comments to the manuscript and to the project planning and data collection efforts. Much of the basic data collection, compilation and preliminary interpretations were accomplished by James Wilson, Justim Blum, Thomas Zakaria, Nancy Donnelly, David Dunbar, and Debbie Wallace. Jodi Lehman developed and implemented computer programs to analyze portions of the hydrologic data. Dale Fain participated in the borehole data collection at Gibson Dome No. 1. V-Anne Chernock substantially improved the clarity of the manuscript through her editorial comments. The authors are grateful for these efforts.

REFERENCES

Anderson, R. Y., and Kirkland, D. W., 1980, Dissolution of salt deposits by brine density flow: Geology, v. 8, p. 66-69.

Baars, D. L., 1962, Permian system of the Colorado Plateau: American Association of Petroleum Geologists Bulletin, v. 46, no. 2, p. 149-218.

Baars, D. L., 1972, Red Rock Country: The Geologic History of the Colorado Plateau: Doubleday — Natural History Press, New York, 254 p.

Baars, D. L., and Seager, W. R., 1970, Stratigraphic control of petroleum in White Rim Sandstone (Permian) in and near Canyonlands National Park, Utah: American Association of Petroleum Geologists Bulletin, v. 54, no. 5, p. 709-718.

Baars, D. L., Parker, J. W., and Chronic, J., 1967, Revised stratigraphic nomenclature of Pennsylvanian system, Paradox Basin: American Association of Petroleum Geologists Bulletin, v. 51, no. 3, p. 393-403.

Back, W., 1966, Hydrochemical facies and ground-water flow patterns in the northern part of Atlantic Coastal Plain: U.S. Geological Survey Professional Paper 498-A, 42 p.

Berry, F. A. F., and Hanshaw, B. B., 1960, Geologic evidence suggesting membrane properties of shales: 21st International Geologic Congress, Abstract, p. 209.

Carpenter, A. B., and Miller, J. C., 1969, Geochemistry of saline subsurface water, Saline County (Missouri): Chemical Geology, v. 4, p. 135-167.

Carpenter, A. B., 1978, Origin and chemical evolution of brines in sedimentary basins: Oklahoma Geological Survey Circular 79, p. 60-77.

Chebotarev, I. I., 1955, Metamorphism of natural waters in the crust of weathering: Geochimica et Cosmochimica Acta, v. 8, p. 22-48.

Collins, A. G., 1975, Geochemistry of oilfield waters: Elsevier Scientific Publishing Company, New York, N.Y.

Cooley, M. E., Harshburger, J. W., Akens, T. P., and Hardt, W. F., 1969, Regional hydrogeology of the Navajo and Hopi Indian reservations, Arizona, New Mexico and Utah: U.S. Geological Survey Professional Paper 521-A, p. A1-A61.

Earlougher, R. C., 1977, Advances in Well Test Analysis: Society of Petroleum Engineers of AIME, Dallas, Texas, p. 74-103.

Feltis, R. D., 1966, Water from bedrock in the Colorado Plateau of Utah: Utah State Engineer, Division of Water Rights, Technical Publication No. 15, 82 p.

Foster, M. D., 1950, The origin of high sodium bicarbonate waters in the Atlantic and Gulf Coastal Plains: Geochimica et Cosmochimica Acta, v. 1, p. 33-48.

Freese, R. A., and Cherry, J. A., 1979, Groundwater: Prentice-Hall, Inc., Englewood Cliffs, N.J., 604 p.

Galloway, W. E., Kreitler, C. W., and McGowe, J. H., 1978, Depositional and ground-water flow systems in the exploration of uranium: Research Colloquim Proceedings, Sept. 8-9, 1978, presented by the Texas Bureau of Economic Geology, p. V1-1-V1-62.

Hanshaw, B. B., and Hill, G. A., 1969, Geochemistry and hydrodynamics of the Paradox Basin region, Utah, Colorado, and New Mexico: Chemical Geology, v. 4, p. 263-294.

Hanshaw, B. B., and Back, W., 1979, Major geochemical processes in the evolution of carbonate-aquifer systems: Journal of Hydrology, v. 43, p. 287-312.

Hintze, L. F., 1973, Geologic history of Utah: Brigham Young University Geology Studies, v. 20, part 3, p. 1-181.

Hite, R. J., 1968, Salt deposits of the Paradox Basin, southeast Utah and southwest Colorado: Geological Society of America Special Paper 88, p. 319-330.

Hite, R. J., 1970, Shelf carbonate sedimentation controlled by salinity in the Paradox Basin, southeast Utah: Northern Ohio Geological Society, Third Symposium on Salt, v. 1, p. 48-66.

Hite, R. J., 1978, Geology of the Lisbon Valley potash deposits, San Juan County, Utah: U.S. Geological Survey Open File Report 78-148, 21 p.

Hite, R. J., and Lohman, S. W., 1973, Geologic appraisal of Paradox Basin salt deposits for waste emplacement: U.S. Geological Survey Open File Report 73-114, 75 p.

Horner, D. R., 1951, Pressure build-up in wells: Third World Petroleum Congress Proceedings, Section II, E. J. Brill, Leider, Holland, p. 503-521.

Huntoon, P. W., 1977, The hydrogeologic feasibility of developing ground-water supplies in the northern part of Canyonlands National Park and Bridges National Monument, Utah: Wyoming Water Resource Research Institute, 24 p.

Huntoon, P. W., 1979a, The feasibility of developing ground-water supplies in and adjacent to the Glen Canyon National Recreation area and Canyonlands National Park west of the Colorado and Green rivers, Utah: Wyoming Water Resources Research Institute, 15 p.

Huntoon, P.W., 1979b, The occurrence of ground water in the Canyonlands area of Utah, with emphasis on water in the Permian section: Four Corners Geological Society Guidebook, 9th Field Conference, p. 39-46.

Huntoon, P.W. and H.R. Richter, 1979, Breccia pipes in the vicinity of Lockhart Basin, Canyonlands area Utah: Four Corners Geological Society Guidebook, 9th Field Conference, p. 47-54.

Huntoon, P.W., 1981, Fault controlled ground-water circulation under the Colorado River, Marble Canyon, Arizona: Ground Water, v. 19, no. 1, p. 20-27.

Irwin, J.H., 1966, Geology and availability of ground water on the Ute Mountain Indian Reservation, Colorado and New Mexico: U.S. Geological Survey Water-Supply Paper 1576-G, 105 p.

Jobin, D.A., 1962, Relation of the transmissive character of the sedimentary rocks of the Colorado Plateau to the distribution of uranium deposits: U.S. Geological Survey Bulletin 1124, 151 p.

Johnson, K., 1980, Earth Resource Associates, personal communication with McCulley, B. L., Woodward-Clyde Consultants, 24 November.

Jones, R. W., 1959, Origin of salt anticlines of Paradox Basin: Bulletin of the American Association of Petroleum Geologists, v. 43, no. 8, p. 1869-1895.

Lane, A. C., 1908, Mine waters and their field assay: Geological Society of America Bulletin, v. 19, p. 501-512.

Maxey, George B., 1964, Hydrostratigraphic units: Journal of Hydrology, v. 2, p. 124-129.

Mayhew, E. J., and Heylmun, E. B., 1965, Concentrated subsurface brines in the Moab region, Utah: Utah Geological and Mineral Survey Special Studies No. 13, 28 p.

Mayhew, E. J., and Heylmun, E. B., 1966, Complex salts and brines of the Paradox Basin, in Rau, J. L. (ed.), Second Symposium on Salt, v. 1: Geology, Geochemistry Mining: Northern Ohio Geological Society, Cleveland, Ohio, p. 221-235.

McGill, G. E., and Stromquist, A. W., 1975, Origin of graben in the Needles district, Canyonlands National Park, Utah: Four Corners Geological Society Guidebook, 8th Field Conference, Canyonlands, p. 235-244.

Molenaar, C. M., 1975a, Nomenclature chart of the Canyonlands and adjacent areas, in Canyonlands Country, A Guidebook: Four Corners Geological Society, p. 142.

Molenaar, C. M., 1975b, Some notes on Upper Cretaceous stratigraphy of the Paradox Basin, in Canyonlands Country, A Guidebook: Four Corners Geological Society, p. 191-192.

Piper, A. M., 1944, A graphic procedure in the geochemical interpretation of water analyses: American Geophysical Union Trans., v. 25, p. 914-923.

Richter, H. R., 1980, Ground water resources in the part of Canyonland's National Park east of the Colorado River and contiguous Bureau of Land Management Lands, Utah: MS Thesis, University of Wyoming, Laramie, Wyoming, 80 p.

Rittenhouse, G., 1967, Bromine in oil-field waters and its use in determining possibilities of origin of these waters: American Association of Petroleum Geologists Bulletin, v. 15, no. 12, p. 2430-2440.

Ritzma, H. R., and Doelling, H. H. (eds.), 1969, Mineral Resources, San Juan County, Utah, and Adjacent Areas: Utah Geological and Mineralogical Survey Special Studies No. 24, Part I, 125 p.

Sugiura, R., and Kitcho, C., 1980, Collapse Structures in the Paradox Basin: in preparation for the RMAG Guidebook to the Paradox Basin.

Sumsion, C. T., 1969, Ground water occurrence in the Spanish Valley area, Grand and San Juan Counties, Utah: Geological Society of America Meeting Abstracts, Rocky Mountain Section, p. 79-80.

Valyashko, M. G., 1956, Geochemistry of bromine in the processes of salt desposition and the use of the bromine content as a genetic and prospecting criterion: Geochemistry, no. 6, p. 570-589.

Wengerd, S. A., and Matheny, M. L., 1958, Pennsylvanian system of Four Corners Region: American Association of Petroleum Geologists Bulletin, v. 42, no. 9, p. 2048-2106.

Wengerd, S. A., 1970, Western Paradox Basin is a potential oil giant in Pennsylvanian rocks: the Oil and Gas Journal, Part I; p. 172-178, 183-184; Part II: p. 96-102.

White, D. E., 1965, Saline waters of sedimentary rocks: American Association of Petroleum Geologists Memoir 4, p. 342-366.

Arrioca Colorado

GEOTECHNICAL ASPECTS OF THE SEARCH FOR A PERMANENT REPOSITORY FOR THE DURANGO URANIUM TAILINGS PILE

Robert M. Kirkham[1], Robert W. Blair[2], and W. Rahe Junge[3]

ABSTRACT

From 1942 to 1962 uranium and vanadium were recovered from ore processed at a mill in Durango, Colorado. Tailings from this operation were placed in two waste piles located at the base of Smelter Mountain and adjacent to the Animas River. In their present condition the radioactive tailings are considered a potential health hazard by the Federal government, and the long-term stability of the pile is threatened by flooding and erosion along the Animas River.

A Federal program entitled the Uranium Mill Tailings Remedial Action Program was established in response to the Uranium Mill Tailings Control Act of 1978. This program provides for the safe and environmentally sound stabilization, disposal, and control of abandoned uranium tailings throughout the country. Twenty-four inactive tailings piles in the Western United States are being considered for remedial action. The Durango tailings pile is on the high priority list and is one of four piles currently being evaluated for relocation.

The Federal government requested that the State of Colorado cooperate in the selection of candidate relocation sites for the Durango pile. An initial concern was to assure that any proposed site be geotechnically suitable for tailings disposal. To accomplish this, the Colorado Geological Survey, with assistance from other geoscientists, developed a site selection process that used geotechnical aspects as initial criteria. Nine potential sites within a 30-mile radius of Durango were identified during this process. A committee composed of state, county, and municipal representatives selected three preferred candidate sites from the nine potential sites. Their recommendations were based not only on geotechnical parameters, but also on social, political, economic, and ecologic considerations. Additionally, the committee recommended further consideration of a fourth site that did not meet the geotechnical criteria, but afforded the opportunity to use conveyors to transport the tailings and thus avoid truck haulage problems. These four candidate sites are currently being studied in detail by the U.S. Department of Energy prior to selection of the final site.

INTRODUCTION

During the 1940s, 1950s, and 1960s uranium ore was processed at a number of mills in Colorado. Tailings from this milling was often dumped in unsuitable locations that now pose potential hazards to the general public. Such hazards will persist into the future and possibly worsen because of increasing pressures and dispersion of the tailings material by geologic, hydrologic, and meteorologic forces. The uranium mill tailings at Durango, Colorado, pose such a hazard.

In 1978 the Federal legislature passed the Uranium Mill Tailings Control Act to provide for the safe and environmentally sound stabilization, disposal, and control of abandoned uranium tailings throughout the country. The Uranium Mill Tailings Remedial Action Program (UMTRAP) was established in response to this legislation and is administered by the U.S. Department of Energy (DOE). Twenty-four abandoned uranium tailings piles in the Western United States qualify for UMTRAP. The Durango tailings pile is on the DOE high-priority list and is one of four sites currently being studied for relocation.

To aid in the accomplishment of this program, the DOE requested that the State of Colorado assist in identifying candidate sites within a 30-mile radius of Durango for the removal and permanent disposal of the tailings. The state, with assistance from R. M. Kirkham and the Four Corners

Environmental Research Institute, developed and conducted a two-phase site selection process to achieve this request. The initial and dominant concern was to recognize sites that were geotechnically suitable for relocation. This was accomplished during Phase I of the site selection process.

Nine potential sites that are geotechnically acceptable were identified during Phase I. These potential sites were reviewed and further evaluated by the Site Selection Committee during Phase II. Three of these nine sites were recommended by the Committee as preferred candidate sites. A fourth site that did not meet the geotechnical criteria, but did offer use of conveyor transportation was also recommended. These four sites are being studied in detail by the DOE for the preparation of an environmental impact statement on the proposed relocation project and to facilitate selection of a final site.

This paper summarizes the placement objectives, site selection process, and proposed potential sites. It also includes the recommendations of the Site Selection Committee.

HISTORY OF THE DURANGO TAILINGS PILE

Ford, Bacon and Davis Utah Inc. (1977) described the history of milling operations at the Durango Mill. The mill was built on the site of an old lead smelter by the United States Vanadium Corporation (USV) in 1942 just southwest of downtown Durango. USV furnished vanadium to the Metals Reserve Company, a company formed by the Federal government for the purchase of strategic materials needed in

[1] Consulting Geologist. Bailey. CO 80421

[2] Department of Geology. Fort Lewis College. Durango. CO 81301

[3] Colorado Geological Survey. Denver. CO 80203

World War II. The mill operated until 1946 and was then shut down. In 1949 the mill was reopened when the Vanadium Corporation of America (VCA) contracted to sell uranium to the Atomic Energy Commission. The mill permanently closed in March, 1962. VCA retained ownership of the mill site and adjoining property until 1967, when VCA merged into Foote Mineral Company. During 1976 and 1977 Foote Mineral Company sold the tailings to Ranchers Exploration and Development Corporation. Ranchers, present owners of the tailings piles, proposed that the Durango tailings be relocated and reprocessed at the Long Hollow site in 1978. This proposed project experienced delays during licensing, and has been withdrawn from consideration because of the current low price of yellowcake.

During its life the Durango mill processed approximately 1.5 million tons of uranium ore. The amount of extracted uranium and vanadium is not known precisely, but the uranium values remaining within the Durango tailings are reported to be the richest in the country. Reprocessing of the tailings must be considered not only for economic reasons, but also because of the mandate of the Uranium Tailings Control Act of 1978.

PREFERRED METHOD OF TAILINGS DISPOSAL

Uranium tailings constitute a technologically enhanced source of natural radiation by virtue of the physical and chemical processing of the ore and potential redistribution of the contained radionuclides by wind and water transport (Landa, 1980). The redistribution of these radionuclides can be controlled for hundreds and possibly thousands of years by selecting disposal sites that optimize geologic, hydrologic, meteorologic, and geochemical conditions, and by proper design, construction, and maintenance of the disposal site.

To achieve this containment the U.S. Nuclear Regulatory Commission (NRC) promulgated the recently enacted Uranium Mill Licensing Requirements. In Appendix A to 10 CFR Part 40, the NRC suggests that the "prime option" for disposal is placement of the tailings in trenches below the ground surface. Dewatering of the tailings during processing and/or in situ drainage systems are recommended by the NRC.

The Colorado Geological Survey (1981) considers disposal of dewatered tailings in trenches excavated into thick, relatively impermeable shale as the most effective, practical method to satisfy the long-term containment objectives suggested by the NRC regulations for the Durango tailings pile. All nine potential sites identified within a 30-mile radius of Durango appear to be amenable to this type of tailings disposal.

PLACEMENT OBJECTIVES

To insure the safe, long-term containment of uranium tailings material in Colorado, a number of general placement objectives have been established by the Colorado Geological Survey (1981):

1. Tailings disposal areas should be located at as remote a site as possible to reduce the potential population exposure and the likelihood of human intrusion.

2. Tailings disposal areas should be located at a site where disruption and dispersion by natural forces are eliminated or minimized.

3. Tailings should be placed below the ground surface, but above the water table in trenches or pits excavated into relatively impervious shale whenever possible.

4. Tailings should be covered with a minimum of three meters of earth materials calculated to reduce the surface exhalation of radon from the tailings to less than two picocuries per square meter per second above background levels and designed to minimize root and animal penetration.

5. Reclamation of the tailings disposal area should include a full, self-sustaining vegetative cover or riprap to retard erosion by water and wind, and to inhibit salt leaching. The final contour slopes should be as close as possible to the natural surface, but not steeper than 5h:1v.

6. Contamination of surface and ground waters due to seepage of toxic materials should be minimized through the use of physical and/or chemical controls.

7. Tailings disposal areas should not adversely affect unique historic, archaeologic, wildlife, or ecologic areas.

8. The final tailings repository should be designed so that it remains isolated and requires minimal maintenance for hundreds or thousands of years.

SITE SELECTION PROCESS

Candidate sites for relocating the Durango tailings pile were determined and comparatively rated through a two-phase selection process. Phase I of this process consisted of a series of steps in which potential sites were identified a 30-mile radius of the Durango tailings pile. Phase II involved review and evaluation of these potential sites by a Site Selection Committee composed of state, county, and municipal representatives. This committee, after due consideration of pertinent geologic, social, economic, ecologic, and political factors, recommended candidate sites for the permanent disposal of the tailings.

PHASE I: The first step of Phase I was to determine which geologic formations possessed acceptable permeability, thickness, and lateral lithologic continuity characteristics. Such suitable formations must have beds of low or very low permeability that are at least 150 feet thick and are laterally persistent for many square miles. In the study area the Cretaceous Mancos Shale and Lewis Shale meet these criteria. Both formations are laterally continuous marine deposits that are commonly over 1,500 feet thick and are dominantly shale.

Several other formations in the study area contain thick sequences of shale, but also have interbedded channel sandstone and conglomerate beds that locally serve as important sources of ground water. These formations, the Cretaceous-Tertiary Animas Formation and Tertiary San Jose and Nacimiento Formations, were considered possibly suitable as disposal host rocks.

During the second step of Phase I all areas underlain by suitable formations and selected areas underlain by possibly suitable formations were analyzed for surface slopes. The most favorable slopes range from two to five percent, but all areas with slopes of less than ten percent were examined. Areas with acceptable lithologic and slope characteristics that were at least one-fourth square mile in size were designated as target areas.

Ten target areas were identified within a 30-mile radius of Durango. The outline of these areas is shown in Figure 1. They include the Florida Mesa, Horse Gulch, Pine Ridge, Indian Creek, Long Hollow, Rabbit Mountain, Thompson Park, Weber Mountain, Mud Creek, and Mancos Valley target areas.

The third step of Phase I involved the evaluation of target areas with regard to the following criteria, and selection of potential sites by excluding areas that did not meet the

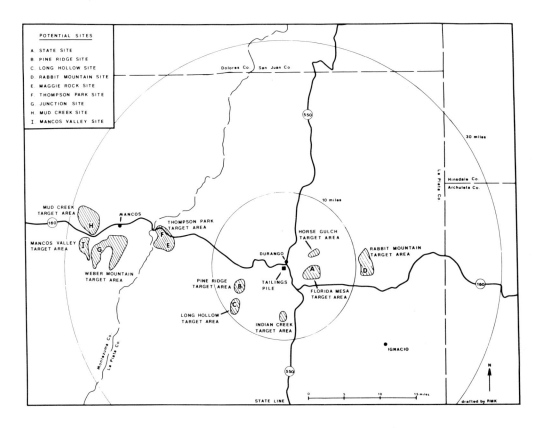

Figure 1. Map showing the locations of the target areas and potential sites geotechnically suitable for disposal of the Durango tailings pile.

criteria. All of the following areas were automatically disqualified as potential sites:

1. areas of insufficient size (a minimum of 200 to 300 acres for the Durango tailings pile);

2. areas subject to extensive flooding;

3. areas with substantial ground-water resources or recharge;

4. areas of complex geologic structure (e.g., abundant faulting, folding, and jointing);

5. areas susceptible to geologic hazards that could disrupt the repository (e.g., subsidence, active faulting, unstable or potentially unstable slopes, rapid erosion);

6. areas of Quaternary glaciation;

7. areas of Quaternary igneous activity;

8. areas with known mineral, geothermal, archaeologic, cultural, historic, wildlife, or ecologic resources that could be adversely impacted;

9. areas of substantial surface water, springs, and present or planned bodies of water;

10. areas of concentrated human habitation (towns, subdivisions, etc.);

11. wilderness areas and wild and scenic river areas.

Consideration of these criteria with regard to the target areas resulted in the selection of potential sites (Figure 1). Several target areas were eliminated because they did not meet the above constraints. The Horse Gulch target area was dropped because it did not contain a large enough area of acceptable slopes. Furthermore, this target area has a high erosion potential, as evidenced by the deep gullies that have recently cut through parts of the area. The Indian Creek site was ruled out because of thick gravel deposits on the site, possible shallow ground-water problems, high erosion potential, mineral resource conflicts, and site proximity to the Animas River. Additionally, this site was located on Indian land, and the Southern Ute Tribe expressed disinterest in accepting the tailings on their land.

Nine potential sites were recommended for relocation, and/or reprocessing of the Durango uranium mill tailings. In order of distance from the pile, they were the State site, Pine Ridge site, Long Hollow site, Rabbit Mountain site, Maggie Rock site, Thompson Park site, Junction site, Mud Creek site, and Mancos Valley site.

The fourth and final step of Phase I was the geotechnical evaluation and ranking of the potential sites by the use of a grading matrix. The grading matrix, shown in Figure 2, was used to rank each individual site by addressing a number of geologic, hydrologic, and meteorologic factors. Each factor was assigned a rank value from one to five in the matrix based on the characteristics of the particular site being evaluated. Some factors were more important than others and were weighted twice the rank value. The total site score was calculated by adding all factor scores. Results from this grading matrix are included in a following section on site descriptions.

PHASE II. Potential sites were reviewed and evaluated during Phase II by the Site Selection Committee. Recommendations by the committee were based not only on geotechnical characteristics, but also on other factors that must be considered for an acceptable disposal site. These

GEOTECHNICAL RATING MATRIX FOR POTENTIALLY
SUITABLE URANIUM MILL TAILINGS
DISPOSAL OR REPROCESSING SITES

SITE DESIGNATION: _____ SITE LOCATION:_____

FACTOR	RANK 1	RANK 2	RANK 3	RANK 4	RANK 5	WEIGHT	Factor Score
1. Surficial materials lithology	gravel or sand	very fine sand or sandy silt	silt	silty clay	clay	1	
2. Surficial materials thickness (if clay or silty clay, site ranks 5)	>25 ft.	15 to 25 ft.	10 to 15 ft.	5 to 10 ft.	0 to 5 ft.	1	
3. Host rock lithology	sandstone, limestone, or conglomerate	very fine sandstone or sandy siltstone	siltstone	silty shale or claystone	shale or claystone	2	
4. Host rock thickness (if conglomerate or sandstone, site ranks 1)	< 50 ft.	50 to 100 ft.	100 to 200 ft.	200 to 500 ft.	>500 ft.	2	
5. Host rock relative lateral continuity	very discontinuous		somewhat continuous		very continuous	2	
6. Land slope	>10%		<2% or 5% to 10%		2% to 5%	2	
7. Susceptibility to natural slope failures	moderate to high		low		very low	2	
8. Dip of underlying rocks	highly folded or >45°	30° to 45°	20° to 30°	10° to 20°	0° to 10°	1	
9. Presence of fracturing (joints & shear zones)	closely-spaced open joints		moderately-spaced open joints		sparse or closed joints	1	
10. Distance from known faulting	< 1/2 mile	1/2 to 1 mile	1 to 2 miles	2 to 5 miles	>5 miles	1	
11. Present erosional/depositional setting	intense gullying	moderate gullying	small rills	sheet erosion	no erosion or undergoing deposition	1	
12. Long-term potential for future erosion	high		moderate		low	1	
13. Conflict with mineral resources	serious conflicts		minor conflicts		no conflicts	1	
14. Aquifer characteristics of surficial materials	produces moderate amounts of good quality water	produces minor amounts of good quality water	produces moderate amounts of poor quality water	produces minor amounts of poor quality water	produces no water	2	
15. Aquifer characteristics of host rock	produces moderate amounts of good quality water	produces minor amounts of good quality water	produces moderate amounts of poor quality water	produces minor amounts of poor quality water	produces no water	2	
16. Depth to 1st underlying important bedrock aquifer	< 50 ft.	50 to 100 ft.	100 to 200 ft.	200 to 500 ft.	>500 ft.	2	
17. Water quality in 1st underlying important bedrock aquifer	excellent	good	average	poor	very poor	1	
18. Distance to nearest spring, perennial stream, perennial lake, or major irrigation ditch	on site	0 to 1/2 miles	1/2 to 1 miles	1 to 2 miles	2 miles	1	
19. Size of drainage basin above site	>5 sq. miles	2 to 5 sq. miles	1 to 2 sq. miles	½ to 1 sq. miles	<½ sq. mile	1	
20. Evaporation to precipitation ratio	<1		1 to 2		>2	1	

(left margin brackets: GEOLOGIC FACTORS for items 1–13; HYDROLOGIC AND METEOROLOGIC FACTORS for items 14–20)

Total Site Score _____

Figure 2.   Rating matrix used to comparatively rank the geotechnical characteristics of the recommended potential sites.

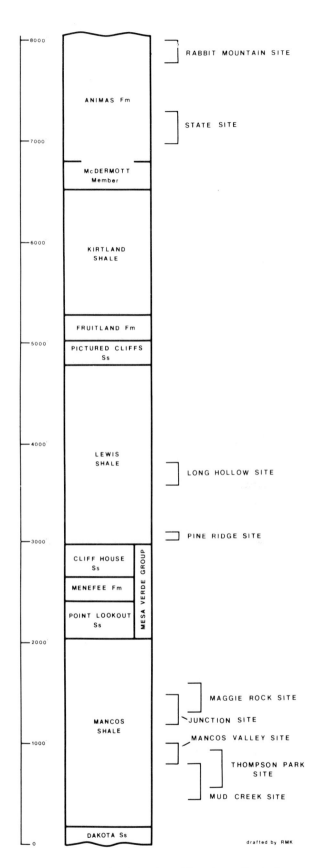

Figure 3. Generalized stratigraphic column illustrating the approximate stratigraphic position of the recommended potential sites.

factors included, but were not limited to, transportation elements, land use, land ownership, wildlife, archaeologic, historical, cultural, and ecologic impacts, local attitudes to particular sites, reclamation potential, economics, and site remoteness. The Site Selection Committee designated the Long Hollow, Pine Ridge, and Rabbit Mountain sites as the preferred candidate sites. A site in Bodo Canyon about one mile southwest of the tailings pile was also recommended for further consideration. Although this site did not meet the geotechnical criteria, the Committee felt that the advantages related to conveyor transport justified additional study of the site.

SUMMARY DESCRIPTION OF POTENTIAL SITES

The geotechnical suitability of all nine sites was comparatively ranked using a grading matrix. Certain sites were significantly better than others, but all sites appeared to be geotechnically feasible. Results of the grading matrix evaluation, along with individual site scores are as follows:

1. Maggie Rock site - 124
2. Junction site - 122
3. Long Hollow site - 119
4., 5., & 6. Mud Creek, Mancos Valley, and Thompson Park sites - 118
7. Rabbit Mountain site - 103
8. State site - 102
9. Pine Ridge site - 97

An important element in the grading matrix evaluation was the thickness of shale or claystone beneath a site. Figure 3 illustrates the approximate stratigraphic position of each site.

Two sites, the Maggie Rock and Junction sites, ranked slightly higher than other sites. Both sites have excellent geotechnical characteristics, but both also are a considerable distance from the existing pile. The Maggie Rock site is in a very scenic area and is partly owned by the Ute Mountain Tribe. Land acquisition would probably prove to be very difficult. This area also is irrigated farm land. The Junction site is adjacent to a proposed BLM wilderness area. Although utilization of this site would probably not affect the wilderness properties of the area under study, it is likely to have encountered considerable opposition from environmentalists. Additionally, the Junction site is irrigated farm land and is near known archaeologic sites.

Four sites, the Mancos Valley, Long Hollow, Mud Creek, and Thompson Park sites, received similar scores that were slightly less than the top two ranking sites. All four are very good from geotechnical aspects, but only the Long Hollow site does not involve considerable haulage. The Mancos Valley site has a higher erosion potential than do the other three. Mesa Verde National Park is only one-half mile from the Mancos Valley site and important archaeologic resources are nearby. Additionally, utilization of this site would conflict with mineral resource development. A producing oil well is on the far northwest corner of the site and several other wells are close by. Considerable exploration drilling is presently being conducted adjacent to the site.

The Long Hollow site was proposed for use by Ranchers Exploration and Development Corporation. This site has a minor perched ground-water problem, but the main citizen opposition to utilization of this site centered around transportation problems related to the use of the Wildcat Canyon road. An alternate road through Ridges Basin could be upgraded and used as the haul route to avoid this problem.

The Thompson Park site is in a very scenic setting and is highly visible from U.S. Highway 160. This site also is irrigated agricultural land. The Mud Creek site is one of the more remote sites, but it is a major wildlife wintering area and is on a wildlife migration route. Considerable road improvement and construction would be required for a haul route to this site.

Three sites, the Rabbit Mountain, State, and Pine Ridge sites, scored noticeably lower than the other potential sites, but are nonetheless apparently acceptable from a geotechnical standpoint. Rabbit Mountain and State sites are underlain by the Animas Formation, a possibly suitable formation that locally is an important source of ground-water in the region. The Rabbit Mountain site also has an erosion problem on part of the site. Additionally, the site includes small areas of excessive slopes and is confined to a relatively narrow valley. The State site consists of low rolling hills that could cause some excavation problems.

Only 50 to 100 feet of Lewis Shale underlies the Pine Ridge site. Furthermore, an anticline, syncline, and fault extend through or near the Pine Ridge site. These features suggest bedrock fracturing may be high at the site. An existing subdivision is close to the Pine Ridge site, and part of the site may be subdivided in the near future.

CONCLUSION

Nine potential sites that are geotechnically suitable for the permanent disposal of the Durango uranium tailings pile have been identified and comparatively ranked using a geotechnical grading matrix. Three of these sites, the Long Hollow, Rabbit Mountain, and Pine Ridge sites, have been chosen by the Site Selection Committee as preferred candidate sites, based not only on the geotechnical factors, but also on political, social, ecologic, and economic parameters. The Committee also recommended that a fourth site in Bodo Canyon be studied in greater detail. This site did not meet the geotechnical criteria, but the problems associated with truck haulage could be avoided with this site by use of a conveyor transport system.

These preferred sites are currently being studied in depth by the U.S. Department of Energy. Final selection of the actual repository site for the Durango tailings pile will be made after completion of this detailed investigation.

REFERENCES CITED

Colorado Geological Survey, 1981, Preliminary report on potential sites suitable for relocation and/or reprocessing of the Durango uranium mill tailings pile: Colorado Geological Survey open-file report 81-1, prepared with assistance from R. M. Kirkham and the Four Corners Environmental Research Institute.

Ford, Bacon and Davis Utah Inc., 1977, Phase II — Title I, Engineering assessment of inactive uranium mill tailings — Durango site, Durango, Colorado: report prepared by Ford, Bacon and Davis Utah Inc., for the U.S. Department of Energy, Report No. GJT-6.

Landa, E., 1980, Isolation of uranium mill tailings and their component radionuclides from the biosphere — some earth science perspectives: U.S. Geological Survey Circ. 814, 32 p.

A PARADOXICAL CLARIFICATION OF AN EXPENSE ACCOUNT

March 1, 1957

Mr. Santo Puglisi
Intergallatic Resources, Ltd.
Smileyburg, Kansas 64720

Dear Sir:

To clarify a situation from which arose two tow charges, either of which would stagger the imagination, I should like to state the circumstances which resulted in a total experience that ordinarily would shatter the emotions.

Sunday evening, February 17, I left Durango to scout Northwest Production Company's #1 Northeast, SE NW SW of Section 16, Township 27 North-Range 2 West, Rio Arriba Country, New Mexico, offsetting nearly half of a township of Indian lands up for bid at yesterday's land sale. My country road map indicated no road within thirty miles of the rig, neither was there the usual contractor's sign pointing down any of the reservation roads leading off New Mexico Highway 44. New Mexico Highway #95, which runs from Regina (13 miles north of Cuba) to Lindrith (12 miles) to Gavilan (9 miles) to the Apache Reservation (12 miles) to Burford Lake (10 miles) and to Tierra Amarilla (24 miles), seemed indicated as it would pass within eight miles of the rig and should bring me within view of the derrick lights.

Frankly, at the reservation gate, which was reached at midnight, there were no tracks of heavy equipment, but, being that close, I drove eight miles north to be due east of the location. No derrick lights and a road that was getting no better caused me to turn around and head back. Three miles up the line, where the road is narrow as it starts to take itself up and out of a wide canyon, the car had insufficient traction to make a not-too abrupt hill-curve. Four passes at it failed and, after spending several hours chaining up on mud-grip treads and adobe mud, four more passes with tire chains failed, so I headed north again for Tierra Amarilla.

At a point ten miles inside the reservation there is a cluster of five dwellings, two of which are occupied by Indian brothers. There was a big slough at the edge of the barnyard, the reason for turning around the first time, so I went to the house expecting to find Apache-speaking Apaches and was surprised to see an adjoining hut occupied by a cowboy who was wrangling wild horses on the reservation. Also present was an old duffer of eighty some years who is also connected with a horse. The cowboys were on starvation meals, as it had been too far and too muddy for them to ride out, and were existing largely from the charity of the Indians who weren't doing much better.

The Apaches, who can speak English, told me prospects were dim for getting out by spring. But, after eating breakfast of a cup of old coffee and a sourdough biscuit, I took off and stuck myself in another barnyard slough. The two Indians helped me get going after four hours labor, an incident of which was that the base of the bumper jack flew between an Indian's legs when we shoved the car away from the ruts. Three miles down the line the car stuck again in old ruts, so I walked back to the settlement in a storm of rain and snow, dragging my feet the last mile because the adobe mud would ball up on them like cement.

Getting my strength back on coffee and sourdough biscuits, I jumped aboard a horse and rode in the rain to an abandoned ranger station a mile away to use the field phone hanging on an outside wall. The contact was the Agency at Dulce and any conversation with the outside had to be relayed back and forth by an Indian Monitor. Dulce was disinclined to do much about it, claiming that a road had been washed out, so I had them call Denver and Northwest Production in Albuquerque. Northwest had a "cat", but it was busy fighting the crews in and out through four miles of mud and also there were several long canyons between us which would force an all-day detour. Northwest told me to stand by for a pickup, so I returned to the settlement and, foregoing dinner, stretched out on the adobe floor for some sleep.

Biscuits and coffee, and then jockeying back to the ranger station to learn where the pickup was. The truck, a four-wheel drive International, got in about 1 P.M., and, after fighting the car for several hours, suspecting the power glide was getting in bad shape and lacking the power to tow deadweight, the driver had it fought back to Lindrith at 4:45 P.M. He had to hustle over to some wells and said he'd give me a lift to Cuba on his way back. Having to be in Albuquerque for scout check, I called three scouts' offices in Farmington. All had left so I called Durango and caught Continental's scout on his way out of the office. We agreed to meet in Cuba, and, allowing time, I called a filling station-cafe there and asked them to look out for a certain car and certain person. Northwest's driver had not returned. Also, the "gooks" in Cuba had paid no attention to my call, discovered when Conoco called me at 9. Conoco slugged his way through the mud to Lindrith and on the way back to Cuba he went too far on the shoulder by swinging too wide for approaching headlights. The headlights belonged to the car of a drilling crew of El Paso Natural Gas and the car was in the ditch. A following pickup had tied on, so I walked down and lent my shoulder to the enterprise to guarantee assistance. We came off the shoulder easily and made it to Albuquerque at 2 A.M.

In bed at 4 and up at 7, I made scout check, rode back to Durango with Union's scout, and spent all Wednesday night posting maps, editing reports and writing a scout letter. Thursday I was on the phone to New Mexico Highway Department, to Dulce and to Durango garages. Dulce's superintendent was full of the usual bureaucratic bogwash, the Santa Fe office of the New Mexico Highway Department didn't even know the number of its patrol station at Chama, and in the meantime a garage here had located me a Dodge Powerwagon, operated by an Al Crawford of Hesperus.

Northwest's driver had told me it would take all of that power to take me off the reservation, so I contracted the going price of $7.00 per hour, with no standby time of $2.50 per hour as was being paid by General Petroleum to get their crews in and out on a Granite test southwest of Durango. We took off at 3 P.M. Thursday and were looking at the car at 8:00. The Dodge went through the roads easily, so easy that I expected to be in Durango by sunup. I had Al turn around and back up to tie onto the car. My hitch on the bumper broke it, so I had Al swing around to utilize the winch line. The car had to be abandoned Tuesday on the road between a small hogback and pond, and all turning had to be after a backup of a quarter of a mile away. After one catheading the Dodge had to back again and got stuck in a spot where water had seeped in under the road. It was then 2 A.M. so we walked the half-mile to the settlement and slept four hours on the floor. Breakfast changed from coffee and biscuits, as on the way down I had stopped at Lindrith to get some grub for the cowboys who had fed me. They told us Thursday night they had to ride out in the morning or starve.

Al and I went back to work and ran the winch line back under the truck to tie onto a tree. The winch shear-pin broke, so I walked back to the settlement to find something for a deadman. The cowboys were riding out and one of the horses drug a 4-foot sill down to the Dodge. We set a deadman and the truck walked out. During intermittent drizzle and clear skies we fought the car out of the worst of the draw, lack of trees being a big handicap. The biggest obstacle of all, however, was adobe mud, the likes of which had never been seen by 1) the Dodge driver who has lived in the Four Corners Area for 48 years and has pulled out twenty cars and hundreds of oilfield and uranium trucks and 2) one of New Mexico's largest dirt contractors. In fact, the car's transmission was intact—the lack of power was because the balling adobe all but had the wheels cemented. In taking off the chains I had to pry the wheels off with a shovel and the chains off with a jack handle. The end of the draw found us at the settlement hungry and thirsty. The cowboys had ridden off with the grub, leaving Al and I an onion for lunch.

I took the wheels off again and dug the adobe out to speed the show up as the car was capable of traveling with its own power. Another half-mile, though, and the adobe had it locked. The Dodge tied on again and we made two miles progress, the car getting hot enough to boil out the Zerone. With my wheels barely turning, the Dodge lacked the traction and we lacked trees for winching. We were forced to give up and return to Gavilan for rest and food, a difficult drive because of the near freezing weather and because of tie rod troubles. Earlier in the day, the adobe was plowed once too often and sucked the right tie rod out. This we fixed with muscle and bailing wire. It held up to the extent that it dropped out only twice more to Gavilan. And somewhere along the way we had to, I disremember, either cut some ruts or tie onto a tree. We reached Gavilan at 7:00 P.M. and had an outside chance for success the next day if there was a hard-enough freeze.

There was no such luck. Crawford and I had worked ourselves into a near stupor. The adobe was still in control. The Dodge had run by now a fair-sized bill and I felt compelled to plunge like a losing gambler. Gavilan Lodge had an electric welder, so we fixed the tie rod for all time. Also, two miles north of Gavilan there was parked a D-8 "cat". I learned, though, that it was ready for survey because of a cracked block and thus of no use. Crawford and I drove down to Lindrith, the nearest phone, and I called the Denver Office which gave me the option of using my own judgement. I said that I stuck the car and that I would get it out. There being nothing accomplished sitting in a bar all day, I told Crawford we were going back to work. We left Gavilan at noon with a truckload of anchors, an extra 200 feet of cable which I requisitioned from somebody's junk pile, fifty gallons of gas, and thirty gallons of water. The adobe was still there when we

planted a deadman. After peeling off the foot or so of soft adobe, the rest of the hole had to be spudded with a wrecking bar. Walking out 150 feet of winch line and fighting every step of the way, moving the car just 150 feet, having to spud another anchor hole, having to jam the winch line back onto the spool, and standing in a driving rain-snow while doing it, we returned to Gavilan at 7:00 P.M.

Discussing the "cat" some more I learned that it belonged to Walt Swafford, a dirt contractor in Cuba. I also learned that Walt had an Austin-Western road patrol. Crawford and I drove down to Lindrith in the rain-snow and I called Walt. His price was $12.00 per hour for use of the blade. He also said he was actually having his first time in town in three years but agreed to come out and would be there one hour after daylight. Returning to Gavilan, the footfeed got stuck and the truck went off the shoulder. In the rain and snow we did about thirty minutes shoveling. The same place in Cuba that ruined things Tuesday night did so again Sunday morning and failed to wake him. He made it from Cuba to Gavilan by 10, with no breakfast, and we set sail, with the winch line respooled and the footfeed repaired. Snow was still lying on top of the mud and the mud was soft, prospects excellent. Walt, possibly a little rocky and speedy, was in the ditch when we came around the bend four miles up the line. He tried to lift the scraper out on its blade, unsuccessfully, so we tied onto it with the power wagon. The winch shear pin broke again and the only spare pin didn't have the strength.

We took off in the Dodge to get Walt's gin truck. Walt was afraid to use his "cat" as he was going to trade it in for a new one. He decided to use the "cat", so we crawled up to the scraper. Another small crisis developed when the starting motor crank got lost in the shuffle. Luckily, Crawford was able to keep full throttle on the "cat", and the blade came out easily. The drain plug to the "cat" got lost when we drained the water and the middle finger on his left hand got mashed when I "weeviled off" and dropped the boom of the front blade on it. We made it to the car without further incident and the scraper tied on. By this time we had lost some of the advantage of the rain, the adobe starting to firm up again. But with all six wheels driving and with chains on the front wheels, the scraper barely made it up the hill which thwarted me the previous Sunday. The second small slope was even tougher, this even with my car in low gear. My wheels were barely turning and at certain times weren't turning at all during the six miles to the gate. Huge balls of adobe spun off my rear wheels. One ball the size of an oil drum even sucked off a hubcap. We had to stop once momentarily to let the Dodge use the scraper for a deadman to get off a soft shoulder. We made the gate just as the sun broke through the clouds prior to sunset.

Walt, probably the finest operator in New Mexico, gave me the perfect tow job. However, five miles north of Gavilan, the scraper had used up all diesel fuel. The Dodge had gone ahead of us and when it returned we put some gas in the tank of the scraper for the trip up the last big hill. After eating gas fumes from a diesel exhaust for two miles I had the car in position for the Dodge to take it to Gavilan. I was then able to drive toward Lindrith.

Success eluded me again when, going through a mudhole, the motor stalled and the battery showed up with no power. The Dodge tied on again for a fast tow to get me started, but the generator lacked the power to kick the motor in. Slack developed in the tow line and when the Dodge tightened up, the left front frame was torn loose. The right frame being cemented with adobe, the bumpers not matching, and an axle assembly being impractical, the only place left to hook onto was a reinforcement indentation on the bottom of the fly wheel housing. Every time the chain would slack, the hook would drop out. All three of us had taken turns lying in the mud and water and were tired and hungry. We left the car at the side of the road and drove into Cuba at midnight.

Walt gave my check an endorsement so that I could buy a new battery, nothing else being obtainable. Crawford and I drove back to the car, installed the battery and made it back to Durango at 6 without any more trouble. At the so-called "Dulce highway" which runs up the reservation from New Mexico Highway 44, I parked the car and climbed into the Dodge for a forty-mile trip to Northwest's rig. Fifteen miles in, I chanced across the driver who got me off the reservation the previous Tuesday. He told me the rig had been shut down since Saturday night because of the rounds. Two "cats" were buried on the location, the crews were confronted with an 8 mile round trip walk, and to plug a casing leak would entail a Halliburton charge of $15-20,000 just to fight their trucks in and out. He also said that his inability to swing back through Lindrith was caused by burying his truck on one of the roads. Sage Drilling Company, Northwest's contractor, indicates that drilling will not resume until at least Saturday.

To sum all this up, I would say that Swafford's job was nearly perfect. Crawford worked like a horse and I had nothing better to do. The torn frame "teed" me off and the shear pin business got a little old. However, I understand that when I called, he had just returned to the house after being released by General Petroleum. For an incident of Colorado mud, General Petroleum wound up wanting his services badly the day after he was released. General Petroleum's location also saw a D-6 "cat" suck the front wheels out from under a FWD water truck which was buried.

Crawford stated that he had no idea that the job would be so tough and would have recommended leaving the car there indefinitely had he known, which brings the matter down to Amerada and myself.

Perhaps if I had it all over to do again, I'd suggest leaving the car there. The period of time would be indefinite and the status of the car upon return would be even more uncertain. Of the over-all economics of such a situation I'm certain. I got the car in and I got it out. It would still be there, however, had there not been a heavy rain Saturday night, a fact which becomes a bit of a paradox — mud so bad that only rain can improve the situation, for the time had come when I no longer had the strength to race a shovel against the clock.

My car has only 26,000 miles on it and faces a repair bill quoted at $251.05 unless other damage is uncovered. This, plus the towing charges, is the third time in nine months my car has been stacked. The first time was for free because the insurance carrier for the construction company is picking up the tab when T.R. Kelty, the adjuster here, receives the release which I signed last summer and forwarded to Tulsa, covering being picked off by a rockslide. The second incident in November when a horse in closed-range country ran into my car could have been for free had not circumstances indicated an impracticable lawsuit. This last time, though indicating I would be better equipped with a bicycle, could have been avoided by my using the popular telephone-black top system of scouting. But I believe that Amerada, a corporation which I enjoy hustling for, is entitled to something better when an important test is being drilled.

Very truly yours,

Richard H. Ruggles

rhr:rm

Durango and La Plata Mountains. (Photo by Jack Rathbone)

FIRST DAY

ROAD LOG FROM DURANGO, COLORADO TO TELLURIDE, COLORADO, VIA SILVERTON AND OURAY, COLORADO

September 28, 1981

DRIVING DISTANCE: 127.8 Miles
STARTING TIME: 8:30 A.M.
ASSEMBLY POINT: Corner Sawyer Street and La Posta Road (this is on the frontage road to Highway 550 south of Durango, across from City of Durango Service Center Building).

TRIP SPEAKERS

Dick Ullrich, Don Baars, Vickey Price, John Campbell, Paul Weimer

SUMMARY

The trip today examines the stratigraphic sequence from the Cretaceous to the Precambrian. We descend through the section as we travel northward toward the Silverton caldera and the Uncompahgre uplift, and Precambrian metasediments are seen just south of Ouray. The trip from Ouray to Telluride crosses Dallas Divide. Westward stratigraphic thickening off the ancient Uncompahgre uplift is seen on the west side of Dallas Divide.

ROAD LOG: D. L. Baars; New Mexico Geological Society 19th Field Conf. Guidebook, 1968; Rocky Mtn. Assoc. of Geologists, Road Logs of Colo., 1960. Compiled by Dennis Irwin

Cumulative
Mileage

STOP 1 — Discussion of Tertiary-Cretaceous stratigraphy. Viewing the stratigraphy clockwise starting at south and proceeding down section: Animas Formation caps ridge and is underlain by purple McDermott Formation (Tertiary?); light colored slopes are Upper Cretaceous Kirtland-Fruitland Formations; sandstone beneath prominent landslide is Pictured Cliffs, it overlies the Lewis Shale (both are also Upper Cretaceous). Looking to northwest and continuing down section; Smelter Mountain at south end of Durango is capped by Cliffhouse Sandstone underlain by the Menefee shales and then the Point Lookout Sandstone, lowest slope is Mancos Shale. View just west of north is a dip slope of the Dakota Formation.

.9

.9 At 9:00 Point Lookout Sandstone grading downward into Mancos Shale.

.1

1.0 At 3:00 dipping to southeast the most easterly and stratigraphically highest sandstone is the Cliffhouse, it is underlain to left by Menefee shales and coals and then the Point Lookout.

.3

1.3 Animas River bridge. Looking west the highest sandstone on the skyline is Pictured Cliffs underlain by Menefee shales and then Point Lookout Sandstone and Mancos Shale. Peaks on skyline are La Plata Mountains, Tertiary intrusives.

.4

1.7 VCA tailings pile at 9:00. Uranium-vanadium ores from Colorado Plateau mines were processed here during the 1950's and early 1960's. Pile is to be moved because of local fears of contamination.

.4

2.1 Intersection highways 550 and 160. Go north into Durango on 550.

Figure 1.   Looking west across Durango. (photo by C.D. Irwin) Kch = Cliffhouse; Kmf = Menefee; Kpl = Point Lookout; Kmc = Mancos

.8

2.9   Stop light, go left.

.2

3.1   Cross Animas River. Largest brown trout in state was caught from hole just to right of bridge, 26 pounds. Dip slope seen ahead to left is Dakota, the obvious structure is the Durango anticline.

1.4

4.5   Stop light. Ridge to east capped by Point Lookout Sandstone. TURN RIGHT.

.1

4.6   Animas River.

.3

4.9   Road is between 2 terminal moraines of late Wisconsin (Pinedale) advance; houses built on top of moraines have beautiful view of Animas Valley and San Juan Mountains to north.

.9

5.8   Stop sign, turn left.
South dipping slope to left (Animas City Mountain) is capped by Dakota-Burro Canyon(?) Sandstone (Cretaceous).

Underlying slope is Morrison Formation, and upper white cliff is Junction Creek Sandstone which is separated from the lower white colored Entrada Sandstone by the slope-forming Wanakah Formation (Summerville equivalent)—all Jurassic in age. Redbeds at base of outcrop are in the Dolores Formation (Triassic). Steep slopes at base of distant cliffs are Cutler Formation (Permian) and bedded gray rocks on far mountain are Hermosa Group (Pennsylvanian).

.9

6.7   Upper slopes at 12:00 are in Morrison Formation with basal ledgy sandstone of possible Salt Wash Member. Upper white sandstone is the Junction Creek.

.4

7.1   Divergence in dips across valley at 10:00 is due to northeast plunge of Durango anticline which intersects valley.

.4

7.5   Contact between Entrada Formation (Jurassic) and Dolores Formation (Triassic) at 2:00. Vertical cliff-forming

Figure 2. **View looking northeast across Animas River. (photo by C.D. Irwin) Kd = Dakota; Jm = Morrison; Jjc = Junction Creek; Jwk = Wanakah; Trw = Wingate; Trd = Dalores; Pc = Cutler**

sandstone above redbed slope may be Wingate Sandstone (Triassic).

.8

8.3 Alternating ledges and slopes above valley at 10:00 is the Cutler Formation (Permian).

.3

8.6 Resistant ledgy redbeds at 1-3:00 are in the Cutler. Channeling at upper contact is visible in gully at 3:00.

.5

9.1 Good view of Cutler through Dakota at 10:00 and Cutler at 2:00.

.4

9.5 Waterfall in Cutler (when water is present) at 10:00.

.1

9.6 Hermosa Mountain at 12:00, capped by red Cutler overlying gray rocks of the type section of Hermosa Group.

1.3

10.9 West Needles Mountains in Precambrian metamorphic complex at 12:00.

.6

11.5 Top of Hermosa Group at 10:00. Resistent ledges at base of cliff are limestones at top of Hermosa.

.8

12.3 Junction, continue straight ahead. Road to left crosses valley to U.S. Highway 550.

.1

12.4 Base of Hermosa Mountain at 10:00 is in poorly exposed shale and gypsum of the Paradox Formation. Base of Cutler Formation (Permian) in middle of cliff at 3:00.

.6

13.0 Cliff at right is massive gritstone of lower Honaker Trail Formation.

.3

13.3 Good view of Honaker Trail, capped by Cutler redbeds at 2-3:00.

.3

13.6 View of Paradox Formation at base of Hermosa Mountain at 10:00. Hermosa Mountain is the type section for the Hermosa Group.

1.2

14.8 Distant view of Engineer Mountain on left side of canyon; Potato Hill is prominent peak in center; West Needle Mountains are on right. Steep lower slope at 10:00 on the flank of Hermosa Mountain is thick clastic sequence underlying the Paradox Formation and overlying the Pinkerton Trail Formation (both are in the Hermosa Group).

.2

15.0 Roadcut in dark gray shales of Paradox Formation.

.4

15.4 Fork in road, go left. Road to right is logging road access to Missionary Ridge.

.2

15.6 View of Hermosa Cliffs in distance at 11:00. Massive beds at base of valley at 1:00 are Leadville and Ouray Formations (Mississippian-Devonian). Lower valley at 12:00 is Precambrian (?) granite.

.6

16.2 Good view of pre-Paradox clastics at 9-11:00. Engineer Mountain at 12:00.

.6

16.8 Tuffaceous thermal spring deposits in valley at 10:00.

.2

17.0 Lower cliffs at 2-3:00 are carbonates of Leadville and Ouray Formations. Landslide topography seen in middle slopes below Hermosa outcrops.

.3

17.3 Lower cliffs ahead in Leadville Limestone overlying Ouray Limestone. Shale notch separating carbonates is top of Ouray.

.1

17.4 Sharp left turn. Road lies upon glacial outwash terrace of Wisconsin advance (Pinedale?).

.2

17.6 Granite outcrop on right.

.6

18.2 Granite outcrop on right.

.3

18.5 Good exposures of Leadville and Ouray, covered Elbert (Upper Devonian) slope and Ignacio Quartzite (Cambrian) in lower cliffs at 9:00.

.1

18.6 Baker's Bridge across Animas River in granite gorge. The first mining camp in southwestern Colorado was established here in 1861, on the east bank of the river, by a group of about 100 people under the leadership of Charles Baker. Little gold was found, however, and the Indians were a constant hazard. When the Civil War began the party disbanded and returned east. Baker later returned and was killed by Indians as he was preparing to lead an exploring party into the Grand Canyon.

.4

19.0 Yellowish deposits on hillside at 12:00 are deposits from springs which flow from fracturing associated with a normal fault which transects the valley. This fault can be seen displacing the Leadville at 8:00 across the valley.

.1

19.1 Junction with County Road 250, turn right, do not continue straight. Type section of Pinkerton Trail Formation at 12:00.

.1

19.2 Good exposures of Leadville and Ouray at 9-11:00. Highway in Elbert Formation.

.2

19.4 Roadcut in Ignacio Quartzite.

.2

19.6 Ignacio Quartzite on left.

.1

19.7 Granite outcrops at 12-3:00.

.3

20.0 Roadcuts in granite. Note mafic dike in roadcut to east.

.4

20.4 Ignacio Quartzite on left.

.3

20.7 Hermosa Cliffs on skyline.

.5

21.2 **STOP 2** — Walk up railroad tracks to inspect Mississippian-Cambrian section and discussion of same. At 10:00 Leadville Limestone caps ridge, underlain by Ouray Limestone below shale break; tree covered slope is in Elbert Formation. Lower cliffs are McCracken and Ignacio overlying granite. Shalona Lake on right.

North along the railroad tracks the Precambrian-Cambrian boundary is exposed with the Ignacio Formation (Cambrian) lying on Baker's Bridge Granite (Precambrian). Northwest of the

Figure 3.   Looking southwest from railroad tracks at Shalona Lake. (photo by D.L. Baars) Leadville is cliff at upper left; Ouray below shale notch; tree covered slope in Elbert; lower cliffs are McCracken & Ignacio

highway/railroad intersection is the abandoned Rockwood Quarry, dug in the Leadville Limestone. The underlying Ouray Formation is exposed in the cliffs below and east of the quarry. The McCracken Sandstone Member of the Elbert is exposed along the railroad. The uppermost part of the Leadville Limestone, exposed in the rim of the quarry, is a residuum composed of fragments of Leadville Limestone encased in red clay of the over-lying Molas Formation. Solution channels and cavities deep in the limestone are filled with Molas red clay.

The quarry floor lies about 10 feet above the base of the Leadville. Quarrying was not carried deeper stratigraphically because the underlying beds are too siliceous. The upper half of the Leadville, below the breccia, is composed of massive beds of white, coarsely crystalline limestone, containing crinoid stems and other fossils. Some beds are oolitic and others, particularly in the lower part, contain lenses and nodules of dark-gray chert. The oolitic strata are rich in endothyrid foraminifera.

The thickness of the Leadville is about 100 feet. It is separated from the underlying Ouray Formation by a bed of lime shale, 3-5 feet thick, that forms a notch in the cliff face, exposed in the cliffs east of the quarry. Late Devonian fossils are present in the Ouray; and Mississippian fossils are present in the Leadville. The Ouray is about 70 feet thick; it is similar to the Leadville but somewhat more siliceous. The lower 15-20 feet of Ouray Limestone is thin bedded and contains thin shale partings.

The Elbert Formation is about 40 feet thick here and is composed of interbedded sandstones (the McCracken Member), shaly limestones and shales. The Ignacio Quartzite is 70′ thick at this locality. It consists of dull-red, light tannish-red, and tannish-white quartzite in beds about two feet thick interbedded with beds of dull-red sandy shale one to four inches thick. The formation, however, is irregular in thickness and character. At some places it consists largely of sandstone and reddish shale. Locally it contains a cobblestone conglomerate at its base. An excellent exposure of this is seen along the railroad north of the highway. The Ignacio is believed to be equivalent to the Sawatch Quartzite, which is widespread in the Front Range, Sawatch Range, White River Uplift, and areas adjacent to these ranges.

.1

21.3 Cross railroad tracks. Rockwood quarry at 1:00.

1.1

22.4 Highway on Molas Formation (Pennsylvanian).

.7

23.1 Hermosa Cliffs (strata of Hermosa Group) to west, Engineer Mountain at 1:00, West Needle Mountains at 2:00. Highway level is about at the Leadville-Molas contact; above, to the west, in ascending order, are the Pinkerton Trail Formation, the talus-covered Paradox Formation, and the higher cliffs of the Honaker Trail Formation. These three formations constitute the Hermosa Group. Wisconsin stage glaciers in this part of the canyon were more than 2,000 feet thick and reached nearly to the tops of the Hermosa Cliffs.

.3

23.4 Roadcut in Pinkerton Trail Formation.

.2

23.6 Tamaron resort entrance to right.

.3

23.9 Outcrops of pre-Pennsylvanian rocks along Elbert Creek at right.

.6

24.5 Landslide deposits on left.

.2

24.7 Haviland Lake road to right.

1.5

26.2 Pinkerton Trail Formation in roadcut. Mississippian at 3:00.

.5

26.7 Electra Lake junction (originally Ignacio Reservoir). Ignacio Quartzite type section. Electra Lake is the source of water for the hydroelectric plant at Tacoma. A dam across Elbert Creek forms the lake which is supplied chiefly by a flume from Cascade Creek about 5 miles to the north. The water from the lake drops about 500 feet to a penstock; then enters the pipeline and plunges 200 feet to the turbines, with a 450 pound pressure at the plant. The northeast edge of the lake is bounded by the Electra Lake gabbro (1,460 m.y.).

.6

27.3 View of the East Needle Mountains at 2:00, dominated by Pidgeon Peak

13,972'. The West Needle Mountains, with Twilight Peak, 13,158', the highest mountain at 1:00. The East Needles are composed mostly of Eolus Granite (1,460 m.y.) and the West Needles are Twilight Gneiss (1,780 m.y.).

1.2

28.5 Bridge over Elbert Creek, type section of The Elbert to the west; highway on Molas Formation.

.7

29.2 Potato Hill (also locally called Spud Mountain) at 12:00. Molas regolith in roadcut.

.1

29.3 Uppermost Leadville in outcrop on right.

.5

29.8 Pinkerton Trail Formation in roadcut on left.

.7

30.5 Entrance to Purgatory Ski Area to left.

.1

30.6 Molas regolith in roadcuts on right for next .3 miles.

1.4

32.0 Molas regolith in roadcuts on right.

.7

32.7 Engineer Mountain at 1:00 capped by Tertiary rhyolite sill about 800' thick (note the columnar jointing); underlying redbeds are Cutler Formation (Permian) overlying rocks of the Hermosa Group. Grizzly Peak at 11:00 is a Tertiary quartz monzonite stock.

.6

33.3 Road loops around head of Cascade Canyon. Excellent exposures of the entire Devonian sequence here make this canyon ideal for the study of these beds, especially the Elbert Formation.

.1

33.4 The old Lime Creek road, now little used, angles off to the right and follows the lip of Cascade Canyon.

.5

33.9 Leadville Formation in roadcuts on left.

1.2

35.1 Mill Creek Lodge.

.3

35.4 Leadville Formation in roadcuts on left.

.3

Figure 4.   Engineer Mountain. (photo by J.H. Rathbone)

35.7 Precambrian in gully on right; overlying Cambrian is covered.

.1

35.8 McCracken Sandstone Member of Elbert Formation in roadcut at right overlain by upper Elbert in following gully.

.1

35.4 Leadville Formation in roadcut at right, overlain by basal Molas.

.3

36.2 Tertiary (?) sill of sanadine trachyte porphyry in roadcut in Molas Formation. Note contact metamorphism.

.1

36.3 Ouray-upper Elbert contact on left.

.2

36.5 McCracken Sandstone on left.

.1

Figure 5.   McCracken & Ignacio Formations. (photo by D.L. Baars)

36.6 Cambrian-Precambrian contact. Roadcut exposes lower part of Leadville, and all of Ouray, Elbert, and Ignacio formations and Precambrian gneiss. Clean exposure of Elbert Formation in roadcut.

.8

37.4 Hermosa Group outcropping on Engineer Mountain at 10:00, overlain by Cutler and Tertiary igneous rocks on peak.

1.6

39.0 **STOP 3** — Coalbank Pass, elevation 10,640'. The old stage road, from Durango to Silverton, passed about here, and dropped down into Lime Creek

nearly along route of present highway. With the advent of the automobile, the stage road was abandoned; the first auto road from Cascade Creek was made around the south and east flanks of Potato Hill into Lime Creek Canyon. There for a considerable distance, the road is a narrow ledge blasted out of the face of the cliff. The new Coalbank Hill road, which we are now traveling, reverted back to the old stagecoach line. There is no coal at Coalbank Pass, on Coalbank Hill, nor along Coal Creek.

Faults trending northeast, along drainage northeast of pass are the Coalbank faults, down-to-northeast. Honaker Trail beds are faulted against Precambrian rocks of the Twilight Gneiss with about 750 feet of stratigraphic separation. On the up-thrown block, the gneisses are overlain by the Devonian age McCracken Member of the Elbert Formation in outcrops along the fault; whereas, at the parking area, a quartzite, boulder-cobble conglomerate is between the two units.

West of highway, the Cambrian Ignacio Formation sandstones are between the quartzite conglomerate and the McCracken. Above the McCracken, are thin shales and shaly carbonates of the Elbert Formation, overlain by thin carbonates of the Leadville and Ouray, and several tens of feet of red Molas Formation terra rosa materials. Lower Hermosa carbonates and detrital rocks are the first rocks exposed above the Molas Formation. Middle member limestone benches are at the top of the cliff; 1,523 feet of stratigraphic section is present above the Molas Formation. Cyclic detrital and carbonate (here mostly dolomitic) deltaic and shallow-marine deposits in the lower Honaker Trail Formation are exposed at road level north of the Coalbank Pass fault.

.1

39.1 Crossing large east-west normal fault, down thrown side on north. Entering complex normal fault area.

.2

39.3 Highway parallels fault scarp on right. Highway in Hermosa Group.

.5

39.8 Mountain across valley at 3:00 is Twilight

Peak (13,158'), type area of the Twilight Gneiss which is faulted against Hermosa rocks at 2:00.

.6

40.4 Sharply flexed beds of the Honaker Trail Formation, with a reverse dip to the south. This flexure resulted from periodic uplift of a small horst composed of the Uncompahgre Formation. Angular unconformities in the flexure indicate vertical movement during deposition of the lower Honaker Trail Formation (Desmoinesian).

.3

40.7 Sharply flexed limestone beds in the lower Honaker Trail Formation, north of the Snowden fault, are against Uncompahgre slates and quartzites to the south. The Snowden fault extends from here about 2 miles west and at least 6 miles east to the Animas River. The fault may connect with the Elk Park faults that extend another 10 miles, or so, along the north flank of the Grenadier Range.

Outcrop of Cambrian (?) quartzite conglomerate overlying Precambrian quartzite on small hill below highway.

.4

41.1 Crossing Snowden fault trace. Precambrian outcrops on right, Hermosa Group limestones on left.

.3

SAN JUAN MOUNTAIN STRATIGRAPHIC COLUMN

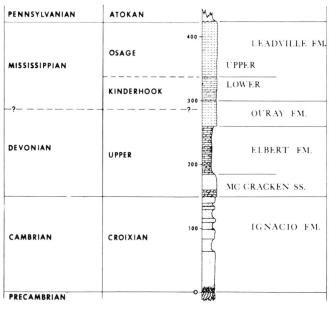

PENNSYLVANIAN	ATOKAN	
MISSISSIPPIAN	OSAGE	LEADVILLE FM.
		UPPER
	KINDERHOOK	LOWER
?	?	OURAY FM.
DEVONIAN	UPPER	ELBERT FM.
		MC CRACKEN SS.
CAMBRIAN	CROIXIAN	IGNACIO FM.
PRECAMBRIAN		

Figure 6.

41.4 Highway crosses axis of a syncline in the Honaker Trail Formation, formed by drag folding along the Snowden fault (to south) and laccolithic (?) intrusion (to north). The doubly-plunging syncline has its low point just to the east of Lime Creek. Roadcut here shows carbonate solution features and channel scour in lower and middle members of the Honaker Trail Formation.

The area, from Lime Creek to slightly beyond Molas Pass, was burned in 1879, in a fire that cleared 26,000 acres. The time period, since the fire, has been insufficient to re-establish a forest cover, despite replanting that began in 1911.

.8

42.2 Hill to the east is the main part of the Tertiary Lime Creek intrusion, probably a laccolith, that intruded and deformed the Honaker Trail Formation. Minor hydrothermal alteration and pyrite mineralization are associated with the intrusion.

.2

42.4 West Lime Creek. Highway is in Hermosa Group to Molas Pass.

4.2

46.6 Molas Pass, elevation 10,910 feet. Highway is cut in the detrital facies of the Lower Member of the Honaker Trail Formation. Molas Lake, 10,488 feet, is seen below to northeast. Grand Turk Mountain, to north, is capped by the San Juan Formation, resting on a thin layer of Telluride Conglomerate, which, in turn, overlies the late Eocene erosion surface. The erosion surface bevels the gently westward-dipping Paleozoic strata, so that the Tertiary conglomerate lies on Cretaceous rocks to the northwest; Triassic age Dolores Formation to the north-northwest; Permian age Cutler Formation to the north; and Pennsylvanian age Honaker Trail Formation to the northeast.

This area has been extensively glaciated during the Pleistocene, as is everywhere apparent. The terraces below are scoured Paleozoic rocks; Storm Peak, beyond Silverton, shows a hanging valley; well-displayed cirques, glacial valleys, and hanging tributaries can be seen east of the Animas Valley. Note especially the west-southwest-trending glacial striae that are common right on top the pass itself, evidence that surely is suggestive of icecap conditions in the San Juans.

From this vantage, structural elements of the Paleozoic Grenadier Highland (horst?) can be seen in the present topography: the Molas-Andrews Lake fault, trending east-northeast and down-to-south, is about on line with Molas Pass; the Snowden fault, trending east and passing along the north slope of Snowden Peak, is down-to-north, with the intervening Molas graben (present-day) represented by the modern Molas Creek Valley. The Molas graben was a high area during the early Paleozoic.

Viewpoint is on a carbonate bed of one of the carbonate-detrital sequences in the Lower Member of the Honaker Trail Formation. This bed is a gray, fossiliferous, lime wackestone to packstone, slightly sandy at the base and intraclastic at top. Fossils include phylloid algae, pelecypods, crinoids, fusulinids, gastropods, foraminifera and brachiopods. Locally, the unit is a coralline boundstone made of *Chaetetes*. The marine section is interspersed with fluvial sandstones.

.2

46.8 Grenadier Mountains to right, formed by steeply dipping upper Precambrian rocks.

.2

50.0 To left fossiliferous gray limestones and shales near the base of the Pinkerton Trail Formation.

.1

50.1 Trinity Peak at 8:00 in the Grenadier Range; Elk Creek Canyon and White Dome at 2:30. Ledgy outcrops along highway are interbedded limestones and shales of Pennsylvanian age.

.1

50.2 Outcrops of Molas Formation in roadcuts.

.5

50.7 South entrance to Molas Lake; TURN RIGHT, Pinkerton Trail limestone and shale to left.

.6

51.3 **STOP 4** — Molas Lake. Borrow-pit excavations show the relationship

Figure 7. Snowden Peak across Little Molas Lake, view to northwest. (photo by D.L. Baars)

between the Leadville Limestone (Mississippian) and the lower Molas Formation (Pennsylvanian). The quarry has excavated into the west side of a paleokarst tower and exposed paleokarst breccias. The Leadville here is a light blue-gray, partly recrystallized, bryozoan-coralline-brachiopodal-crinoidal lime wackestone to packstone. The lower part of the Molas Formation is a red, non-bedded terra rosa residuum that fills solution openings and breccia voids in the Leadville Limestone. The middle member of the Molas is a poorly stratified mixture of transported quartz sand and transported terra rosa material; the upper member shows marine reworking. The Molas-Hermosa contact appears to be gradational, and many of the fossils are common to both formations.

View toward south is dominated by Snowden Mountain (13,077') and the Grenadier Range of the Needle Mountains to the south-southeast.

.2

51.5 North entrance road to Molas Lake. Highway is in Molas Formation.

.8

52.3 Approximate location of small east-west fault, upthrown side on north. Highway cut in Leadville Limestone.

.1

52.4 Highway begins steep descent into Animas River gorge. Outcrops on left of highway are of Leadville and Ouray limestones. Highway parallels small fault on right, along which the limestones are

Figure 8. Grenadier Range and Molas Lake. (photo by D.L. Baars)

displaced against older Precambrian schists and gneisses.

.1

52.5 Approximate top of Elbert Formation (Devonian): for next 1 mile outcrops on left of highway are interbedded shale, limestone, dolomite, and quartzite of the Elbert Formation and the Ignacio Formation.

.7

53.2 Canyon to right was cut by the Animas River and glacier. Cirques and hanging valleys at 3:00. Ignacio Quartzite, Elbert Formation, and Leadville-Ouray Limestone just north of hanging valley at

about same level as highway. Paleozoic outcrops are faulted out by a small northeast-trending fault, and do not appear north of the fault. Below are older Precambrian schists and gneisses.

View northeast of Silverton; junction of Mineral Creek and Animas River; alteration and mineralization along caldera ring-zone. Mt. Kendall, immediately east across the Animas River; outcrop in roadcut of Sultan Mountain intrusive and its contact with Paleozoic sedimentary rocks. Contact metamorphism of sediments to quartzites, hornfels, marbles and skarn.

.3

53.5 Small fault, downthrown to north; Leadville and Ouray Formations faulted against the Elbert Formation.

.2

53.7 Approximate contact of the Ouray and Elbert Formations.

.1

53.8 Small fault displaces Elbert Formation against Ignacio Quartzite; upthrown side on north; drag in Elbert is evident.

.1

53.9 Sharp S turn; view of Silverton at 3:00. Approximate Ignacio-Elbert contact.

.1

54.0 Glacial striations on outcrop to left.

.1

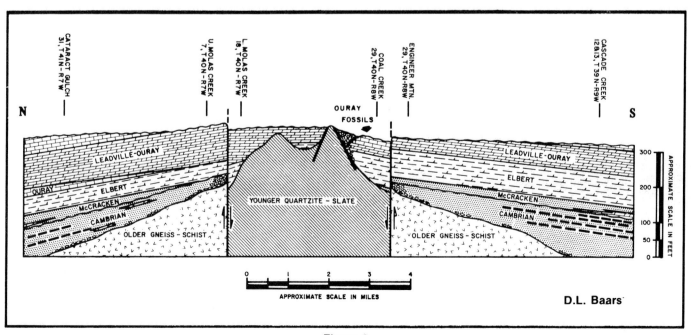

Figure 9.

54.1 Approximate contact of Elbert and Ouray Formations.

.1

54.2 Approximate contact of Leadville-Ouray with Miocene age quartz monzonite pluton. Good view of Silverton and Animas River at 1-2:00.

.2

54.4 View of Silverton at right with Storm King Mountain towering behind the town. Storm King is composed of Miocene pyroxene-quartz latite above a base of the Burns Quartz Latite. The red mountain at 12:00 is composed of the Silverton Volcanic Series (Tertiary).

.6

55.0 Glacially polished outcrop at left.

.1

55.1 Road enters talus slope from Miocene age stock. Silverton and Animas River canyon at 3:00, canyon of Mineral Creek at 12:00. Red rocks on mountain at 12:00 are of Silverton Volcanic Series.

.1

55.2 Silverton City limits.

.2

55.4 Bridge over Mineral Creek.

.2

55.6 Highway junction U.S. 550 and Colo. 110; TURN LEFT to Ouray. View down Animas River Canyon at 4:00. Note river modification of the glaciated canyon; a broad U-shaped canyon deepened and cut to a V-shape by the Animas River. Peaks visible in the distance looking south down the canyon are in the Grenadier Range and the Needle Mountains.

On right, the slopes of Anvil Mountain are altered volcanic rocks of the Silverton Volcanic Series. On left, the slopes of Sultan and Bear Mountains are composed of a Tertiary quartz monzonite intrusive stock. Both mountains are capped with remnants of San Juan Tuff and Telluride Conglomerate (both Tertiary).

.6

56.2 Old North Star mine and mill west of Mineral Creek.

1.4

57.6 Junction with road up south fork of Mineral Creek. Volcanic rocks forming the slopes of Anvil Mountain northeast of valley are highly altered by sulfataric emanations along south fork of Mineral Creek. The Cutler Formation (Permian) is beneath the San Juan Tuff forming the outer rim of the caldera.

The Silverton Volcanic Series rests on the San Juan Tuff at about 11,000 feet on the slopes north of South Fork, but they are below the valley bottom at 9,500 feet on Anvil Mountain to the east. This difference may be due to post-Silverton faulting and to the fact that the Silverton Series thickens markedly inside the caldera rim. Some of the faulting also occurred during accumulation of volcanic rocks in the central caldera basin.

1.1

58.7 Road turns northward and continues along the general trend of the rim belt of the caldera. Volcanic rocks form both walls of the valley, with the San Juan Tuff at valley level on west side and Silverton Volcanic Series on east side.

2.0

60.7 Jeep road to west to town of Ophir over Ophir Pass.

1.9

62.6 Mineral Creek.

.1

62.7 Chattanooga. Mill Creek from the west joins Mineral Creek here. Northward along Mineral Creek is one of the rim faults, with highly altered Silverton Volcanic Series on the east, and a downfaulted wedge of highly altered rhyolite of the Potosi Volcanic Series on the west. Westward, Potosi Rhyolite caps the mountain top in a normal position; but, east of there, the rhyolite has been stepped down by faulting.

2.0

64.7 To north and east of highway, caldera rim step-faulting has gradually lowered blocks of Potosi Rhyolite from their original position on the ridges to the west.

.3

65.0 Red Mountain Pass, 11,075 feet (Ouray County). Outcrops are flows of Picayune Hornblende Latite (Silverton Volcanic Series). The Silverton Railroad was built by Otto Mears and followed in part the

Rainbow Route Toll Road previously constructed by Mears. The railroad was originally projected to Ouray, but the 19-percent grades were beyond the capacity of friction traction.

.5

65.5 Red Mountains No. 1, No. 2, and No. 3, from north to south consist of flows, flow breccias, and pyroclastics of rhyolite and latite together with several rhyolite and quartz latite porphyry intrusives. The rocks are highly altered as the result of late Tertiary hydrothermal activity, and are weathered to shades of yellow, yellow-brown, and red-brown.

.8

66.3 Idarado Mining Company ahead right. The following description of the mine is by J. R. Hillebrand, N.M.G.S., 1968: "The Idarado mine lies beneath the high ridge between Red Mountain Valley and Telluride, and is in both San Miguel and Ouray Counties. The mine contains more than 80 miles of interconnected drifts or crosscuts on or connecting the Ajax-Smuggler, Tomboy, Liberty Bell, Alamo, Virginius, Pandora, Flat, Japan, Flora, Cross, Ansborough, Handicap, Barstow, Montana-Argentine and Black Bear veins. Approximately 100,000 feet of drifts and 37,000 feet of crosscuts are accessible, and are mostly on the Montana-Argentine and Black Bear veins and Ajax section of the Ajax-Smuggler vein.

Access to the mine is through either the Treasury tunnel, whose portal is below Red Mountain Pass at an altitude of 10,600 feet, or the Mill Level tunnel entrance 2 miles east of Telluride, at an altitude of 9,060 feet. The Treasury tunnel intersects the Black Bear vein 8,670 feet from the portal, and the Mill Level tunnel intersects the Argentine vein 7,150 feet from the portal.

It is 6 miles from the Red Mountain plant to the Pandora plant, via interconnecting drifts and raises. There are engineering offices at both plants as a matter of convenience. The Red Mountain plant includes the company general offices, warehouse, carpenter and machine shops, and mine change-room. The Pandora plant consists of the mill and assay office, machine shops, and mine change-room. The flotation mill has a capacity of 1,800 tons per day, making a bullion product and separate concentrates of lead, copper, and zinc."

The mine is currently inactive because of depressed metal prices. Ahead left, Spirit Basin, a cirque, beneath saddle on skyline. The slope up Spirit Gulch is crossed by several northeast-trending faults, part of the fault belt around the Silverton "Caldera" on the northwest. Across canyon, large dumps and snowsheds of the Genesee-Vanderbilt tunnel, one of the large mines of the district; slightly farther north, Yankee Girl mine, the largest producer of the district.

.6

66.9 Sharp curve. Yankee Girl headframe to right.

.1

67.0 Tailings pond at right. Roadcuts in breccias of Picayune Pyroxene Latite (equivalent to San Juan Tuff in part). Champion Basin to right.

.2

67.2 Barstow mine up Commodore Gulch at 11:00. This deposit was one of the few in the Red Mountain district which contained much gold. Site of old mining town of Guston lies to east.

.2

67.4 Commodore Gulch. Northeasterly-trending fault just south of bridge moved Picayune Pyroxene Latite down on the southeast against the San Juan Tuff on the northwest.

.3

67.7 Red Mountain No. 1 at 12:00; and Red Mountain No. 3 at 2:30. Alteration of San Juan Tuff at head of Governor Gulch on left. Milepost 83.

.7

68.4 Joker tunnel on right. This tunnel was successfully driven to drain mines and cut the workings of the district but was never entirely completed as originally planned.

.3

68.7 Below road on west side of Red Mountain Creek is caved portal of the Meldrum tunnel, begun (but not completed) in the 1890's by Andrew Meldrum as a railroad and mine tunnel running nearly due west from Red Mountain Valley on the east to the Pandora Basin near Telluride on the west.

.3

69.0 Mudflows and alluvial fans on left slopes.

.4

69.4 Mount Abrams straight ahead. Ghost town of Red Mountain is through the aspen trees to the right.

.8

70.2 Entering Ironton Flats. These topographic flats may have been formed by alluvial infilling of a small lake formed by mudflows which periodically dammed the valley. The old town of Ironton occupied the upper end of the flats. Lower western slopes of Ironton Valley are largely San Juan Tuff, but eastern side consists of Silverton volcanic flows and breccias. The Silverton and San Juan rocks appear to have graded and intertongued across Ironton Valley as suggested by Kelley (1946).

.4

70.6 Full Moon Gulch left, Saratoga mine right, and Maud S. Mono-Baltic mines on right rear worked replacement deposits in the Ouray Limestone where limestone is in contact with the overlying Telluride Conglomerate or San Juan Tuff. Uncompahgre Quartzite (Precambrian) at base of hill.

.7

71.3 Ahead right, down the canyon, buried hill of Uncompahgre Quartzite (ochre and gray) in the horizontally bedded gray San Juan Tuff.

.4

71.7 Red Mountain Creek.

.3

72.0 Highly jointed cliffs of San Juan Tuff ahead right. This is a well-bedded greenish-to-purplish rhyolitic-to-andesitic fanglomerate, strikingly exposed along the canyon walls between Ironton Flats and Ouray where it reaches a thickness of 1,500-2,500 feet.

.5

72.5 On right is a memorial plaque for R. F. Miller and his two daughters who were swept into the adjacent canyon by an avalanche while putting on tire chains in the slide path.

.1

72.6 Milepost 88

.1

72.7 Riverside slide, site of the tragedy. Large snow slides descend into Red Mountain Creek from both sides of the canyon filling the bottom to 100 feet deep. The slide from the west comes down Curran Creek; the one from the east comes down Riverside Creek. The old Mears toll road was near the bottom of the creek. In winter a tunnel large enough for a stage and six-horse team was sometimes cut 450 feet through the slide. In some years the snow does not melt all summer.

.3

73.0 Bear Creek Slate Member of Uncompahgre Quartzite in roadcuts.

.1

73.1 On curve. Note contact between the black Bear Creek Slate Member and the white Sutton Mill Quartzite Member dipping south.

.4

73.5 Breccia pipe composed of rounded and angular fragments of Precambrian quartzite and slate cemented by pyrite in roadcut at right.

.1

73.6 The Uncompahgre Quartzite comprises all the Precambrian rocks of this part of the mountains and consists principally of alternating quartzite and slate members.

.7

74.3 To right, jeep road over Engineer Mountain to Silverton.

.1

74.4 Uncompahgre River to left.

.6

75.0 To left, buildings at portal of Natalia tunnel. Glacially abraded hummocks and grooves on quartzite around the Natalia mine.

.4

75.4 Bridge over Bear Creek Falls (drop is 227 feet). The term "Million Dollar Highway" has been loosely applied in recent years to the road from Durango to Silverton. Actually it originally meant only the six miles from Ouray to Ironton Park, which cost $1,200,000 when built during the 1920's. The road closely followed the toll road built by Otto Mears, which itself cost $40,000 a mile where it cut solid rock along the cliffs between Bear Creek Falls and State Bridge — an enormous sum in those days. The toll gate was here at the falls. The charter expired in 1900. Note the narrow trail on the left of Bear Creek above the bridge. About $600,000 worth of ore was packed down this trail by burro train from the Grizzly King mine.

The buildings just south of the falls are those of the Sutton Mill built in 1926 (100-ton capacity). The mill was built for the Sutton mine located next to a blade-shaped crag in San Juan Tuff very high on the opposite canyon wall about southwest of here. A very steep tram connected the mine and mill, but much of the ore that was run through the mill came from the Yankee Girl dumps in the Red Mountain district. The mine is reached by road and trail from Ouray along the west side of the canyon.

.1

75.5 Bear Creek Falls turnout. Glacial grooves, scratches and polish are abundantly preserved on the Precambrian rocks of the canyon, and the irregular hummocky surfaces along the western wall of the canyon are the product of glacial scour by the last (Wisconsin) glacier, which as it moved past this point may have been as much as 3,000 feet deep with its terminus some 12 miles down the Uncompahgre Valley. The bouldery debris south of the bridge over Bear Creek Falls may be a remnant of Wisconsin till or kame terrace material. In this area the canyon bottom does not appear to have been deepened more than about 50 feet by Recent stream erosion.

Note large ripple marks in Precambrian down low across canyon. These are common in roadcuts all along the canyon. The dip across the canyon is 61° N., 35° W.

.3

75.8 Tunnel on highway. This was driven in 1912, through Bear Creek Slate Member of the Uncompahgre Formation.

.3

76.1 Note conglomerate bed in Uncompahgre Quartzite in roadcuts on right.

.2

76.3 Note glaciated surfaces on left. Grooved and polished surfaces are widespread on both sides of the canyon in this area.

.1

76.4 At 9:00 on timbered skyline, rim of Devonian Elbert Formation lying on Precambrian slate faulted against Precambrian quartzite to the south.

.3

76.7 Approximate location of Ouray fault which brings Precambrian up on north side. Leadville and Ouray Limestone on south side. Fault trends across valley to right and up small gully to right of Box Canyon sign.

.2

76.9 Parking area with view of Ouray. Leadville Limestone in road and up on west wall of canyon. The cliffs east and west of Ouray are formed chiefly by the Hermosa Formation, which dips north and plunges under the valley about one mile north of Ouray. The Leadville-Ouray Limestone is exposed in Box Canyon on southwest edge of town. The large cirque-like amphitheater southeast of town is formed almost entirely in the San Juan Tuff (Tertiary).

.2

77.1 Amphitheater campground road.

.7

77.8 Road up Canyon Creek to Camp Bird and Revenue mines. Note lower extent of glaciation and Recent gorge beneath bridge, cut by Uncompahgre River since disappearance of the last (Wisconsin) valley glacier from this point. It was down this road that ores from the Revenue, and other mines in the Sneffels district having their portals on this side, were packed and hauled to Ouray. Strings of 50 pack mules and burros were not an uncommon sight. In later years teams were used. Just before reaching the Camp Bird is the famous "Water Hole Slide". One year the slide ran just as the ore teams were passing. Five men and twenty-six horses perished.

The Camp Bird mine was actively worked from 1896 to June 30, 1916, when it was closed to await the results of a new adit, which, driven 11,000 feet by June 1918, cut the vein 450 feet below the lowest old workings. Development work on the vein from the new level failed to find sufficient new ore to operate the 60-ton mill. From 1896 to 1919 this mine yielded $27,269,768 in value of recovered gold, silver, lead, and copper; and the profit of

Figure 10. Devonian Ouray and Precambrian contact in Box Canyon at Ouray. (photo by J.H. Rathbone)

the mines and mill exclusive of depreciation was $17,731,788, or 186 percent. The discoverer of this mine was Thomas F. Walsh, eventual owner of the "Hope" diamond.

The mine remained idle until 1926 when Joe King, John Moore, Ed Lavender, and Charles Bell, Sr., organized King Lease, Inc. and took a lease from Camp Bird Ltd. to mine a pillar of ore known to have been left in the "hematite stope" by the old company on the No. 3 or "Boardinghouse Level". The mine has been a consistent and profitable producer of gold (bullion), silver, copper, lead, and zinc ever since with minor interruption. Total production now exceeds $35 million.

.4

78.2 Road bends left and becomes Main Street, Ouray. This area, often called the Switzerland of America, was first entered by prospectors in July, 1875 crossing the mountains from Silverton. The town was incorporated in October, 1876 and by 1877, two years after the first gold discovery, a newspaper "The Ouray Times" was being circulated. Ouray takes its name from Chief Ouray, "The Arrow", who was peacebearer between the Ute Indians and the Whites. After gold was discovered in the San Juans, Chief Ouray was chosen by the Utes to represent them in all treaties, and he and his wife, Chipeta, became very well known in this district.

Ouray is the center of the Uncompahgre or Ouray mining district. This is the only mining district in the San Juan region where the relationship between the older and younger periods of Tertiary mineralization may be determined by direct observation. The older veins are terminated upward against the Telluride erosion surface, whereas the younger veins cut both the older rocks and the overlying volcanic formations. The most productive deposits have been in the older rocks (Mississippian through Cretaceous); the gold and silver-lead mineralization was probably related to intrusion of rather small dikes, laccoliths and sheets in the Ouray domal structure.

.2

78.4 Beaumont Hotel on left in center of town.

.5

78.9 Ouray municipal swimming pool and goldfish ponds. About 1920 a pair of two-foot long alligators were placed in the small natural warmwater ponds now holding goldfish, and in 10 years they grew to a length of 6 feet. Near the pool once stood the First and Last Chance Saloon, aptly named to serve both those arriving or departing town.

.3

79.2 To left, thick beds of Hermosa Group cut by dikes. Cutler Formation caps the cliff.

.6

79.8 On left, monoclinal flexure affects Cutler beds. Dolores Formation (Triassic) truncates the monocline and unconformably overlies the Cutler Formation on the south, and the Hermosa beds on the north of the monocline.

The cross-section, index map and following text on this area is taken from a paper by R.J. Weimer in the RMAG 1980 Symposium, Colorado Geology, p. 23-35.

The magnitude of the truncation is about 2,000 feet and the entire Cutler is absent on the east side of the river valley in the ampitheater.

The paleodrape seen in the photograph occurred after the Cutler Formation was deposited. Uplift of the Sneffels horst offset the Precambrian about 3,500 feet by brittle deformation across a fault zone 1.5 miles wide. The overlying Hermosa and Cutler Formations were folded, and subsequent erosion removed all of the Cutler from the Snefels horst and reduced the entire area to a plain. During the Late Triassic, conglomeratic sandstones, siltstones and shales of the Dolores Formation covered this erosional surface. The tensional nature of segments of the drape fold is indicated by the injection of Tertiary dikes and hydrothermal solutions into open fractures. Recurrent movement along the Ouray and other faults and regional northward tilting occurred during the Laramide orogeny.

.3

80.1 Ouray city limits, north side.

.1

80.2 Foot of monocline to left; Rotary Park to right.

.5

80.7 Road to Lake Lenore, Bachelor mine, and

Figure 11. Ouray; cliffs on left are Hermosa. (photo by J.H. Rathbone)

Banner-American mill. The Bachelor occupies the south side of Dexter Creek; the Calliope was on the north side. Both were important producers of high-grade silver-lead ores during the late 1880's and 1890's. The Bachelor production exceeded $3,000,000.

              .2

80.9 On left, Corbett Creek canyon and Whitehouse Mountain (skyline) capped by Silverton pyroxene andesite (?) and Potosi volcanics overlying 2,000 feet of San Juan Tuff. Excellent exposures of Cutler in canyon walls next 1.5 miles. Burbank (1930) described the Cutler Formation as follows:

"The Cutler formation lies conformably upon the Hermosa formation. The upper 300 feet of the Hermosa resembles the Cutler much more closely than it does the lower and middle Hermoas below it, and consequently the division between the Hermosa and Cutler formations cannot be sharply drawn. The only logical division that could be made was to place the base of the Cutler at the top or near to the top of the highest fossiliferous limestone, or shale, of Hermosa age. The conditions about Ouray indicate, however, that there is little assurance that uniformity can be obtained by such a method. The upper limits of the Hermosa and the base of the Cutler must therefore be considered only as an arbitrary division. There is exposed approximately 2,150 feet of the Cutler formation along the Uncompahgre Valley between Ouray and the vicinity of Corbett Creek . . .

Figure 12. Photograph of paleodrape fold and uncomformity at base of Dolores Formation (Trd). View west wall of Uncompahgre River Valley. (photo by R.J. Weimer)

The unconformity shown between the Dolores and Cutler Formations is not apparent from the valley floor. Cross-section of the same event is below; index map follows.

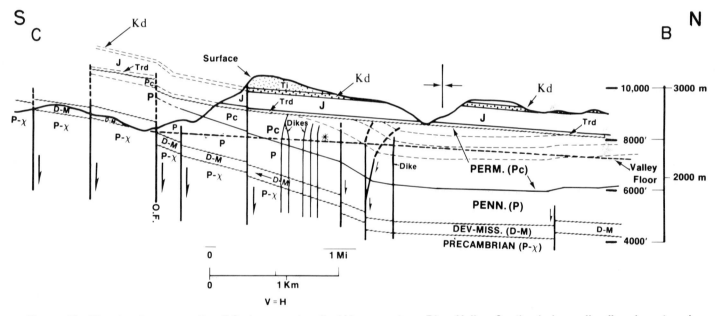

Figure 13. Structural cross section BC along west wall of Uncompahgre River Valley. Section below valley floor is restored. O.F. is Ouray fault; symbols for formations are: P-x = Precambrian; D-M = Elbert, Ouray and Leadville; P = Molas and Hermosa; Pc = Cutler; Trd = Dolores; J = Jurassic; Kd = Dakota; Ti = Tertiary intrusion; * = approximate surface position of a core hole by Bear Creek Mining Company. drilled to a depth of about 2,000 ft (610 m).

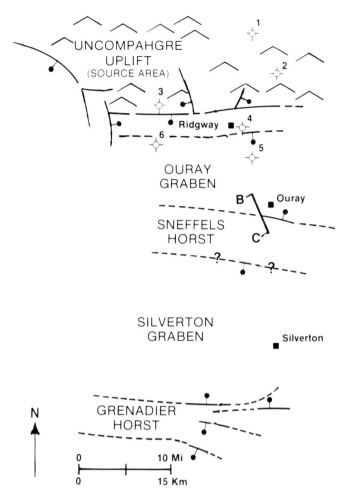

Figure 14. Map showing Paleozoic paleotectonic elements on west and northwest flank of San Juan dome, Colorado.

The lower part of the Cutler is characterized by red sandy and limy shales, similar to the thinner parting shales in the upper Hermosa, but the thick sandstone and conglomerate beds like those of the upper Hermosa, gradually become less prominent in the basal part of the Cutler. The Cutler sandstones alternate with the sandy and limy shales, and are mostly less than 20 feet in thickness. The colors are pink or purplish in the coarser grits, while the finer sandstones are brick red. Cross-bedding is characteristic of many of the sandstones, and is particularly prominent in some because of the altenations of light and dark bands.

About 1,450 feet above its base a series of very coarse, heavy conglomerates makes its appearance in the Cutler formation. These conglomerates contain well-rounded boulders, a considerable

number of which are as much as 6 to 10 inches in diameter; they consist largely of Precambrian rocks, granites, schists, greenstones, and quartzites. The lower beds of conglomerate contain, however, many boulders of pitted limestone which appear to have been derived from the Ouray limestone."

.6

81.5 Dexter Creek.

.4

81.9 Note Cutler beds dipping south toward shallow syncline.

.5

82.4 Sequence on hillside at 3:00 is Dakota capping hill, covered Morrison, Entrada at mine dumps capped by thin Pony Express Limestone; then Dolores red beds (mostly covered) and Cutler in lower part of hill.

.1

82.5 Cutler Creek, type locality of the Cutler Formation. Dolores beds exposed in slope above.

1.0

83.5 Bridge over Cutler Creek.

.6

84.1 Entrada Sandstone (Jurassic) pronounced white outcrop ahead right; below is Dolores mudstone and sandstone, and lower yet is Cutler sandstone, conglomerate, and mudstone.

.6

84.7 The Dolores-Cutler contact is at the color break on the hill up to the right between the brighter red above and the darker red below. The Dolores is only about 100 feet thick in this area.

.8

85.8 Highway at Dolores-Cutler contact. Dike forms prominent wall to right.

1.6

87.4 On left side of valley, Morrison, Dakota and Mancos are exposed.

.2

87.6 Hot springs on left. At 12:00 terminal moraine of Wisconsin advance of Uncompahgre glacier. Earlier Durango till is present several hundred feet above valley bottom, along both sides, and a few miles farther north than the Wisconsin terminal moraine.

Uncompahgre is an Indian name meaning "water rushing over red rocks".

.8

88.4 Straight ahead, at 12:00, Morrison Formation capped by Dakota on upthrown side of Ridgway fault. Bare slopes to left front are Mancos Shale (Cretaceous). Ridgway "till", a mudflow, overlies Mancos and is overlain by Telluride Conglomerate and San Juan Tuff near top of pointed hill to left front.

.8

89.2 Junction with Colorado State Highway 62 west to Telluride and Naturita. East-west fault crosses highway just to north. Mancos Shale in valley is faulted down against Morrison Formation in hills beyond. Turn left.

.2

89.4 Bridge over Uncompahgre River. Entering Ridgway. Turn right to City. Park for **STOP 4.**

.3

89.7 Mancos Shale exposed in cliffs ahead.

.5

90.2 Leaving Ridgway.

.3

90.5 Looking back at Ridgway the peaks seen in the distance are as follows: Uncompahgre Peak (14,286') at 10:00, this is the highest visible peak; Matterhorn Peak (13,589'), the small point just to the right; and Wetterhorn Peak (14,017'), is behind at about 10:30.

.7

91.2 San Miguel Mountains ahead.

.9

92.1 Ascending Mancos Shale. To north upthrown block of Morrison is seen faulted against Mancos at base of hill.

1.7

93.8 Bridge across Dallas Creek. Mancos Shale is exposed in vicinity.

2.8

96.6 Dike in Mancos Shale in road cut.

1.2

97.8 Basalt in road cut and alongside road for next .5 miles.

.6

98.4 Looking back downhill across covered Mancos Shale, a fault scarp is visible on the far ridge. Dakota Sandstone seen capping the ridge is on the north upfaulted block. This fault probably coincides with the ancient Permo-Pennsylvanian Uncompahgre fault.

.2

98.6 Crossing igneous dike.

1.1

99.7 Entering San Miguel County.

.1

99.8 Dallas Divide, elevation 8,970'. Mount Sneffels (14,150') is the high peak at 7:30. Davis Oil Co. McClure #1 was drilled and abandoned in 1963 about 2 miles north of here. The well bottomed in Leadville Limestone (Miss.) at 5,539' without significant shows. Dakota in road cut.

1.1

100.9 Dakota outcrop. Note carbonaceous shale.

.2

101.1 At 8:00; North Pole Peak (12,990') and Hayden Peak (13,158').

.1

101.2 Approximate base of Dakota. Road is in Morrison Formation for next four miles.

1.0

102.2 Milepost 10.

1.3

103.5 Dallas Divide ski area on left. Dakota Sandstone capping hill.

.6

104.1 Abandoned railroad trestle on left.

.6

104.7 Morrison exposures.

1.0

105.7 Pony Express Limestone Member of Wanaka (Summerville) Formation overlies Entrada Sandstone, both are Jurassic age deposits.

.2

105.9 Crossing Alder Creek fault. Entrada is exposed in roadcut on upthrown east block.

.2

106.1 Tributary of Leopard Creek on left.

.8

106.9 Brushy Basin Shale Member of Morrison Formation (Jurassic) exposed on right.

.3

107.2 Milepost 5.

.5

Figure 15. Wilson Peak. (photo by D.L. Baars)

107.7 Salt Wash Sandstone Member of Morrison exposed on right in roadcuts.

.8

108.5 Outcrop of thinly-bedded Pony Express Limestone. Overlying it is the Bilk Creek Sandstone Member of the Wanakah Formation.

.1

108.6 Entrada-Dolores contact on right.

.3

108.9 Entrada-Dolores contact at 3:00. Dolores is Triassic age.

.3

109.2 Mine at 3:00.

1.2

110.4 Approximate contact of Dolores and Cutler Formations (the Triassic-Permian boundary). Road to left leads to Leopard vanadium mines.

In the next two miles the highway will cross many northwest-southeast-trending normal faults of small magnitude, most but not all are down to the northeast.

1.0

111.4 Base of aerial tram of the Omega mine.

.7

112.1 Looking back at hillside one can see the Omega mine which produced vanadium ore from the Entrada Sandstone.

.1

112.2 Road junction of Colorado State Highway 62 and Colorado State Highway 145. Turn left to Placerville (.3 miles) and Telluride.

Cutler Formation exposed at roadside, very conglomeratic.

.3

112.5 Placerville store. Road is in Cutler for next 5 miles.

.4

112.9 Leaving Placerville.

.2

113.1 Clastic dike in Cutler seen in road cut at bend. Note channels in Cutler on left.

.5

113.6 Clastic dike seen in reentrant at left.

.3

113.9 At 2:30, gravels that were placered for gold are about 100 feet in thickness.

.2

114.1 Kerr McGee Placerville Unit No. 1 well site on right above road. This dry hole, drilled in 1960, bottomed in Precambrian at a depth of 6,244 feet. The lithology in this well through the Pennsylvanian section shows an intermediate position between the limestones, shales and evaporites of the Paradox Basin and the thick arkosic material shed from the Uncompahgre-San Luis Uplift. The section in the Kerr McGee well is dominantly fine-, medium- and coarse-grained, somewhat arkosic sands with some thin limestone stringers separated by beds of dark gray to black shale.

Much of the Pre-Pennsylvanian section is missing because of erosion. The well drilled out of Molas into a Cambrian section consisting of sands, dolomites and green shale. Formation tops include Cutler at the surface, Hermosa at 2936', Paradox at 4522', Molas at 5664', Cambrian at 5804' and Precambrian at 6156'. The well was drilled upon a highly faulted, west-plunging anticline that is easily mapped from surface exposures. No significant shows were observed.

.7

114.8 Road to right goes up Fall Creek.

.6

115.4 Lower tram house of aerial tram to the Fall Creek mine is right of road.

.5

115.9 Sawpit store.

.1

116.0 Milepost 80.

.9

116.9 Small dike roughly parallels road about 200 feet vertically up slope on left at 8:00.
.4

117.3 Excellent exposure of Cutler-Dolores contact across canyon. White quartz-pebble conglomerate at base of brick-red Dolores overlies the purplish-red Cutler.

The Cutler Formation which underlies the Dolores Formation and overlies the Rico Formation is considered to be Permian in age. However, the Rico varies in age from Des Moines in the San Juan Mountains to Virgil in the central Paradox Basin. Therefore, the Cutler in this area is probably partly Pennsylvanian in age. It is composed of lenses of arkosic and conglomeratic pink and maroon sandstone interstratified with red siltstone and is dominantly a stream and flood plain deposit. The large cobbles in the conglomerate indicate a nearby source which in this case would be the ancestral San Luis uplift a short distance to the east, or, farther north, the Uncompahgre uplift. In the western Paradox basin the lower part of the Cutler interfingers with Wolfcampian age carbonates of the Elephant Canyon Formation and the upper part interfingers with eolian and shallow marine sands of the Cedar Mesa Formation.

The Dolores Formation overlies the Cutler, underlies the Entrada and is late Triassic in age. In this area it is about 300 to 450 feet thick. The basal 5-10 feet is a conglomerate containing limestone pebbles that grades upward into a white sandstone. The remainder of the formation consists mostly of thick-bedded red mudstone with many intercalated thin beds of micaceous sandstone, sandy shale and red shaly siltstone. The top 50-100 feet is a yellowish-gray sandy mudstone, calcareous sandstone and limestone conglomerate that is probably a Wingate Sandstone equivalent. The remainder of the formation correlates with the Chinle Formation.

Note dike in Cutler at 11:00.
.4

117.7 Light-gray quartz-pebble conglomerate in small reentrant to left of road is basal unit of Dolores Formation.
.3

118.0 Milepost 78.
.5

118.5 Silver Pick Road and Big Bear Creek to right. This is also the abandoned townsite of Vanadium. The ruins you see are the remains of the old Primos Chemical Company mill. The first vanadium from the Placerville district was processed here in the late 1910's and early 1920's. Moreover, the first uranium ore in the United States was recovered at this mill.
.3

118.8 Basalt dike exposed in bend of road, it can be seen again exposed in small reentrant on left side of road 100 feet ahead.
.3

119.1 Mouth of Summit Creek at left.
.3

119.4 Entrada Sandstone is well exposed at top of Dolores Formation on both sides of the river. It is the uppermost cliff-forming ledge of tan to reddish-brown to buff sandstone above the conspicuously cross-bedded sandstones in the Dolores. Entrada is Upper Jurassic in age, thickness here is 30-55 feet.
.8

120.2 Small fans built into San Miguel River from drainage to south.
.1

120.3 Dolores Formation on right.
.3

120.6 Pony Express Member of Wanakah Formation is black band part way up hill to left. It overlies the Entrada Sandstone and underlies the Bilk Creek Sandstone.

The Wanakah Formation is of late Jurassic age, it underlies the Junction Creek Sandstone and overlies the Entrada Sandstone. As generally recognized, the Wanakah Formation consists of three members: The Pony Express Limestone Member at the base, the Bilk Creek Sandstone Member in the middle, and the "Marl" Member at the top.

The Pony Express Limestone ranges from 10-25 feet in thickness. The bottom of the Pony Express is a black dense limestone, this is overlain in places by about the same amount of dark-gray limestone breccia formed by the leaching of gypsum. The upper part, when present, is composed of a gray, massive, somewhat sandy limestone.

The Bilk Creek Sandstone consists of 20-30 feet of very fine- to fine-grained, irregularly bedded sandstone. It is topped by the so-called Carnelian Sandstone, this is about 18 inches of resistant sandstone containing red chalcedony grains.

The "Marl" Member is about 70 feet thick and consists of mostly reddish siltstones with a few nodular sandstones that weather to form a smooth slope. This unit is lithologically similar to and physically continuous with the Summerville Formation.

.3

120.9   Milepost 75. Road maintenance buildings on right.

.6

121.5   Well-exposed section of Mesozoic rocks to left of road. In descending order:
Dakota Sandstone — 195': forms cliff at rim of canyon.
Morrison Formation
    Brushy Basin Member— 307'
    Salt Wash Member   — 320'
Junction Creek Sandstone — 26'
Wanakah Formation
    "Marl" Member   — 69'
    Bilk Creek Sandstone — 23'
    Pony Express Member — 13'
Entrada Sandstone — 54'
Dolores Formation — top 40' exposed here.

.2

121.7   Bilk Creek Canyon to right. Mancos and Dakota at 12:00.

.1

121.8   South Fork Road to right leads to Ilum (3 miles) and Ames (7 miles). Ames is the site of the first operating power station producing high voltage alternating current for power purposes.

By 1890, fuel for operating the mines in this area had become so expensive that a cheaper fuel bill was imperative or mine closures would certainly result.

L. L. Nunn, a part time lawyer, decided alternating current produced by water power was the answer. He convinced Westinghouse Corp. to participate by providing a 3,800 volt generator. Nikola Tesla designed the motor. There were no

electrical engineers in 1890 so Nunn formed the "Telluride Institute" and enrolled students from Cornell University in New York. The students designed and built the proper electrical equipment, erected poles, strung wire, built the dam and water conduits to the Pelton waterwheels. Learning as they went and working for $30 per month plus room and board the project was completed in 1891. It was successful from the first time the circuit was closed and fuel costs dropped 80 percent. By 1894 the entire city of Telluride plus most of the mines and mills in the district were wired and using electricity.

.5

122.3   Junction Creek Sandstone, which overlies red "Marl" Member of the Wanakah Formation (Summerville), is exposed in roadcut on left.

.3

122.6   Salt Wash Member of Morrison Formation exposed in roadcut on left.

.4

123.0   The double-peaked ridge at 3:00, up the Lake Fork of the San Miguel River, is San Bernado Mountain. Ridges of medial and lateral moraines of the Lake Fork glacier can be seen on Sunshine Mesa, along the west side of the Lake Fork Valley.

.1

123.1   Brushy Basin Member of Morrison exposed in road cuts on left.

.1

123.2   Road crosses normal fault of northwest trend. Northeast side of fault is downthrown about 200 feet.

.3

123.5   For the next 0.1 mile the road crosses a landslide. Mancos is seen in the trough of a small faulted syncline to the north of the road.

.2

123.7   For the next 0.3 miles along the north side of the road, and across the Main Fork to the south, there are exposures of breached terminal and recessional moraines of the Main Fork glacier. Both stratified and unstratified glacial materials are present, having a total thickness of about 500 feet. Dakota Sandstone crops out along the south side of the Main Fork Valley.

.2

123.9 Milepost 72.

.1

124.0 Top of Keystone Hill.

.1

124.1 Cross Remine Creek. Abandoned townsite of Keystone on left.

.3

Figure 16. **View north across Telluride. (photo by D.L. Baars)**

124.4 Society Turn, intersection with Highway 145 south. Continue straight. Society Turn is so called because in the 1890's and 1900's Telluride society would ride this far on Sunday afternoons to see and be seen and then return. A small amount of coal has been mined from the Dakota Formation just north of this junction.

.2

124.6 Intersection with Deep Creek road to left.

.9

125.5 Top of the Salt Wash Member of the Morrison Formation is exposed on lower hill slopes at left.

.2

125.7 Recessional moraine extends across valley at right.

.1

125.8 Mouth of Eide Creek to left. Dallas Peak can be seen at 10:00.

.4

126.2 Road crosses Mill Creek.

.4

126.6 Exposed in large cliff to left of road, from base up:

Dolores — red beds.

Wingate — thin-bedded, yellow-brown unit at top of red beds.

Entrada — thin, buff-colored, smooth cliff-forming unit.

Pony Express — thin black unit.

Bilk Creek — thin sandstone at top of Pony Express.

"Marl" Member — vegetation-covered slope.

Junction Creek — sandstone ledges visible through openings in tree covered slope high up.

.8

127.4 Mouth of Butcher Creek on left.

.4

127.8 Telluride city limits.

The first permanent settlers in the valley of the San Miguel were a group of prospectors including the Remine brothers who located the first placer claims in the valley in August of 1875. In October of 1875 John Fulton filed the first lode claim on what became known as the Sheridan Group. From this group of claims came the Smuggler, Union and Mendota mines, some of the largest producers in the district.

By 1880 most of the large mines had been located and two town sites had been established. The first, San Miguel, was legally incorporated on Oct. 10, 1877 while the second, Columbia, one mile to the east, was officially located and plotted on Jan. 10, 1878. Columbia became the larger of the two towns because of its slightly closer proximity to the mines and its wider streets which more easily accomodated the large freight wagons. In 1881 the name Columbia was changed to Telluride to help solve the confusion of two Columbias, the other was also a mining camp but in California. San Miguel County was created in February of 1883 and Telluride was chosen as the county seat.

In 1889 the San Miguel Valley Bank, located two doors east of the Sheridan Hotel, was relieved of $24,000 by Butch Cassidy and the Wild Bunch. They escaped into Utah by riding south through Rico and Dolores.

Otto Mears suceeded in bringing the railroad into Telluride from Ridgway over Dallas Divide by December of 1890 and one year later it was connected over Lizard Head Pass to Rico and Durango. Freight rates for ore were set at $60.00 per ton.

On the Fourth of July, 1903, William Jennings Bryan delivered his famous Cross of Gold speech from a platform in front of the Sheridan Hotel.

Later that same summer the miners in Cripple Creek went out on strike, so did the Telluride miners, out of sympathy. Typical wages at that time were $3.00 a day for a miner for an eight-hour day, outside laborers earned $2.50 for a ten-hour day and mill men were paid $4.00 for a twelve-hour day. Work was seven days a week with two holidays per year. The conflict between labor and management culminated with several shoot-outs at individual mine sites, fatalities, the arrival of the National Guard and the imposition of martial law.

Several years later a young man named Jack Dempsey washed dishes here at a local bordello named The Senate before he went into prize fighting.

The majority of the mines east of Telluride were eventually bought by the Idarado Mining Company. In 1955 a new 1,800 tons of ore per day mill was constructed and by 1964 as much ore and milled concentrates was being produced as was produced by all the mines in the region during the boom at the turn of the century.

Figure 17.   Ophir Needles, south of Telluride. (photo by D.L. Baars)

The Idarado mine shut down several years ago. The increase in gold price brought forth an announcement of plans to resume mining, however depressed base metal prices and the instability of gold prices have prevented this from happening. (Reference: "Telluride, From Pick to Powder" by R. L. & S. C. Fetter, 1979.)

SECOND DAY

ROAD LOG FROM TELLURIDE, COLORADO TO MOAB, UTAH, VIA PARADOX VALLEY AND LISBON VALLEY

September 29, 1981

DRIVING DISTANCE: 157.3 Miles
STARTING TIME: 8:00 A.M.
ASSEMBLY POINT: West city limits of Telluride.

TRIP SPEAKERS

C. M. Molenaar, Robert Hite, K. T. Smith, Harvey Merrell

SUMMARY

The trip today travels from Telluride to Moab through the Salt Anticline region and looks at various of these features (Paradox Valley, Pine Ridge, Lisbon Valley and Sinbad Valley).

ROAD LOG: D. L. Baars; C. M. Molenaar; Rocky Mountain Assoc. of Geologists, Road Logs of Colo., 1960; Four Corners Geol. Soc., 3rd Field Conf., 1960 and 9th Field Conf., 1979. Log compiled by Dennis Irwin.

Cumulative Mileage

Telluride city limits, west end.

.4

.4 Mouth of Butcher Creek on right.

.8

1.2 To left is intersection with old "Boomerang" road to Turkey and Gold King basins, site of the Alta mine. Name refers to the number of switchbacks along the route. In the large cliff exposure on the right of the road, the red beds are the Dolores Formation. The thin-bedded, yellow-brown unit at the top of the red beds is the Wingate Sandstone equivalent. The thin, buff-colored, smooth cliff-forming unit above is the Entrada Sandstone, here it is abnormally thin. Next above is a thin black unit, which is the Pony Express Limestone Member of the Wanakh Formation. The Pony Express is capped by the thin-bedded Bilk Creek Sandstone Member of the Wanaka. The "Marl" Member of the Wanakh forms the vegetation-covered slope above. Basal ledges of the Junction Creek Sandstone are visible in openings in the tree cover farther up the slope. The Cutler Formation shows in scattered outcrops in the trees below the main cliff exposures.

.4

1.6 Road crosses Mill Creek. This is the site of the old town of San Miguel, the original settlement in the Main Fork Valley. The San Juan tuff is well exposed in the high steep cliffs visible up Mill Creek valley.

.2

1.8 Campbell Peak can be seen up Eider Creek to right. Here the Silverton volcanic series is only four feet thick, and the Potosi to the east and west lies directly on the San Juan tuff.

.2

2.0 Mouth of Eide Creek at right. Alluvial fan at mouth of creek.

.1

2.1 Recessional moraine extends across valley at left.

.2

2.3 Top of the Salt Wash Member of the Morrison Formation is exposed on lower hill slopes at right.

.9

3.2 Intersection with Deep Creek road to right.

.2

3.4 Society Turn, intersection with Highway 145 south. Stay right.

.3

3.7 Cross Remine Creek.

.1

3.8 Top of Keystone Hill. For the next 0.3 mile along the north side of road, and across the Main Fork, to the south, there are exposures of breached terminal and recessional moraines of the Main Fork glacier. Both stratified and unstratified glacial materials are present, having a total thickness of about 500 feet. Dakota Sandstone crops out along the south side of the Main Fork Valley.

.1

3.9 Milepost 72.

.4

4.3 For the next 0.1 mile the road crosses a landslide. Mancos is moving down the trough of a small faulted syncline to the north of the road.

.3

4.6 Road crosses normal fault of northwest trend. Northeast side of fault is downthrown about 200 feet.

.1

4.7 Brushy Basin Member of Morrison exposed in road cuts on right.

.1

4.8 The sharp mountain summit at 10:00 up the canyon of the Lake Fork of the San Miguel River is Sunshine Mountain. The double peaked ridge left of Sunshine Mountain is San Bernado Mountain, and at the head of the drainage is the west shoulder of Sheep Mountain. Ridges of medial and lateral moraines of the Lake Fork glacier can be seen on Sunshine Mesa, along the west side of the Lake Fork Valley.

.4

5.2 Salt Wash Member of the Morrison exposed in roadcut.

.3

5.5 Junction Creek Sandstone, which overlies red "Marl" Member of the Wanakh Formation, is exposed in roadcut.

.6

6.1 Bilk Creek Canyon to left.

.2

6.3 Well exposed section of Mesozoic rocks to right of road. In descending order:
Dakota Sandstone — 195', sandstones and thin carbonaceous shales; forms cliff at rim of canyon.
Morrison Formation (Upper Jurassic):
  Brushy Basin Member — 307', red and green mudstones with a few thin lenticular sandstones, some conglomeratic sandstone at base.
  Salt Wash Member — 320', lenticular channel-filling cross-bedded sandstones with some interbedded mudstone.
Junction Creek Sandstone — 26', even-bedded sandstone which weathers to form a smooth vertical cliff.
Wanakah Formation
  "Marl" Member — 69', mostly reddish siltstones with a few thin nodular sandstones; weathers to form a smooth slope.
  Bilk Creek Sandstone Member — 23', irregularly bedded sandstone with a thin "carnelian" sandstone at the top.
  Pony Express Limestone Member — 13', dense black fetid limestone; forms prominent black band seen on right side of road.
Entrada Sandstone — 54', light-colored cross-bedded sandstone; weathers to form a smooth rounded cliff.
Dolores Formation (Upper Triassic) — about 450' thick but only 40' of reddish siltstones are exposed here.

.6

6.9 Milepost 75. Road maintenance buildings on left.

.6

7.5 Dolores Formation on right.

.1

7.6 Small fans built into San Miguel River from drainage to south.

.8

8.4 Entrada Sandstone is well-exposed at the top of the Dolores Formation on both sides of river. It is the uppermost cliff-forming ledge of tan to reddish-brown, to buff sandstone above the conspicuously cross-bedded sandstones in the Dolores.

.3

8.7 Mouth of Summit Creek at right.

.3

9.0 Side of basalt dike is well exposed in small reentrant to right of road. This same dike is exposed in the bend of the road 100′ ahead and can be seen across the canyon at 11:00.

.3

9.3 Big Bear Creek to left.

.2

9.5 Prominent dike at 7:00. It is unique in this area because it weathers into a slot between walls of baked sedimentary rocks instead of standing out as a resistant ridge. The dike ranges in composition from minette (a variety of mica-seyenite composed mostly of biotite and orthoclase) to olivine basalt. It has been traced for more than three miles.

.3

9.8 Milepost 78.

.2

10.0 Basalt dike across canyon at 12:00.

.1

10.1 Light-gray quartz-pebble conglomerate in small reentrant right of road is basal unit of Dolores Formation.

.4

10.5 Excellent exposure of Cutler (Upper Pennsylvanian and Permian) - Dolores (Upper Triassic) contact across canyon at 10:00. White quartz-pebble conglomerate at base of brick-red Dolores overlies the purplish-red Cutler.

.4

10.9 Small dike roughly parallels road about 200 feet vertically up slope at 2:00.

.9

11.8 Milepost 80.

.1

11.9 Sawpit store. Gravel-filled channel at 12:00 marks pre-Wisconsin course of San Miguel River. Other patches of stream gravel and valley fill can be seen at many places along the road.

.5

12.4 Lower tram house of aerial tram to the Fall Creek mine is left of road.

.6

13.0 Road to left goes up Fall Creek.

.9

13.9 At 9:30, semi-stratified valley fill reaches a thickness of about 100 feet. These pre-

Figure 18. View to north near Sawpit; Dakota caps hill; Morrison and Wanakah below with Entrada cliffs in center of picture. (photo by C.D. Irwin)

Wisconsin gravels were placered for gold in the early 1900's.

.3

14.2 Clastic dike in reentrant at right.

.5

14.7 Clastic dike in roadcut at bend.

.6

15.3 Placerville store.

.3

15.6 Intersection with Colorado highway 62, turn left.

Cross Leopard Creek. Junction with Colorado 62 to Ridgway. West of here numerous rock-held terraces can be seen, most of them north of the river. The river valley is markedly asymmetric; the rocks dip gently south, and the river flows along the south edge of the valley. The north edge of the valley is controlled by the Black King fault. This normal fault trends westerly and dips 65° to 80° north. The north side is downthrown as much as 500 feet. For several miles to the west, "greenstone" pebble, cobble and boulder conglomerates, 5 to 25 feet thick, are common in the Cutler and exposed along the road. The Pony Express Limestone pinches out to the west at about this longitude but the pinchout is not visible from the road. West of this point the Bilk

Creek Sandstone lies directly on the Entrada Sandstone.

.7

16.3 Biotite monchiquite dike exposed at right at road bend.

2.2

18.5 Road across bridge to left follows Specie Creek.

1.3

19.8 Pre-Wisconsin valley fill about 100 feet thick at 10:00 across river. Site of gold placer operations.

.8

20.6 Straight ahead is well exposed gravel-filled pre-Wisconsin channel of the San Miguel River. The adit cut in red beds of the Cutler is at the base of the channel.

.7

21.3 Road crosses normal fault of at least 100 feet displacement. Fault trace is visible at 11:00 along valley wall across river. The Salt Wash Member of the Morrison has been dropped down along the north side of this west-trending fault against the Dolores Formation on the south. Here along the valley wall the throw is about 200 feet. This fault lies slightly en echelon to the Black King fault, which dies out about three-quarters of a mile east of this point. The fault system is continuous westward to a point a few miles south of Norwood, roughly paralleling the road. West of this point the Cutler Formation, also downthrown by the fault, is not exposed, and it is not seen again along the San Miguel River until below Uravan.

.6

21.9 Opposite mouth of Saltado Creek. Conspicuous white bed on both sides of the river is the Entrada Sandstone. The red sandstone cliff below it is formed by the Wingate Sandstone equivalent, in the Dolores Formation. Poorly exposed Bilk Creek Sandstone Member of the Wanaka Formation overlies the Entrada, and is in turn overlain by the "Marl" Member of the Wanaka Formation (Summerville Formation of western Colorado) which forms the talus-covered and tree-bearing slope. The Salt Wash Member of the Morrison makes prominent cliffs for several miles to the west. It has a higher sandstone content here than in most of south-western Colorado, and does not form the three or four discrete ledges

common to the west and southwest. The Brushy Basin Member of the Morrison is exposed just west of the mouth of Saltado Creek, with a very heavy sandstone ledge in its upper part. This sandstone, believed to be the Burro Canyon (Lower Cretaceous), underlies the Dakota, and is only locally present. Dakota Sandstone forms the rim of the canyon on the skyline.

2.0

23.9 Contact between Entrada and Bilk Creek Sandstones is about 10 feet above road at bend in road.

.2

24.1 Road crosses upper contact of Entrada Sandstone.

.3

24.4 Milepost 94.

.3

24.7 Northwest-southeast trending fault on right, down side is to the road.

.4

25.1 San Miguel ranch resort at left.

.2

25.3 Goodenough Gulch and road to Iron Springs Mesa on right.

.3

25.6 Mouth of Beaver Creek at left. Salt Wash cliffs on both sides of Canyon. Well exposed section of Salt Wash, Brushy Basin and Dakota ahead.

.3

25.9 Dakota on skyline ahead.

.6

26.5 Road crosses San Miguel River at foot of Norwood Hill. Climb hill in Morrison, excellent exposures of Summerville and Morrison in canyon to right.

.8

27.3 Salt Wash-Brushy Basin contact in roadcut to left.

.7

28.0 Base of Burro Canyon Formation, massive light-gray conglomeratic sandstone overlain by thin sandstones interbedded with gray and green mudstone.

.1

28.1 Lens of coal in Dakota. Base of Dakota is just below the lens, which nearly channels out the basal Dakota ledge at this point. The basal ledge is present a little farther west. Down stream the San Miguel River cuts along the flank of a broad anticline. In the distance is the Uncompahgre Plateau.

.2

28.3 Bank of wind-blown sand along right side of road, characteristic clastic deposit on mesa tops in southwestern Colorado.

.4

28.7 Top of Norwood Hill. Flat plain between here and Norwood is developed on top of Dakota Sandstone.

.3

29.0 From this spot the following topographic features are visible:

6:30 — Last Dollar Range

7:30-8:30 — Sunshine Mountain; the Mount Wilson group, Little Cone, The Dolores Peaks

9:00 — Groundhog Mountain; Lone Cone, capped by a thick sill or laccolith

11:30 — east-dipping beds on the east limb of the Gypsum Valley anticline

12:30 — west-dipping strata on the west limb of the Paradox Valley anticline

1:00 — Laccolithic La Sal Mountains in the far distance, east-dipping strata on the east limb of the Paradox Valley anticline in the near distance

2:00 — low-lying hills are part of the Uncompahgre Plateau

.9

29.9 Junction with road to Dolores.

.4

30.3 Uncompahgre Uplift at 3:00 on sky line.

1.0

31.3 La Sal Mountains at 1:00. Entering Norwood, elevation 7014′.

.2

31.5 Post Office in Norwood. Road for next fifteen miles is on Quaternary alluvium overlying Dakota Sandstone in most places.

1.6

33.1 La Sal Mountains on sky line at 12:00.

.9

34.0 Montrose County.

2.1

36.1 North and south dips off Paradox Valley structure seen ahead.

1.1

37.2 Dakota in low hill on right.

.7

37.9 Uncompahgre Plateau on sky line ahead.

2.2

40.1 Redvale.

1.8

41.9 View of southeast end of Paradox Valley, collapsed salt anticline, at 12:00. Escarpment on northeast flank is capped by Burro Canyon Formation of Early Cretaceous age.

.4

42.3 San Miguel syncline, the structural depression between the Paradox Valley anticline and the Uncompahgre Plateau, is visible, trending northwest at 12:00.

3.6

45.9 Dakota-Mancos contact.

.8

46.7 Thin coal beds in Dakota exposed in roadcut on right.

.2

46.9 Contact between Dakota and Burro Canyon exposed in roadcut on right. Contact is between 10-foot conglomeratic sandstone and underlying light-green mudstone.

.6

47.5 Junction with Colorado 80 to Gypsum Valley, Slick Rock and Dove Creek.

.4

47.9 Dakota-Burro Canyon contact in roadcut on right.

.2

48.1 Junction with Colorado 90 (to right) to Montrose. Road crosses the Uncompahgre.

.1

48.2 Dakota Sandstone in road cut.

.4

48.6 Dakota-Burro Canyon contact in roadcut on right.

.9

49.5 Contact between Burro Canyon Formation and underlying Brushy Basin Member of Morrison Formation at base of massive conglomeratic sandstone ledge at right.

.5

50.0 Cross Naturita Creek.

    1.2

51.2 Naturita.

    .3

51.5 Junction with Colorado 97, continue straight.

    1.6

53.1 At 2:00 Dakota Sandstone crops out as small ledges near top of hill. Burro Canyon Formation is thicker cliff below.

    .7

53.8 Cross Dry Creek. San Miguel River on right.

    .2

54.0 Road junction, Colorado State Highway 90. Turn left.

    .5

54.5 Burro Canyon — Morrison (Jurassic) contact.

    1.0

55.5 Note fault and rollover in Morrison. This results from salt flowage and/or solution collapse.

    .8

56.3 Dakota-Burro Canyon contact. Entering southeast end of Paradox Valley.

    .8

57.1 Note anticlinal rollover at 8:00 on southwest flank of valley. This is known as the Dry Creek anticline or sometimes Montrose dome, and is associated with salt flowage in the underlying Paradox salt. The Kirby No. 1 Dyer well was drilled on this feature in 1957-58 and was completed for 630 MCFGPD from sandstones in the upper Honaker Trail and lower Cutler Formations. The well produced a small amount of gas and was abandoned in 1964. Four other tests drilled in the vicinity in 1967-69 were dry holes.

    1.8

58.9 Swath on hillside at 9:00 is 6 inch Pacific Northwest pipeline from Naturita-Uravan area.

    .9

59.8 Wingate and Chinle Formations (Triassic) outcrop on right. La Sal Mountains at 1:00. Note numerous uranium mines in Salt Wash Member of the Morrison Formation (Jurassic) at 10-11:00.

    3.6

63.4 A few hundred yards to right is location of the American Liberty No. 1, a dry hole drilled in 1948-51. This well bottomed in salt at 10,846'.

Paradox Valley is the largest of the salt anticlines of the Paradox basin. The valley is underlain by a thick salt core that flowed into its present position from the flanking synclines. The thick section of post-salt Pennsylvanian rocks in the Nucla or San Miguel syncline on the northeast suggests salt flowage from that flank in Pennsylvanian time. A thick section of Permian Cutler Formation in the southwest flanking syncline suggests that the salt flowed from that flank during Permian time. Well data indicate the salt under Paradox Valley to be at least 14,000 feet thick.

    1.7

65.1 Stratigraphic section seen on northeast flank is as follows:
Permian — Cutler (this is exposed further up the valley);
Triassic — Moenkopi, Chinle, Wingate and Kayenta;
Jurassic — Entrada, Summerville and Morrison;
Cretaceous — Burro Canyon.
There are many faults paralleling cliffs due to solution collapse in the salt. Note Entrada Sandstone being cut out by faulting along cliffs at 1-2:00. Low gray hills in valley are leached Paradox outcrops (Penn.).

    2.8

67.9 Cutler exposed in gully to right.

    1.3

69.2 Low hills at 2:00 in foreground are leached Paradox. Chinle-Moenkopi contact on far hill is at color break between light red Chinle and darker Moenkopi. Moenkopi-Cutler contact where Dolores River cuts through cliff is at top of purplish beds.

    2.3

71.5 Intersection with County Road Y11 to right. Turn right and park, road continues through valley and up San Miguel River to Uravan. **STOP 1.** Discussion of Salt Anticline structure and tectonics.

    1.4

72.9 Dolores River bridge. Note pinchout of Navajo Sandstone (Triassic) on walls of canyon up Dolores River.

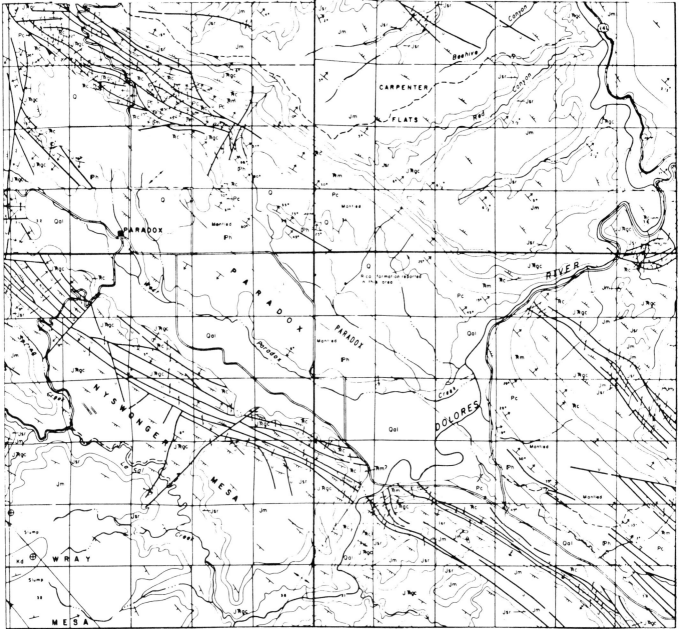

Figure 19. Photogeology west end of Paradox Valley. (Courtesy Texas Instruments)

.3

73.2 Bedrock (look fast so you don't miss it), home of the Flintstones.

.9

74.1 About 1½ miles to right in valley, the Continental Oil Co. Scorup No. 1 well, drilled in 1958, penetrated the base of salt at 14,670 feet and bottomed in the Mississippian Leadville Limestone at 15,000 feet. This is the thickest well penetration of salt in the basin.

About 3 miles to the south in the Dolores River Canyon on the southwest flank, The Union Oil Ayers No. 1-0-30, drilled in 1970-71, encountered only about 800 feet of salt, and bottomed in the Ouray Limestone at 14,400 feet.

About 5 miles southwest of the Continental well, the Shell Oil Co. Wray Mesa No. 1 well, drilled in 1960-61, went directly from Upper Hermosa (Honaker Trail) into the Devonian Elbert Formation, the salt section is completely missing. About 6,000 feet of structural relief on the subsalt formations is indicated between the two wells. A large paleo-fault probably parallels the southwest flank of Paradox Valley.

1.2

75.3 At 1:00, note rollover and fault near end of

valley: Wingate against Morrison. This feature is associated with solution collapse and/or salt flowage.

3.4

78.7 Note faulted mess in Wingate-Kayenta section as flank of salt structure is traversed.

1.5

80.2 **STOP 2.** Overlook of Paradox Valley.

1.0

81.2 Wingate-Chinle contact on right. Note eolian cross-bedding in Wingate. View of Paradox Valley. In far distance to northeast is Uncompahgre Uplift where top of Precambrian can be seen with binoculars. Slope-forming Chinle overlies granitic basement. Burro Canyon is exposed on top. Structural relief on subsalt strata between Continental well in Paradox Valley and Shell Wray Mesa No. 1 well on southwest flank is about 6,000 feet.

.7

81.9 Kayenta-Wingate contact. Navajo Sandstone above.

.7

82.6 Note red to green color change in Kayenta shale.

.1

82.7 Navajo-Kayenta contact above road.

1.1

83.8 Canyon walls of La Sal Creek are: Wingate at very bottom downstream, Kayenta and Navajo (Triassic); (Jurassic) Dewey Bridge Member of Entrada, Entrada, Summerville and Salt Wash Member of Morrison. Note thickness of Navajo compared with zero thickness on immediate flank of Paradox salt anticline.

1.3

85.1 Navajo Sandstone.

3.1

88.2 Colorado-Utah State line.

1.9

90.1 Top Navajo. Note uranium mines in Morrison Formation.

2.2

92.3 Entering "Pine Ridge" Valley. This valley is underlain at depth by a salt anticline which has been relatively inactive since Moenkopi (Triassic) time. The Tenneco Redd Ranch No. 1 well penetrated a normal Mesozoic section and then went into a pre-Moenkopi leached zone and about 9,000 feet of salt. The well bottomed in Mississippian at 12,572 feet. Tidewater drilled a dry Mississippian test about 1½ miles southwest of Tenneco and penetrated almost 6,000 feet of Cutler and only 150 feet of salt. The top of the Mississippian is about 300 feet high to the Tenneco well.

2.6

94.9 La Sal Mountains at 2:00. Mt. Peale is highest mountain in group at 12,721'. Tenneco well site is at 9:00 on side of hill.

2.4

97.3 Highway department road material stockpile area. Enter. **STOP 3.** Lunch. Discussion of evaporites.

.2

97.5 Top of rise. Abajo Mountains at 12:00.

1.8

99.3 Dips ahead are off Lisbon Valley salt anticline.

1.5

100.8 La Sal.

1.3

102.1 Northeast flank of Lisbon anticline is at 9:00. At 11:00, in far distance, are the Henry Mountains (Tertiary stocks). At 10:30 on far skyline is the Monument Uplift. Also seen on far sky line at 9:00 are Abajo Mtns.

1.4

103.5 Road junction to Lisbon Valley. Turn left.

.5

104.0 Straight ahead to Lisbon Valley. Rattlesnake open pit uranium mine in the distance on the right. Ore is in the Salt Wash Member of the Morrison.

1.7

105.7 Stay on paved road. Abajo Mountains at 2:00.

.9

106.6 Junction to Atlas Minerals Big Indian mine to the right. Stay left. Rio Alyom Lisbon Valley mine to the left. Ore is at about 2,600 feet in the Moss Back Member of the Chinle Formation. Cliff-maker on right is Wingate.

.1

106.7 Road is along the Lisbon Valley fault. Cretaceous rocks are exposed in the down-thrown block on the left, the Chinle on the up-thrown block to the right.

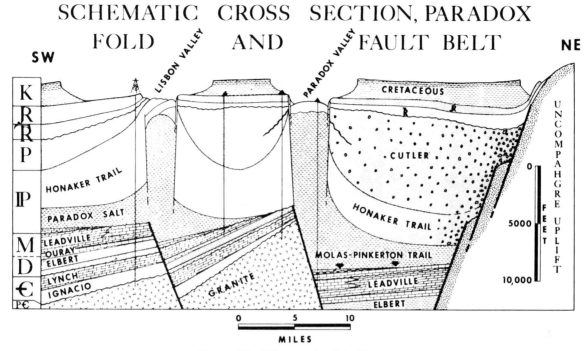

SCHEMATIC CROSS SECTION, PARADOX
FOLD AND FAULT BELT

Figure 20. (Diagram by D.L. Baars)

107.0 .3 Road to left leads to Rio Alyom Lisbon Valley mine.

107.6 .6 Home Stake's Alice mine on right. Uranium ore is in the Moss Back Member of the Chinle. Stay on pavement.

108.5 .9 Open-pit copper mine produces azurite, malachite, etc. from fault zone. The mine is presently controlled by Atlas Minerals.

108.6 .1 Road to left leads to Ranchers Small Fry mine. Straight ahead.

108.7 .1 Copper processing plant was located on the left, operated by Keystone-Wallace. Outcrop of Cutler Formation on the right. During World War II operators of the Big Indian mine attempted to develop a process for flotation of oxidized copper at this mill. Copper ores (malachite and azurite) are in the sandstones and conglomerates of the Dakota-Burro Canyon Formations. Mineralized material is associated with the Lisbon Valley fault which is exposed just in front of old mill. Here the Cutler red beds (on west side) are against the Dakota-Burro Canyon rocks (on the east). The dip of the fault plane varies from 54° to 85° to the northeast.

109.2 .5 Turn left onto dirt road. This road leads down the center of Lisbon Valley along the Lisbon Valley fault.

109.7 .5 **STOP 4.** Discussion of Lisbon Valley structure, oil field, and uranium deposits.

110.2 .5 Return to pavement and turn left on Big Indian Wash road. Cretaceous rocks exposed in hill to left. Road to right in Cutler Formation. View ahead of southwest flank of Lisbon Valley salt anticline.

111.7 1.5 Tree-covered slope on left is dip slope of Upper Pennsylvanian Honaker Trail Formation. The Cutler Formation is in the valley floor (traversed by highway). The bleached zone on the right is in the Moss Back Member; there is no Moenkopi present here.

112.7 1.0 Dirt road to the right goes to the Big Buck mine which produces ore from the upper part of the Cutler Formation. This is one of the oldest mines in the district. Straight ahead.

113.4 .7 The Mi Vida mine is over the ridge to the right. The bleached beds are in the Moss

Back Member of the Chinle. Mines on this side of the ridge open in the Culter, but are operated in the Moss Back.

.6

114.0   Dirt road to right goes to mine that opens in the Cutler, but produces from the Moss Back Member. Prominent massive light-colored sandstone halfway up the slope is an eolian sand at the top of the Cutler Formation. It is cut out up-dip by an angular unconformity between the Cutler and the Chinle Formations. Light-colored thin sandstones near the top of the Cutler are marine.

.2

114.2   Gas and oil wells at this location are part of the Lisbon Valley field. The field was discovered in 1960, with the completion of the Pure Oil Company NW Lisbon No. 1 in the McCracken Sandstone (Devonian) for 587 BOPD after testing condensate and gas from the Redwall Limestone (Mississippian). Subsequent development down the flanks of the structure indicated that the major reserves were in the Redwall. The field is a retrograde condensate field and the structurally highest wells are used as gas injection wells. There are 23 producible wells, but normally only about ten are producing. Production has been averaging about 2,500 BO, 55,000 MCFG and 4,500 BW per day. Cumulative production to date is approaching 43 million barrels of 50° API oil. The oil is piped to Aneth station, about 60 miles south; the gas recycling plant is at the south end of the field. The trap is a complexly faulted anticline or horst(?) (no surface expression) with vertical closure of about 1,600 feet. The reservoir appears to be filled to the spill point and is a dolomitized and leached crinoidal mud bank in the Redwall.

.6

114.8   Dirt road to right goes to Spillar Canyon mine in the Cutler Formation. Little Valley at 12:00 is floored by the Cutler Formation.

.8

115.6   Big Indian monolith ahead is capped by Wingate Sandstone.

1.0

116.6   Road swings back to the west and cuts through Wingate capped by Kayenta.

.5

117.1   Top of Wingate Sandstone at cattle guard.

.5

117.6   Oil tanks on right. Buttes formed in Navajo Sandstone.

.3

117.9   Plateau to the left capped by Dakota-Burro Canyon Sandstones, overlying Morrison Formation, with uranium mines in the Salt Wash Member, then the Summerville and Entrada Formations with the Navajo Sandstone at the base.

.1

118.0   Road about on top of Navajo Formation with overlying Entrada forming rounded hills.

.5

118.5   Road junction, *turn right*. Road leads past Union Oil Companies processing plant seen ahead. Road for next 3 miles is mostly on Navajo Sandstone and aeolian sand, Carmel is very sandy here and is called Dewey Bridge Member of the Entrada Formation, it is difficult to pick in the sand covered flats.

1.3

119.8   Crossing Big Indian Wash.

.3

120.1   Union plant seen to right. Deer Neck Mesa to east.

1.6

121.7   Road intersection. **STOP 5.** Stop here for view of Lisbon oil field. Road to right leads to Mi Vida mine and other producing properties discovered by Charlie Steen. Turn left (west) to continue to Moab.

.2

121.9   Road crosses Dewey Bridge (Carmel)-Navajo contact.

.2

122.1   Casa Colorado Rock at 11:00 is Entrada capped by basal Morrison.

2.7

124.8   Road crosses Dewey Bridge-Navajo contact.

1.5

126.3   Low knobs of Navajo to left and right of road are capped by Dewey Bridge.

.5

126.8   Intersection Highway 163, turn right to Moab.

1.3

128.1 Entrada-Navajo contact in roadcut.

.4

128.5 Hook and Ladder Gulch to right.

.9

129.4 At left is the Coyote Wash syncline which separates the Hart Point terrace from the Hudson Wash anticline. To right is a view of the southwest flank of the Lisbon Valley anticline.

.6

130.0 Entrada bluffs at right.

.4

130.4 Dewey Bridge Member of Entrada in roadcut.

.1

130.5 Dewey Bridge-Navajo contact at left.

1.4

131.9 Slickrock-Dewey Bridge contact at right.

.3

132.2 Wilson Arch in the Slickrock Member of the Entrada Sandstone ahead.

1.1

133.3 White Entrada Sandstone capped by Morrison at left.

.9

134.2 Road to Looking Glass Rock on the left.

.8

135.0 La Sal junction.

.5

135.5 Crossing Coyote Wash.

.3

135.8 Salt Wash Member of Morrison, to right, is mined for uranium at the San Juan and Junction mines. North plunge of Lisbon Valley anticline to right.

1.1

136.9 Pacific Northwest pump station. Axis of Hudson Wash anticline to left. Entrada bluffs at right.

.7

137.6 View of La Sal Mountains at 2:00. At 12:00 in distance, note fractured Navajo outcrops on southwest flank of Spanish Valley salt anticline. Road follows along Carmel or Dewey Bridge Member of Entrada (take your pick) for next few miles. Contorted bedding is common in Carmel in this general area.

.8

138.4 Highway is on top of Navajo dip slope.

.3

138.7 Crossing wash.

.5

139.2 Crossing Navajo-Dewey Bridge contact, Entrada cliffs at right.

.4

139.6 Dewey Bridge-Navajo dip slope on left forms the northwest flank of the Hudson Wash anticline.

.4

140.0 Highway is on Dewey Bridge dip slope.

.5

140.5 Cross-bedding in Navajo at right.

.5

141.0 On left is Dewey Bridge-Navajo contact.

.9

141.9 Hole in the Rock. Man-made home, carved in Entrada Sandstone.

.1

142.0 Note axis of Kings Bottom syncline in Entrada. Massive cliffs are the Slickrock Member. Kane Springs Roadside Park at right.

.6

142.6 Crossing fault. Massive Entrada Sandstone in bottom of gully at right. Entrada-Morrison contact beyond fault at left. (Note apparent reverse drag.)

Roadcut on left exposes red beds overlying Entrada Sandstone. These red beds, which contain irregular masses of chert, have long been considered to be Summerville Formation (lower Summerville of McKnight). However, recent work by O'Sullivan has shown that the regional J-5 unconformity, which is above the Summerville, has truncated the Summerville in the Moab-La Sal Junction area. The red beds in this area are above the J-5 unconformity, and therefore must be younger than Summerville, O'Sullivan includes them in the Morrison Formation. This interpretation, however, has not been completely accepted by all the geologists familiar with this area.

.6

143.2 Small fault at 9:00.

1.1

144.3 Note fractured Navajo Sandstone (Triassic) on hill at 9:00.

.2

144.5 Salt Wash Member of Morrison Formation.

.4

144.9 Road cuts across numerous faults in Morrison collapse block.

.2

145.1 Approaching Spanish Valley salt anticline. Salt Wash in roadcuts.

1.2

146.3 At 4:00, note rollover into Pack Creek graben, a continuation of the Spanish Valley salt structure. Note pediment surface back toward La Sal Mountains. Mancos Shale is exposed below pediment up Valley.

2.4

148.7 Navajo on right side of valley. Moab Tongue of Entrada is resistant, desert-varnish-covered sandstone bed on sky line. On left side of valley is faulted Wingate and Chinle in lower slope and Wingate, Kayenta and Navajo above. Spanish Valley salt anticline is typically faulted along both flanks due to solution of the salt and collapse of the overlying strata, and also to salt flowage. The white rounded knobs at the base of the slope southwest of Moab are leached Paradox gypsum and black dolomitic shale (Penn.) that was intercalated in the salt section. No wells have penetrated the entire salt section in Spanish Valley proper.

.8

149.5 Pacific Northwest pipeline paralleling road at 9:00.

Figure 21. Moab and Spanish Valley. (photo by D.L. Baars)

1.5

151.0 At 3:00 is a collapse fold in the Moab anticline.

1.4

152.4 Low hills at 9:00 are within the collapse area of the structure.

.7

153.1 Cap rock on scarp at 9:00 is Navajo, beneath is Kayenta and Wingate.

.7

153.8 Entrada outcrops visible behind Navajo rim at 3:00.

1.7

155.5 Road junction; go straight.

1.8

157.3 South traffic signal, Moab, Utah.

THIRD DAY

ROAD LOG FROM MOAB, UTAH TO DURANGO, COLORADO VIA DEAD HORSE POINT, UTAH

September 30, 1981

DRIVING DISTANCE: 222.7 Miles
STARTING TIME: 8:00 A.M.
ASSEMBLY POINT: Assemble at abandoned service station on east side of Main Street at north end of town; La Hacienda Restaurant is just south of assembly point and B.P.O.E. is uphill to right.

TRIP SPEAKERS

D. L. Baars, Robert Norman, Robert Lauth, Nick Thomaidis

SUMMARY

This morning we will travel to Dead Horse Point where we can overlook Canyonlands National Park, Cane Creek anticline, the Texasgulf potash plant, and view some interesting Permian stratigraphy. From Dead Horse Point we will return to Durango by way of Monticello, Utah and Cortez, Colorado.

ROAD LOG: Road log taken from: Rocky Mountain Assoc. of Geologists, Road Logs of Colo., 1960; Four Corners Geological Society, 8th Field Conf., 1975 and 9th Field Conf., 1979. Log compiled by Donald L. Baars and Dennis Irwin.

Cumulative
Mileage

Road log starts at intersection of U.S. Highway 163 and Utah State Highway 128. This is 2 miles north of assembly point.

Continue north across Colorado River on U.S. 163.

.3

.3   Wingate-Chinle (Triassic) contact in roadcut.

.5

.8   At 12:00, strata on hillside above railroad are Virgil portion of Honaker Trail Formation (Penn.). The uranium processing plant of Atlas Minerals on the left. This plant, with a capacity of 1,000 tons per day, uses carbonate leaching and ion exchange. A vanadium circuit is also present. Ore supply comes from the Lisbon Valley, La Sal, Cane Creek, Dry Valley, White Canyon, and Green River areas.

.8

1.6   Road junction. Stay Right. Road to left follows the river to Texasgulf Inc. potash mine on the Cane Creek anticline.

.1

1.7   At 12:00, are Navajo Sandstone (Triassic?) and Entrada Sandstone (Jurassic). Note contorted bedding in the lower red Dewey Bridge Member of the Entrada.

1.3

3.0   Crossing Moab fault, a high-angle normal fault caused by salt flowage. The Entrada Sandstone is in fault contact with the upper part of the Honaker Trail Formation. Stratigraphic throw is about 2,000 feet.

.2

3.2   The section exposed here is the base of the Cutler Formation (Permian) and top 400 feet of the Honaker Trail Formation. Virgilian fusulinids were collected in one of the upper limestone beds. The total Honaker Trail in this area is about 1,900 feet thick. Note the cyclic nature of the Honaker Trail and the various sedimentary features. Note truncation of the Cutler by the Moenkopi (Triassic) on hillside across the road.

.1

3.3 Highway parallels Moab fault. Well location at wide spot on right ahead is Delhi Taylor No. 2 which was a potash stratigraphic test. This well went into salt at 2,340 feet and bottomed near the base of salt at 9,424 feet. Delhi-Taylor has drilled about 10 potash tests in this area (known as the Seven mile anticline). The other wells went only a short way into the salt section. This structure is presently classed as a potash reserve.

1.7

5.0 Moenkopi-Cutler contact on left is at color break between brighter red Cutler and red-brown Moenkopi. The Cutler Formation is generally thought of as an arkosic wedge of fluvial origin coming off the ancestral Uncompahgre uplift. However, in this area and west, many of the fluvial deposits have been locally reworked by eolian processes resulting in much interbedding of fine-grained eolian sands between the fluvial deposits. Most of the brighter red, more massive sandstone beds seen here are eolian sandstones with dominant cross-bedding dips to the southeast. The purplish-red, coarser, poorly sorted arkosic beds are fluvial sandstones in which the dominant cross-bedding dips are to the southwest.

2.3

7.3 At 1:00, green hillside in distance is green shale of the Brushy Basin Member of the Morrison Formation (Jurassic). At 11:30 is fault contact (Moab fault) between Chinle on left and Brushy Basin on right, a stratigraphic throw of about 2,000 feet.

1.1

8.4 Bridge. At 3:00 exhumed sandstone channel in Salt Wash Member of Morrison. Current direction was easterly.

.3

8.7 Road junction. Dead Horse Point road. Turn left.

.3

9.0 At 1:00 the basal sandstone of the Chinle Formation is exposed near the base of a green shale where a uranium road has been cut. Uranium is being mined in this area from lenses of carbonaceous sandstone and mudstone pebble

conglomerate in the basal Chinle Formation. The Moss Back Member of the Chinle, which is the host rock for many deposits to the south, is not recognized here. The Moenkopi-Cutler contact is at the top of bright red, massive sandstone bed.

1.3

10.3 At 8-10:00, note thinning of Chinle strata in uppermost part above prominent sandstone bed and below Wingate.

.7

11.0 Wingate-Chinle contact. Note large-scale eolian crossbeds in Wingate.

1.1

12.1 Kayenta-Wingate contact.

.9

13.0 Navajo-Kayenta contact. View of section from Wingate Sandstone (Triassic) up to Salt Wash Member of Morrison Formation (Jurassic). Note Moab Tongue intertonguing with Summerville; to the east it merges with the Entrada and to the west it pinches out a short distance west of the Green River.

1.7

14.7 At 4:30, note lenticular sandstone bar (?) "buildup" in Dewey Bridge Member of the Entrada.

.4

15.1 Note contorted bedding in Dewey Bridge Member in cliffs at right.

1.6

16.7 In distance to north are the Book Cliffs which are made up of Mesaverde Group (Upper Cretaceous) sediments dipping north into the Uinta Basin.

1.1

17.8 At 3:00 in far distance is the San Rafael Swell. Navajo Sandstone hogbacks can be seen on the steep, east flank of the uplift.

1.3

19.1 Pure Big Flat Unit No. 5 (Bartlett Flat field) on left. This well was completed for 450 BOPD from the Cane Creek marker, *a "clastic" break within the salt section*. This unit averages 50 to 100 feet in thickness and consists of interbedded black shale, dense dolomitic shale and anhydrite. Where productive, it is probably a fractured reservoir. Total production from this well between 1962

Figure 22. Shafer dome, view to south of Dead Horse Point. (photo by J.H. Rathbone)

Figure 23. Cane Creek anticline and La Sal Mountains from Dead Horse Point. (photo by J.H. Rathbone)

and 1965 was approximately 49,000 barrels of 43° gravity oil. This well has been abandoned or shut-in because of collapsed casing and a decline in production rate. A 330-foot easterly offset was a dry hole. The top of the salt in the No. 5 well is at 4,230 feet; the base salt is at 7,288 feet. A subcommercial amount of oil was recovered from the Mississippian.

A few other wells in this general area have encountered production in the Cane Creek marker but in most cases, production rates declined rapidly after high initial production rates. One exception is the Southern Natural Gas Company Long Canyon No. 1 which has produced almost 800,000 barrels of oil since 1962. A one-half mile offset was dry in the Cane Creek marker.

1.5

20.6   Roadcuts are in Kayenta.

.6

21.2   At 2:00, in far distance are the Henry Mountains, which are Tertiary stocks and laccoliths.

1.2

22.4   Road junction. Turn left. Small hill on left is Navajo Sandstone.

.7

23.1   La Sal Mountains at 12:00. Abajo Mountains at 2:00 and Monument Uplift at 2:30. About a mile to the right is the Big Flat field, a small Mississippian oil field. The discovery was made by Pure Oil Company in 1957. Three wells were productive but the casing collapsed in 2 of the wells within a few years of their completion. High pour point oil and an inert gas cap, which created producing problems, also contributed to economic difficulties. In 1971 the Big Flat Unit was finally terminated with a total cumulative production of 83,469 BO; 52,395 MCFG and 41,950 BW. At the surface, Big Flat is a broad dome with about 200 feet of closure; however, at the Mississippian level, it is completely faulted.

1.1

24.2   Road juction. Turn right.

4.9

29.1   Dead Horse Point Visitor Center.

1.5

30.6   **STOP 1.** Walk out to rim for spectacular

view overlooking the Colorado River and Canyonlands National Park to the southwest. Vertical drop to river is about 2,000 feet. The section exposed is from Kayenta-Wingate, on top, to Honaker Trail in the river gorge to the left. Prominent bench below is a Permian limestone bed locally known as the "Shafer Limestone". It pinches out a short distance to the east.

Note pinchout of White Rim Sandstone at top of Permian section on canyon walls to right. This unit forms the prominent rim of the intermediate bench around the mesa to the southwest. It is a beach-dune complex(?) with common large-scale, festoon cross-bedding separated by zones with planar bedding. It thickens rapidly westward where it eventually intertongues with the Toroweap and lower part of the Kaibab Formations. The White Rim Sandstone is stained or saturated with tarry oil over a large area a few miles west of the confluence of the Green and Colorado Rivers, this is the Elaterite Basin deposit.

Shafer dome, which is to the left front, is a small salt structure. The Texasgulf Inc. potash mining operation constructed the obvious evaporation pans on the west flank of the Cane Creek anticline for the precipitation of salts from brine wells in the anticline.

Turn around, retrace route to Moab.

33.5

64.1   South traffic signal, Moab, Utah. Driving south along fault that forms west side of Moab anticline. Rounded orange sandstone knobs of Navajo lie on rubble from Kayenta Formation. Chinle-Moss Back-Cutler beds form the lower two-thirds of the cliffs and are somewhat mantled by rubble. White, rounded hills at base are Paradox gypsum which flowed up near the fault.

Rounded light orange Navajo Sandstone bluffs on left represent the east flank of the Moab anticline. The rubbly beds seen in front of the Navajo bluffs are within the collapsed part of the structure.

La Sal Mountains at 10:00-12:00.

1.8

65.9   Road junction; go straight.

1.0

66.9 At 1:00-4:00 are slump blocks of Wingate and Kayenta and older beds on the collapse side of the fault zone.

.7

67.6 At 9:00 are Entrada outcrops visible behind the Navajo rim.

.7

68.3 At 3:00 the cap rock on the scarp is now Navajo, beneath is the Kayenta and Wingate.

.7

69.0 Low hills at 3:00 are within the collapse area of the structure.

1.4

70.4 At 9:00 is a collapse fold in the Moab anticline. At 12:00 Mancos Shale slopes may be seen in the background.

1.5

71.9 At 3:00 is the Pacific Northwest pipeline paralleling the road.

3.0

74.9 Morrison beds within Moab anticline at 11:00. South Mountain at 11:00; North Mountain at 9:00; Pleistocene gravel terrain low at 8:00-10:00.

.4

75.3 Mancos beds in notch at 10:30.

.5

75.8 At 2:00 is part of the associated collapse on the southwest edge of the Moab anticline. The Morrison on the left is faulted against the Kayenta-Wingate on the right.

.7

76.5 Road or highway cuts across numerous faults in the Morrison collapse block.

.4

76.9 Salt Wash Member of the Morrison Formation in normal position.

.2

77.1 Pacific Northwest gas line at 12:00 cutting through Morrison.

.8

77.9 Inactive Lookout uranium mine at 2:00 in the Salt Wash Member of the Morrison Formation. This is one of the many small mines in the Moab mining area.

.7

78.6 Fault at 11:00.

.2

78.8 Crossing fault. Massive Entrada Sandstone in bottom of gully at left.

Entrada-Morrison contact beyond fault at right. (Note apparent reverse drag.)

.6

79.4 Kane Springs Roadside Park at left. Massive cliffs are the Slickrock Member of the Entrada Sandstone.

.2

79.6 Slickrock-Dewey Bridge contact. You are now in King's Bottom syncline. The red beds ahead are Dewey Bridge with massive Navajo Sandstone below.

.5

80.1 Slickrock-Dewey Bridge-Navajo at 12:00.

.3

80.4 At left is Dewey Bridge-Navajo contact.

.5

80.9 Cross-bedding in Navajo at right.

.2

81.1 Contorted Dewey Bridge bedding at 11:00.

.3

81.4 Highway is on Dewey Bridge dip slope.

.4

81.8 Dewey Bridge-Navajo dip slope on right forms the northwest flank of the Hudson Wash anticline.

.4

82.2 Crossing Navajo-Dewey Bridge contact, Entrada cliffs at left.

.5

82.7 Crossing wash.

.3

83.0 Highway is on top of Navajo dip slope.

.8

83.8 View of La Sal Mountains at 8:00.

.7

84.5 Pacific Northwest pump station. Axis of Hudson Wash anticline to the right. Entrada bluffs at left.

1.1

85.6 The north plunge of the Lisbon Valley anticline at 9:30 with the King's Bottom syncline at the left.

Note numerous drill roads at the San Juan and Junction uranium mines. Ore here comes from the Salt Wash Member of the Morrison Formation seen to the left. This is part of the Brown's Hole locality of the Moab mining area.

.3

85.9 Crossing Coyote Wash.

.5

86.4 La Sal junction; go straight. White cliffs of Entrada Sandstone ahead.

.8

87.2 Road to Looking Glass Rock on the right.

.9

88.1 White Entrada Sandstone capped by Morrison at right.

1.1

89.2 Wilson arch in the Slickrock Member of the Entrada Sandstone ahead.

.3

89.5 Slickrock-Dewey Bridge contact at right.

.2

89.7 Abajo Mountains ahead.

.6

90.3 Entrada Sandstone overlain by thin Summerville and basal Morrison at 1:00. At 2:00 the green dip slope is the top of the Navajo.

.6

90.9 Dewey Bridge-Navajo contact at left.

.1

91.0 Dewey Bridge in roadcut.

.4

91.4 Entrada bluffs at left.

.6

92.0 At right is the Coyote Wash syncline which separates the Hart Point terrace from the Hudson Wash anticline.

To the left is a view of the southwest flank of the Lisbon Valley anticline.

.2

92.2 Dewey Bridge-Navajo contact at 2:00.

.5

92.7 Plateau on sky line at 9:00-10:00 capped by Dakota.

.6

93.3 Entrada-Navajo contact in roadcut.

.7

94.0 Abajo Mountains ahead.

.9

94.9 Crossing Hatch Wash.

.4

95.3 Navajo cross-bedding and Entrada-Navajo contact.

.8

96.1 Top of Navajo.

.4

96.5 Southwest flank of Lisbon Valley

anticline at 9:00. Entrada Sandstone capped by Morrison forms surface at 1:00-3:00.

.6

97.1 Road to Anticline Overlook, Canyonlands National Park to right.

.5

97.6 Mesa at 10:00 is capped by Dakota Sandstone which overlies sequentially downward the Burro Canyon, Morrison, Summerville and Entrada formations. Uranium is produced from the Salt Wash Member of the Morrison here in the Dry Valley mining area. Southwest flank of the Lisbon Valley anticline visible at 7:00-9:00 in the Wingate Sandstone. Storage tanks of the Lisbon Valley oil field visible at 9:00. The Lisbon Valley uranium mining area is located just east of the Wingate escarpment.

5.2

102.8 At 11:00 is Church Rock, an outlier of Entrada Sandstone. It is capped by the Moab Tongue which overlies the Slickrock Member with the Dewey Bridge Member at the base.

At 12:00 the sky line is capped by Dakota, the slopes are Morrison, and the base is Entrada.

1.2

104.0 Road to right leads to Indian Creek State Park and Canyonlands National Park. Continue straight.

1.4

105.4 Entrada forms low cliffs to right and left. Sky line capped by Dakota-Burro Canyon sandstones.

1.6

107.0 Crossing small fault, trace seen at 3:00.

.4

107.4 Top of Entrada Sandstone; overlying redbeds are Summerville Formation. Road begins ascent through the Morrison Formation.

3.4

110.8 Dakota-Burro Canyon cliffs on both sides.

1.5

112.3 Road is on the approximate top of the Dakota. The Abajo Mountains to the right are Tertiary igneous intrusives.

4.2

116.5 Lone Cone and the Wilson Peaks at 8:30,

San Juan Mountains at 9:00, La Plata Mountains at 10:00, Ute Mountains at 11:00.

1.3

117.8   Enter Monticello.

.6

118.4   Intersection Highways 163 and 666. County Library on left. **STOP 2.** We will stop for lunch at the park area east (behind) of the library.

Continue east on 666 after lunch.

.7

119.1   Highway on approximate top of Dakota. Lone Cone at 12:00.

2.3

121.4   Red color of fields is from red dust that some geologists have titled the Dove Creek loess. Dust came from red beds exposed to south in Monument Valley and/or from the north in Canyonlands area.

.4

121.8   Dakota exposed in stream with Morrison at base.

4.7

126.5   Weathered Mancos Shale at 9:00.

1.3

127.8   Weathered Mancos in roadcut.

2.3

130.1   Road to Eastland.

.5

130.6   Mancos in roadcut.

2.5

133.1   Mancos Shale in roadcut.

1.3

134.4   Road to right leads to Ucolo and Summit Point hamlets.

1.3

135.7   Colorado-Utah state line.

.6

136.3   Dakota exposed in stream cut at left.

1.7

138.0   Dakota to left.

1.7

139.7   Ute Mountain, Tertiary laccolith at 1:00. Legend says that one day one of the Gods became angry with the Utes so he put all of the clouds in his pockets and laid down to sleep. The clouds seen around the peaks are those that are escaping from his pockets. One day he will awake, then he will help to drive all the enemies of the Utes away from their lands.

2.3

142.0   Junction Highway 141 to Naturita.

1.5

143.5   Enter Dove Creek, Pinto Bean capitol of the world.

1.0

144.5   Leave Dove Creek, Dakota exposed in creek.

3.9

148.4   Note black shales in Dakota at 9:00.

1.8

150.2   Dip slope to southwest is off Dove Creek anticline, low area is Dove Creek syncline, axial strike is northwest-southeast.

1.0

151.2   Dakota exposed in canyon.

1.0

152.2   Dakota exposure, note black shales.

1.2

153.4   Cahone.

2.2

155.6   La Plata Mountains at 10:00.

.3

155.9   Enter Montezuma County.

2.3

158.2   Dove Creek syncline to west with anticlinal beyond. The Dove Creek anticline is about 18 miles long and plunges to the northwest. The discovery well was completed in 1948 and it has been offset by four dry holes. Total production is less than 90,000 BO & 1 BCFG. Most of the acreage in the field is now part of the Cow Canyon Unit operated by Mobil Oil Corp. for carbon dioxide development from the Mississippian.

1.4

159.6   Pleasant View.

1.6

161.2   Dakota in roadcut.

3.3

164.5   Yellow Jacket.

1.4

165.9   Canyons southwest of highway are tributary to McElmo Canyon and are rimmed with Dakota sandstone.

1.3

167.2 Mancos and Mesaverde on sky line ahead. Dakota to east.

2.6

169.8 Overhead irrigation flume. Road crosses small fault. Dakota in roadcut.

1.8

171.6 Descending south dips of extreme northwest portion of San Juan basin.

.4

172.0 Arriola.

1.9

173.9 Graneros Shale in roadcut.

1.6

175.5 Auto graveyard on left.

2.6

178.1 Dakota at 9:00, notice overlying dark shale.

.8

178.9 Cortez.

.5

179.4 Road intersection, stay left to Durango.

.4

179.8 Left to Durango on Main Street (Highway 160).

2.0

181.8 East city limits of Cortez which is also the eastern end of the McElmo syncline. Most of the topography in this area is held up by the Dakota Sandstone.

1.6

183.4 Fault crosses road at 10:00. Mancos Shale faulted down against Dakota Sandstone in hills north of road. Fault is down to west, about 200' of throw.

1.2

184.6 Coal in Dakota on left.

.5

185.1 McElmo Creek.

.6

185.7 Dakota in roadcut to right.

.4

186.1 Mancos Shale capped by Point Lookout Sandstone at 2:00.

.9

187.0 Outlier of Dakota Sandstone to north.

.9

187.9 Thin limestones in roadcut to left are probably Greenhorn.

1.3

189.2 Mancos Shale dead ahead.

.8

190.0 Entrance to Mesa Verde National Park. Authorized June 29, 1906.

"Type" locality of the Mesaverde from U.S.G.S. Bulletin 896, pages 1355-1356.

"Named by W. H. Holmes in 1877 and divided into (descending) (1) Upper escarpment sandstone (Cliff House) 190' thick; (2) Middle coal (Menefee) consisting of 800-900' of sandstone, shale, marl and lignite; (3) Lower escarpment sandstone (Point Lookout) 120' thick. The group represents a portion of the Cretaceous transgressive-regressive deposition of sediments between underlying Mancos Shale and overlying Lewis Shale."

.3

190.3 Point Lookout gas field to left. About a dozen shallow gas wells have been drilled in this area of which four produced gas from the Dakota. The tourist camp at the top of the hill adjacent to the old entrance to Mesa Verde used gas from these wells. The wells are now almost entirely depleted.

4.2

194.5 At 3:00 at a distance of about 3.5 miles, a Tertiary igneous plug may be seen to the right of the Mancos River valley. It is immediately below the Mesaverde-capped scarp on Weber Mountain.

2.5

197.0 Entering Mancos.

.5

197.5 Turn right to City Park. **STOP 3.** Discussion of Bug Canyon field, "southern shelf" geology and Tertiary-Cretaceous problem.

.5

198.0 Mancos River bridge, leaving Mancos.

The Mancos River valley is the type section for the Mancos Shale from U.S.G.S. Bulletin 896, pages 1276-1277.

"In 1899 W. Cross named the Mancos shale for the occurrence in Mancos Valley. The shale is dark-gray in color and contains non-persistent beds of sandstone and limestone. The thickness varies from 1200-2000'. The Mancos shale grades into the underlying Dakota sandstone and overlying Mesa Verde group."

1.6

199.6 Abandoned saw mill on right. Highway traverses along essentially horizontal Mancos Shale. East fork of Mancos Creek on right.

1.0

200.6 The prominent hogback to the left at 9-10:00 is a Tertiary igneous intrusion.

.6

201.2 Road climbs hill on Mancos Shale. Milepost 60.

1.7

202.9 Top of Mancos Hill.

.1

203.0 La Plata County.

.1

203.1 Milepost 62. Overlooking Thompson Park to right. Grain and hay farming in this region is dependent upon irrigation and consequently is limited mostly to valleys.

.6

203.7 Thompson Park. Dakota Sandstone forms dip slopes to north.

.3

204.0 Point Lookout Sandstone capping scarp on right.

1.0

205.0 Good exposure of Mancos Shale in roadcut on left.

2.1

207.1 Mancos Shale on left.

.6

207.7 The highway along here is usually undergoing some form of maintenance because the Mancos is actively sliding to the right.

2.3

210.0 Another area of creeping Mancos Shale and perpetual highway maintenance.

.4

210.4 Divide between La Plata River and Cherry Creek drainages.

1.2

211.6 Hesperus Ski Area on right.

.4

212.0 Abandoned coal mine in Menefee on right at 3:00.

.2

212.2 Road up La Plata River canyon on left provides access to many of the early but now abandoned mines.

.4

212.6 Bridge over La Plata River. There was much placer mining in this valley in early days.

.1

212.7 Road to original Fort Lewis A & M College on right. In 1953 Great Western Drilling Company drilled a 10,214' Devonian test on the college campus.

.6

213.3 Note high level terrace gravels in roadcut on left.

.4

213.7 Top hill, divide between Animas and La Plata river drainages. La Plata Mountains to left; highest peak is Hesperus at 13,225', which is capped by Mancos strata.

.6

214.3 Point Lookout at 10:00.

1.6

215.9 Milepost 76.

.2

216.1 Entrance to Durango West on left.

.4

216.5 At 4:00 is Pictured Cliffs scarp along north rim of San Juan basin.

.6

217.1 Mancos Shale exposed in roadcuts.

.2

217.3 Entering axial trace of Perins Peak syncline.

.6

217.9 Milepost 78. Exposures on either side show the transitional nature between the Lewis and Mesaverde Formations. Road is slightly east of the syncline axis.

.6

218.5 Victory and Morning Star coal mines on left. Mines are now abandoned, coal was mined from the Menefee and used locally. Leaving axial portion of Perins Peak syncline.

.4

218.9 Abandoned coal mine at 3:00. Approximate Mesaverde-Mancos contact.

.4

219.3 Twin Buttes at 1:00.

.4

219.7 Entering Lightner Creek valley. Twin

Figure 24. Durango with Durango anticline to north. Hill to left capped by Dakota, then Morrison with Junction Creek Sandstone cliffs near base. (photo by C.D. Irwin)

Buttes on left capped by Point Lookout. The old abandoned town of Perins, which was a prosperous coal mining town, is just in back of these buttes. Railroad once serviced this town.

       .3

220.0 Axial trace of Durango anticline.

       .3

220.3 Abandoned coal mine in Menefee high on hillside at 3:00.

       .2

220.5 Perins Peak at 9-10:00.

       .5

221.0 Wildcat Canyon road to right.

       .8

221.8 Bridge over Lightner Creek. Point Lookout forms escarpment seen on sky line ahead.

       .9

222.7 Bridge over Animas River and Durango city limits.

Engineer Mtn.

We're big city enough to supply the money you need. Hometown enough to supply it fast.

Allen Thomas, Vice President

We've been working with the region's independents for years, providing money and a broad range of service—from production loans to lease drafts services.

To get money where it can do the most good at the right time, we have organized our staff to meet the very exacting demands of the energy industry. Not only do the officers we assign to each company have enough authority to make most decisions independently, but we also make sure a backup officer is kept current and ready to fill in. That way we can respond quickly and consistently. Over the years our independent customers have appreciated that response.

Our people are bankers. And they know the industry's problems. That combination assures innovative solutions and a working relationship that keeps things moving.

If you would like to know more about our lending capacities, quick decisions and hometown service, call the Better Bankers. We would like to demonstrate that there is more to being a natural resources bank than a committee at the end of a WATS line.

Central Bank
of Denver

The Better Bankers.℠
1515 Arapahoe Street/Denver, Colorado 80292
(303) 893-3456/Member FDIC

Ⓒ CENTRAL BANCORPORATION, INC.

PARADOX BASIN
100 WELL SYNTHETIC SEISMOGRAM STUDY
WITH
ACCOMPANYING VELOCITY MAPS AND DIGITIZED DATA

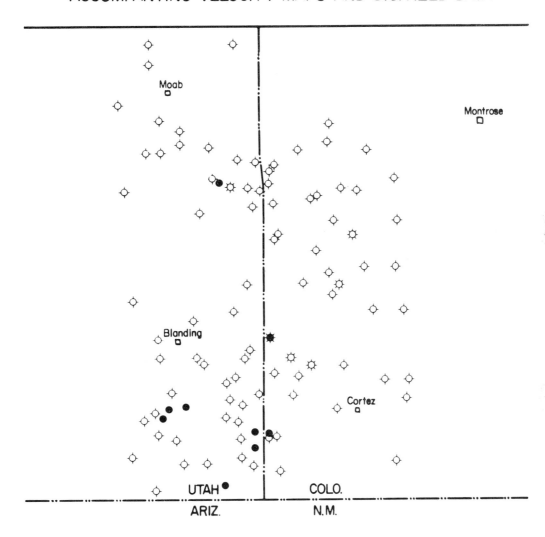

LAND AND MARINE SEISMIC DATA PROCESSING
STRATIGRAPHIC PROCESSING AND INTERPRETATION
SEISMIC MODELING
HARDWARE AND SOFTWARE SALES
DIGITIZING

FOR MORE INFORMATION PLEASE WRITE OR CALL:

DENVER PROCESSING CENTER, INC.

910 15th STREET SUITE 200
DENVER, COLORADO 80202
(303) 571-1170
ATTN. JACK BARNES

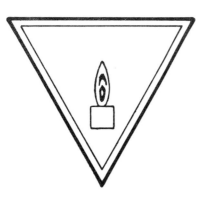

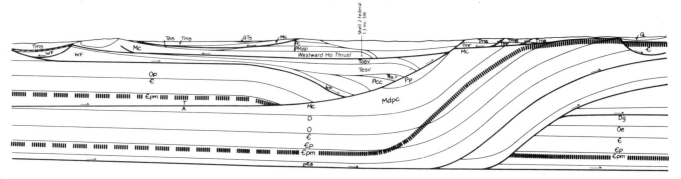

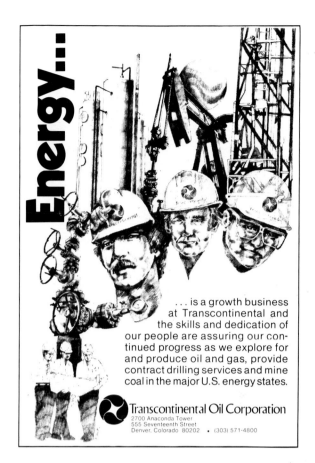

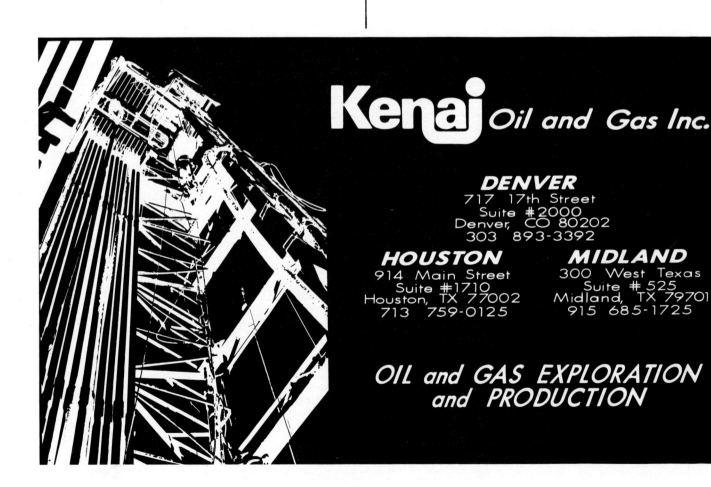

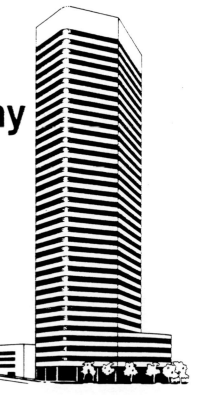

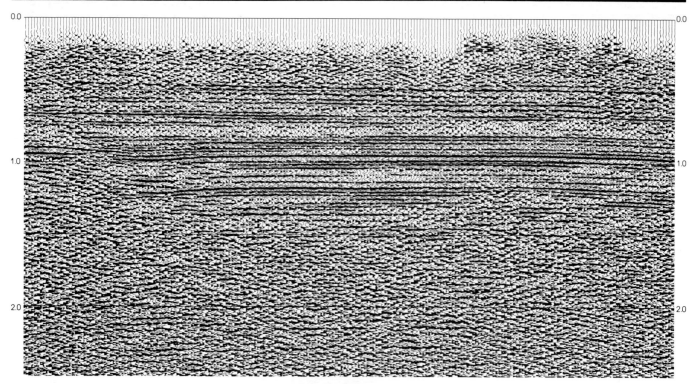

Conventionally Processed
Paradox Basin Data

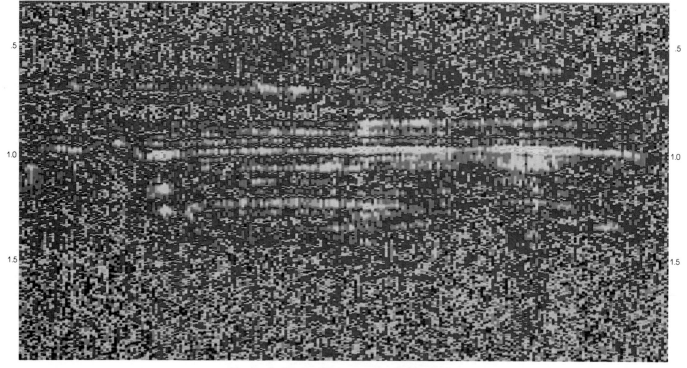

Reflection Strength Display
of Paradox Basin Data

PARADOX BASIN SPECULATIVE SURVEY

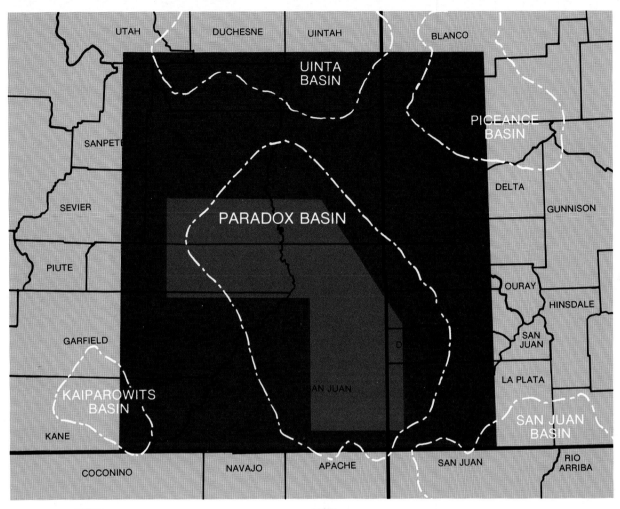

■ 1979 - 1980 Coverage   ■ 1981 - Proposed Coverage

Sefel Geophysical has available for purchase
870 miles of speculative seismic data in Southeastern Utah

The current data were acquired during 1979 - 1980
and an additional 1500 miles are proposed for 1981

A Vibroseis™ energy source
was used to collect the 1200 % CDP coverage
and Sefel state-of-the-art processing resulted in a highly
interpretable data package

For more information   Sefel Geophysical
please call or write: 201 S. Cherokee Street
                              Denver, CO 80223
                              (303) 722-5793 / Telex 450104

TM CONOCO

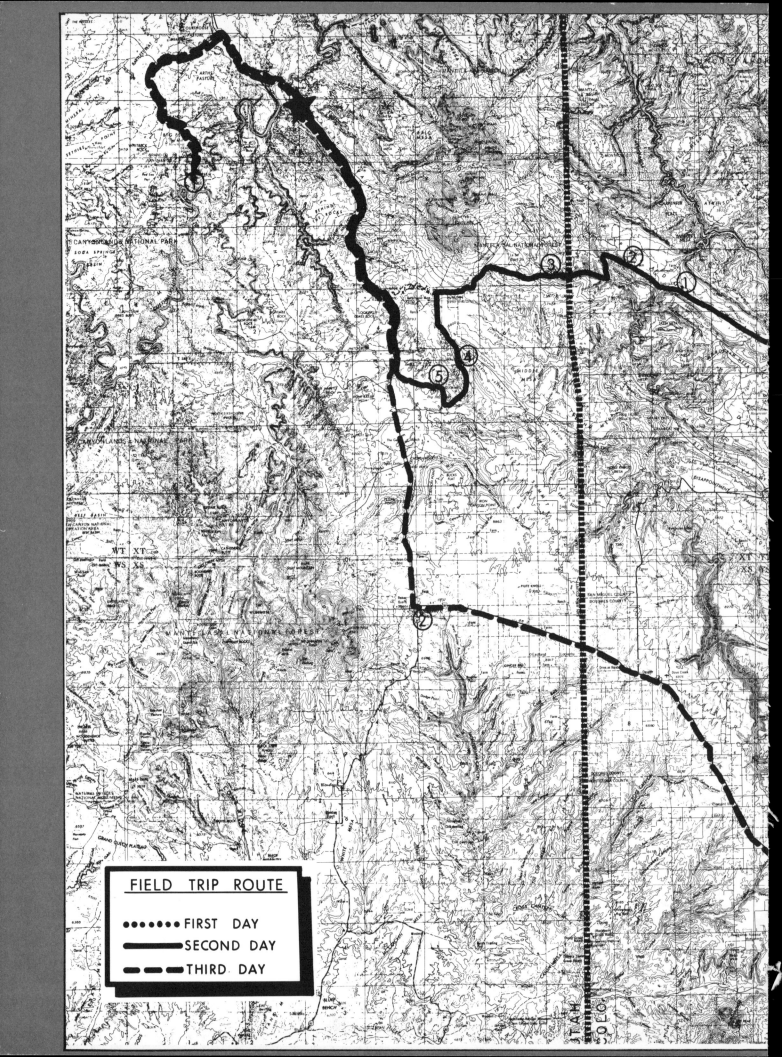

FIELD TRIP ROUTE

• • • • • • • FIRST DAY

——————— SECOND DAY

— — — — THIRD DAY